Core Connections Algebra 2
Second Edition*, Version 4.0

Managing Editors / Authors

Judy Kysh (Both Edition)
San Francisco State University
San Francisco, CA

Evra Baldinger (First Edition)
University of California, Berkeley
Berkeley, CA

Michael Kassarjian (2nd Edition)
CPM Educational Program
Encino, CA

Contributing Authors

Karen Arth
Central High School East
Fresno, CA

Mark Atkinson
North Salem High School
Salem, OR

Carlos Cabana
San Lorenzo High School
San Lorenzo, CA

John Cooper
Del Oro High School
Loomis, CA

Elizabeth Coyner
Christian Brothers High School
Sacramento, CA

Scott Coyner
Christian Brothers High School
Sacramento, CA

Dolores Dean
Holy Family High School
Broomfield, CO

Ernest Derrera
Roosevelt High School
Johnston, CO

Leslie Dietiker
Michigan State University
East Lansing, MI

Misty Nikula
Whatcom Day Acadamy
Bellingham, WA

Bob Petersen
Rosemont High School
Sacramento, CA

Norm Prokup
The College Preparatory School
Oakland, CA

Barbara Shreve
San Lorenzo High School
San Lorenzo, CA

Estelle Woodbury
San Lorenzo High School
San Lorenzo, CA

Karen Wootton
CPM Educational Program
Odenton, MD

Technical Managers

Hannah Coyner
Sacramento, CA

Sarah Maile
Sacramento, CA

Claire Taylor
Sacramento, CA

Program Directors

Leslie Dietiker, Ph.D.
Boston University
Boston, MA

Lori Hamada
CPM Educational Program
Fresno, CA

Brian Hoey
CPM Educational Program
Sacramento, CA

Judy Kysh, Ph.D.
Departments of Education and Mathematics
San Francisco State University, CA

Tom Sallee, Ph.D.
Department of Mathematics
University of California, Davis

*Based on *Algebra 2 Connections*

e-book Manager
Carol Cho
Director of Technology
Martinez, CA

e-book Programmers
Rakesh Khanna
Daniel Kleinsinger
Kevin Stein

e-book Assistants
Debbie Dodd
Shirley Paulsen
Wendy Papciak
Anna Poehlmann
Jordan Wight

Assessment Manager
Karen Wootton
Director of Assessment
Odenton, MD

Assessment Website
Elizabeth Fong
Michael Huang
Daniel Kleinsinger

Illustration
Kevin Coffey
San Francisco, CA

Homework Help Manager
Bob Petersen
CPM Educational Program

Homework Help Website
Carol Cho
Director of Technology

Parent Guide with Extra Practice
Bob Petersen (Managing Editor)
CPM Educational Program
Sacramento, CA

Scott Coyner
Christian Brothers High School
Sacramento, CA

Brian Hoey
Christian Brothers High School
Sacramento, CA

Sarah Maile
CPM Educational Program
Sacramento, CA

Karen Wooton
CPM Educational Program
Odenton, MD

Technical Manager
Rebecca Harlow
Sarah Maile

Technical Assistants
Stephanie Achondo
Eric Baxter
Diego Breedlove
Carrie Cai
Mary Coyner
Bethany Firch
Rebecca Harlow
Leslie Lai
Michael Li
James McCardle
Wendy Papciak
Iris Perez
Eduardo Ramirez
Andrea Smith
Christy Van Beek
Alex Yu

Robert Ainsworth
Rebecca Bobell
Duncan Breedlove
Alex Contreras
Carmen de la Cruz
Elizabeth Fong
Dana Kimball
Keith Lee
Jerry Luo
Nyssa Muheim
Atlanta Parrott
Steven Pham
John Ramos
Rachel Smith
Megan Walters

Erica Andrews
Delenn Breedlove
Elizabeth Burke
Hannah Coyner
Matthew Donahue
Miguel Francisco
Madeline Kimball
Michael Leong
Eli Marable
Alexandra Murphy
Ryan Peabody
Anna Poehlmann
Ali Rivera
Claire Taylor
Sarah Wong

2 3 4 5 6   16 15 14 13   Version 4.0

Printed in the United States of America   ISBN: 978-1-60328-115-7

A Note to Students:

Welcome to a new year of math! In this course, you will learn to use new models and methods to think about problems as well as solve them. You will be developing powerful mathematical tools and learning new ways of thinking about and investigating situations. You will be making connections, discovering relationships, figuring out what strategies can be used to solve problems, and explaining your thinking. Learning to think in these ways and communicate about your thinking is useful in mathematical contexts, other subjects in school, and situations outside the classroom. The mathematics you have learned in the past will be valuable for learning in this course. That work, and what you learn in this course, will prepare you for future courses.

In meeting the challenges of this course, you will not be learning alone. You will cooperate with other students as a member of a study team. Being a part of a team means speaking up and interacting with other people. You will explain your ideas, listen to what others have to say, and ask questions if there is something you do not understand. In this course, a single problem can often be solved several ways. You will see problems in different ways than your teammates do. Each of you has something to contribute while you work on the lessons in this course.

Together, your team will complete problems and activities that will help you discover mathematical ideas and develop solution methods. Your teacher will support you as you work, but will not take away your opportunity to think and investigate for yourself. Each topic will be revisited many times and will connect to other topics. If something is not clear to you the first time you work on it, you will have more chances to build your understanding as the course continues.

Learning math this way has an advantage: as long as you actively participate, make sure everyone in your study team is involved, and ask good questions, you will find yourself understanding mathematics at a deeper level than ever before. By the end of this course, you will have a powerful set of mathematical tools to use to solve new problems. With your teammates you will meet mathematical challenges you would not have known how to approach before.

In addition to the support provided by your teacher and your study team, CPM has also created online resources to help you, including help with homework, and a parent guide with extra practice. You will find these resources and more at www.cpm.org.

We wish you well and are confident that you will enjoy this next year of learning!

Sincerely,
The CPM Team

Core Connections Algebra 2
Student Edition

INVESTIGATIONS AND FUNCTIONS

1

Chapter 1   Investigations and Functions

Welcome to Algebra 2! This chapter will introduce you to the ways you will be working as well as several of the big ideas in this course. You will share your current mathematical knowledge with your study team as you work together to solve problems. Some of these ideas you will revisit later in the course and connect to new mathematical ideas. You will learn to work with a graphing calculator to help you discover qualities of functions and systems of functions.

Guiding Question

Mathematically proficient students construct reasonable arguments and critique the reasoning of others.

As you work through this chapter, ask yourself:

As I investigate functions, am I analyzing the function thoroughly and clearly communicating my reasoning to others?

Chapter Outline

Section 1.1   In this section, you will get to know the members of your study team. You will work with your team to develop skills and techniques for using a graphing calculator to help you explore functions and intersections, and you will present your results to the class.

Section 1.2   Here, you will find multiple ways to represent a geometric relationship, summarize your results, and present your results to the class. You will also analyze the family of exponential functions and investigate a non-linear non-exponential function. You will develop your understanding of what it means to investigate a function.

1.1.1 How can I work with my team to figure it out?

Solving Puzzles in Teams

Welcome to Algebra 2! This first chapter will challenge you to use different problem-solving strategies. You will also be introduced to different tools and resources that you can use throughout the course as you investigate new ideas, solve problems, and share mathematical ideas.

1-1. **BUILDING WITH YARN**

Work with your team to make each of the shapes you see below out of a single loop of yarn. You may make the shapes in any order. Before you start, review the Team Roles that are described on the next page. Use these roles to help your study team work together today. When you make one of the shapes successfully, call your teacher over to show off your accomplishment.

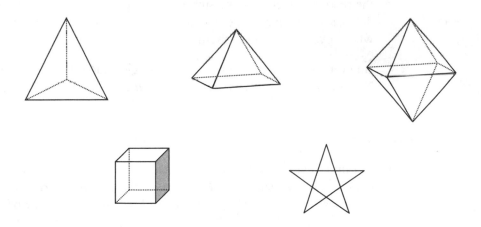

Team Roles

Resource Manager: If your name comes first alphabetically:

- Make sure your team has all of the necessary materials, such as yarn for problem 1-1 or the resource pages for problem 1-2.

- Ask your teacher a question when the *entire* team is stuck. Before raising your hand, you might ask your team, *"Does anyone have an idea? Should I ask the teacher?"*

- Make sure your team cleans up materials by delegating tasks. You could say, *"I will put away the _____ while you _____ ."*

Facilitator: If your name comes second alphabetically:

- Start your team's discussion by reading the question aloud and then asking, *"Which shape should we start with?"* or *"How can we work together to make this shape?"*

- Make sure that all of the team members get any necessary help. You do not need to answer all of the questions yourself. A good Facilitator regularly asks, *"Do we understand what we are supposed to do?"* and *"Who can answer _____'s question?"*

Recorder/Reporter: If your name comes third alphabetically:

- Be sure all team members are able to reach the yarn and have access to the resource pages. Make sure resource pages and work that is being discussed are placed in the center of the table or group of desks in a spot where everyone can see them.

- Be prepared to share your team's strategies and results with the class. You might report, *"We tried ___ , but it didn't work, so we decided to try ___ ."*

Task Manager: If your name comes fourth alphabetically:

- Remind the team to stay on task and not to talk to students in other teams. You can suggest, *"Let's try working on a different shape,"* or *"Are we ready to try the function machines in a different order?"*

- Keep track of time. Give your team reminders, such as, *"I think we need to decide now so that we will have enough time to ..."*

1-2.   FUNCTION MACHINES

Your teacher will give you a set of four function machines. Your team's job is to get a specific output by putting those machines in a particular order so that one machine's output becomes the next machine's input. As you work, discuss what you know about the kind of output each function produces to help you arrange the machines in an appropriate order. The four functions are reprinted below.

$f(x) = \sqrt{x}$ $g(x) = -(x-2)^2$

$h(x) = 2^x - 7$ $k(x) = -\frac{x}{2} - 1$

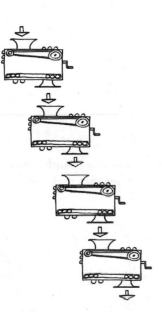

a.   In what order should you stack the machines so that when 6 is dropped into the first machine, and all four machines have had their effect, the last machine's output is 11?

b.   What order will result in a final output of 131,065 when the first input is 64?

METHODS AND MEANINGS

Functions

A relationship between inputs and outputs is a **function** if there is no more than one output for each input. Functions are often written as $y =$ some expression involving x, where x is the input and y is the output. The following is an example of a function.

$$y = (x-2)^2$$

x	−2	−1	0	1	2	3	4	5
y	16	9	4	1	0	1	4	9

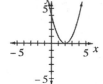

In the example above the value of y depends on x, so y is also called the **dependent variable** and x is called the **independent variable**.

Another way to write a function is with the notation " $f(x) =$ " instead of " $y =$ ". The function named "f" has output $f(x)$. The input is x.

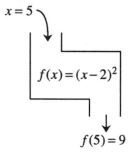

In the example at right, $f(5) = 9$. The input is 5 and the output is 9. You read this as, "f of 5 equals 9."

The set of all inputs for which there is an output is called the **domain**. The set of all possible outputs is called the **range**. In the example above, notice that you can input any x-value into the equation and get an output. The domain of this function is "all real numbers" because any number can be an input. The outputs are all greater than or equal to zero, so the range is $y \geq 0$.

$x^2 + y^2 = 1$ is not a function because there are two y-values (outputs) for some x-values, as shown below.

$$x^2 + y^2 = 1$$

x	−1	0	0	1
y	0	−1	1	0

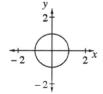

1-3.   KEEPING A NOTEBOOK

> You will need to keep an organized notebook for this course. Below is one method of keeping a notebook. Ask your teacher if you should follow these guidelines or if there is another system you should follow.
>
> • The notebook should be a sturdy, three-ring, loose-leaf binder with a hard cover.
>
> • The binder should have dividers to separate it into five sections:
>
> TEXT   TESTS AND QUIZZES
> HOMEWORK   LINED AND GRAPH PAPER
> CLASSWORK/NOTES
>
> You should put your name inside the front cover of your notebook so it will be returned to you if you lose it. Put your phone number and address (or the school's address, if you prefer) on the inside front cover. It will also help to put your name in large, clear letters on the outside so if someone sees it they can say, *"Hey, Julia, I saw your notebook in the cafeteria under the back table."*
>
> Your notebook will be your biggest asset for this course and will be the primary resource you will use to study, so take good care of it!

1-4.   "Find $f(3)$" means to find the output of function $f(x)$ for an input of $x = 3$. For the function $f(x) = \frac{1}{x-2}$, find each of the following values.

    a.   Find $f(4)$. (This means find the output of the function when $x = 4$.)

    b.   Find x when $f(x) = 1$. (This means find the input that gives an output of 1.)

1-5.   Angelica is working with function machines. She has the two machines $g(x) = \sqrt{x-5}$ and $h(x) = x^2 - 6$. She wants to put them in order so that the output of the first machine becomes the input of the second. She wants to use a beginning input of 6.

    a.   In what order must she put the machines to get a final output of 5?

    b.   Is it possible for her to get a final output of –5? If so, show how she could do that. If not, explain why not.

1-6.   An average school bus holds
        45 people. Sketch a graph
        showing the relationship
        between the number of students
        who need bus transportation and
        the number of buses required.
        Be sure to label the axes.

1-7.   In this course, you will learn shortcuts that allow you to sketch many different
        types of graphs quickly and accurately. However, when the directions ask you
        to *graph an equation* or to *draw a graph*, this means it is not just a sketch you
        should do quickly. You need to:

        •   Use graph paper.   •   Label key points.

        •   Scale your axes appropriately.   •   Plot points accurately.

        On separate sets of axes, graph each of the following equations. If you do not
        remember any shortcuts for graphing, you can always make an $x \to y$ table.

        a. $y = -2x + 7$ b. $y = \frac{3}{5}x + 1$

        c. $3x + 2y = 6$ d. $y = x^2$

1-8.   The graph for part (d) of problem 1-7 is different from the other three graphs.

        a.   Explain how the graph is different from the other three graphs.

        b.   What in the equation of part (d) makes its graph different?

        c.   What is the graph of part (d) called?

1-9.   Write down everything you know about the equation $y = mx + b$. You should
        include what this general equation represents, as well as what each of the
        different letters represents. Be as thorough as possible.

1.1.2 How can I use my graphing calculator?

· ·
Using a Graphing Calculator to Explore a Function

In Algebra 1 you learned that multiple representations such as situations, tables, graphs, and equations along with their interconnections are useful for learning about functions. A graphing calculator can be a very useful tool for generating different representations quickly. Today, you will use this tool to explore a function. You will describe your function completely to the class.

1-10.   Your team will use graphing calculators to learn about one of the
following functions.

   i. $y = 2\sqrt{9-x} - 4$ *ii.* $y = \sqrt{100 - x^2}$

   iii. $y = 3\sqrt{x+4} - 6$ *iv.* $y = 3\sqrt{4-x} - 3$

   v. $y = -2\sqrt{25 - x^2} + 8$ *vi.* $y = -3\sqrt{x+9} + 4$

   vii. $y = 2\sqrt{25 - x^2} - 1$ *viii.* $y = \sqrt{4-x} - 1$

Your Task: Describe your team's function in as much detail as possible. Use your graphing calculator to help you generate a table and a complete graph of your function. Remember that drawing a complete graph means:

- Use graph paper.
- Scale your axes appropriately.
- Label key points.
- Plot points accurately.

As you work, keep your graphing calculators in the middle of your workspace, so that you can compare your screens and all team members can see and discuss your results. Be sure to record what you learn as you explore your function. As a team, you will be preparing a report about your function for the class. Consider the Discussion Points below as you work.

Discussion Points

What are the key points on the graph? Where are they exactly?

Can we identify at least five integer inputs that give integer values as outputs?

Are there values of *x* or *y* that do not make sense?

How high or low does the graph go?

Did the graphing calculator show an accurate graph?

How can we be sure the graph is complete?

1-11.   When your team has completed a table and drawn a
complete graph, prepare a report for the whole class.

The class will get the most out of your presentation
if you focus on what was particularly interesting
about your function or what you learned. Rather
than saying, *"We plugged in a 2 and got a 5,"*
consider using statements such as, *"We decided to try an input of 2 because we
wanted to know what happened to the left of x = 3."*

The following sentence starters can help you make a meaningful and interesting
presentation.

"At first we were confused by…"

"This makes sense because…"

"We weren't sure about… , so we tried…"

"Something interesting that we noticed about our graph is…"

As you prepare your presentation, your teacher will provide you with poster-
making supplies. Reread the task statement of problem 1-10 (labeled "Your
Task") and be sure to include all relevant information and ideas in your
presentation.

METHODS AND MEANINGS

MATH NOTES

Linear Equations

A **linear equation** is an equation that forms a line when it is
graphed. This type of equation may be written in several
different forms. Although these forms look different, they are
equivalent; that is, their graphs are all the same line.

Standard Form: An equation in $ax + by = c$ form, such as $6x - 3y = 18$.

Slope-Intercept Form: An equation in
$y = mx + b$ form, such as $y = 2x - 6$.

You can find the **slope** (also known as
the **growth factor**) and the
y-intercept of a line in $y = mx + b$
form quickly. For the equation
$y = 2x - 6$, the slope is 2, while the
y-intercept is (0, –6).

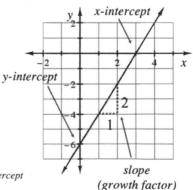

$$y = 2x - 6 \quad \text{y-intercept}$$
$$\quad\quad\uparrow$$
$$\quad slope$$

1-12.   Junior is saving money in his piggy bank. He starts with 10 cents and adds two pennies each day. Create an $x \rightarrow y$ table and a graph for the function for which x represents the number of days since Junior started saving money and y represents the total money he has saved.

1-13.   Use the Zero Product Property and factoring, when necessary, to solve for x. The Math Notes box for Lesson 1.1.4 may be useful, if you need help.

a. $(x+13)(x-7)=0$ b. $(2x+3)(3x-7)=0$

c $x(x-3)=0$ d. $x^2-5x=0$

e. $x^2-2x-35=0$ f. $3x^2+14x-5=0$

1-14.   Terri's project for the Math Fair was a magnificent black box that she called a function machine. If you put 3 into her machine, the output would be 8. If you put in 10, the output would be 29; and if you put in 20, it would be 59.

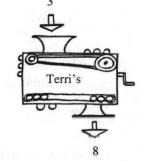

a.   What would her machine do to the input 5? What about –1? What about x? Making an input $\rightarrow$ output table may help.

b.   Write an equation for Terri's machine.

1-15.   Nafeesa graphed a line with a slope of 5 and a y-intercept of $(0, -2)$.

a.   Find an equation for her line.   b.   Find the value of x when $y=0$.

1-16.   In each of the following equations, what is y when $x=2$? When $x=0$? Where would the graph of each equation cross the y-axis?

a. $y=3x+15$ b. $y=3-3x$

1-17.   Carmichael made a function machine. The inner workings of the machine are visible in the diagram at right. What will the output be in each of the following cases?

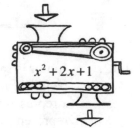

$x^2 + 2x + 1$

a.   If 3 is dropped in?

b.   If −4 is dropped in?

c.   If −22.872 is dropped in?

1-18.   Does the temperature outside depend on the time of day, or does the time of day depend on the temperature outside? This may seem like a silly question, but to sketch a graph that represents this relationship, you first need to decide which axis will represent which quantity.

a.   When you graph an equation such as $y = 3x - 5$, which variable (the x or the y) *depends* on the other? Which is not dependent? (That is, which is *in*dependent?) Explain.

b.   Which variable is *dependent*: temperature or time of day? Which variable is *independent*?

c.   Sketch a graph (with appropriately named axes) that shows the relationship between temperature outside and time of day.

1-19.   Jill needs to cut a smaller piece from a 30-foot length of lumber. Create multiple representations ($x \rightarrow y$ table, graph, and equation) for the function with x-values that are the length of the piece Jill cuts off and y-values that are the length of the piece that is left over. Which representation best portrays the situation? Why? Explain.

1-20.   Make a table and graph the function $f(x) = \frac{1}{2}x^2$. Describe all of the possible input and output values.

1-21.   Given $f(x) = -\frac{2}{3}x + 3$ and $g(x) = 2x^2 - 5$, complete parts (a) through (f) below.

    a.   Calculate $f(3)$.   b.   Solve $f(x) = -5$.

    c.   Calculate $g(-3)$.   d.   Solve $g(x) = -7$.

    e.   Solve $g(x) = 8$.   f.   Solve $g(x) = 9$.

1-22.   Gerri made a function machine. Below are four pictures of her machine. (Note that these are all pictures of the same function machine.) Find the equation for Gerri's function machine.

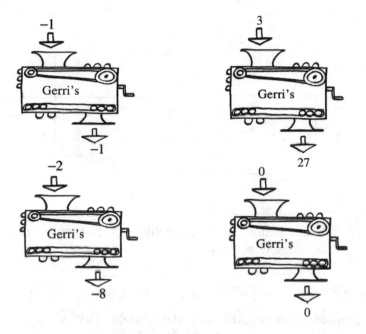

1-23.   Examine each graph below. Based on the shape of the graph and the labels on the axes, write a sentence to describe the relationship that each graph represents. Then state which axis represents the independent variable and which one represents the dependent variable.

a.

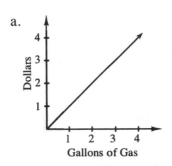

b.

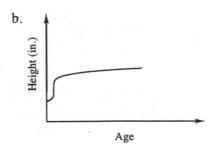

c.

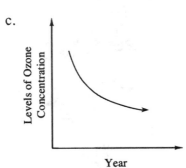

d.

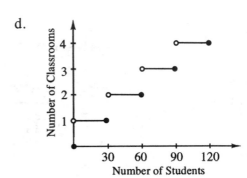

e.   What are all of the possible inputs of the graph in part (d)? What are all of the possible outputs?

1-24.   Consider triangles ABC and ADE at right. Give a convincing argument why $\triangle ABC \sim \triangle ADE$. Then use what you know about similar triangles to complete each of the following ratios for the triangles.

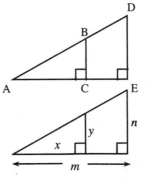

a.   b.

1-25.   Note: The stoplight icon to the right of a problem indicates that there is an error in the problem.

Find the error in the solution at right. Explain what the error is and solve the equation correctly. Show how to check your solution to be sure that it is correct.

$$3(x-2) - 2(x+7) = 2x + 17$$
$$3x - 6 - 2x + 14 = 2x + 17$$
$$x + 8 = 2x + 17$$
$$-9 = x$$

14

1.1.3 Which values are possible?

Domain and Range

In Lesson 1.1.2 you worked with your graphing calculator to see complete graphs of functions and to determine what information was useful to describe those functions completely. In this lesson you will look at more functions, this time thinking about the input and output values that are possible. You will also learn to use some additional tools on your graphing calculator that will allow you to see a complete graph. As you work with your team, remember to ask each other questions such as:

What values are possible?

Can we see the complete graph?

What other information can we use to describe the function?

1-26.   Jerrod and Sonia were working with their team on problem 1-2 to put the function machines in order. These functions are reprinted for you below.

$f(x) = \sqrt{x}$ $g(x) = -(x-2)^2$

$h(x) = 2^x - 7$ $k(x) = -\frac{x}{2} - 1$

a.   Jerrod first put an input of 6 into the function $g(x) = -(x-2)^2$ and got an output of -16. He wanted to try $f(x) = \sqrt{x}$ as his next function in the order, but he thinks there might be a problem using -16 as an input. Is there a problem? Explain.

b.   Because it is not possible to take the square root of -16, it can be said that -16 is not in the **domain** of the function $f(x)$. The **domain** of a function is the collection of numbers that are possible inputs for that function. With your team, find two other numbers that are *not* part of the domain of $f(x)$. Then describe the domain. In other words, what are all of the numbers that *can* be used as inputs for the function $f(x)$?

c.   Sonia claimed that $g(x)$ could not possibly be the last function in the order for problem 1-2. She justified her thinking by saying, *"Our final output has to be 11, which is a positive number. The function g(x) will always make its output negative, so it can't come last in the order."* Discuss this with your team. Does Sonia's logic make sense? How did she know that the output of $g(x)$ would never be positive?

Problem continues on next page. →

1-26.   *Problem continued from previous page.*

   d.   Because the outputs of the function $g(x)$ do not include certain numbers, it can be said that positive numbers are not part of the **range** of the function $g(x)$. The **range** of a function is the set of all of the possible values that can be outputs. With your team, describe the range of the function $g(x)$. In other words what are all of the values that *can* be outputs of the function?

1-27.   Use your graphing calculator to help you draw a complete graph of $y = (x+1)(x-9)$.

   a.   Describe the graph completely.

   b.   What window settings allow you to see the complete graph?

   c.   How are the settings related to domain and range?

1-28.   Use your graphing calculator to draw a complete graph of $y = (x-12)^2 + 11$.

   a.   What happens when you use the standard window?

   b.   What window settings did you use to see enough of the graph to help you visualize and draw a complete graph?

   c.   What are the domain and range of the function?

1-29.   Now you will reverse your thinking to create a graph with a given domain and range.

   a.   Sketch a function that has a domain of all real numbers between and including −3 and 10 (written $-3 \le x \le 10$) and a range of all real numbers between and including −4 and 6 (written $-4 \le y \le 6$). You do not have to write an equation for your function. Verify your endpoints with your team. Be creative.

   b.   Sketch a function with a domain of all real numbers and a range of the values 2, 4, 5, and 8 (written $y = 2, 4, 5, 8$).

      The domain of all real numbers can be written $-\infty < x < \infty$. The symbols $-\infty$ and ∞ represents positive and negative **infinity**. They mean that the domain goes on without ending in the positive and negative direction. Infinity is not a number; it is a concept.

1-30.   How can a graphing calculator help you find the solution to a
system of equations? Consider this system:

$$5x - y = 35$$
$$3x + y = -3$$

   a.   First graph the system in a standard window. Can you
see the solution on your screen?

   b.   To find the solution you will need to change the window on your
calculator. Discuss with your team what maximum value, minimum value,
and scale you should use for the x- and y-axes in order to see the
intersection. After you have decided, check your conclusion on the
graphing calculator.

   c.   Use a "trace" function on your calculator to find the solution from the
graphs. Then solve the system algebraically.

   d.   Discuss the two methods with your team. Explain which one your team
prefers and why.

1-31.   What does the graph of $y = x + \frac{1}{(x+2)^2} - 3$ look like? Graph the
equation on your calculator. Use the trace and/or zoom buttons to
find the x- and y-intercepts. What is the domain of this function?
What is the range?

1-32.   Use your graphing calculator to help you sketch the graphs of $y = \frac{1}{x} - 4$ and
$y = \frac{1}{x-4}$. Are the graphs the same? Should they be? Explain why or why not.

1-33.

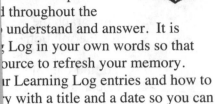

34 - c b

39 - c

reflect on your
Learning Log.
s and examples
throughout the
understand and answer. It is
Log in your own words so that
ource to refresh your memory.
r Learning Log entries and how to
y with a title and a date so you can

ing you know about domain and
eas. Title this entry "Domain and

Ⓜ ETHODS AND MEANINGS

MATH NOTES

Domain and Range

The set of possible values for the input of a function is called the **domain** of the function. This set consists of every input value for x for which the function is defined.

The **range** of a function is the set of possible values of the output. This set contains every y-value that the function can generate.

Domain and **range** are often written with **inequality notation** as shown in the examples below.

The symbols $-\infty$ and ∞ represents positive and negative **infinity**. They mean that the domain goes on without ending in the positive or negative direction. Infinity is not a number; it is a concept.

If the domain is any number between and including –2 and 7:	$-2 \leq x \leq 7$
If the range is any number greater than but excluding 4:	$y > 4$ or $4 < y < \infty$
If the domain is all real numbers except for –3:	$x \neq -3$
If the domain is all real numbers:	$-\infty < x < \infty$

Core Connections Algebra 2

1-34.   Examine $g(x)$ graphed at right.

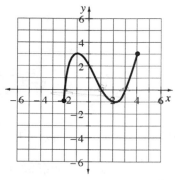

a.   Which x-values have points on the graph? That is, describe the domain of $g(x)$.

b.   What are the possible outputs for $g(x)$? That is, what is the range?

c.   Ricky thinks the range of $g(x)$ is: $-1, 0, 1, 2$, and 3. Is he correct? Why or why not?

d.   Draw a graph for another function with the same domain and range as $g(x)$.

1-35.   Consider the functions $f(x) = 3x^2 - 5$ and $g(x) = \sqrt{x-5} + 2$.

a.   Find $f(5)$.   b.   Find $g(5)$.

c.   Find $f(4)$.   d.   Find $g(4)$.

e.   Find $f(x) + g(x)$.   f.   Find $g(x) - f(x)$.

g.   Describe the domain of $f(x)$.   h.   Describe the domain of $g(x)$.

i.   Why is the domain of one of these functions more restrictive than the other?

1-36.   Nissos and Chelita were arguing over a math problem. Nissos was trying to explain to Chelita that she had made a mistake in finding the x-intercepts of the function $y = x^2 - 10x + 21$. *"No way!"* Chelita exclaimed. *"I know how to find x-intercepts! You make the y equal to zero and solve for x. I know I did this right!"* Here is Chelita's work:

Step 1: $x^2 - 10x + 21 = 0$, so $(x+7)(x+3) = 0$.

Step 2:   Therefore, $x + 7 = 0$ or $x + 3 = 0$.

Step 3:   So $x = -7$ or $x = -3$.

Nissos tried to explain to Chelita that she had done something wrong. What is Chelita's error? Justify and explain your answer completely.

1-37.   As you have found when using a graphing calculator, equations must be solved for y; that is, they must be written in y-form. Rewrite each equation below so that it can be entered into a graphing calculator.

  a. $x = 3y + 6$ b. $x = 5y - 10$

  c. $x = y^2$ d. $x = 2y^2 - 4$

  e. $x = (y - 5)^2$

1-38.   Given $f(x) = 2x - 7$, complete parts (a) through (c) below.

  a. Compute $f(0)$.

  b. Solve $f(x) = 0$.

  c. What do the answers to parts (a) and (b) tell you about the graph of $f(x)$?

1-39.   Gregory planted a lemon tree in his back yard. When he planted the tree, it was 2 feet tall. He noticed that it has been growing 3 inches every week.

  a. Create multiple representations ($x \rightarrow y$ table, graph, and equation) to represent the relationship between the days that have passed and the height of the tree.

  b. If the tree continues growing at this rate, when will it be 6 feet tall? How can you see this in each of the representations?

  c. State the possible inputs and outputs of the graph.

1-40.   Solve each of the following equations. Be sure to check your solutions.

  a. $4(x - 1) - 2(3x + 5) = -3x - 1$ b. $3x - 5 = 2.5x + 3 - (x - 4)$

1.1.4 How can I represent intersections?

Points of Intersection in Multiple Representations

Throughout this course, you will represent functions in several different ways, and you will find connections between the various representations. These connections will give you new ways to investigate functions and to justify your conclusions.

How can these connections help you understand more about systems of equations? In this lesson, you will make connections between ways of representing a system of equations as you use your graphing calculator to find the points of intersection in multiple representations.

1-41.   INTERSECTION INVESTIGATION

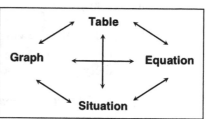

In Lesson 1.1.3, you used the features of your graphing calculator to find a point of intersection of two graphs. Can you use other representations as well? What about other strategies? Are all strategies equally accurate? Which do you prefer?

Your Task: Work with your team to find *as many ways as you can* (with *and* without your graphing calculator) to determine the points of intersection of the functions $f(x) = 2x^2 - 5x + 6$ and $g(x) = -2x^2 - x + 30$. Be sure to think about tables, graphs, and equations as you work. Be prepared to share each of your methods to the class.

Hint: If you are using a TI83+/84+ calculator, explore the [TABLE], [TBLSET], and [CALC] features on your graphing calculator. For other calculators, your teacher will give you guidance.

Discussion Points

How can we find it using graphs?

How can we find it in tables?

How can we find it using equations?

Further Guidance

1-42. Jason and his team were working on finding the points of intersection of $f(x) = 2x^2 - 5x + 6$ and $g(x) = -2x^2 - x + 30$. He suggested, *"Maybe we could start by looking at the graphs of the functions."*

    a. Use your graphing calculator to help you graph $f(x)$ and $g(x)$.

    b. Adjust the viewing window so that you can see all of the points of intersection. How accurately can you approximate the coordinates of these points by looking at the graph? Give it a try.

    c. Use the "trace" feature to get a more accurate approximation of each of the points.

    d. With your team, explore the [CALC] feature of your TI83/84+ graphing calculator. Can you find a way to make the graphing calculator calculate your points of intersection for you? How accurate are your results? Be prepared to share your method to the class.

1-43. Aria was in Jason's team. She had another idea and asked, *"Can't we find the points of intersection by comparing the tables of our two functions?"*

    a. What did Aria mean? How can you find points of intersection by looking at tables?

    b. Use your graphing calculator to make tables for $f(x)$ and $g(x)$. To do this, you will need to explore the [TABLE] and [TBLSET] features of your TI83/84+ calculator.

    c. Find all of the points of intersection in the tables. How accurate are these results?

    d. Can you think of any circumstances in which using a table might not be an efficient or accurate strategy for finding points of intersection? Explain.

1-44. Delilah listened to Jason and Aria explain their ideas. She said, *"I thought of another way! We have a method for using the equations to find points of intersection even without the graphing calculator, don't we?"*

    a. What method is Delilah referring to?

    b. Use Delilah's method to find the points of intersection of these two functions.

――――――   *Further Guidance*   ――――――
section ends here.

Core Connections Algebra 2

1-45.   Rhianna says she can draw different functions that have the same *x-intercepts* and the same domain and range. Her teammates say, *"No, that's impossible!"* But Rhianna insists, *"It is possible, we just need to sketch the graphs."*

   a.   What if the *x*-intercepts are $(-5, 0)$, $(2, 0)$, and $(6, 0)$, the domain is $-5 \leq x \leq 7$, and the range is $-4 \leq y \leq 10$? Is more than one function possible? Give examples to help explain why or why not.

   b.   What if the *x*-intercepts are $(-4, 0)$ and $(2, 0)$, the domain is all real numbers, and the range is $y \geq -8$? Is there more than one function possible? Give examples of multiple functions or explain why there can be only one.

METHODS AND MEANINGS

Solving a Quadratic Equation

MATH NOTES

In a previous course, you learned how to solve **quadratic equations** (equations that can be written in the form $ax^2 + bx + c = 0$). Review two methods for solving quadratic equations below.

Some quadratic equations can be solved by **factoring** and then using the **Zero Product Property**. For example, the quadratic equation $x^2 - 3x - 10 = 0$ can be rewritten by factoring as $(x-5)(x+2) = 0$. The Zero Product Property states that if $ab = 0$, then $a = 0$ or $b = 0$. So if $(x-5)(x+2) = 0$, then $(x-5) = 0$ or $(x+2) = 0$. Therefore, $x = 5$ or $x = -2$.

Another method for solving quadratic equations is using the **Quadratic Formula**. This method is particularly helpful for solving quadratic equations that are difficult or impossible to factor. Before using the Quadratic Formula, the quadratic equation you want to solve must be in standard form (that is, written as $ax^2 + bx + c = 0$).

In this form, a is the coefficient of the x^2-term, b is the coefficient of the x-term, and c is the constant term. The Quadratic Formula is stated at right.

$$x = \frac{-b \pm \sqrt{b^2 - 4ac}}{2a}$$

This formula gives two possible solutions for x. The two solutions are shown by the "$\pm$" symbol. This symbol (read as "plus or minus") is shorthand notation that tells you to evaluate the expression twice: once using addition and once using subtraction. Therefore, Quadratic Formula problems usually must be simplified twice to give:

$$x = \frac{-b + \sqrt{b^2 - 4ac}}{2a} \quad \text{or} \quad x = \frac{-b - \sqrt{b^2 - 4ac}}{2a}$$

Of course if $\sqrt{b^2 - 4ac}$ equals zero, you will get the same result both times.

To solve $x^2 - 3x - 10 = 0$ using the Quadratic Formula, substitute $a = 1$, $b = -3$, and $c = -10$ into the formula, as shown below, then simplify.

$$x = \frac{-(-3) \pm \sqrt{(-3)^2 - 4(1)(-10)}}{2(1)} = \frac{3 \pm \sqrt{49}}{2} = \frac{3+7}{2} \text{ or } \frac{3-7}{2}$$

$$x = 5 \quad \text{or} \quad x = -2$$

         Core Connections Algebra 2

1-46.   Use any method to find the point of intersection of $f(x) = 3x - 5$ and $g(x) = -4x + 9$.

1-47.   Compute for $f(x) = \frac{1}{x}$.

    a. $f(\frac{1}{2})$
    b. $f(\frac{1}{10})$
    c. $f(0.01)$
    d. $f(0.007)$

1-48.   Solve each of the following quadratic equations. If you need help, refer to the Math Notes box for this lesson.

    a. $x^2 - 8x + 15 = 0$
                                                    b. $2x^2 - 5x - 6 = 0$

1-49.   Consider the points $(-5, 0)$ and $(0, 3)$.

    a.   Plot the points and find the distance between them. Give your answer both in simplest radical form and as a decimal approximation.

    b.   Find the slope of the line that passes through both points.

1-50.   Stacie says to Cory, *"Reach into this standard deck of playing cards and pull out a card at random. If it is the queen of hearts, I'll pay you $5.00."* (Note: A standard deck of playing cards contains 52 cards, each of which is unique.)

    a.   What is the probability that Cory gets Stacie's $5.00?

    b.   What is the probability that Stacie keeps her $5.00?

1-51.   Find the error in the solution at right. Identify the error and solve the equation correctly.

$$4.1x = 9.5x + 23.7$$
$$-4.1x = -4.1x$$
$$5.4x = 23.7$$
$$\frac{5.4x}{5.4} = \frac{23.7}{5.4}$$
$$x = 4.39$$

1-52.   Solve each of the following equations.

    a. $3.9x - 2.1 = 11.2x + 51.7$
                                          b. $\frac{1}{5}x - 2 = \frac{13}{25} - 0.7x$

1.2.1 How can I represent a function?

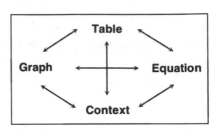

Modeling a Geometric Relationship

Mathematics can be used to model physical relationships to help us understand them better. Mathematical models can assume the form of a series of diagrams, a situation, a table, an equation, or a graph. In this course, you will be given situations to explore by gathering and interpreting data. You will learn to generalize your information so that you can make predictions about cases that you did not actually test. In this lesson, you will analyze a geometric relationship and look for connections among its multiple representations.

1-53.   ANALYZING DATA FROM A GEOMETRIC RELATIONSHIP

Each team will make paper boxes using the instructions given below. Based on the physical models, your team will represent the relationship between the height of the box and its volume in multiple ways.

If it has not been done already, cut a sheet of centimeter grid paper to match the dimensions that your teacher assigns your team. Then, cut the same size square out of each corner, and fold the sides up to form a shallow box (with no lid) as shown below.

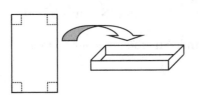

Dimensions

22 cm × 16 cm   18 cm × 10 cm

22 cm × 14 cm   15 cm × 15 cm

20 cm × 15 cm   15 cm × 10 cm

20 cm × 9 cm   12 cm × 9 cm

Your Task: As a team you will investigate the relationship between the height of a box (the **input**) and its volume (the **output**). You can build as many boxes as necessary to establish this relationship. Be sure to build all of your boxes out of paper of the same size. Record your information using multiple representations – including diagrams, a table, and a graph. Also record any thoughts, observations, and/or general statements that come up in your discussion of the problem.

Discussion Points

How can we collect data for this relationship?

How much data is enough?

What are all the possible inputs for our function?

How are the different representations related?

Further Guidance

1-54. Begin your investigation by building several boxes, taking measurements, and collecting data.

a. As a team, choose a starting input value. Note that this value is the same as *the length of the side of one of the squares cut from the corner of your grid paper* and becomes the height of your box. Now make the first box and determine its volume. Label the box with its important information. Work in the middle of your workspace so that everyone understands what is being measured or calculated, and be sure everyone agrees on the result before recording the information in an input → output table on your own paper.

b. Each team member should now choose a *different* input value and build a new box or draw a diagram using this new value. Calculate the volume of your box. Share your input and output values with the rest of your team and record everyone's data in your input→output table.

c. Use the data in your table to create a graph to represent the situation.

——————————— *Further Guidance* ———————————
section ends here.

1-55.   **GENERALIZING**

Now you will generalize your results. Generalizing is an important mathematical process. A common way to generalize is to write an equation using algebra.

a.   Draw a diagram of one of your boxes. Since this shape is being used to generalize, you want it to represent a relationship between *any* possible input and its output. Therefore, instead of labeling the height with a number, label the height of this box x.

b.   Work with your team to calculate the volume (or y-value) for a height of x. It may help you to remember how you calculated the volume when the height was a number and use the same strategy for your new input of x.

1-56.   **LOOKING FOR CONNECTIONS**

Put your $x \to y$ table, graph, and equation in the middle of your workspace. With your team, discuss the questions below.

As you address each question, remember to give reasons when you can. Also, if you make an observation, discuss how that observation relates to your table, graph, and equation.

a.   Is the domain of the relationship limited? That is, are there some input values that would not make sense? Why or why not? How can you tell using the graph? The $x \to y$ table? Using the equation? Using the boxes themselves (or diagrams of the boxes)?

b.   Is the range of the relationship limited? That is, what are all of the possible outputs (volumes)? Are there any outputs that would not make sense? Why or why not?

c.   Should you connect the points on your graph with a smooth curve? That is, should your graph be *continuous* or *discrete*? Explain.

d.   What is different about your graph for this problem when compared to others you have seen in previous courses? What special points or features does it have?

e.   Work with your team to find as many other connections as you can among your geometric models, your table, your equation, and your graph. How can you show or explain each connection?

1-57.   What graph do you get when you use the graphing calculator to draw the graph of your equation? Explain the relationship between this and the graph you made on your own paper.

1-58.   Organize your findings into a stand-alone poster that shows everything you
         have learned about all of the representations of your function as well as the
         connections between the representations. Use colors, arrows, words, and any
         other useful tools you can think of to make sure that someone reading your
         poster would understand all of your thinking.

METHODS AND MEANINGS

Triangle Trigonometry

There are three **trigonometric ratios** you can use to solve for the
missing side lengths and angle measurements in any right
triangle: tangent, sine, and cosine.

In the triangle below, when the sides are described relative to the
angle θ (the Greek letter "theta"), the opposite leg is y and the
adjacent leg is x. The hypotenuse is h regardless of which acute
angle is used.

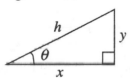

$$\tan \theta = \frac{\text{opposite leg}}{\text{adjacent leg}} = \frac{y}{x}$$

$$\sin \theta = \frac{\text{opposite leg}}{\text{hypotenuse}} = \frac{y}{h}$$

$$\cos \theta = \frac{\text{adjacent leg}}{\text{hypotenuse}} = \frac{x}{h}$$

In general, for any uniquely determined triangle, missing sides and
angles can be determined by using the **Law of Sines** or the **Law of
Cosines**.

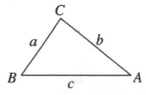

$$\frac{\sin A}{a} = \frac{\sin B}{b} = \frac{\sin C}{c}$$
and
$$c^2 = a^2 + b^2 - 2ab\cos C$$

1-59.   Make a table and graph for $h(x) = x^3 - 4$. Find the domain, range, and
         intercepts.

1-60.   For each diagram below, write and solve an equation to find the value of each
         variable. Give your answer to part (d) in both radical and decimal form. For a
         reminder of the trigonometry ratios, refer to the Math Notes box for this lesson.

a. 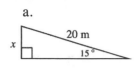   b. 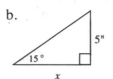   c.   d.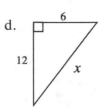

1-61.   Consider the equation $4x - 6y = 12$.

         a.   Predict what the graph of this equation looks like. Justify your answer.

         b.   Solve the equation for y and graph the equation.

         c.   Explain clearly how to find the x- and y-intercepts.

         d.   Which form of the equation is best for finding the x- and y-intercepts
               quickly? Why?

         e.   Find the x- and y-intercepts of $2x - 3y = -18$. Then use the intercepts to
               sketch a graph quickly.

1-62.   Name the domain and range for each of the following functions.

a. 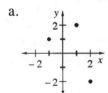   b. 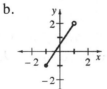   c. 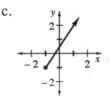   d.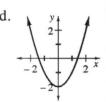

1-63.   Find the error in the solution at right. Explain what
         the error is and solve the equation correctly. Be
         sure to check your answer.

$$\frac{5}{x} = x - 4$$
$$x \cdot \frac{5}{x} = x - 4$$
$$5 = x - 4$$
$$x = 9$$

1-64.   Solve each of the following equations. Be sure to check your answers.

         a. $\frac{6}{x} = x - 1$ b. $\frac{9}{x} = x$

1-65.   Compute each of the following values for $f(x) = \frac{1}{x-2}$.

   a. $f(2.5)$ b. $f(1.75)$

   c. $f(2)$ d.   Justify your answer for part (c).

1-66.   Graph the following functions and find the x- and y-intercepts.

   a. $y = 2x + 3$ b. $f(x) = 2x + 3$

   c.   How are the functions in (a) and (b) the same? How are they different?

1-67.   A 3-foot indoor children's slide must meet the ground very gradually and make an angle of 155°, as shown in the diagram at right. Find the height of the slide (y) and the length of the floor it will cover (x).

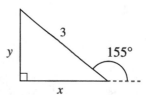

1-68.   Find the domain and the range for each of the following functions.

   a. 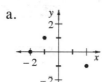   b. 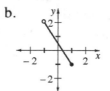   c. 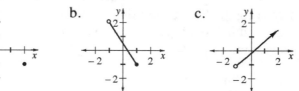   d.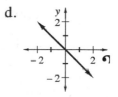

1-69.   Write one or two equations to help you solve the following problem.

A rectangle's length is four times its width. The sum of its two adjacent sides is 22 cm. How long is each side?

1-70.   Solve each of the following equations.

   a. $\frac{3}{x} + 6 = -45$ b. $\frac{x-2}{5} = \frac{10-x}{8}$ c. $(x+1)(x-3) = 0$

1-71.   Consider $f(x) = x^2 - 2x + 6$ and $g(x) = 2x + 11$.

   a.   Use any method to find the points of intersection of $f(x)$ and $g(x)$.

   b.   Calculate $f(x) + g(x)$.

   c.   Calculate $f(x) - g(x)$.

1-72.   Rearrange each equation below by solving for x. Write each equation in the form $x =$ _____ . (Note that y will be in your answer).

    a. $y = \frac{3}{5}x + 1$ b. $3x + 2y = 6$

    c. $y = x^2$ d. $y = x^2 - 100$

1-73.   Consider circles of different sizes. Create multiple representations of the function ($x \rightarrow y$ table, equation, and graph) with inputs that are the radius of the circle and outputs that are its area.

1-74.   Consider the points $(-2, 5)$ and $(5, 2)$ as you complete parts (a) and (b) below.

    a.   Plot the points and find the distance between them. Give your answer both in simplest radical form and as a decimal approximation.

    b.   Find the slope of the line that goes through the two points.

1-75.   If the number 1 is the output for Carmichael's function machine shown at right, how can you find out what number was dropped in? Find the number(s) that could have been dropped in.

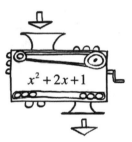

$x^2 + 2x + 1$

1-76.   What value of x allows you to find the y-intercept? Where does the graph of each equation below cross the y-axis? Write each answer as an ordered pair.

    a. $y = 3x + 6$ b. $x = 5y - 10$

    c. $y = x^2$ d. $y = 2x^2 - 4$

    e. $y = (x - 5)^2$ f. $y = 3x^3 - 2x^2 + 13$

1-77.   Find the error in the solution at right. Describe the error and solve the equation correctly.

$3x + 2 = 10 - 4(x - 1)$

$3x + 2 = 6(x - 1)$

$3x + 2 = 6x - 6$

$8 = 3x$ so $x = \frac{8}{3}$

1.2.2 How can I investigate a function?

Function Investigation

What does it mean to describe a function completely? In this lesson you will graph and investigate a family of functions with equations of the form $f(x) = \frac{1}{x-h}$. As you work with your team, keep the multiple representations of functions in mind.

1-78.   **INVESTIGATING A FUNCTION, Part One**

Your team will investigate functions of the form $f(x) = \frac{1}{x-h}$, where h can be any number.

As a team, choose a value for h between -10 and 10. For example, if $h = 7$, then $f(x) = \frac{1}{x-7}$.

Your Task: On a piece of graph paper, write down the function you get when you use your value for h. Then make an $x \to y$ table and draw a complete graph of your function. Is there any more information you need to be sure that you can see the entire shape of your graph? Discuss this question with your team and add any new information you think is necessary.

Discussion Points

How can we be sure that our graph is complete?

How can we get output values that are greater than 1 or less than -1?

Further Guidance

1-79.   This function is different from others you have seen in the past. To get a complete graph, you will need to make sure your table includes enough information.

a.   Make an $x \rightarrow y$ table with integer x-values from 5 less than your value of h to 5 more than your value of h. For example, if you are working with $h = 7$, you would begin your table at $x = 2$ and end it at $x = 12$. What do you notice about all of your y-values?

b.   Is there any x-value that has no y-value for your function? Why does this make sense?

c.   Plot all of the points that you have in your table so far.

d.   Now you will need to add more values to your table to see what is happening to your function as your input values get close to your value of h. Choose eight input values that are very close to your value of h and on either side of h. For example, if you are working with $h = 7$, you might choose input values such as $6.5, 6.7, 6.9, 6.99, 7.01, 7.1, 7.3$, and 7.5. For each new input value, calculate the corresponding output and add the new point to your graph.

e.   When you have enough points to be sure that you know the shape of your graph, sketch the curve.

——————   *Further Guidance*   ——————
section ends here.

1-80.   Now you will continue your investigation of $f(x) = \frac{1}{x-h}$.

a.   Each team member should choose a different value of h and make a complete $x \rightarrow y$ table and graph for your new function.

b.   Examine all of your team's functions. Together, generate a list of questions that you could ask about the functions your team created. Be as thorough as possible and be prepared to share your questions with the class.

c.   The graph of some functions contains an **asymptote**. To learn more about asymptotes, read the Math Notes box at the end of this lesson.

d.   As your teacher records each team's questions, copy them into your Learning Log. Title this entry "Function Investigation Questions" and label it with today's date.

1-81.   INVESTIGATING A FUNCTION, Part Two: SUMMARY STATEMENTS

Now you are ready for the most important part of your investigation: summary statements! Summary statements are a very important part of this course, so your team will practice making them. A summary statement is a statement about a function *along with a thorough justification*. A strong summary statement should be justified with multiple representations ($x \rightarrow y$ table, graph, equation, and situation, if applicable).

a.   Read the example summary statement below about the range of the function $y = x^2$. Discuss it with your team and decide if it is justified completely.

Statement: The function $y = x^2$ has a range of all real numbers greater than or equal to zero ($y \geq 0$). **First justification:** You can see this when you look at the graph, because you can see that the lowest point on the graph is on the *x*-axis.

Second justification: You can also see this in the table, because none of the *y*-values are negative.

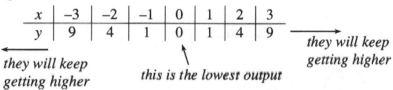

x	−3	−2	−1	0	1	2	3
y	9	4	1	0	1	4	9

they will keep getting higher   *this is the lowest output*   *they will keep getting higher*

Third justification: It makes sense with the equation, because if you square any number, the answer will be positive. For example, $(-2)^2 = 4$ and $3^2 = 9$.

---

b.   Use your "Function Investigation Questions" Learning Log entry from problem 1-80 to help you make as many summary statements about your functions as you can. Remember to justify each summary statement in as many ways as possible.

1-82.   SHARING SUMMARY STATEMENTS

With your team, choose one summary statement that you wrote that you find particularly interesting. Write the summary statement along with its justification so that it can be displayed for the whole class to see. Include sketches of graphs, $x \rightarrow y$ tables, equations, circles, arrows, colors, and any other tools that are helpful.

1-83.   What will the graph of $f(x) = \frac{1}{x+25}$ look like?

a.   Discuss this question with your team and make a sketch of what you predict the graph will look like. Give as many reasons for your prediction as you can.

b.   Use your graphing calculator to graph $f(x) = \frac{1}{x+25}$. Do you see what you expected to see? Why or why not?

c.   Adjust the viewing window if needed. When you see the full picture of your graph, make a sketch of the graph on your paper. Label any important points.

d.   How close was your prediction?

Graphs with Asymptotes

A mathematically clear and complete definition of an asymptote requires some ideas from calculus, but some examples of graphs with **asymptotes** should help you recognize them when they occur. In the following examples, the dotted lines are the asymptotes, and the equations of the asymptotes are given. In the two lower graphs, the y-axis, $x = 0$, is also an asymptote.

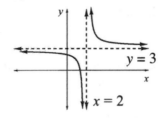

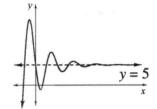

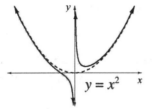

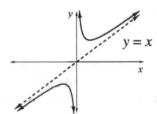

As you can see in the examples above, asymptotes can be diagonal lines or even curves. However, in this course, asymptotes will almost always be horizontal or vertical lines. The graph of a function has a **horizontal asymptote** if as you trace along the graph out to the left or right (that is, as you choose x-coordinates farther and farther away from zero, either toward infinity or toward negative infinity), the distance between the graph of the function and the asymptote gets closer to zero.

A graph has a **vertical asymptote** if, as you choose x-coordinates closer and closer to a certain value, from either the left or right (or both), the y-coordinate gets farther away from zero, either toward infinity or toward negative infinity.

1-84.   Use any method to find the points of intersection of $f(x) = 2x^2 - 3x + 4$ and $g(x) = x^2 + 5x - 3$.

1-85.   Solve each equation for x.

   a. $-2(x + 4) = 35 - (7 - 4x)$ b. $\frac{x-4}{7} = \frac{8-3x}{5}$

1-86.   Make a complete graph of the function $f(x) = \sqrt{x} - 2$, label its x- and y-intercepts, and describe its domain and range.

1-87.   Write and solve an equation or a system of equations to help you solve the following problem.

   A cable 84 meters long is cut into two pieces so that one piece is 18 meters longer than the other. Find the length of each piece of cable.

1-88.   Carlo got a pet snake as a birthday present. On his birthday, the baby snake was just 26 cm long. He has been watching it closely and has noticed that it has been growing 2 cm each week.

   a.   Create multiple representations ($x \rightarrow y$ table, graph, and equation) of the function for which the inputs are the weeks since Carlo's birthday and the outputs are the length of the snake.

   b.   If the snake continues to grow at the same rate, when will it be 1 meter (100 cm) long? How can you see this in each representation?

1-89.   What value of y allows you to find the x-intercept? For each of the equations below, find where its graph intersects the x-axis. Write each answer as an ordered pair.

   a. $y = 3x + 6$ b. $x = 5y - 10$

   c. $y = x^2$ d. $y = 2x^2 - 4$

   e. $y = (x - 5)^2$ f. $y = x^3 - 13$

1-90.   Make a complete graph of the function $h(x) = 2x^2 + 4x - 6$ and describe its domain and range.

1-91.   Solve each equation below for the indicated variable.

     a. $y = mx + b$ for x b. $A = \pi r^2$ for r

     c. $V = LHW$ for W d. $2x + \frac{1}{y} = 3$ for y

1-92.   Create multiple representations ($x \rightarrow y$ table, graph, and equation) of the function $g(x) = \frac{2}{x}$. Then make at least 3 summary statements.

1-93.   Suppose you want to find where the lines $y = 3x + 15$ and $y = 3 - 3x$ cross, and you want to be more accurate than the graphing calculator or graph paper will allow. You can use algebra to find the *point of intersection*.

     a.   If you remember how to do this, find the point of intersection using algebra and be prepared to explain your method to your team tomorrow in class. If you do not remember, then do parts (b) through (e) below.

     b.   Since $y = 3x + 15$ and $y = 3 - 3x$, what must be true about $3x + 15$ and $3 - 3x$ when their y-values are the same?

     c.   Write an equation that does not contain y and solve it for x.

     d.   Use the x-value you found in part (c) to find the corresponding y-value.

     e.   Where do the two lines cross?

1-94.   The *Salami and More Deli* sells a 5-foot submarine sandwich for parties. It weighs 8 pounds. Assuming that the weight per foot is constant, what would be the length of a 12-pound sandwich?

1-95.   If $h(x) = x^2 - 5$, where does the graph of $h(x)$ cross the x-axis? Make a sketch of the graph.

1-96.   Graph the following equations.

    a. $y - 2x = 3$

    b. $y - 3 = x^2$

    c.   State the x- and y-intercepts for each equation.

    d.   Where do the two graphs cross? Show how you can find these two points without looking at the graphs.

1-97.   Match the law, equation, or formula in Column I with its corresponding name from Column II.

Column I

    a. $x = \frac{-b \pm \sqrt{b^2 - 4ac}}{2a}$

    b. $\frac{\sin A}{a} = \frac{\sin B}{b}$

    c. $c^2 = a^2 + b^2$

    d. $c^2 = a^2 + b^2 - 2ab \cos C$

Column II

    1.   Law of Cosines

    2.   Law of Sines

    3.   Pythagorean Theorem

    4.   Quadratic Formula

1.2.3 What do they have in common?

The Family of Linear Functions

In Lesson 1.2.2, your team investigated functions of the form $f(x) = \frac{1}{x-h}$, where h could be any number. You learned that as you changed h, the graph changed, but the basic shape stayed the same. In this lesson, you will think about functions of the form $f(x) = mx + b$.

1-98.   Consider functions of the form $y = mx + b$.

    a.   What do x and y represent in this function? What do m and b represent? Which ones can you change?

    b.   With the rest of the class, explore the effects of m and b on the function $y = mx + b$. What effect does m have on the graph? What effect does b have on the graph?

    c.   For this function, m and b are called **parameters** (as h was for $f(x) = \frac{1}{x-h}$), whereas x and y are called **variables**. With your team, explain the difference between a parameter and a variable.

    d.   What do all of the functions of the form $y = mx + b$ have in common? Since they all have the same basic relationship between x and y, they can be called a **family of functions**.

1-99.   With your team, examine each group of equations below and discuss what you would see if you drew the graphs of the four equations on one set of axes. Write a description of what you imagine you would see. (You do not actually have to draw them.)

    a. $x + 2y = 10$
           $y = -\frac{1}{2}x + 3$
           $-4y = 2x + 8$
           $y = -\frac{1}{2}x$

    b. $5x + y = -3$
           $y = -\frac{1}{2}x - 3$
           $3x - 4y = 12$
           $5y - 2x = -15$

1-100. Parts (a) through (f) below are six representations of a relationship between an input and an output. With your team, decide whether each relationship is linear and write a clear summary statement justifying your decision. If the relationship is linear, graph it and find its equation. If it is not linear, describe the growth.

a.

Pieces of Bread	Grams of Fiber
0	0
1	5
2	10
3	15
4	20

b. *Killer Fried Chickens charges $7.00 for a basic bucket of chicken and $0.50 for each additional piece. The input is the number of extra pieces of chicken ordered, and the output is the total cost of the order.*

c.

x	y
10	0
5	5
3	7
2	8
1	9
0	10

d.

x	y
10	1
5	2
4	2.5
2	5
1	10
0.5	20

e. *James planted a bush in his yard. The year he planted it, the bush produced 17 flowers. Each year, the branches of the bush split, so the number of flowers doubles. The input is the year after planting, and the output is the number of flowers.*

f.

x	y
0	−7
2	−2
4	3
6	8
8	13

1-101. Work with your team to create one new table and one new situation that display linear relationships. Be sure to justify how you can tell that your table and situation are linear.

1-102. Without using a graph, decide whether the relationship shown in the table at right is linear. Write a clear summary statement justifying your ideas. Be prepared to share your ideas with the class.

x	y
1	0.5
4	−7
10	−22
15	−34.5

1-103. LEARNING LOG

In your Learning Log, explain how you can recognize a linear relationship in a table or the description of a situation. Be sure to include examples. Title this entry "Recognizing Linear Relationships" and label it with today's date.

Core Connections Algebra 2

1-104. Find the slope and intercepts of $3x + 4y = 12$. Sketch a graph.

1-105. Write an equation for the line that passes through the points $(2, 0)$ and $(0, -3)$. Remember that drawing a diagram (in this case, drawing the graph) can be very helpful.

1-106. Solve each equation below. Give solutions in both radical and decimal form.

   a. $x^2 + 3x - 3 = 0$ b. $3x^2 - 7x = 12$

1-107. Jason loves to download music. *Downloads R Us* sells songs only in packages of three, and it charges $2.00 for each package of three songs. Jason's favorite group just released their *Greatest Hits* CD, which has 17 songs on it. Jason wants to buy all 17 songs from *Downloads R Us*. How much should Jason expect to pay?

1-108. Make a sketch of a graph showing the relationship between the number of people on your school's campus and the time of day.

1-109. For each graph below, what are the domain and range?

   a. 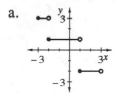   b. 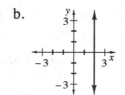   c.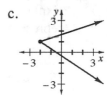

1-110. Uyregor has a collection of six-sided number cubes. He takes one out to roll it.

   a.   What are all possible outcomes that can come up?

   b.   What is the probability that a 4 comes up?

   c.   What is the probability that the number that comes up is less than 5?

1.2.4 What can I learn about it?

Function Investigation Challenge

In this lesson, you will have a chance to show your understanding of investigation as you work with a new function.

1-111.   In this activity you will investigate the function $f(x) = \frac{5}{(x^2+1)} - 1$.

   a.   Take a moment to look over your Learning Log entry entitled "Function Investigation Questions." Are there any questions you should add to your list? Discuss this with your team and make any necessary additions to your Learning Log.

   b.   Now investigate $f(x) = \frac{5}{(x^2+1)} - 1$ completely. Be sure to make clear summary statements that are justified using multiple representations.

1-112.   Recently, Kalani and Lynette took a trip from Vacaville, California to Los Angeles. The graph at right represents their trip.

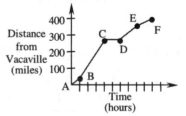

   a.   Explain what each line segment in the graph represents.

   b.   About how many miles is it from Vacaville to Los Angeles? How do you know?

   c.   Using the graph shown above, sketch a graph that would represent their *speed* while traveling. Take your time to think this through carefully and be sure to label the axes.

1-113.   Solve each equation below for x.

   a. $10 - 2(2x + 1) = 4(x - 2)$ b. $5 - (2x - 3) = -8 + 2x$

1-114. The right triangle shown at right has a height ($m\overline{BC}$) of 12 cm, and its area is 60 square cm. Find $m\angle B$ and the length of the hypotenuse.

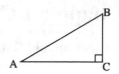

1-115. The longer leg of a right triangle is three inches more than three times the length of the shorter leg. The area of the triangle is 84 square inches. Find the perimeter of the triangle.

1-116. Imagine that you are adding water to the beakers shown below (labeled A, B, and C). Sketch a graph for each beaker to show the relationship between the volume of water added and the height of the water in each beaker. Put all three graphs on one set of axes (you may want to use colored pencils to distinguish the graphs). What are the independent and dependent variables?

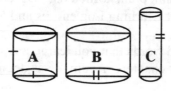

1-117. Sketch a few different equilateral triangles. Create multiple representations ($x \rightarrow y$ table, graph, equation) of the function with inputs that are the length of one side of an equilateral triangle and outputs that are its perimeter.

1-118. Have you ever wondered why so many equations are written with the variables x and y? Suppose you are reaching into a bag that contains all the letters of the English alphabet, and you pull out one letter at random to use as a variable in equations.

  a. What is the probability that you pull out an x?

  b. If you got an x, now what is the probability that you will pull out a y?

Chapter 1 Closure   What have I learned?

Reflection and Synthesis

The activities below offer you a chance to reflect
about what you have learned during this chapter.
As you work, look for concepts that you feel very
comfortable with, ideas that you would like to learn
more about, and topics you need more help with.
Look for connections between ideas as well as
connections with material you learned previously.

①   TEAM BRAINSTORM

What have you studied in this chapter? What ideas were important in what you
learned? With your team, brainstorm a list. Be as detailed as you can. To help
get you started, a list of Learning Log entries and Math Notes boxes are below.

What topics, ideas, and words that you learned *before* this course are connected
to the new ideas in this chapter? Again, be as detailed as you can.

How long can you make your list? Challenge yourselves. Be prepared to share
your team's ideas with the class.

Learning Log Entries
- Lesson 1.1.3 – Domain and Range
- Lesson 1.2.2 – Function Investigation Questions
- Lesson 1.2.3 – Recognizing Linear Relationships

Math Notes
- Lesson 1.1.1 – Functions
- Lesson 1.1.2 – Linear Equations
- Lesson 1.1.3 – Domain and Range
- Lesson 1.1.4 – Solving a Quadratic Equation
- Lesson 1.2.1 – Triangle Trigonometry
- Lesson 1.2.2 – Graphs With Asymptotes

The following is a list of the vocabulary used in this chapter. Make sure that you are familiar with all of these words and know what they mean. Refer to the glossary or index for any words that you do not yet understand.

asymptote	dependent variable	domain
equation	function	graph
independent variable	infinity	input
investigate	situation	symmetry
output	range	x-intercept
$x \rightarrow y$ table	y-intercept	

Make a concept map showing all of the connections you can find among the key words and ideas listed above. To show a connection between two words, draw a line between them and explain the connection, as shown in the model below. A word can be connected to any other word as long as you can justify the connection. For each key word or idea, provide an example or sketch that shows the idea.

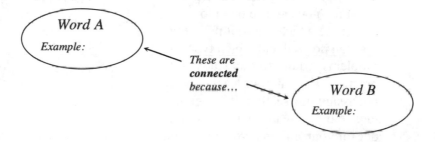

Your teacher may provide you with vocabulary cards to help you get started. If you use the cards to plan your concept map, be sure either to re-draw your concept map on your paper or to glue the vocabulary cards to a poster with all of the connections explained for others to see and understand.

While you are making your map, your team may think of related words or ideas that are not listed above. Be sure to include these ideas on your concept map.

③   PORTFOLIO: EVIDENCE OF MATHEMATICAL PROFICIENCY

Your teacher may have instructed you to take a
photograph of the poster you made for Lesson 1.1.2
as evidence of your early understanding about
describing functions. If so, include the photograph
in your portfolio.

Explain everything you know about $y = x^2 - 4$ and
$y = \sqrt{x + 4}$.

Your teacher may give you the Chapter 1 Closure Resource Page: Function
Investigations Graphic Organizer page to work on (or you can download this
from www.cpm.org). A Graphic Organizer is a tool you can use to organize
your thoughts and communicate your ideas clearly.

④   WHAT HAVE I LEARNED?

Most of the problems in this section
represent typical problems found in
this chapter. They serve as a gauge
for you. You can use them to
determine which types of problems
you can do well and which types of
problems require further study and
practice. Even if your teacher does
not assign this section, it is a good
idea to try these problems and find
out for yourself what you know and what you still need to work on.

Solve each problem as completely as you can. The table at the end of the
closure section has answers to these problems. It also tells you where you
can find additional help and practice with problems like these.

CL 1-119.   Given the functions $f(x) = \sqrt{x + 4}$ and $g(x) = x^2 - x$, find the value of each
expression below.

a. $f(5)$ b. $g(-1)$

c. x if $f(x) = 10$ d. x if $g(x) = 6$

CL 1-120.   Describe the domain and range for each function shown below.

a.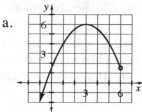

b.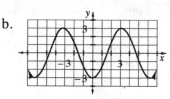

CL 1-121.   For each pair of equations below, determine where the graphs intersect.

a. $y = 3x + 15$
      $y = 3 - 3x$

b. $y = x^2 - 3x - 8$
      $y = 2$

CL 1-122.   Graph the function $f(x) = x^2 - 2x - 8$. Identify the domain and range and identify any special points such as the intercepts and vertex.

CL 1-123.   Graph each equation below and find the x- and y-intercepts.

a. $y = -\frac{3}{2}x + 8$

b. $2x - 3y = -6$

CL 1-124.   Find an equation for each line described below.

a.   The line that passes through the point (2, 8) and has a slope of –5.

b.   The line that passes through the points (–3, 4) and (5, –4).

c.   The line that passes through the points (–2, 4) and (4, –5).

CL 1-125.   Solve each equation below.

a. $\frac{x+2}{5} = \frac{10-2x}{3}$

b. $\frac{3}{x} - 1 = 8$

c. $x^2 + 3x = 18$

CL 1-126.   Solve for y.

a.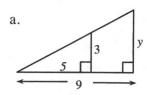

b.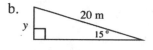

CL 1-127.   Micah was given $200 for his birthday. Each week he spends $15 on comic books. In how many weeks will his birthday money be gone?

Create multiple representations ($x \rightarrow y$ table, graph, and equation) for the relationship between the weeks since Micah's birthday and how much money he has left. How does each representation show the solution to the problem?

CL 1-128.   Check your answers using the table at the end of this section. Which problems do you feel confident about? Which problems were hard? Have you worked on problems like these in math classes you have taken before? Use the table to make a list of topics with which you need help and a list of topics you need to practice more.

Answers and Support for Closure Activity #4
What Have I Learned?

Note: MN = Math Note, LL = Learning Log

Problem	Solutions		Need Help?	More Practice
CL 1-119.	a. 3	b. 2	Lesson 1.1.1	Problems 1-4, 1-5, 1-17, 1-21, and 1-35
	c. $x = 96$	d. $x = -2$ or 3	MN: 1.1.1	
CL 1-120.	a. Domain: $-\infty < x < 6$ Range: $-\infty < y \le 6$		Lesson 1.1.3	Problems 1-34, 1-35, 1-62, 1-68, and 1-86
	b. Domain: all real numbers Range: $-3 \le y \le 3$		MN: 1.1.3 LL: 1.1.3	
CL 1-121.	a. $(-2, 9)$		Lesson 1.1.4	Problems 1-46, 1-69, 1-71, 1-84, 1-87, and 1-93
	b. $(5, 2), (-2, 2)$		MN: 1.1.4	
CL 1-122.			Lessons 1.2.2 and 1.2.4	Problems 1-20, 1-59, 1-90, and 1-95
	Domain: all real numbers;		MN: 1.1.3	
	Range: $y \ge -9$		LL: 1.2.2	
	Intercepts: $(-2, 0), (4, 0)$, and $(0, -8)$			
	Vertex: $(1, -9)$			
CL 1-123.	a.		MN: 1.1.2	Problems 1-7, 1-61, 1-66, and 1-104
	Intercepts: $(5\frac{1}{3}, 0)$ and $(0, 8)$			
	b.			
	Intercepts: $(-3, 0)$ and $(0, 2)$			

Problem	Solutions	Need Help?	More Practice
CL 1-124.	a. $y = -5x + 18$ b. $y = -x + 1$ c. $y = -\frac{3}{2}x + 1$	MN: 1.1.2	Problem 1-15, 1-49, 1-74, and 1-105
CL 1-125.	a. $x = \frac{44}{13}$ b. $x = \frac{1}{3}$ c. $x = -6$ or 3	Explanations and practice of topics from previous courses are available in the *Core Connections Algebra Parent Guide with Extra Practice,* available free at www.cpm.org.	Problems 1-36, 1-48, 1-52, 1-63, 1-64, 1-70, 1-85, and 1-106
CL 1-126.	a. $y = \frac{27}{5} = 5.4$ b. $y \approx 5.18$	MN: 1.2.1	Problems 1-24, 1-60, and 1-67
CL 1-127.	$y = 200 - 15x$, where y represents the total amount of money left and x represents the numbers of weeks that have passed	Lesson 1.1.2	Problems 1-12, 1-19, 1-39, and 1-88

Week	$
0	200
1	185
2	170
3	155
4	140
5	125

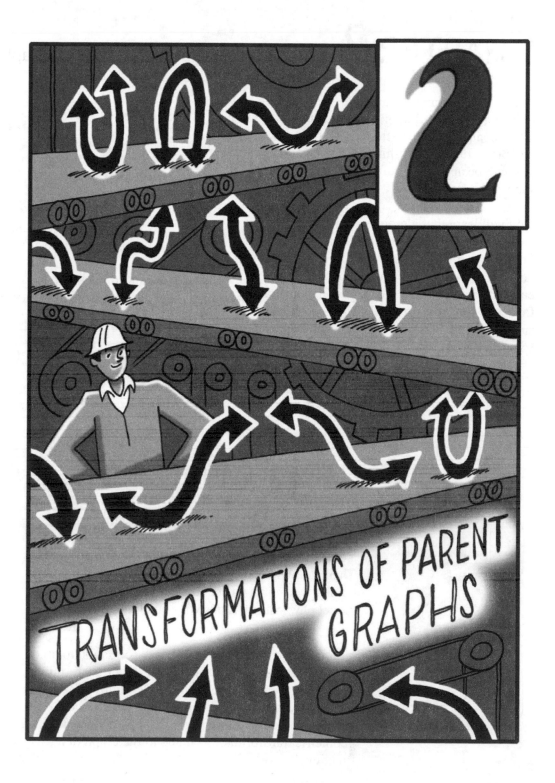

2

TRANSFORMATIONS OF PARENT GRAPHS

CHAPTER 2   Transformations of Parent Graphs

In the first section of Chapter 2, you will learn how to change the equation of a parabola to make it fit a set of nonlinear data. After you learn how to stretch, compress, reflect, and shift the graph of $f(x) = x^2$, you will be able to create a variety of parabolic shapes and sizes.

You will learn that a graph's transformations are clearly recognizable when its equation is written in graphing form. Understanding this form will help you learn how to rewrite equations so that they are easier to graph. You will also use the quadratic family of functions to model physical situations, such as the arc of a jumping rabbit and the path of a soccer ball.

In Section 2.2, you will apply these same types of transformations to other parent functions.

Guiding Question

Mathematically proficient students model with mathematics.

As you work through this chapter, ask yourself:

How can I model this everyday situation with mathematics?

Chapter Outline

Section 2.1 In this section, you will learn how to shift, stretch, compress, and flip the graph of $f(x) = x^2$. You will write a general equation for the family of quadratic functions. Then you will learn how to graph a quadratic function quickly when it is written in graphing form. You will model physical situations with quadratic functions.

Section 2.2 You will apply the concepts of transformation to other parent functions, and you will learn that transforming each parent function creates a whole family of functions. You will write a general equation for a family of functions. You will learn how the equation predicts the geometric transformations made to the graph of a function.

2.1.1 How can an equation help me predict?

Modeling Non-Linear Data

This chapter will help you develop the power to manipulate functions so that they are useful in a wide variety of situations. Today's lesson focuses on collecting data and finding a function to model the trend in that data. You will then generalize your results and make predictions beyond the range of data you can measure. Discuss the following focus questions with your team while you work:

What will the graph look like?

Should we connect the data points?

How can we find an equation that fits the data?

2-1.   SHRINKING TARGETS LAB

What is the relationship between the radius of a disk and its mass? If you double the radius of the disk, does the mass also double?

To answer these questions, your team will use scissors, a scale, and a Lesson 2.1.1 Resource Page. You will measure the weight of at least 8 different circular disks of varying radii (the plural of "radius"). Find your first data point by cutting out the large circle, measuring its radius, and using the scale to weigh it carefully. Repeat this process for circles of different radii.

After your team has collected its data, answer the questions below.

a.   Look at your data with your team and predict what you think the graph will look like. Justify your prediction.

b.   Enter your data in the graphing calculator and plot it. Sketch the graph of your data on your paper.

c.   Consider the shrinking targets situation, what do you predict the *x*- and *y*-intercepts should be? What do they represent? Does the graph of your equation have these same intercept(s)? If not, explain completely why not.

Problem continues on next page. →

2-1.   *Problem continued from previous page.*

   d.   What kind of equation do you think will model your data? Will your
        model predict the intercepts correctly?

   e.   Work with your team to find an equation that fits your data. Test the
        accuracy of your team's equation by entering it into your graphing
        calculator. If necessary, adjust your equation to make its graph fit your
        data and the *x*- and *y*-intercepts better. Once you are satisfied with your
        model, sketch the graph of your equation on your graph of data points
        from part (b).

   f.   What would be the mass of a target with a radius twice as large as the
        largest one you measured? How do you know?

2-2.   What more can be said about the equation you used to model your data from
        the Shrinking Targets Lab? Consider this as you answer the questions below.

   a.   What are all of the acceptable input and output values (domain and range)
        for the activity in Shrinking Targets Lab? Do they match the domain and
        range of the function you used to model your data? If not, why are they
        different?

   b.   In part (a), you may have noticed that your equation only makes sense as
        a model for your data for part of its domain. Therefore, to accurately
        describe your model, you can add a condition to your equation, such as,
        "This equation is a good model when _____."

        What condition can you add to describe when your model is valid?

2-3.   Look back at the adjustments you made to your equation in problem 2-1 in
        order to make it fit your data. What did you change in your equation, and what
        effects did your changes have on its graph? Discuss these questions with your
        team and be prepared to share your ideas with the class.

MATH NOTES

METHODS AND MEANINGS

Exponential Functions

An **exponential function** has the general form $y = a \cdot b^x$, where a is the **initial value** (the y-intercept) and b is the **multiplier** (the growth). Be careful: The independent variable x has to be in the exponent. For example, $y = x^2$ is *not* an exponential equation, even though it has an exponent.

For example, in the multiple representations below, the y-intercept is $(0, 4)$ and the growth factor is 3 because the y-value is increasing by multiplying by 3.

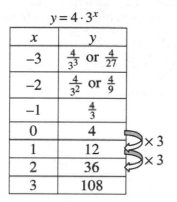

$$y = 4 \cdot 3^x$$

x	y
-3	$\frac{4}{3^3}$ or $\frac{4}{27}$
-2	$\frac{4}{3^2}$ or $\frac{4}{9}$
-1	$\frac{4}{3}$
0	4
1	12
2	36
3	108

$\times 3$
$\times 3$

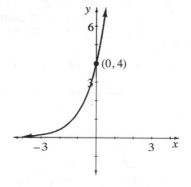

To increase or decrease a quantity by a percentage, use the multiplier for that percentage. For example, the multiplier for an increase of 7% is $100\% + 7\% = 1.07$. The multiplier for a decrease of 7% is $100\% - 7\% = 0.93$.

2-4.   Jamilla was moving to a new city. She
        researched the rates charged by the local utility
        company for water. She found the listing of
        charges below. She expects that her family may
        use up to 1,000 cubic feet of water each month.

        • $12.70 monthly service fee

        • First 300 cubic feet of water used:
           $3.90 per 100 cubic feet, or fraction thereof

        • After the first 300 cubic feet:
           $5.20 per 100 cubic feet, or fraction thereof

        a. Sketch a graph of the cost of Jamilla's possible water usage in one
            month. Be sure to consider what the cost would be for partial units such
            as 220 or 675 cubic feet of water.

        b. Is this graph a function? Why or why not?

        c. What are the domain and range of this graph?

2-5.   For each equation in parts (a) through (d) below, find the input value that
        gives the *smallest* possible output. In other words, find the *x*-value of the
        lowest point on the graph. Then find the input value that gives the *largest*
        possible output (or the *x*-value of the *highest* point on the graph).

        a. $y = (x-2)^2$ b. $y = x^2 + 2$ c. $y = (x+3)^2$ d. $y = -x^2 + 5$

        e. Where on the graphs of each of the above equations would you find the
            points with the smallest or largest *y*-values?

2-6.   Sketch $y = x^2$, $y = -3x^2$, and $y = -0.25x^2$ on the same set of axes. What does a
        negative coefficient do to the graph?

2-7.   Your results from this problem will be useful in the parabola investigation that you will do in Lesson 2.1.2.

   a.   Draw the graph of $y = (x-3)^2$. If you are drawing the graph by hand be sure to use the domain $0 \le x \le 6$.

   b.   How is this graph different from the graph of $y = x^2$?

2-8.   Consider the sequence with the initial value 256, followed by 64, 16, ...

   a.   Write the next three terms of this sequence, then find an equation for the sequence.

   b.   If you were to keep writing out more and more terms of the sequence, what would happen to the terms?

   c.   Sketch a graph of the sequence. What happens to the points as you go farther to the right?

   d.   What is the domain of the sequence? What is the domain of the function with the same equation as this sequence?

2-9.   Write the equation for each graph.

   a.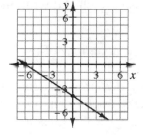

   b.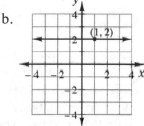

   c.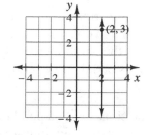

   d.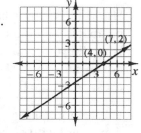

2-10.   The slope of $\overline{AB}$ is 5, with points $A(-3,-1)$ and $B(2,n)$. Find the value of n and the distance between points A and B.

2.1.2 How can I shift a parabola?

• •

Parabola Investigation

In Algebra 1 you learned about slope and y-intercept, ideas that allow you to write equations and sketch graphs of any line. During this lesson you will work on developing similar tools for parabolas.

2-11.   PARABOLA LAB, Part One

What happens to a parabola's graph when you change the numbers in the equation? To get a better sense of the different ways to transform the graph of a parabola, as a team complete the investigation outlined below. As you work, be sure to sketch the graphs you see in your graphing calculator carefully and record the equations you enter.

a.   On graph paper, graph the equation $y = (x-2)(x-2)$. Be sure to label any important points on your graph, including the lowest point on the graph, called the **vertex**. (If the graph were to open downward, the vertex would be the highest point on the graph.) Also sketch and write the equation of the line of symmetry of your graph.

b.   Use your graphing calculator to find the equations of two parabolas with *different* graphs that also open upward and still have a vertex at $(2, 0)$. Add sketches of these two new graphs to your graph from part (a), along with their equations. As you work, keep track of any ideas you try along with their results, even if they do not answer this question, as they may help you later.

c.   Use your graphing calculator to find the equations of two different parabolas that open *downward*, each with its vertex on the x-axis at $x = 2$. How did you change the equation so that the parabola would open downward? Add sketches of these graphs and their equations to your axes. What are their lines of symmetry?

d.   Use your graphing calculator to find the equation of a parabola that opens downward with a vertex at $(-4, 0)$. What is the equation of your parabola's line of symmetry?

e.   Choose a new point on the x-axis and find at least three equations of parabolas that touch the x-axis only at that one point.

2-12.   PARABOLA LAB, Part Two

Polly Parabola had been the manager of the Parabola Department of Functions of America, but she has decided to start her own company called "Professional Parabola Productions." She needs your help. See her memo below.

MEMO

To: *Your Study Team*
From: Ms. Polly Parabola, CEO
Re: *New Parabola Possibilities*

I am starting a new company specializing only in parabolas. To win over new customers, I need to be able to show them that we know more about parabolas than any of the other function factories around, especially since every company already sells $y = x^2$.

My customers will need all sorts of parabolas, and we need the knowledge to make them happy. I would love to offer parabolas that are completely new to them.

Please investigate all different kinds of parabolas. Determine all the ways that you can change the equation $y = x^2$ to change the shape, direction, and location of a parabola on a graph.

Remember that I'm counting on you! I need you to uncover the parabola secrets that our competitors do not know.

Sincerely,
Ms. Polly Parabola

Your Task: Work with your team to determine all of the ways you can change the graph of a parabola by changing its equation. Be prepared to share your ideas with the class. As other teams contribute ideas to a class discussion, write down any new ideas.

Start by choosing one transformation from the list generated by the class; then find a way to change the equation $y = x^2$ to create this transformation. Whenever you figure out a new transformation, record a clear summary statement before moving on to the next transformation. Be prepared to explain your summary statement to Ms. Polly Parabola.

Discussion Points

What changes can we make to a parabola's graph?

What changes can we make to the equation $y = x^2$?

How do changes in the equation relate to changes in the graph?

2-13.   Graph the parabola $y = x^2$. Be sure to label any important points. When you are sure that your graph is complete and accurate, trace over it in colored pencil.

a.   Find a way to change the equation is to make the $y = x^2$ parabola *stretch vertically*. That is, to make the graph look narrower, so the points in the parabola seem to rise away from the vertex more quickly. The new parabola should have the same vertex and orientation (i.e., open up) as $y = x^2$. Record the equations you try, along with their results. Write down the results even when they are wrong – they may come in handy later on.

b.   Find a way to change the equation to make the $y = x^2$ parabola *compress vertically*. That is, to make the graph look flatter, so that the points seem to rise away from the vertex less quickly. Record the equations you try, along with their results and your observations.

c.   Find a way to change the equation to make the same parabola *open downward*. The new parabola should be congruent (the same shape and size) to $y = x^2$, with the same vertex, except it should open downward so its vertex will be its highest point. Record the equations you try, their results, and your observations.

d.   Find a way to change the equation to make the $y = x^2$ parabola *move 5 units down*. Your new parabola should look exactly like $y = x^2$, but the vertex should be at $(0, -5)$. Record the equations you try, along with their results. Include a comment about moving the graph up as well as down.

e.   Find a way to change the equation to make the $y = x^2$ parabola *move 3 units to the right*. Your new parabola should look exactly like $y = x^2$, except that the vertex should be at the point $(3, 0)$. If you need an idea to get started, review your work on problem 2-11. Record the equations you try, along with their results. Include a comment about how to move the parabola to the left as well as how to move it to the right.

f.   Find a way to change the equation to make the $y = x^2$ parabola *move 3 units to the left*, as in part (e), AND *stretch vertically*, as in part (a). Record the equations you try, along with their results.

——————   *Further Guidance section ends here.*   ——————

2-14.   Find a way to change the equation to make the $y = x^2$ parabola *vertically compressed, open down, move six units up, and move two units to the left.* Where is the vertex of your new parabola?

2-15.   Now that you are a parabola expert, you can impress Ms. Polly Parabola!

   a.   Make up your own fancy transformation and show her how you can change your equation to create it.

   b.   Write a general equation for a parabola that could be shifted or stretched in any direction by any amount. Be prepared to share your ideas with the class.

2-16.   Explain the differences between an *accurate sketch* and a *careful graph*.

2-17.   If $p(x) = x^2 + 5x - 6$, find:

   a.   Where $p(x)$ intersects the y-axis.

   b.   Where $p(x)$ intersects the x-axis.

   c.   If $q(x) = x^2 + 5x$, find the intercepts of $q(x)$ and compare the graphs of $p(x)$ and $q(x)$.

   d.   Find $p(x) - q(x)$.

2-18.   Solve for z in each equation below.

   a. $4^z = 8$ b. $4^{2z/3} = 8^{(z+2)}$

   c. $3^z = 81^2$ d. $5^{(z+1)/3} = 25^{1/z}$

2-19.   Simplify each of the following expressions. Be sure that your answer has no negative or fractional exponents.

   a. $(\frac{1}{81})^{-1/4}$ b. $x^{-2}y^{-4}$ c. $(2x)^{-2}(16x^2y)^{1/2}$

2-20.   Daniela, Kieu, and Duyen decide to go to the
movies one hot summer afternoon. The theater is
having a summer special called Three Go Free.
They will get free movie tickets if they each buy
a large popcorn and a large soft drink. They take
the deal and spend $22.50 on food, drinks and
movie tickets. The next week, they go back
again, only this time, they each pay $8.00 for
their ticket, they each get a large soft drink, but
they share one large bucket of popcorn. This
return trip costs them a total of $37.50.

a.   Find the price of a large soft drink and the price of a large bucket of
popcorn.

b.   Did you write two equations or did you use another method? If you used
another method, write two equations now and solve them. If you already
used a system of equations, skip this part.

2-21.   Plot each pair of points and find the distance between them. Give answers in
both square-root form and as decimal approximations.

a. $(3,-6)$ and $(-2,5)$ b. $(5,-8)$ and $(-3,1)$ c. $(0,5)$ and $(5,0)$

d.   Write the distance you found in part (c) in simplified square-root form.

2-22.   The amount of profit (in millions) made by Scandal Math, a company that
writes math problems based on tabloid articles, can be found by the equation
$P(n) = -n^2 + 10n$, where n is the number of textbooks sold (also in millions).
Find the maximum profit and the number of textbooks that Scandal Math must
sell to realize this maximum profit.

2-23.   Your friend is taking an algebra class at a different school where
she is not allowed to use a graphing calculator.

a.   Explain to her how she can get a good sketch of the graph of
the function $y = 2(x+3)^2 - 8$ without using a calculator *and*
without having to make an $x \rightarrow y$ table. Be sure to explain how to locate
the vertex, whether the parabola should open up or down, and how its
shape is related to the shape of the graph of $y = x^2$.

b.   Your friend also needs to know the *x*- and *y*-intercepts. Show her how to
find them without having to draw an accurate graph or use a graphing
calculator.

2-24.   Consider the equations $y = 3(x-1)^2 - 5$ and $y = 3x^2 - 6x - 2$.

   a.   Verify that they are equivalent by creating a table or graph for each equation.

   b.   Show algebraically that these two equations are equivalent by starting with one form and showing how to get the other.

   c.   Notice that the value for a is 3 in both forms of the equation, but that the numbers for b and c are different from the numbers for h and k. Why do you think the value for a would be the same number in both forms of the equation?

2-25.   Use what you learned in the parabola investigation to write an equation for each of the parabolas described below.

   a.   A parabola opening upward, shifted 8 units right, and 5 units down.

   b.   A parabola with a stretch factor of 10, sitting with its vertex on the x-axis at $x = -6$.

   c.   A downward-opening parabola with vertex $(-7, -2)$ and a vertical compression of 0.6.

2-26.   The point $(3, -7)$ is on a line with a slope of $\frac{2}{3}$. Find another point on the line.

2-27.   Simplify each expression without using a calculator. Remember that to simplify expressions with radicals, you can remove perfect square factors such as in this example: $\sqrt{18} = \sqrt{9 \cdot 2} = \sqrt{9} \cdot \sqrt{2} = 3\sqrt{2}$

   a. $\sqrt{50}$ b. $\sqrt{72}$ c. $\sqrt{45}$

2-28.   Find the value of x.

   a.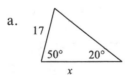

   b.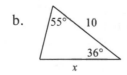

2-29.   Suppose your parents spend an average of $300 each month for your food.

   a.   In five years, when you are living on your own, how much will you be spending on food each month if you are eating about the same amount and inflation averages about 4% per year?

   b.   Write an equation that represents your monthly food bill x years from now if both the rate of inflation and your eating habits stay the same.

2.1.3 How can I graph it quickly?

Graphing a Parabola Without a Table

You have developed several tools that enable you to transform graphs of parabolas by altering their equations. In the next few lessons, you will use this knowledge to do more with the equations and graphs of parabolic functions than ever before. In this lesson, you will figure out how to use your growing knowledge of transforming graphs to make a quick and fairly accurate graph of any parabolic function.

2-30. TRANSFORMING GRAPHS

Use your dynamic graphing tool to support a class discussion about the equation $y = a(x - h)^2 + k$. Refer to the bulleted points below.

- Identify which **parameter** (a, h, or k) affects the orientation, vertical shift, horizontal shift, vertical stretch, and vertical compression of the graph compared to the graph of the parent function $y = x^2$.

- What values stretch the graph vertically? Compress the graph horizontally? Why do those values have these impacts?

- What values cause the graph to flip vertically?

- What values cause the graph to shift to the left? To the right? Why?

- What values cause the graph to shift up or down? Why?

- Are there points on your graph that connect to specific parameters in the equation? Explain.

2-31. For each equation below, predict the coordinates of the vertex, the orientation (whether it opens up or down), and whether the graph will be a vertical stretch or a compression of $y = x^2$. Do not use a graphing calculator. Quickly make an accurate graph based on your predictions. How can you make the shape of your graph accurate without using a table? Be prepared to share your strategies with the class.

a. $y = (x + 9)^2$ b. $y = x^2 + 7$

c. $y = 3x^2$ d. $y = \frac{1}{3}(x - 1)^2$

e. $y = -(x - 7)^2 + 6$ f. $y = 2(x + 3)^2 - 8$

g. Now take out your graphing calculator and check your predictions for the equations in parts (a) through (f). Did you make any mistakes? If so, describe the mistake and what you need to do in order to correct it.

2-32.   Graph each equation below without making a table or using your graphing calculator. Look for ways to go directly from the equation to the graph. What information did you need to make a graph without using a table? How did you find that information from the equation? Be ready to share your strategies with the class.

   a. $y = (x-7)^2 - 2$ b. $y = 0.5(x+3)^2 + 1$

2-33.   In problem 2-32, you figured out that having an equation for a parabola in **graphing form** ($y = a(x-h)^2 + k$) allows you to know the vertex, the orientation, and the stretch factor, and that knowing these attributes allows you to graph without having to make a table. How can you make a graph without a table when the equation is given in **standard form** ($y = ax^2 + bx + c$)? Consider the equation $y = 2x^2 + 4x - 30$.

   a.   What is the orientation of $y = 2x^2 + 4x - 30$? That is, does it open upward or open downward? How could you change the equation to make the graph open the opposite way?

   b.   What is the stretch factor of $y = 2x^2 + 4x - 30$? Justify your answer.

   c.   Can you identify the vertex of $y = 2x^2 + 4x - 30$ by looking at the equation? If not, talk with your team about strategies you could use to find the vertex without using a table or graphing calculator and then apply your new strategy to the problem. If your team is stuck consider doing parts (*i*) through (*iii*) below.

        i.   What are the x-intercepts of the parabola?

        ii.   Where is the vertex located in relation to the x-intercepts? Can you use this relationship to find the x coordinate of the vertex?

        iii. Use the x-coordinate of the vertex to find its y-coordinate.

   d.   Make a quick graph of $y = 2x^2 + 4x - 30$ and write its equation in graphing form.

2-34.   Rewrite each equation in graphing form and then sketch a graph. Label each sketch so that it is possible to connect it to the equation.

   a. $p(x) = x^2 - 10x + 16$ b. $f(x) = x^2 + 3x - 10$

   c. $g(x) = x^2 - 4x - 2$ d. $h(x) = -4x^2 + 4x + 8$

METHODS AND MEANINGS

Forms of Quadratics

There are three main forms of a quadratic function: standard form, factored form, and graphing form. Study the examples below. Assume that $a \neq 0$ and that the meaning of $a, b,$ and c are different for each form below.

Standard form: $f(x) = ax^2 + bx + c$. The y-intercept is $(0, c)$.

Factored form: $f(x) = a(x+b)(x+c)$. The x-intercepts are $(-b, 0)$ and $(-c, 0)$.

Graphing form (vertex form): $f(x) = a(x-h)^2 + k$. The vertex is (h, k).

Similarly, there are three forms of a single-variable quadratic equation.

Standard form: Any quadratic equation written in the form $ax^2 + bx + c = 0$.

Factored form: Any quadratic equation written in the form $a(x+b)(x+c) = 0$.

Perfect Square form: Any quadratic equation written in the form $(ax-b)^2 = c^2$.

Solutions to a quadratic equation can be written in **exact form (radical form)** as in:

$$x = \frac{-3+\sqrt{5}}{2} \quad \text{or} \quad x = \frac{-3-\sqrt{5}}{2}$$

Solutions can also be estimated and written in **approximate decimal form**:

$$x = -0.38 \quad \text{or} \quad x = -2.62$$

2-35.   Solve each of the following equations *without using the Quadratic Formula.*

   a. $y^2 - 6y = 0$ b. $n^2 + 5n + 7 = 7$

   c. $2t^2 - 14t + 3 = 3$ d. $\frac{1}{3}x^2 + 3x - 4 = -4$

   e.   Zero is one of the solutions of each of the above equations. What do all
         of the above equations have in common that causes them to have zero as
         a solution?

2-36.   Find the vertex of each of the following parabolas by averaging the
         x-intercepts. Then write each equation in graphing form.

   a. $y = (x - 3)(x - 11)$ b. $y = (x + 2)(x - 6)$

   c. $y = x^2 - 14x + 40$ d. $y = (x - 2)^2 - 1$

2-37.   Did you need to average the *x*-intercepts to find the vertex in part (d) of the
         preceding problem?

   a.   What are the coordinates of the vertex for part (d)?

   b.   How do these coordinates relate to the equation?

2-38.   Scientists can estimate the increase in carbon dioxide in the atmosphere by
         measuring increases in carbon emissions. In 1998 the annual carbon emission
         was about eight gigatons (a gigaton is a billion metric tons). Over the last
         several years, annual carbon emission has been increasing by about one
         percent.

   a.   At this rate, how much carbon will be emitted in 2010?

   b.   Write a function, $C(x)$, to represent the amount of carbon emitted in any
         year starting with the year 2000.

2-39.   Make predictions about how many places the graph of each equation below
         will touch the x-axis. You may first want to rewrite some of the equations in a
         more useful form.

    a. $y = (x - 2)(x - 3)$ b. $y = (x + 1)^2$

    c. $y = x^2 + 6x + 9$ d. $y = x^2 + 7x + 10$

    e. $y = x^2 + 6x + 8$ f. $y = -x^2 - 4x - 4$

    g.   Check your predictions with your calculator.

    h.   Write a clear explanation describing how you can tell whether the
          equation of a parabola will touch the x-axis at only one point.

2-40.   Simplify each of the following expressions. Be sure that your answer has no
         negative or fractional exponents.

    a. $64^{1/3}$ b. $(4x^2 y^5)^{-2}$ c. $(2x^2 \cdot y^{-3})(3x^{-1}y^5)$

2-41.   Suppose you have a 3 by 3 by 3 cube. It is painted on all six faces and then cut
         apart into 27 pieces, each a 1 by 1 by 1 cube. If one of the cubes is chosen at
         random, what is the probability that:

    a.   Three sides are painted?   b.   Two sides are painted?

    c.   One side is painted?   d.   No sides are painted?

2.1.4 How can I rewrite it in graphing form?

Rewriting in Graphing Form

In Lesson 2.1.3, you used the method of averaging the intercepts to change the equation of a parabola from the standard form $f(x) = ax^2 + bx + c$ to the graphing form $f(x) = a(x-h)^2 + k$ by finding the x-intercepts and averaging them to find the x-value of the vertex. Next you substituted to find the y-value, and then used the coordinates of the vertex for h and k.

What can you say about a parabola that cannot be factored or that does not cross the x-axis? How can you write its equation in graphing form? In a previous course you may have learned how to complete the square for quadratics and this strategy can help you write the graphing form for a parabola.

2-42.   In this investigation you will compare two methods of changing a quadratic equation from standard form to graphing form.

  a.   Write the equation of the parabola $y = x^2 - 2x - 15$ in graphing form using two methods. First, use the method of averaging the intercepts. Then, use the method of completing the square. Find the x-intercept(s), the y-intercept(s), and the vertex of the parabola, and sketch the graph.

  b.   Write $y = x^2 + 8x + 10$ in graphing form. Find the intercepts and vertex, and sketch the graph. Do both strategies work for this parabola?

  c.   Can you use both methods to sketch $y = x^2 + 2x + 4$? Do both strategies still work?

  d.   Discuss the two strategies with your team. Then respond to the following Discussion Points.

Discussion Points

When does the method of averaging the intercepts work better?

When does the method of completing the square work better?

Which method was more efficient and why?

2-43.   Jessica was at home struggling with her homework. She had missed class and could not remember how to **complete the square**. She was supposed to use the method to change $f(x) = x^2 + 8x + 10$ to graphing form. Then her precocious younger sister, Anita, who was playing with algebra tiles, said, *"Hey, I bet I know what they mean."* Anita's Algebra class had been using tiles to multiply and factor binomials. Anita explained, *"$f(x) = x^2 + 8x + 10$ would look like this,"*

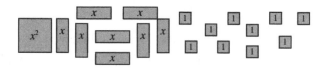

"Yes," said Jessica, *"I took Algebra 1 too, remember?"*

Anita continued, *"And you need to make it into a square!"*

"OK," said Jessica, and she arranged her tiles as shown in the picture below.

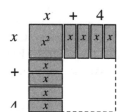

"Oh," said Jessica. *"So I just need 16 small unit tiles to fill in the corner."*

"But you only have 10," Anita reminded her.

"Right, I only have ten," Jessica replied. She put in the 10 small square tiles then drew the outline of the whole square and said:

*"Oh, I get it! The **complete square** is $(x+4)^2$ which is equal to $x^2 + 4x + 16$. But my original expression, $x^2 + 8x + 10$, has six fewer tiles than that, so what I have is $(x+4)^2$, minus 6."*

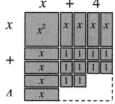

"Yes," said Anita. *"You started with $x^2 + 8x + 10$, but now you can rewrite it as $x^2 + 8x + 10 = (x+4)^2 - 6$."*

Use your graphing calculator to show that $f(x) = x^2 + 8x + 10$ and $f(x) = (x+4)^2 - 6$ are equivalent functions.

2-44.   Help Jessica with a new problem. She needs to complete the square to write $y = x^2 + 4x + 9$ in graphing form. Draw tiles to help her figure out how to make this expression into a square. Does she have too few or too many unit squares this time? Write her equation in graphing form.

2-45. How could you complete the square to change $f(x) = x^2 + 5x + 2$ into graphing form? How would you split the five x-tiles into two equal parts?

Jessica decided to use force! She cut one tile in half, as shown below. Then she added her two unit tiles.

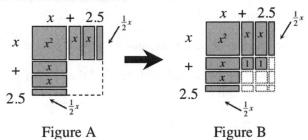

Figure A   Figure B

a. How many unit tiles are in the perfect square?

b. Does Jessica have too many or too few tiles in her original expression? How many?

b. Write the graphing form of the function.

c. Now use your work on problems 2-43 through part (b) of problem 2-45 to complete problem 2-42.

———————   *Further Guidance*   ———————
section ends here.

2-46. Use the strategy of your choice to write each function below in graphing form.

a. $f(x) = x^2 + 6x + 7$ b. $f(x) = x^2 - 4x + 11$

c. $f(x) = x^2 + 5x + 2$ d. $f(x) = x^2 - 7x + 2$

2-47. How can you use a quadratic equation in graphing form to make a quick sketch of the parabola?

a. What is the vertex and y-intercept of the graph of $y = (x-3)^2 - 25$? Explain how you found the y-intercept.

b. Find the x intercepts of $y = (x-3)^2 - 25$ algebraically. Explain how you found the x-intercepts.

c. Obtain the Lesson 2.1.4 Resource Page and justify each step in solving the equation in part (b) for x when $y = 0$.

d. Find the exact vertex, y-intercept, and x-intercepts of $y = (x+5)^2 - 8 = 0$. Make a sketch of the parabola, then check your sketch with your graphing calculator.

2-48.   GENERALIZATION CHALLENGE I

Jeremy had an idea, *"What if we start with the equation in standard form? I bet we can find a way to get the vertex so we don't have to solve the equation or change it to graphing form every time. Let's start with $y = ax^2 + bx + c$ and find the x-intercepts for its graph."*

a.   Solve the general quadratic equation to get the x-intercepts.

b.   How can you use the x-intercepts to find the line of symmetry? What is the line of symmetry?

c.   What is the vertex of the graph of $y = ax^2 + bx + c$?

2-49.   GENERALIZATION CHALLENGE II

Jessica had another idea. She said, *"Couldn't we just start with $y = ax^2 + bx + c$ and complete the square?"*

Jeremy objected, *"But what do we do about the ax^2?"*

a.   How can you rewrite the equation so the coefficient of x is one? Do it.

b.   What is the square that needs to be completed?

c.   What expression has to be added to complete the square?

d.   Rewrite the equation in the form $\frac{y}{a} = (x + \underline{})^2 + \underline{}$, and multiply by a.

e.   What is the vertex? Is the result the same as in problem 2-48? How do you know?

METHODS AND MEANINGS

Finding Graphing Form and Vertex of Parabolas

Starting with the graphing form of a quadratic equation and rewriting it to get standard form is straightforward algebra. But starting with a quadratic equation in standard form and rewriting it to get graphing form is more difficult. You have used two strategies to rewrite standard form in graphing form: **averaging the intercepts** and **completing the square**.

For example, change $y = x^2 + 3x - 10$ to graphing form.

Averaging Intercepts:

x-intercept is where $y = 0$.

Solve $0 = x^2 + 3x - 10$

$0 = (x+5)(x-2)$

The x-intercepts are $(-5,0)$ and $(2,0)$

Axis of symmetry: $x = \frac{-5+2}{2} = -\frac{3}{2}$

By evaluating for x, find $y = -\frac{49}{4}$

Vertex: $(-\frac{3}{2}, -\frac{49}{4})$

Completing the Square:

Make a perfect square from $x^2 + 3x$:

1.5	$1.5x$	2.25
x	x^2	$1.5x$
	x	1.5

$(x+1.5)^2 = x^2 + 3x + 2.25$

The original expression, $x^2 + 3x - 10$, is 12.25 fewer than $(x+1.5)^2$. So,

$y = x^2 + 3x - 10 = (x+1.5)^2 - 12.25$.

Since graphing form is $y = a(x-h)^2 + k$,

vertex: $(-1.5, -12.25) = (-\frac{3}{2}, -\frac{49}{4})$

In general, how are h and k in $y = a(x-h)^2 + k$ related to b and c in $y = ax^2 + bx + c$? By averaging the two solutions given by the Quadratic Formula, or by completing the square, the axis of symmetry is $y = -\frac{b}{2a}$, and the vertex is $\left(-\frac{b}{2a}, c - \frac{b^2}{4a}\right)$, so $h = -\frac{b}{2a}$ and $k = c - \frac{b^2}{4a}$.

2-50.   For each quadratic function below use the method of completing the square or averaging the intercepts to rewrite it in graphing form. Then, state the axis of symmetry and give the vertex of each parabola. Try to use each method at least once.

   a. $f(x) = x^2 + 6x + 15$ b. $y = x^2 - 4x + 9$

   c. $f(x) = x^2 - 8x$ d. $y = x^2 + 7x - 2$

2-51.   Represent the number you would have to add to an expression of the form $x^2 + bx$ to make a complete square.

2-52.   How is $y = 2^x$ different from $y = -(2^x)$? Sketch the graph of $y = -(2^x)$.

2-53.   Throughout this book, key problems have been selected as "checkpoints." Each checkpoint problem is marked with an icon like the one at left. These checkpoint problems are provided so that you can check to be sure you are building skills at the expected level. When you have trouble with checkpoint problems, refer to the review materials and practice problems that are available in the Checkpoint Materials section at the back of your book.

This problem is a checkpoint for finding the distance between two points and finding the equation of a line. It will be referred to as Checkpoint 2A.

For each pair of points, determine the distance between them. Then find the equation for a line through them.

   a. $(-2,4)$ and $(4,7)$ b. $(3,4)$ and $(3,-1)$

   c. $(-7,20)$ and $(3,-5)$ d. $(1,-2)$ and $(5,-2)$

Check your answers by referring to the Checkpoint 2A materials located at the back of your book.

If you needed help solving these problems correctly, then you need more practice. Review the Checkpoint 2A materials and try the practice problems. Also, consider getting help outside of class time. From this point on, you will be expected to do problems like these quickly and easily.

2-54.   The Quadratic Formula can be used to help solve $4x^3 + 23x^2 - 2x = 0$.
Show or explain how.

2-55.   Find the value of x.

a.
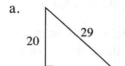

b.
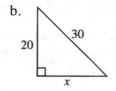

c.
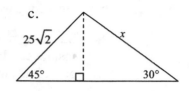

2-56.   A dart hits each of these dartboards at random. What is the probability that the dart will land in the unshaded area?

a.

b.

2-57.   If $\frac{2}{3}$ of A is $\frac{5}{12}$, and $\frac{4}{3}$ of B is $\frac{8}{9}$, which is larger, A or B?

2-58.   Examine the diagram at right. Imagine spinning the rectangle around the y-axis. Think of a rectangular flap attached to the y-axis so that the rectangle will revolve around the y-axis.

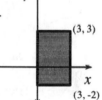

a.   Draw the resulting shape.

b.   Find the volume of this shape.

2-59.   What is a line of symmetry?

a.   Draw a figure that has a line of symmetry.

b.   Draw a figure that has *two* lines of symmetry.

c.   Can you find a basic geometric shape that has an infinite number of lines of symmetry?

2-60.   Find the point where $y = 3x - 1$ intersects $2y + 5x = 53$.

2-61.   Lettie just got her driver's license. Her friends soon nicknamed her "Leadfoot" because she is always going 80 mph on the freeway even though the speed limit is 65 mph.

   a.   At this speed, how long will it take her to travel 50 miles?

   b.   How long would it take her if she drove the 50 miles at 65 mph?

   c.   Speeding tickets carry fines of about $200 and usually increase the cost of insurance. If Lettie gets a ticket on this trip, then what would be her cost per minute of time saved?

2-62.   Solve for the indicated value. Leave your answer in exact form.

   a. $x =$ _____

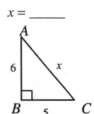

   b. $m\angle C =$ _____

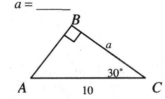

   c. $m\angle B =$ _____

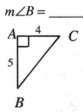

   d. $a =$ _____

2-63.   Below are two situations that can be described using exponential functions. They represent a small sampling of the situations where quantities grow or decay by a constant percentage over equal periods of time. For each situation:

   • Find an appropriate unit of time (such as days, weeks, years).

   • Find the multiplier that should be used.

   • Identify the initial value.

   • Write an exponential equation in the form $f(x) = ab^x$ that represents the growth or decay.

   a.   A house purchased for $120,000 has an annual appreciation of 6%.

   b.   The number of bacteria present in a colony is 180 at noon, and it increases at a rate of 22% per hour.

2.1.5 How can I model the data?

. . . .

Mathematical Modeling with Parabolas

In the past few lessons, you have determined how to move graphs of parabolas around, that is, to transform them, on a set of axes. You have also learned how to write quadratic equations in graphing and in standard form. In this lesson you will put these new skills to work as you use parabolas and their equations to model situations.

2-64.   JUMPING JACKRABBITS

The diagram at right shows a jackrabbit jumping over a three-foot-high fence. To just clear the fence, the rabbit must start its jump at a point four feet from the fence.

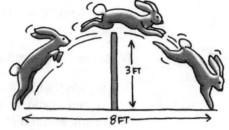

Sketch the situation and write an equation that models the path of the jackrabbit. Show or explain how you know your sketch and equation fit the situation.

Discussion Points

How can we make a graph fit this situation?

What information do we need in order to find an equation?

How can we be sure that our equation fits the situation?

2-65.   Sketch the path of the jackrabbit on your paper. Choose where to place the x- and y-axes in your diagram so that they make sense and make the problem easier. Label as many points as you can on your sketch.

    a.   What is the shape of the path of the jackrabbit? What kind of equation would best model this situation?

    b.   What point on your graph can tell you about the values of h and k in the equation? Write the values for h and k into the general equation. Is your equation finished?

    c.   With your team, find a strategy to find the exact value of a. Will any of the points on your diagram help? Be prepared to share your strategy with the class.

    d.   What are the domain and range for your model?

    e.   Did any team in your class get a different equation? If so, write down their equation and show how it can also model the path of the jackrabbit. What choices did that team make differently that resulted in the different equation?

———————   *Further Guidance*   ———————
section ends here.

2-66.   When Ms. Bibbi kicked a soccer ball, it traveled a horizontal distance of 150 feet and reached a height of 100 feet at its highest point. Sketch the path of the soccer ball and find an equation of the parabola that models it.

2-67.   At the skateboard park, the hot new attraction is the *U-Dip,* a cement structure embedded into the ground. The cross-sectional view of the *U-Dip* is a parabola that dips 15 feet below the ground. The width at ground level, its widest part, is 40 feet across. Sketch the cross-sectional view of the *U-Dip*, and find an equation of the parabola that models it.

2-68.   LEARNING LOG

With your team, discuss all of the different forms you know for the equation of a parabola. In your Learning Log, write down each form, along with a brief explanation of how that form is useful. Title this entry, "Forms of a Quadratic Function" and label it with today's date.

Core Connections Algebra 2

2-69.   FIRE! CALL 9-1-1!

A fireboat in the
harbor is helping put
out a fire in a
warehouse on the pier.
The distance from the
barrel (end) of the
water cannon to the
roof of the warehouse
is 120 feet, and the
water shoots up 50 feet
above the barrel of the water cannon.

Sketch a graph and find an equation of the parabola that models the path of the
water from the fireboat to the fire. Give the domain and range for which the
function makes sense in relation to the fireboat.

2-70.   Draw accurate graphs of $y = 2x + 5$, $y = 2x^2 + 5$, and $y = \frac{1}{2}x^2 + 5$ on the same
set of axes. Label the intercepts.

a.   In the equation $y = 2x + 5$, what does the 2 tell you about the graph?

b.   Is the 2 in $y = 2x^2 + 5$ also the slope? Explain.

2-71.   Think about how you might sketch a parabola on a graph.

a.   Do the sides of a parabola ever curve back in like the figure at
right? Explain your reasoning.

b.   Do the sides of the parabola approach straight vertical lines as
shown in the figure at right? (In other words, do parabolas have
asymptotes?) Give a reason for your answer.

2-72.   Find the equation of an exponential function that passes through each pair of
points.

a. $(2, 9)$ and $(4, 324)$ b. $(-1, 40)$ and $(0, 12)$

2-73.   Find the *x*- and *y*-intercepts of the graphs of the two equations below.

a. $y = 2x^2 + 3x - 5$

b. $y = \sqrt{2x - 4}$

2-74.   The vertex of a parabola, point (h, k), locates its position on the coordinate graph. The vertex thus serves as a **locator point** for a parabola. Other families of functions that you will be investigating in this course will also have locator points. These points have different names, but the same purpose for each different type of graph. They help you place the graph on the axes.

Sketch graphs for both of the following equations. On each sketch, label the locator point.

a. $y = 3x^2 + 5$

b. $f(x) = -(x - 3)^2 - 7$

2-75.   If $g(x) = x^2 - 5$, find the value(s) of *x* so that:

a. $g(x) = 20$

b. $g(x) = 6$

2.2.1 How can I transform any graph?

Transforming Other Parent Graphs

You have been learning how to move a parabola around a set of axes, write equations, sketch graphs, and model situations. The graph of $y = x^2$ is called the **parent graph** for the family of parabolas because every other parabola can be seen as a transformation of that one graph.

2-76.   In this investigation you will use what you have learned about transforming the graph of $y = x^2$ to transform four other parent graphs. In fact, your team will figure out how to use what you have learned to transform the graph of *any* function!

Your Task: As a team, determine how you can make the graph of any function move left, right, up, and down and how you can stretch it vertically, compress it vertically, and flip it. Each team member should investigate one of the following parent functions: $y = x^3$, $y = \frac{1}{x}$, $y = \sqrt{x}$, $y = |x|$, and $y = b^x$. (If you are investigating $y = b^x$, your teacher will give you a value to use for b.)

- Remember that to investigate completely, you should sketch graphs, identify the domain and range, and label any important points or asymptotes.

- Then graph and write an equation to demonstrate each transformation you find.

- Finally, find a general equation for your family of graphs.

Discussion Points

How can we move a parabola?

How can we use our ideas about moving parabolas to move other functions?

What changes can we make to the equation?

2-77.   First, investigate your parent graph.

    a.   Graph your equation on a full sheet of graph paper.

    b.   As a team, place your parent graphs into the middle of your workspace. For each graph, identify the domain and range and label any important points or asymptotes.

2-78.   For your parent graph:

    a.   Find and graph an equation that will shift your parent graph left or right.

    b.   Find and graph an equation that will shift your parent graph up or down.

    c.   Find and graph an equation that will stretch or compress your parent graph vertically.

    d.   Find and graph an equation that will flip your parent graph upside-down.

2-79.   One way of writing an equation for a parabola is to use graphing form: $y = a(x - h)^2 + k$. This equation tells you how to shift or stretch the parent graph, $y = x^2$, to get any other parabola.

    a.   Explain what each parameter (a, h, and k) represents for the graph of a parabola.

    b.   As a team, write general equations for each given parent equation. Be ready to explain how your general equations work; that is, tell what effect each part has on the orientation (right-side-up or upside-down), relative size (stretched or compressed), horizontal location (left or right shift), and vertical location (up or down shift).

Further Guidance
section ends here.

Core Connections Algebra 2

2-80.　　As a team, organize your work into a large poster that shows clearly:

- Each parent graph you worked with,

- Examples of each transformation you found, and

- Each general equation.

Use tools such as colors, arrows, and shading to show all of the connections you can find. Then add the following problems for other teams to solve:

- Show the graph of a function in your family for which other teams need to find the equation.

- Give an equation of a function in your family that other teams will graph.

2-81.　　While watering her outdoor plants, Maura noticed that the water coming out of her garden hose followed a parabolic path. Thinking that she might be able to model the path of the water with an equation, she quickly took some measurements. The highest point the water reached was 8 feet, and it landed on the plants 10 feet from where she was standing. Both the nozzle 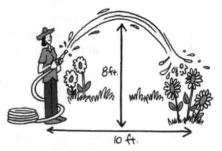 of the hose and the top of the flowers were 4 feet above the ground. Help Maura write an equation that describes the path of the water from the hose to the top of her plants. What domain and range make sense for the model?

2-82.　　Draw the graph of $y = 2x^2 + 3x + 1$.

　　a.　Find the x- and y-intercepts.

　　b.　Where is the line of symmetry of this parabola? Write its equation.

　　c.　Find the coordinates of the vertex.

2-83.　　Change the equation in problem 2-82 so that the parabola has only one x-intercept.

2-84.   Simplify each expression. Remember you can simplify radicals by removing perfect square factors (e.g. $\sqrt{12} = \sqrt{4 \cdot 3} = 2\sqrt{3}$).

   a. $\sqrt{24}$ b. $\sqrt{18}$ c. $\sqrt{3} + \sqrt{3}$ d. $\sqrt{27} + \sqrt{12}$

2-85.   Below are two more situations that can be described using exponential functions. They represent a small sampling of the situations where quantities grow or decay by a constant percentage over equal periods of time. For each situation:

   - Find an appropriate unit of time (such as days, weeks, years).

   - Find the multiplier that should be used.

   - Identify the initial value.

   - Write an exponential equation in the form $f(x) = ab^x$ that represents the growth or decay.

   a.   The value of a car with an initial purchase price of $12,250 depreciates by 11% per year.

   b.   An investment of $1000 earns 6% annual interest, compounded monthly.

2-86.   Rewrite each of the following expressions so that your answer has no negative or fractional exponents.

   a. $16^{5/4}$ b. $(x^5 y^4)^{1/2}$ c. $(x^2 y^{-1})(x^{-3} y)^0$

2-87.   Harvey's Expresso Express, a drive-through coffee stop, is famous for its great house coffee, a blend of Colombian and Mocha Java beans. Their archrival, Jojo's Java, sent a spy to steal their ratio for blending beans. The spy returned with a torn part of an old receipt that showed only the total number of pounds and the total cost, 18 pounds for $92.07. At first Jojo was angry, but then he realized that he knew the price per pound of each kind of coffee ($4.89 for Colombian and $5.43 for Mocha Java). Show how he could use equations to figure out how many pounds of each type of beans Harvey's used.

2-88.   Lilia wants to have a circular pool put in her backyard. She wants the rest of the yard to be paved with concrete.

    a.   If her yard is a 50 ft. by 30 ft. rectangle, what is the radius of the largest pool that will fit in her yard?

    b.   If the concrete is to be 8 inches thick, and costs $2.39 per cubic foot, what is the cost of putting in the concrete? No concrete will be used in the pool. (Reminder: Volume = (Base Area) · Depth).

2-89.   Consider a line with a slope of 3 and a y-intercept at (0, 2).

    a.   Sketch the graph of this line.

    b.   Write the equation of the line.

    c.   Find the initial term and the next three terms of the sequence $t(n) = 3n - 1$. Plot the terms on a new set of axes next to your graph from part (a) above.

    d.   Explain the similarities and differences between the graphs and equations in parts (a) through (c). Are both continuous?

2-90.   The Gross National Product (GNP) of the United States in 1960 was $1.665 \cdot 10^{12}$ dollars. Until 1989 it increased at a rate of 3.17% per year. Use this information to answer each of the questions below.

    a.   What was the GNP in 1989?

    b.   Write an equation to represent the GNP t years after 1960, assuming that the rate of growth remained constant.

    c.   Do you think the rate of growth really remains constant? Explain.

2-91.   Write each expression in simpler radical form.

    a. $\sqrt{x} + \sqrt{y} + 5\sqrt{x} + 2\sqrt{y}$ b. $(2\sqrt{8})^2$

    c. $\frac{\sqrt{50}}{\sqrt{2}}$ d. $\sqrt{\frac{3}{4}}$

2-92.   Multiply each of the following expressions.

   a. $2x^2(3x+4x^2y)$ b. $(x^3y^2)^4(x^2y)$

2-93.   Sketch a graph and draw the line of symmetry for the equation
         $y = 2(x-4)^2 - 3$. What is the equation of the line of symmetry?

2-94.   People who live in isolated or rural areas often
         have their own tanks that hold propane gas to run
         appliances like stoves, washers, and water
         heaters. Some of these tanks are made in the
         shape of a cylinder with two hemispheres on the
         ends, as shown in the picture at right. (Recall
         that a hemisphere is half of a sphere, and the
         volume of a sphere is found by using $V = \frac{4}{3}\pi r^3$.)

         The Inland Propane Gas Tank Company wants to make tanks with this shape,
         and to offer models in different sizes. The cylindrical portion of each of the
         different tanks will be 4 meters long. However, the radius, r, will vary among
         the different models.

         a.   One of the tank models has a radius of 1 meter. What is its volume?

         b.   If the radius is doubled, will the volume double? Explain. Then calculate
              the volume of the larger tank with $r = 2$ m.

         c.   Write an equation that will let the Inland Propane Gas Tank Company
              determine the volume of a tank with any size radius.

2-95.   Write a possible equation for each of these graphs. Assume that one mark on each axis is one unit. When you are in class, check your equations on a graphing calculator and compare your results with your teammates.

a.

b.

c.

d.

e.

f.

g.

h.

i.

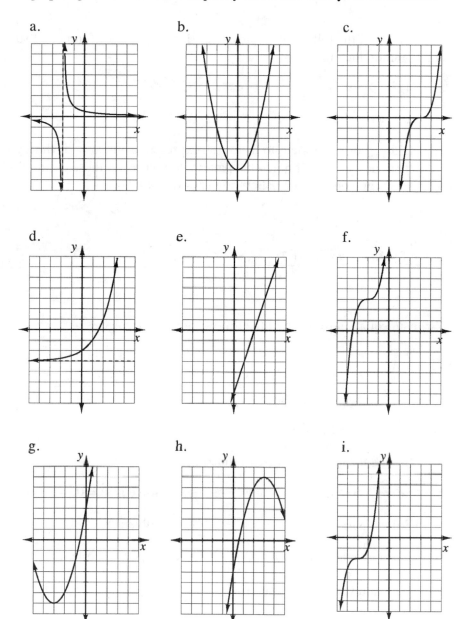

2-96.   By mistake, Jim graphed $y = x^3 - 4x$ instead of $y = x^3 - 4x + 6$. What should he do to his graph to get the correct one?

2-97.   Simplify each radical expression.

    a. $(3\sqrt{2})^2$ b. $\sqrt{\frac{9}{4}}$ c. $\sqrt{\frac{1}{3}}$ d. $(3+\sqrt{2})^2$

2-98.   Factor each of the following expressions. Look for the difference of squares and common factors.

    a. $4x^2 - 9y^2$ b. $8x^3 - 2x^7$

    c. $x^4 - 81y^4$ d. $8x^3 + 2x^7$

    e.   Did you use a shortcut to factor the expressions in parts (a) through (c)? If so, describe it. If not, what pattern do you see in these expressions? How can you use that pattern to factor quickly?

2-99.   Solve for x: $ax + by^3 = c + 7$.

2-100.   Write an equation for each of the following sequences.

    a. $20, 14, 8, \ldots$ b. $-6, -24, -96, \ldots$

2-101.   Given $f(x) = x^3 + 1$ and $g(x) = (x+1)^2$:

    a.   Sketch the graphs of the two functions.

    b.   Solve $f(x) = 9$.   c.   Solve $g(x) = 0$.

    d.   Solve $f(x) = -12$.   e.   Solve $g(x) = -12$.

    f.   For how many values of x does $f(x)$ equal $g(x)$? Explain.

    g.   Find and simplify an expression for $f(x) - g(x)$.

2.2.2 What is the significance of (h, k)?

Describing (h, k) for Each Family of Functions

In Lesson 2.2.1, you learned that you could apply your knowledge of transforming parabolas to transform several other parent functions. In this lesson, you will consolidate your knowledge of each of the parent functions that you know and you will identify the importance of the point (h, k) for each parent function and its family.

2-102.   Think about the parent graph for parabolas, $y = x^2$.

      a.   Write the equation of a parabola that will be the same as the parent graph, but shifted four units to the right.

      b.   Does the strategy you used to move parabolas horizontally also work for other parent graphs? Justify your answer.

      c.   You have learned that the general equation for a parabola is $y = a(x - h)^2 + k$. To move the graph of $y = x^2$ h units to the *right*, you replaced x^2 with $(x - h)^2$. Work with your team to justify why replacing x with $(x - h)$ moves a graph to the right. Think about multiple representations as you discuss this and be prepared to share your ideas with the class.

2-103.   With your team, brainstorm a list of all of the families of functions that you have learned about so far in your study of algebra.

2-104.   Obtain copies of the Parent Graph Toolkit (Lesson 2.2.2 Resource Page) from your teacher. Work with your team to complete a Toolkit entry for each of the parent graphs you have studied so far in this course.

2-105.   What is the equation of the parent graph of a line? Use what you have learned about transforming parent graphs to write the general equation of a transformed line.

   a.   Use this general equation of a line to write the equation of a line with slope $\frac{4}{5}$ that passes through the point $(3, 9)$.

   b.   A line passes through the points $(-1, 5)$ and $(8, -2)$. Substitute each of these into the general equation to create a system of equations. Now solve this system to find the slope. Is this how you have found slope in the past?

2-106.   LEARNING LOG

What can the point (h, k) tell you about the how to graph a function from its equation? How can it help you write the equation for a function given its graph? Discuss these questions with your team and then answer them in a Learning Log entry. Be sure to include examples to help you illustrate your ideas. Title this entry "How to use (h, k)" and label it with today's date.

METHODS AND MEANINGS

MATH NOTES

Point-Slope Equations for Lines

If you think of $y = x$ as a parent equation, then the general equation for the family of lines can be written as

$$y = a(x - h) + k .$$

When this equation is rewritten as $y - k = a(x - h)$ it is often called the **point-slope** form of the equation for a line that contains the point (h, k) and has slope a.

For example, if you know a line contains the point $(7, -8)$ and has slope -4 then the equation can be written $y - (-8) = -4(x - 7)$ or $y + 8 = -4(x - 7)$.

2-107.   Use the point (h, k) to help you write a possible equation for each graph shown below.

a.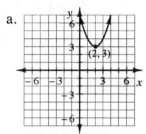

b.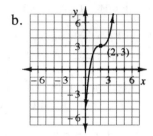

c.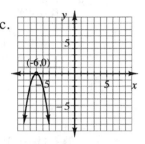

2-108.   Find the domain and range for each of the graphs in the previous problem.

2-109.   For each of the following equations, describe how d transforms the parent graph.

a. $y = dx^3$

b. $y = x^2 - d$

c. $y = (x - d)^2 + 7$

d. $y = \frac{1}{x} + d$

2-110.   Find the equation of an exponential function that passes through each pair of points.

a. $(3, 0.05)$ and $(5, 0.0125)$

b. $(1, 16)$ and $(4, 128)$

2-111.   Rewrite each of the following expressions so that your answers have no negative or fractional exponents.

a. $5^{-2} \cdot 4^{1/2}$

b. $\dfrac{3xy^2z^{-2}}{(xy)^{-1}z^2}$

c. $(3m^2)^3 (2mn)^{-1} (8n^3)^{2/3}$

d. $(5x^2y^3z)^{1/3}$

2-112.   Tino is a businessman who flies to sales conferences regularly. He flies from Seattle to Kansas City once each month and from Seattle to Los Angeles once every 3 months (March, June, September, and December). The flight to Kansas City adds 1500 miles each way to his frequent flier account, while flying to Los Angeles adds 950 miles each way to his account. In January last year, he started with 12,000 miles in his account. In June and December he withdrew 25000 miles from his account for a ticket to Florida for vacation.

   a.   Make a table and a graph that shows the balance in Tino's frequent flier account at the end of each month last year.

   b.   What was the highest number of miles that Tino had in his account during the year? In which month did this occur?

   c.   How many miles did Tino have in his account at the beginning of this year?

   d.   If Tino continues this same pattern of flying will he have enough miles to go on both of his usual vacations this year? Why or why not?

2-113.   Solve each equation for x (that is, put it in $x = $ ___ form).

   a. $y = 2(x - 17)^2$ b. $y + 7 = \sqrt[3]{x + 5}$

2-114.   Where do the following pairs of lines intersect?

   a. $y = 5x - 2$ b. $y = x - 4$
        $y = 3x + 18$ $2x + 3y = 17$

2-115.   Write each expression below in simplest radical form.

   a. $\sqrt{75} + \sqrt{27}$ b. $\sqrt{x} + 2\sqrt{x}$ c. $(\sqrt{12})^2$ d. $(3\sqrt{12})^2$

2-116.   If $g(x) = x^2 - 5$, find:

   a. $g\left(\frac{1}{2}\right)$ b. $g(h + 1)$

2-117.   Graph these two lines on the same set of axes: $y = 2x$ and $y = -\frac{1}{2}x + 6$.

   a.   Find the x- and y-intercepts for each equation.

   b.   Shade the region bounded by the two lines and the x-axis.

   c.   What are the domain and range of the region? How did you find these values?

   d.   Find the area of this region. Round your answer to the nearest tenth.

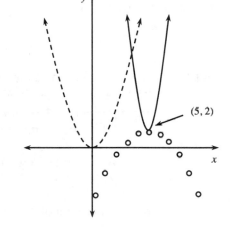

2-118.   The graph of $y = x^2$ is shown as a dashed curve at right. Estimate the equations of the two other parabolas.

2-119.   Find the x- and y-intercepts and the vertex of $y = x^2 + 2x - 80$. Then sketch the graph and write the equation in graphing form.

2-120.   Is -578 a term in the sequence defined by $t(n) = -5n + 7$? Justify your answer.

2.2.3 How can I move a function?

Transformations of Functions

In your Geometry course you transformed figures just like you transformed parent graphs in this course. Today you will look more at geometric transformations and you will explore what happens when you take the opposite of x before applying the operations of the function. That is, you will investigate $f(-x)$.

2-121.   In Geometry, you called the transformation of figures "translations," "reflections," "rotations," and "dilations." Refer to your Parent Graph Toolkit from problem 2-104 and/or your Learning Log entry in problem 2-106 as you complete parts (a) through (d) below.

    a.   What kind of a geometric transformation have you made when you replace $f(x)$ with $f(x)+k$? Be as specific as you can.

    b.   What kind of geometric transformation occurs when you replace $f(x)$ with $-f(x)$? Be as specific as you can.

    c.   What kind of transformation is $f(x-h)$?

    d.   What kind of transformation is $a \cdot f(x)$? Be specific.

2-122.   Investigate the transformation $y = f(-x)$ as directed below.

    a.   For each of the parent graphs you have investigated so far, investigate what happens to the graph when you replace x with $-x$. For each parent function, draw the original and the new graph on the same set of axes in different colors.

    b.   For each parent equation, substitute $-x$ for x and algebraically simplify the result.

    c.   Describe the geometric transformation that occurs when you replace $f(x)$ with $f(-x)$.

2-123.   Functions can be categorized as **even** or **odd functions**. With your team sort
the functions you investigated in problem 2-122 into the following three
groups:

EVEN FUNCTIONS: All functions where $f(-x) = f(x)$.

ODD FUNCTIONS: All functions where $f(-x) = -f(x)$.

FUNCTIONS THAT ARE NEITHER EVEN nor ODD.

2-124.   LEARNING LOG

How will the graph of a function change when $-x$ replaces
x in the function $f(x)$? How can you tell from its graph
whether a function will be even? How can you tell from its
equation whether a function will be even? Discuss these
questions with your team and then answer them in a Learning Log entry. Be
sure to include examples. Title this entry "Reflections and Even Functions"
and label it with today's date.

METHODS AND **M**EANINGS

MATH NOTES

General Equations for Families

If $y = f(x)$ is an equation for a parent graph, then the general equation for the family of functions with similar characteristics as $f(x)$ can be written as:

$$y = a \cdot f(x - h) + k$$

Where (h, k) is the point corresponding to $(0, 0)$ in the parent graph and, relative to the parent graph, the function has been:

- Vertically stretched if the absolute value of a is greater than 1.
- Vertically compressed if the absolute value of a is less than 1.
- Reflected across the x-axis if a is less than 0.

So far in this chapter you have worked with the following families of functions:

Parent	Family	General Equation
$y = x$	Line	$y = a(x - h) + k$
$y = \lvert x \rvert$	Absolute Value	$y = a\lvert x - h \rvert + k$
$y = x^2$	Parabola	$y = a(x - h)^2 + k$
$y = x^3$	Cubic	$y = a(x - h)^3 + k$
$y = \frac{1}{x}$	Hyperbola	$y = a(\frac{1}{x-h}) + k$
$y = \sqrt{x}$	Square Root	$y = a\sqrt{x - h} + k$
$y = b^x$	Exponential	$y = ab^{(x-h)} + k$

Review & Preview

2-125.   Decide whether each of the following functions is even, odd, or neither. Show or explain your reasoning.

a. $y = \frac{2}{3}x + 1$ b. $y = (x + 2)^2$ c. $y = \lvert x \rvert - x^2$

2-126. For each of the following functions sketch the graph of the original and of $y = f(-x)$.

   a. $f(x) = 2|x - 4| + 3$

   b. $f(x) = \dfrac{1}{x + 4}$

   c.   Is either of these functions odd or even? Justify your answer.

2-127. A parabola has vertex $(2, 3)$ and contains the point $(0, 0)$. Find an equation that represents this parabola.

2-128. For each equation below, find the x- and y-intercepts and the locator point (h, k), then write the equations in graphing form.

   a. $y = 7 + 2x^2 + 4x - 5$

   b. $x^2 = 2x + x(2x - 4) + y$

2-129. Consider the system of equations at right:

$$3y - 4x = -1$$
$$9y + 2x = 4$$

   a.   What is the parent of each equation?

   b.   Solve this system algebraically.

   c.   Find where the two graphs intersect.

   d.   Explain the relationship between parts (b) and (c) above.

2-130. Write an equation for each of the following sequences.

   a. $10, 2.5, 0.625, \ldots$

   b. $-2, -8, -14, \ldots$

2-131. Find the intercepts, the locator point (h, k), the domain, and the range for each of the following functions.

   a. $y = |x - 4| - 2$

   b. $y = -|x + 1| + 3$

2.2.4 How can I transform circles?

Transforming Non-Functions

In this lesson, you consider two new parent equations that are different from the ones you have seen in the past because they are not functions. You will investigate them and apply the knowledge you have gained in this chapter to transform them. You will identify ways in which these new equations are different from the functions with which you have been working.

2-132. Begin by fully investigating $x = y^2$ and $x^2 + y^2 = 25$ as follows.

a. Without using your graphing calculator, make a table and a graph for each equation.

b. Marabel and Lissa were working on this problem. Marabel was making a table for $x = y^2$. For an x-value of 4, she found a y-value of 2. Lissa was watching and said, *"Wait! When x is 4, there is also another possible value for y."* What did Lissa mean? Look back at your tables and decide if there are more points you could add.

c. Now describe $x = y^2$ and $x^2 + y^2 = 25$ completely. This includes finding the domain and range of each equation, finding the important points such as intercepts, and describing what happens to y as x increases.

d. How are these relationships different from others you have been working with?

2-133. Rewrite $x = y^2$ and $x^2 + y^2 = 25$ so that you can graph them with your graphing calculator. When you have rewritten both equations, try graphing them using your calculator. Do they look like the graphs you made in problem 2-132?

Core Connections Algebra 2

2-134.   TRANSFORMATIONS OF NON-FUNCTIONS

In order to graph the equation of the circle on your graphing calculator, you had to express the non-function as two functions. Now apply your knowledge of transforming functions to learn about transforming circles.

Your Task: As a team, transform the graphs of $y = \pm\sqrt{25 - x^2}$ horizontally and vertically. Then find a general equation for this family of circles using h, and k. Be prepared to share your findings and your strategies with the class.

Discussion Points

How did we change the equation in other families so that the graph moves vertically? So that it moves horizontally?

How can we rewrite the two functions for a circle the same way?

2-135.   Write your <u>general equations</u> for a circle in standard form by rewriting the equation $y = \pm\sqrt{-(x-h)^2 + 25} + k$ to isolate 25 on one side of the equation. What information does the locator point (h, k) give about the graph of the circle?

2-136.   A circle has a special characteristic, its radius, which defines its size.

a.   Refer back to the graph of $x^2 + y^2 = 25$. What is the radius? How is the radius of the circle related to the equation?

b.   What would be the equation of a circle that has its center at $(5, -7)$ with radius 10? With radius 12?

c.   Now generalize the connection between the radius and the equation of a circle. Write a general equation for a circle with any center (h, k) and radius r.

d.   Given the equation $(x-3)^2 + (y+7)^2 = 169$, how can you find the radius of the circle?

2-137. Consider the equation $(x-4)^2 + (y+1)^2 = 16$.

    a.   What is the shape of the graph? How can you tell?

    b.   What information can you learn about the graph just by looking at the equation?

    c.   Sketch a graph of $(x-4)^2 + (y+1)^2 = 16$.

2-138. Look at your work from problem 2-133. The non-function $x = y^2$ had a graph that is called a "sleeping parabola."

    a.   How could you transform the equation $y = \pm\sqrt{x}$ to move the graph horizontally and vertically? How could you transform the equation to stretch or compress the graph, or to "flip" it vertically?

    b.   Write a general equation for transforming the sleeping parabola family $y = \pm\sqrt{x}$ by using a, h, and k.

    c.   Write the equation for a sleeping parabola in standard form by isolating x on one side of the equation.

2-139. Write the equation $y = x^2 + 7x - 8$ in graphing form.

2-140. You are standing outside the school, waiting to cross the street, when you hear booming music coming from an approaching car.

    a.   Sketch a graph that shows the relationship between how far away from you the car is and the loudness of the music.

    b.   Which is the dependent variable and which is the independent variable?

2-141. The Green Streak Taxi Company charges a $3.00 base fee plus $2.50 per mile. The cab driver sets his meter at $3.00 and the meter adds $0.25 each one-tenth of a mile. Draw a graph to represent this fare structure. Describe the domain and range of your graph.

2-142.   Write an equation for a function that is odd, and explain how you can tell it is odd from its graph, its table and its equation.

2-143.   Explain the difference between the graphs of $y = \frac{1}{x}$ and $y = 4(\frac{1}{x+5}) + 7$.

2-144.   Multiply the expressions in parts (a) through (c) to remove the parentheses.

   a. $(x-1)(x+1)$ b. $2x(x+1)(x+1)$ c. $(x-1)(x+1)(x-2)$

   d.   Find the x- and y-intercepts of $y = x^3 - 2x^2 - x + 2$. The factors in part (c) should be useful.

2-145.   Solve the following systems of equations. In other words, find values of a and b that make each system true. Be sure to show your work or explain your thinking clearly.

   a. $2 = a \cdot b^0$ b. $\frac{1}{2} = a \cdot b^0$
        $\frac{1}{2} = a \cdot b^2$ $2 = a \cdot b^2$

2-146.   A parabola has vertex $(3, 5)$ and contains the point $(0, 0)$.

   a.   If this parabola is a function, find its equation.

   b.   Suppose this parabola is not a function, but is a "sleeping" parabola. Find its equation.

2-147.   Sketch the graph of $y = 2(x-1)^2 + 4$.

   a.   Now rewrite the equation $y = 2(x-1)^2 + 4$ without parentheses. Remember the Order of Operations!

   b.   What would the difference be between the graphs of the two equations above? This is sort of a trick question, but explain your reasoning.

   c.   What is the parent function of $y = 2(x-1)^2 + 4$?

   d.   What is the parent function of $y = 2x^2 - 4x + 6$?

2-148. Consider the equation $(x-5)^2 + (y-8)^2 = 49$.

    a.   What can you tell about the graph just by looking at the equation?

    b.   Sketch a graph of $(x-5)^2 + (y-8)^2 = 49$.

2-149. A line passes through the points $(0, 2)$ and $(1, 0)$.

    a.   Find the slope of the line.

    b.   Find the slope of a line parallel to the given line.

    c.   Find the slope of a line perpendicular to the given line.

    d.   Find the product of the slopes you found in parts (b) and (c).

    e.   Make a conjecture about the product of the slopes of any two perpendicular lines. Test your conjecture by creating more examples.

2-150. Give the equations of two functions, $f(x)$ and $g(x)$, so that $f(x)$ and $g(x)$ intersect at exactly:

    a.   One point.   b.   Two points.   c.   No points.

2-151. Find the x- and y-intercepts for the following parabolas.

    a. $y = (x+12)^2 - 144$ b. $y = (x-8)^2 - 4$

2-152. This problem is a checkpoint for solving linear systems in two variables. It will be referred to as Checkpoint 2B.

    Solve the system of linear equations at right. $5x - 4y = 7$
                                                                 $2y + 6x = 22$

Check your answers by referring to the Checkpoint 2B materials located at the back of your book.

If you needed help solving these problems correctly, then you need more practice. Review the Checkpoint 2B materials and try the practice problems. Also, consider getting help outside of class time. From this point on, you will be expected to do problems like these quickly and easily.

2.2.5 Can I combine functions?

Transforming Piecewise-Defined Functions

Often the equation for a single familiar function describes a part of a situation, but then is not a good description for the rest of the situation. A step graph is one kind of **piecewise-defined function**. The graphs of these situations are functions, but a single equation is not sufficient to describe them. Describing them requires two (or more) different equations for different inputs. Today you will build new functions by using pieces of familiar functions. Phone plans and water rates are situations that can be modeled using step functions.

2-153.   The Horizon Phone Company offers a basic monthly voice phone plan where you pay $40.00 for the first 450 minutes and then $0.45 per minute after that. The graph at right shows how the plan works.

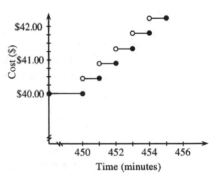

  a.   This is a piecewise-defined function with many pieces. Describe each piece and the domain and range for the function overall. Then describe the domain and range for the first few pieces.

  b.   Write an equation for each part of the domain.

2-154.   With your team, create a piecewise-defined function with at least three "pieces." The function does not need to be a step-function with horizontal line segments, but it needs to meet the definition of a function. Make a table and a graph for your function, and write an equation for each part. Be sure to state the domain for each part, as well as the domain for the whole function.

2-155. Here is another piecewise-defined function, $F(x)$, defined in the domain $-4 \le x \le 7$ by the graph below.

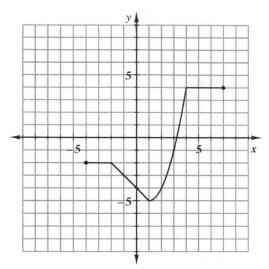

a. Because there is no single equation that represents the whole graph, it is often useful to make a more complete table than you might usually make. On your paper, fill in a table for the function like the one below.

x	−4	−3	−2	−1	0	1	2	3	4	5	6	7
$F(x)$												

b. Use the graph and the table that you made to write equations for each part of the piecewise-defined function. Be sure to state the domain for each part.

2-156. TEAM TRANSFORMATION CHALLENGE

Obtain the Lesson 2.2.5A Resource Page. Use the resource page to show the graph, the table, and the equations for each of the following transformations of the piecewise-defined function in problem 2-155.

a. $y = -F(x)$

b. $y = \frac{1}{2} F(x)$

c. $y = F(x) + 4$

d. $y = F(x - 4)$

2-157.   GRAPHS OF ODD AND EVEN FUNCTIONS

Your goal in this investigation is to determine whether a function is odd or even by looking at its graph.

a.   Use your graphing calculator to graph the following functions, and make a quick sketch of each graph on your paper. Be sure to label each graph.

$f(x) = x^2$ $f(x) = (x+5)^2$ $f(x) = x^2 + 5$

$f(x) = x^3$ $f(x) = (x+5)^3$ $f(x) = x^3 + 5$

$f(x) = \frac{1}{x}$ $f(x) = -2.5x$

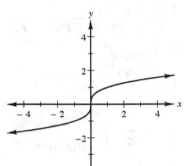

b.   Determine which of the functions above are odd, even, or neither. Can you find an efficient way to do this with your graphing calculator?

c.   How can you tell by looking at the graph whether a function is odd, even, or neither?

d.   Classify the function at right as odd, even, or neither. Explain.

2-158.   Write an equation for an even function of your own. Now write another function of your own that is odd. Show that your functions meet the even/odd criteria. The functions you use do not have to be parent functions.

2-159.   Write an equation for a function that is neither even nor odd. Show that it is neither.

2-160.   AN ADDITIONAL CHALLENGE

In general, a transformation for the parent function $F(x)$ in problem 2-155 can be represented by $y = aF(x - h) + k$. With your team, choose your own values for a, h, and k and show the table, graph, and equations for your transformed $F(x)$.

2-161.   **LEARNING LOG**

In the last few lessons, you have developed the ability to
create a family of functions by transforming *any* parent
function. Does the function you start with (the parent)
affect how you will transform it? If so, how? If not, why not? Are there any
parent graphs that are hard for you to transform? Why or why not? Write a
Learning Log entry answering these questions. Title it "Transform Any
Function" and label it with today's date.

METHODS AND **M**EANINGS

Even and Odd Functions

When a function $f(-x) = f(x)$, the function f is called an **even
function**. For example, for the function $f(x) = x^2$:

$$f(-x) = (-x)^2 = x^2 = f(x)$$

Thus, $f(x) = x^2$ is an even function.

When $f(-x) = -f(x)$, the function f is called an **odd function**. For
example for the function $f(x) = x^3$:

$$f(-x) = (-x)^3 = -x^3 = -f(x).$$

Therefore, $f(x) = x^3$ is an odd function.

2-162.   Write a set of equations for the piecewise-
defined function shown on the graph at right.
Be sure to include the domain for each part of
the function.

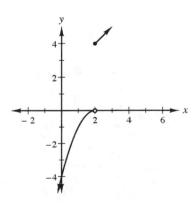

2-163.   Write an equation for a function that is even.
Then explain how you can tell it is even from
its graph, its table, and its equation.

Core Connections Algebra 2

2-164.   Use your knowledge of absolute value functions to find the equation of the graph at right.

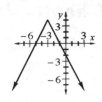

2-165.   Write an equation for each of the circles shown in the graphs below.

a.

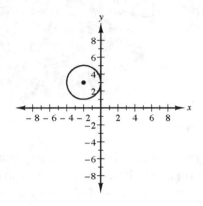

b.

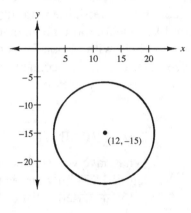

2-166.   Use the technique of completing the square to express $y = x^2 - 5x + 7$ in graphing form and state the vertex.

2-167.   Shortcut Shuneel claims he has a shortcut for finding the vertex of a parabola. While using his shortcut on $y = 2x^2 + 3x + 1$, he ended up with $y = 2(x + \frac{3}{4})^2 - \frac{7}{2}$. Is Shuneel's new equation correct? Why or why not?

2-168.   Remember function machines? Each of the following pictures shows how the same machine changes the given x-value into a corresponding $f(x)$ value. Find the equation for this machine.

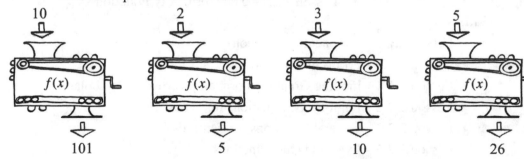

2-169.   If $x^2 + kx + 18$ is factorable, what are the possible values of k?

Chapter 2 Closure What have I learned?

Reflection and Synthesis

The activities below offer you a chance to
reflect about what you have learned during this
chapter. As you work, look for concepts that
you feel very comfortable with, ideas that you
would like to learn more about, and topics you
need more help with. Look for connections
between ideas as well as connections with
material you learned previously.

①   TEAM BRAINSTORM

        What have you studied in this chapter? What ideas were important in what you
        learned? With your team, brainstorm a list. Be as detailed as you can. To help
        get you started, a list of Learning Log entries and Math Notes boxes are below.

        What topics, ideas, and words that you learned *before* this chapter are
        connected to the new ideas in this chapter? Again, be as detailed as you can.

        Next consider the Standards for Mathematical Practice that follow Activity ③:
        Portfolio. What Mathematical Practices did you use in this chapter? When did
        you use them? Give specific examples. How long can you make your list?
        Challenge yourselves. Be prepared to share your team's ideas with the class.

Learning Log Entries
     •   Lesson 2.1.5 – Forms of a Quadratic Function
     •   Lesson 2.2.2 – How to use (h, k)
     •   Lesson 2.2.3 – Reflections and Even Functions
     •   Lesson 2.2.5 – Transform Any Function

Math Notes
   •   Lesson 2.1.1 – Exponential Functions
   •   Lesson 2.1.3 – Forms of Quadratics
   •   Lesson 2.1.4 – Finding Graphing Form and Vertex of Parabolas
   •   Lesson 2.2.2 – Point-Slope Equations for Lines
   •   Lesson 2.2.3 – General Equations for Families
   •   Lesson 2.2.5 – Even and Odd Functions

②   MAKING CONNECTIONS

Below is a list of the vocabulary used in this chapter. Make sure that you are familiar with all of these words and know what they mean. Refer to the glossary or index for any words that you do not yet understand.

compress	dilate	domain
even function	function	general equation
graphing form	(h, k)	horizontal shift
odd function	parameter	parent graph
piecewise-defined function	range	reflection
standard form	step function	stretch factor
transformation	translation	variable
vertex	vertex form	vertical shift

Make a concept map showing all of the connections you can find among the key words and ideas listed above. To show a connection between two words, draw a line between them and explain the connection. A word can be connected to any other word as long as you can justify the connection.

While you are making your map, your team may think of related words or ideas that are not listed here. Be sure to include these ideas on your concept map.

③ PORTFOLIO: EVIDENCE OF MATHEMATICAL PROFICIENCY

This section gives you an opportunity to show growth in
your understanding of key mathematical ideas over time as
you complete this course. Several options are presented
below. Follow your teacher's directions for which options
you should complete.

- Explain everything that you know about $y = x^2 - 4$ and
  $y = \sqrt{x+4}$.

- Your teacher may give you the Chapter 2 Closure Resource Page:
  Transformations Graphic Organizer to complete. Use it to organize and
  show everything that you know about transforming the parent graph(s)
  your teacher gives you.

- The function $g(x)$ is graphed at right.
  Graph each of the following functions.

  $y = 2g(x) + 3$ $y = -g(x-1)$

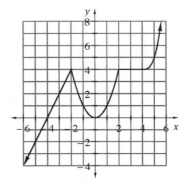

- In Section 2.1, you generalized about how to write
  equations in graphing form by completing the square.
  For example, you learned how to complete the square
  by analyzing actual squares that represented the
  algebraic quantities you were working with, such as in
  the expression represented by the tiles at right. Then
  you generalized the process to complete the square for
  expressions involving negative and fractional terms, which are not easy to
  represent with tiles. Consider this as you answer the questions below.

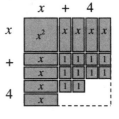

  i.   In general, what can you do to complete the square for a quadratic
       function, no matter what the x term is?

  ii. Use the general strategy you described in part (*i*) above to complete
       the square for the quadratic equation $f(x) = x^2 - 4.5x + 17$

- Consider the Standards for Mathematical Practice that follow. What
  Mathematical Practices did you use in this chapter? When did you use
  them? Give specific examples.

Core Connections Algebra 2

BECOMING MATHEMATICALLY PROFICIENT
The Common Core State Standards For Mathematical Practice

This book focuses on helping you use some very specific Mathematical Practices. The Mathematical Practices describe ways in which mathematically proficient students engage with mathematics everyday.

Make sense of problems and persevere in solving them:

Making sense of problems and persevering in solving them means that you can solve problems that are full of different kinds of mathematics. These types of problems are not routine, simple, or typical. Instead, they combine lots of math ideas and everyday situations. You have to stick with challenging problems, try different strategies, use multiple representations, and use a different method to check your results.

Reason abstractly and quantitatively:

Throughout this course, everyday situations are used to introduce you to new math ideas. Seeing mathematical ideas within a context helps you make sense of the ideas. Once you learn about a math idea in a practical way, you can "**reason abstractly**" by thinking about the concept more generally, representing it with symbols, and manipulating the symbols. **Reasoning quantitatively** is using numbers and symbols to represent an everyday situation, taking into account the units involved, and considering the meaning of the quantities as you compute them.

Construct viable arguments and critique the reasoning of others:

To **construct a viable argument** is to present your solution steps in a logical sequence and to justify your steps with conclusions, relying on number sense, facts and definitions, and previously established results. You communicate clearly, consider the real-life context, and provide clarification when others ask. In this course, you regularly share information, opinions, and expertise with your study team. You **critique the reasoning of others** when you analyze the approach of others, build on each other's ideas, compare the effectiveness of two strategies, and decide what makes sense and under what conditions.

Model with mathematics:

When you **model with mathematics**, you take a complex situation and use mathematics to represent it, often by making assumptions and approximations to simplify the situation. Modeling allows you to analyze and describe the situation and to make predictions. For example, you model when you use multiple representations, including equations, tables, graphs, or diagrams to describe a situation. In situations involving the variability of data, you model when you describe the data with equations. Although a model may not be perfect, it can still be very useful for describing data and making predictions. When you interpret the results, you may need to go back and improve your model by revising your assumptions and approximations.

Use appropriate tools strategically:

To **use appropriate tools strategically** means that you analyze the task and decide which tools may help you model the situation or find a solution. Some of the tools available to you include diagrams, graph paper, calculators, computer software, databases, and websites. You understand the limitations of various tools. A result can be check or estimated by strategically choosing a different tool.

Attend to precision:

To **attend to precision** means that when solving problems, you need to pay close attention to the details. For example, you need to be aware of the units, or how many digits your answer requires, or how to choose a scale and label your graph. You may need to convert the units to be consistent. At times, you need to go back and check whether a numerical solution makes sense in the context of the problem.

You need to **attend to precision** when you communicate your ideas to others. Using the appropriate vocabulary and mathematical language can help make your ideas and reasoning more understandable to others.

Look for and make use of structure:

To **looking for and making use of structure** is a guiding principal of this course. When you are involved in analyzing the structure and in the actual development of mathematical concepts, you gain a deeper, more conceptual understanding than when you are simply told what the structure is and how to do problems. You often use this practice to bring closure to an investigation.

There are many concepts that you learn by looking at the underlying structure of a mathematical idea and thinking about how it connects to other ideas you have already learned. For example, you understand the underlying structure of an equation such as $y = a(x - h)^2 + b$ which allows you to graph it without a table.

Look for and express regularity in repeated reasoning:

To **look for and express regularity in repeated reasoning** means that when you are investigating a new mathematical concept, you notice if calculations are repeated in a pattern. Then you look for a way to generalize the method for use in other situations, or you look for shortcuts. For example, the pattern of growth you notice in a geometric sequence results in being able to write a general exponential equation that highlights the growth and starting point.

WHAT HAVE I LEARNED?

Most of the problems in this section represent
typical problems found in this chapter. They
serve as a gauge for you. You can use them
to determine which types of problems you
can do well and which types of problems
require further study and practice. Even if
your teacher does not assign this section, it is
a good idea to try these problems and find out
for yourself what you know and what you still need to work on.

Solve each problem as completely as you can. The table at the end of the
closure section has answers to these problems. It also tells you where you
can find additional help and practice with problems like these.

CL 2-170.   Chucky and Angelica were reviewing equations of parabolas for their
upcoming math test. They disagreed on what the equation would look like
for a parabola whose vertex was at $(-4, 3)$.

a.   Help them write an equation for a parabola that opens upward from its
vertex at $(-4, 3)$. What is the equation of its line of symmetry?

b.   Chucky wants the same parabola to open down and Angelica wants it
to be compressed. Show them how to change your original equation
to meet both of their desires. Does the line of symmetry change?

c.   Move your parabola from part (b) 7 units to the right and 8 units down
and stretch it vertically so that it is thinner than the original parabola.
What is the equation of the parabola? What is the equation of its line
of symmetry?

CL 2-171.   For each equation, give the locator point (h, k) and the equation of any
asymptotes, and then draw the graph.

a. $f(x) = -|x+2|-1$ b. $y = \frac{1}{x}+2$

c. $y = \frac{1}{x+5}-2$ d. $y = -x^3 + 5$

CL 2-172.   For each of the functions in problem 2-171 sketch the graph of $y = f(-x)$.

CL 2-173. Gloria the grasshopper is working on her hops. She is trying to jump as high and as far as she can. Her best jump so far was 28 cm long, and she reached a height of 20 cm. Sketch a graph and write an equation of the parabola that describes the path of her jump.

CL 2-174. Use what you know about transforming parent graphs to write an equation for each of the graphs described below.

    a. A parabola stretched by a factor of 0.25, opening downward and shifted 12 units down and 3 units left.

    b. A cubic with a stretch factor of 2 and a locator point at $(-6, 1)$.

    c. A hyperbola, $y = \frac{1}{x}$, but with asymptotes at $y = -6$ and $x = 2$.

CL 2-175. Find the equation of the exponential functions with a horizontal asymptote at $y = 0$ through the following pairs of points.

    a. $(2, 99)$ and $(6, 8019)$ b. $(-1, 50)$ and $(2, 25.6)$

CL 2-176. Write an equation for each of the following sequences.

    a. $10, 7, 4, \ldots$ b. $-2, -8, -32, \ldots$

CL 2-177. For each of the equations below, complete the following:

- Find the x- and y-intercepts.
- Find the vertex.
- Sketch a graph of each parabola on its own set of axes.
- Write the equation in graphing form.

    a. $y = x^2 + 8x + 12$ b. $y = (x - 4)(x + 2)$

    c. $y = x^2 - 6x - 9$ d. $y = x^2 + 5x + 1$

CL 2-178. Factor each of the following expressions.

    a. $2x^2 + 7x - 4$ b. $8x^2 + 24x + 10$

CL 2-179. Dinner at David's costs $8.95 today and has been increasing an average of 7% per year.

a. What will it cost in 10 years? b. What did it cost 10 years ago?

CL 2-180. If $g(x) = (x+1)^2$, complete each part below.

a. $g(5)$ b. $g(2m+4)$ c. x if $g(x) = 9$

CL 2-181. Solve each equation for y.

a. $4 - 2(x+y) = 9$ b. $x = 2(y-1)^2 + 2$

CL 2-182. Check your answers using the table at the end of this section. Which problems do you feel confident about? Which problems were hard? Have you worked on problems like these in math classes you have taken before? Use the table to make a list of topics you need help on and a list of topics you need to practice more.

Answers and Support for Closure Activity #4
What Have I Learned?

Note: MN = Math Note, LL = Learning Log

Problem	Solution	Need Help?	More Practice
CL 2-170.	a. Answers may vary but should be in the form of $y = a(x+4)^2 + 3$, where a is any positive number. $x = -4$ b. $y = a(x+4)^2 + 3$, where a is between 0 and -1; Line of symmetry does not change. c. $y = a(x-3)^2 - 5$, where a is less than -1. $x = 3$	Lessons 2.1.2, and 2.1.3 MN: 2.1.3 and 2.1.4	Problems 2-31, 2-32, 2-74, and 2-124

CL 2-171.	a. $(-2, -1)$
	
	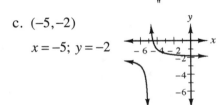
	
	 b. $(0, 2)$
	     $x = 0$; $y = 2$
	
	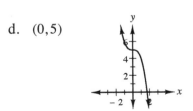
	
	 c. $(-5, -2)$
	     $x = -5$; $y = -2$
	
	 d. $(0, 5)$
		Lessons 2.2.1 and 2.2.2
		
		 MN: 2.2.3
		
		 LL: 2.2.2 and 2.2.5
			Problems 2-74, 2-107, 2-109, 2-118, 2-131, and 2-164

Problem	Solution	Need Help?	More Practice

CL 2-172.   a. 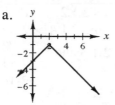   b.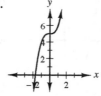

Lesson 2.2.3

LL: 2.2.3

Problems
2-122, 2-126,
and 2-156

c.   d.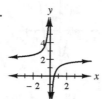

CL 2-173. $y = -\frac{5}{49}x(x-28) = -\frac{5}{49}x^2 + \frac{20}{7}x$

Lesson 2.1.5

LL: 2.1.5

Problems 2-64,
2-66, 2-67,
2-69, and 2-81

CL 2-174.   a. $y = -0.25(x+3)^2 - 12$

b. $y = 2(x+6)^3 + 1$

c. $y = \frac{1}{x-2} - 6$

Lesson 2.2.1
and 2.2.2

Problems 2-25,
2-52, 2-95,
2-96, 2-109,
2-118, and
2-143.

CL 2-175.   a. $y = 11 \cdot 3^x$

b. $y = 40(0.8)^x$

Appendix B
Lesson B.2.2

Problems 2-72
and 2-110

CL 2-176.   a. $t(n) = -3n + 13$

b. $t(n) = -\frac{1}{2}(4)^n$ or $-2(4)^{n-1}$

Both using $t(1)$ as the first term.

Appendix A
Lessons A.2.2
and A.3.2

MN: A.3.2 and
B.2.3

Problems 2-8,
2-100, 2-120,
and 2-130

Problem	Solution		Need Help?	More Practice

CL 2-177.

a. x-int:
$(-6,0),(-2,0)$;
y-int: $(0, 12)$;
vertex: $(-4,-4)$
$y = (x+4)^2 - 4$

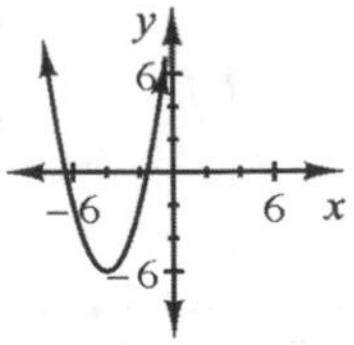

Lessons 2.1.2, 2.1.3, and 2.1.4

MN: 2.1.3 and 2.1.4

LL: 2.1.5

Problems 2-17, 2-34, 2-50, 2-73, 2-82, 2-119, and 2-166

b. x-int: $(-2,0),(4,0)$;
y-int: $(0, -8)$;
vertex: $(1,-9)$;
$y = (x-1)^2 - 9$

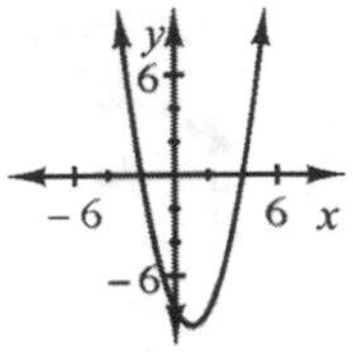

c. x-int: $(3 \pm \sqrt{18},0)$;
y-int: $(0, -9)$;
vertex: $(3,-18)$;
$y = (x-3)^2 - 18$

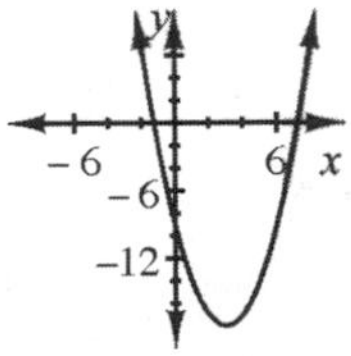

d. x-int: $(\frac{-5 \pm \sqrt{21}}{2},0)$;
y-int: $(0,1)$;
vertex: $(-2.5,-5.25)$;
$y = (x+2.5)^2 - 5.25$

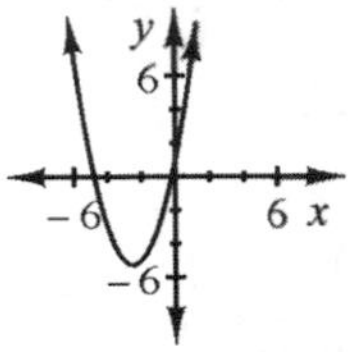

CL 2-178.

a. $(2x-1)(x+4)$

b. $2(2x+5)(2x+1)$

Explanations and practice of topics from previous courses are available in the *Core Connections Algebra Parent Guide with Extra Practice,* available free at www.cpm.org.

Problems 2-35, 2-98, and 2-169

CL 2-179.

a. $17.61

b. $4.55

Appendix B
Lesson B.1.3

Problems 2-29, 2-93, 2-63, and 2-85

CL 2-180.

a. 36

b. $4m^2 + 20m + 25$

c. $2, -4$

Section 1.1

Problems 2-75, 2-101, 2-116, and 2-168

CL 2-181.

a. $y = -x - \frac{5}{2}$

b. $y = \pm\sqrt{\frac{x-2}{2}} + 1$

Topic from previous course.

Problems 1-37, 1-72, 2-99, and 2-113

Chapter 3

Equivalent Forms

In previous chapters, you looked at ways to organize your algebraic thinking using multiple representations such as graphs, tables, and equations. In this chapter, you will focus on rewriting expressions in order to have more useful equivalent forms. You will remind yourself what it means for two expressions or equations to be equivalent. You will then rewrite equations to solve them more easily.

Another focus of this chapter is learning how to combine algebraic fractions (called "rational expressions") and expressions with exponents. By using the special properties of the number 1 and the meaning of exponents, you will be able rewrite long, complicated expressions into simpler forms. You will then multiply, divide, add, and subtract rational expressions.

Guiding Question

Mathematically proficient students construct viable arguments and critique the reasoning of others.

As you work through this chapter, ask yourself:

How can I show that these forms are equivalent?

Chapter Outline

Section 3.1 In this section, you will rewrite expressions and equations to create simpler versions. You will learn a new way to use substitution to rewrite an expression or equation in simpler form.

Section 3.2 You will study the properties of the number 1 and use them to rewrite and simplify rational expressions. You will multiply, divide, add and subtract rational expressions.

3.1.1 Are they equivalent?

Equivalent Expressions

In this chapter you will look at how to rewrite expressions and equations into equivalent forms that will make them more useful. In this lesson, you will begin by identifying equivalent expressions and then work on developing algebraic strategies to show that they are equivalent.

3-1.   Consider the tile pattern at right.

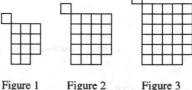

Figure 1   Figure 2   Figure 3

a.   Work with your team to describe what the 100th figure would look like. Then find as many different expressions as you can for the area (the number of tiles) in Figure x. Use algebra to justify that all of your expressions are equivalent.

b.   What information about the pattern is given by various parts of your different expressions?

c.   Write and solve an equation to determine which figure number has 72 tiles. Do you get different results depending upon which expression you choose to use? Explain.

3-2.   Jill and Terrell were looking back at their work on problem 1-53 in Lesson 1.2.1. They had come up with two different expressions for the volume of a paper box made from cutting out squares of dimensions x centimeters by x centimeters. Jill's expression was $(15-2x)(20-2x)x$, and Terrell's expression was $4x^3 - 70x^2 + 300x$.

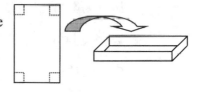

a.   Are Jill's and Terrell's expressions equivalent? Justify your answer.

b.   If you have not done so already, find an algebraic method to determine whether their expressions are equivalent. Be ready to share your strategy.

c.   Gary joined in on their conversation. He had another expression: $(15-2x)(10-x)2x$. Use a strategy from part (b) to decide whether his expression for the volume is equivalent to Jill's or Terrell's. Be prepared to share your ideas with the class.

3-3.   For each of the following expressions, find at least three equivalent expressions. Be sure to justify how you know they are equivalent.

a. $(x+3)^2 - 4$ b. $(2a^2b^3)^3$ c. $m^2n^5 \cdot mn^4$ d. $\frac{(x+1)(2x-1)}{x+2}$

3-4.   LEARNING LOG

What does it mean for two expressions to be equivalent? How can you tell if two expressions are equivalent? Answer these questions in your Learning Log. Be sure to include examples to illustrate your ideas. Title this entry "Equivalent Expressions" and label it with today's date.

3-5.   For each of the following expressions, find at least three equivalent expressions. Which do you consider to be the simplest?

a. $(2x-3)^2 + 5$ b. $(\frac{3x^2y}{x^3})^4$

3-6.   Match each expression on the left with its equivalent expression on the right. Assume that all variables represent positive values. Be sure to justify how you know each pair is equivalent.

a. $\sqrt{4x^2y^4}$ 1. $2x\sqrt{y}$

b. $\sqrt{8x^2y}$ 2. $2y\sqrt{2x}$

c. $\sqrt{4x^2y}$ 3. $2xy^2$

d. $\sqrt{16xy^2}$ 4. $2x\sqrt{2y}$

e. $\sqrt{8xy^2}$ 5. $4y\sqrt{x}$

3-7.   Bonnie and Dylan were both working on simplifying the expression $(\frac{2x^5y^4}{8xy^3})^3$
at right. Each of their first steps is shown below.

Bonnie: $\frac{8x^{15}y^{12}}{512x^3y^9}$ Dylan: $(\frac{x^4y}{4})^3$

Each of them is convinced that they have started the problem correctly. Has either of them made an error? If so, explain the error completely. If not, explain how they can both be correct and verify that they will get the same, correct solution. Which student's method do you prefer? Why?

Core Connections Algebra 2

3-8.   Describe the graphs of the equations given in parts (a) and (b) below. What are their domains and ranges?

   a. $y = 3$ b. $x = -2$ c.   Where do the two graphs cross?

3-9.   Solve this system for m and b: $342 = 23m + b$
                                              $147 = 10m + b$

3-10.   Tanika made this sequence of triangles:

   a.   If the pattern continues, what do you think the next two triangles in the sequence would be?

  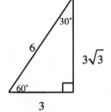

1   2   3

   b.   Write a sentence to explain how to find the long leg and hypotenuse if you know the short leg (i.e., if the base is n units long).

3-11.   Consider the sequence $3, 9, \ldots$

   a.   Assuming that the sequence is arithmetic with $t(1)$ as the first term, find the next four terms of the sequence and then write an equation for $t(n)$.

   b.   Assuming that the sequence is geometric with $t(1)$ as the first term, find the next four terms of the sequence and then write an equation for $t(n)$.

   c.   Create a sequence that begins with 3 that is neither arithmetic nor geometric. For your sequence, write the next four terms and, if you can, write an equation for $t(n)$.

3-12.   Simplify each expression without using a calculator.

   a. $25^{-1/2}$ b. $(\frac{1}{27})^{-1/3}$ c. $9^{3/2}$ d. $16^{-3/4}$

3.1.2 How can I rewrite it?

Rewriting Expressions and Determining Equivalence

In this lesson, you will continue to think about equivalent expressions. You will use an area model to demonstrate that two expressions are equivalent and to find new ways to write expressions. As you work with your team, use the following questions to help focus your discussion:

How can we be sure they are equivalent?

How would this look in a diagram?

Why is this representation convincing?

3-13.   Jonah and Graham are working together. Jonah claims that $(x + y)^2 = x^2 + y^2$. Graham is sure Jonah is wrong, but he cannot figure out how to show it.

a.   Help Graham find as many ways as possible to convince Jonah that he is incorrect. How can he rewrite $(x + y)^2$ correctly?

b.   Are there any values for x and y for which $(x + y)^2 = x^2 + y^2$? In other words, is $(x + y)^2 = x^2 + y^2$ sometimes true? Justify your answer.

3-14.   Do you think that an area model can help rewrite expressions that involve multiplication?

a.   The area model at right relates the expressions $(2x - 3)(3x + 1)$ and $6x^2 - 7x - 3$. With your team, discuss how it can be used to show that these expressions are equivalent. Be prepared to explain your ideas.

	$2x$	-3
$+1$	$2x$	-3
$3x$	$6x^2$	$-9x$

b.   Use an area model to write an expression equivalent to $(5k - 3)(2k - 1)$.

c.   Use an area model to write a product that is equivalent to $x^2 - 3x - 4$.

3-15.   Rewrite each of the following products as a sum and each sum as a product, drawing an area model when appropriate.

a. $2x^2 + 5x + 2$

b. $(3x - 1)(x + 2y - 4)$

c. $(x - 3)(x + 3)$

d. $4x^2 - 49$

e. $(p^2 + 3p + 9)(2p - 1)$

f. $(4 - x)(x^2 + 1) + (3x - 5)$

3-16.   With your team, decide whether the following expressions can be represented with a model and rewrite each expression. Be prepared to share your strategies with the class.

a. $p(p + 3)(2p - 1)$

b. $x(x + 1) + (3x - 5)$

3-17.   Copy each area model below and fill in the missing parts. Then write the two equivalent expressions represented by each model. Be prepared to share your reasoning with the class.

a.

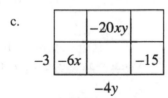

b.

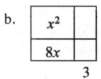

c.

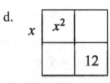

d.

3-18.   Shinna noticed a similarity in parts (c) and (d) of problem 3-15.

a.   Look back at those two problems and their rewritten form. What might Shinna have noticed? Discuss this with your team and be prepared to share your ideas with the class.

b.   Shinna thinks she has found a shortcut that will allow her to rewrite expressions such as those written below without drawing a diagram. What do you think she has figured out? Try your ideas on the expressions shown below.

i. $w^2 - 81$ ii. $4m^2 - 1$ iii. $x^2 - 16y^2$

3-19.   Shinna has noticed that **differences of squares** can be factored easily.

a.   Decide which of the expressions below can be seen as a difference of squares and can therefore be factored using Shinna's shortcut. For each difference of squares, show the squares clearly and then write the product. For example, $16x^2 - 9y^2$ can be rewritten as $(4x)^2 - (3y)^2$ and then as $(4x - 3y)(4x + 3y)$.

   i. $a^2 - 4b^2$ ii. $2x^2 - 16$

   iii. $-x^2 + y^4$ iv. $4a^2 + 9b^2$

b.   Write two more expressions of your own that are differences of squares and show each in factored form.

3-20.   Shinna wants to factor $9x^2y^4 - z^6$. *"Wait!"* she says. *"I think I can see a way to use my shortcut!"*

a.   Discuss this with your team. Is Shinna's expression a difference of squares? If so, what are the squares? If not, explain why. Be ready to share your ideas with the class.

b.   Shinna decided to rewrite her expression so that its structure was simpler to see. She wrote $9x^2y^4 - z^6$ as $U^2 - V^2$. What was she using U to represent? What about V?

c.   George is confused! *"Shinna,"* he says, *"There was no U or V in your problem! What are you doing?"* Explain to George what is going on.

d.   Help Shinna finish factoring the expression $9x^2y^4 - z^6$ by factoring $U^2 - V^2$ and then substituting the original expressions for U and V.

Core Connections Algebra 2

3-21.   How can you use this method of substitution to make use of what you know about other expressions? Work with your team to describe the structure of each of the expressions in parts (a) through (d) below. Use substitution, when appropriate, to make the structure clear. For example, $25x^2 - 100y^4$ is a difference of squares and can be rewritten as $U^2 - V^2$ with $U = 5x$ and $V = 10y^2$.

The following questions might be useful:

What do all of these expressions have in common?

How might we substitute U and V to make rewriting simpler?

a. $a^2 + 2ab + b^2$ b. $x^2 - 6x + 9$

c. $9x^2 + 30xy + 25y^2$ d. $(a+7)^2 - 10(a+7) + 25$

3-22.   Now it's your turn!

a.   Work with a partner to write two really complicated-looking expressions that can actually be rewritten in a different form using substitution. Be sure to write the solutions for your expressions on a separate paper, so that you will be ready to trade expressions with another pair of students.

b.   When you and your partner have been given another pair's expressions, use substitution to rewrite them. Do not let them stump you!

Review & Preview

3-23.   Decide whether each of the following pairs of expressions are equivalent for all values of x (or a and b). If they are equivalent, show how you can be sure. If they are not, justify your reasoning completely.

a. $(x+3)^2$ and $x^2 + 9$ b. $(x+4)^2$ and $x^2 + 8x + 16$

c. $(x+1)(2x-3)$ and $2x^2 - x - 3$ d. $3(x-4)^2 + 2$ and $3x^2 - 24x + 50$

e. $(x^3)^4$ and x^7 f. ab^2 and a^2b^2

3-24.   Look back at the expressions in problem 3-23 that are not equivalent. For each pair of expressions, are there any values of the variable(s) that would make the two expressions equal? Justify your reasoning.

3-25.   Jenna wants to solve the equation $2000x - 4000 = 8000$.

      a.   What easier equation could she solve instead that would give her the same solution? (In other words, what equivalent equation has easier numbers to work with?)

      b.   Justify that your equation in part (a) is equivalent to $2000x - 4000 = 8000$ by showing that they have the same solution.

      c.   Now Jenna wants to solve $\frac{3}{50} - \frac{x}{50} = \frac{7}{50}$. Write and solve an equivalent equation with easier numbers that would give her the same answer.

3-26.   Find an equation for each sequence below. Then describe its graph.

      a.

n	$t(n)$
3	8
5	2
7	−4

      b.

n	$t(n)$
1	40
2	32
3	25.6

3-27.   For the function $h(x) = -3x^2 - 11x + 4$, find the value of $h(x)$ for each value of x given below.

      a. $h(0)$ b. $h(2)$ c. $h(-1)$ d. $h(\frac{1}{2})$

      e.   For what value(s) of x does $h(x) = 0$?

3-28.   Find the x-intercepts for the graph of $y - x^2 = 6x$.

3-29.   Multiply each pair of polynomial functions below to find an expression for $f(x) \cdot g(x)$.

      a. $f(x) = 2x$, $g(x) = (x + 3)$ b. $f(x) = (x + 3)$, $g(x) = (x - 5)$

      c. $f(x) = (2x + 1)$, $g(x) = (x - 3)$ d. $f(x) = (x + 3)$, $g(x) = (x + 3)$

3-30.   Describe how the graph of $y + 3 = -2(x + 1)^2$ is different from $y = x^2$.

3-31.   Given the parabola $f(x) = x^2 - 2x - 3$, complete parts (a) through (c) below.

     a.   Find the vertex by averaging the x-intercepts.

     b.   Find the vertex by completing the square.

     c.   Find the vertex of $f(x) = x^2 + 5x + 2$ using your method of choice.

     d.   What are the domain and range for $f(x) = x^2 + 5x + 2$?

3-32.   Simplify each of the following expressions, leaving only positive exponents in your answer.

     a. $(x^3 y^{-2})^{-4}$ b. $-3x^2(6xy - 2x^3 y^2 z)$

3-33.   Determine if each of the following functions are odd, even or neither.

     a. $y = 3x^3$ b. $y = x^2 + 16$ c. $y = \frac{x^4}{2}$

3-34.   You decide to park your car in a parking garage that charges \$3.00 for the first hour and \$1.00 for each hour (or any part of an hour) after that.

     a.   How much will it cost to park your car for 90 minutes?

     b.   How much will it cost to park your car for 118 minutes? 119 minutes?

     c.   How much will it cost to park your car for 120 minutes? 121 minutes?

     d.   Graph the cost in relation to the length of time your car is parked.

     e.   Is this function continuous?

     f.   Describe how the graph of this function will change if the parking garage raises their parking rate so that the first hour is now \$5.00.

3-35.   Give the equation of each circle below in graphing form.

     a.   A circle with radius of 12 centered at the point (–2, 13).

     b.   A circle with center (–1, –4) and radius 1.

     c.   A circle with equation $x^2 + y^2 - 6x + 16y + 57 = 0$. (Hint: Complete the square for both x and y.)

3-36.   Giuseppe decides that he really wants some ice cream, so he leaves the house at
3:00 p.m. and walks to the ice cream parlor. He arrives at 3:15 (the ice cream
parlor is 6 blocks away). He buys an ice cream cone and sits down to eat it. At
3:45 he heads back home, arriving at 4:05. Find Giuseppe's average walking
rate in blocks per hour for each of the following situations.

   a.   His trip to the ice cream parlor.

   b.   His trip back home.

   c.   The entire trip including the time spent eating.

3.1.3   How can I solve it?

Solving by Rewriting

In the past few lessons, you have worked on recognizing and finding equivalent
expressions. In this lesson, you will apply these ideas to solve equations. As you work,
use the questions below to keep your team's discussion productive and focused.

How can we make it simpler?

Does anyone see another way?

How can we be sure the equations are equivalent?

3-37.   Graciela was trying to solve the quadratic equation $x^2 + 2.5x - 1.5 = 0$. *"I think
I need to use the Quadratic Formula because of the decimals,"* she told Walter.
Walter replied, *"I'm sure there's another way! Can't we rewrite this equation
so there aren't any decimals?"*

   a.   What is Walter talking about? Rewrite the equation so that it has no
        decimals.

   b.   Rewrite your equation again, this time expressing it as a product.

   c.   Now solve your new equation. Be sure to check your solution(s) using
        Graciela's original equation.

3-38.   SOLVING BY REWRITING

Rewriting $x^2 + 2.5x - 1.5 = 0$ in problem 3-37 gave you a new, equivalent equation that was much easier to solve. With your team, find an equivalent equation or system that you think might be easier to solve for parts (a) through (f) below. Then solve your new equation or system and check your answer(s) using the original equations.

a. $100x^2 + 100x = 2000$

b. $15x + 10y = -20$
$7x - 2y = 24$

c. $\frac{1}{3}x^2 + \frac{x}{2} - \frac{1}{3} = 0$

d. $\frac{4}{x^2} + \frac{12}{x} + 9 = 0$

e. $\frac{x-3}{x} + \frac{2}{x-1} = \frac{5-x}{x}$

f. $\frac{\sqrt{x^2-15x}}{2y} = 5$
$3\sqrt{x^2 - 15x} - 3y = 27$

3-39.   Graciela and Walter were working on solving the system of equations in part (f) of problem 3-38. They tried to rewrite both equations in $y=$ form so that they could set them equal to each other.

$2y \cdot \frac{\sqrt{x^2-15x}}{2y} = 2y \cdot 5$ $\sqrt{x^2 - 15x} = 10y$ $y = \frac{\sqrt{x^2-15x}}{10}$
                                    $\Rightarrow$ $\Rightarrow$
$\frac{3\sqrt{x^2-15x}-3y}{3} = \frac{27}{3}$ $\sqrt{x^2 - 15x} - y = 9$ $y = \sqrt{x^2 - 15x} - 9$

Graciela and Walter realized they had a big mess to try to solve. "*Wait,*" Graciela said. "*There's an easier way. Let's use substitution to make this system simpler!*"

a.   Discuss this idea with your team. Does it make sense?

b.   Walter and Graciela decided to try this new idea, but they were not sure the best choice for what expression to replace with a new variable. They came up with these two options:

$U = x^2 - 15x$ or $U = \sqrt{x^2 - 15x}$

To help Graciela and Walter decide, rewrite the original system from problem 3-38 part (f) twice, each time using a different version of U. Which version of U looks like it will make the system easier to solve?

c.   Solve your new system for U and y.

d.   Now what? Since your job in solving a system in x and y is to find values for both of those variables, you are not done. Work with your team to find a way to get the value of x from the value you found for U. Be ready to share your strategies with the class.

3-40.   Consider each of the following equations and systems. Would substitution make them easier to solve? What expression might you temporarily replace with U? Be ready to share your ideas on substitution with the class. You do not need to actually solve the equation(s).

   a. $(m^2 + 5m - 24)^2 - (m^2 + 5m - 24) = 6$

   b. $2x + y^7 = 6$
         $3x - 2y^7 = -5$

   c. $(4x^2 + 4x - 3)^2 = (x^2 - 5x - 6)^2$

3-41.   MORE EQUIVALENT EQUATIONS

   Rewrite each of the following equations in another form by solving for y. (That is, rewrite the equations in $y =$ form.) Check to be sure your new equation is equivalent to the original equation.

   a. $5x - 2y = 8$ b. $xy + 3x = 2$

3-42.   Rewrite the equation from part (b) of problem 3-41 in yet another form by solving for x. Be ready to share your strategies with the class.

3-43.   None of the three equations below are equivalent. Show that this is true by rewriting the equations with an equivalent equation.

   $2x = 2y - 6$ $xy + 2x = (y + 2)(y + 3)$ $-x = -y - 3$

3-44.   Angelica and D'Lee were working on finding roots of two quadratic equations:
$y = (x - 3)(x - 5)$ and $y = 2(x - 3)(x - 5)$.
Angelica made an interesting claim: *"Look,"* she said, *"When I solve each of them for $y = 0$, I get the same solutions. So these equations must be equivalent!"*

   D'Lee is not so sure. *"How can they be equivalent if one of the equations has a factor of 2 that the other equation doesn't?"* she asked.

   a.   Who is correct? Is $y = (x - 3)(x - 5)$ equivalent to $y = 2(x - 3)(x - 5)$? How can you justify your ideas using tables and graphs?

   b.   Are the solutions of $0 = (x - 3)(x - 5)$ equivalent to the solutions of $0 = 2(x - 3)(x - 5)$? Again, how can you justify your ideas?

Core Connections Algebra 2

METHODS AND MEANINGS

Vocabulary for Expressions

A mathematical **expression** is a combination of numbers, variables, and operation symbols. Addition and subtraction separate expressions into parts called **terms**. For example, $4x^2 - 3x + 6$ is an expression. It has three terms: $4x^2$, $3x$, and 6. The **coefficients** of the terms with variables are 4 and –3. 6 is called a **constant term**.

A single-variable **polynomial** is an expression that involves, at most, the operations of addition, subtraction, and multiplication. Most of the polynomials you will work with can be written as expressions with terms of the following form:

$$(\text{any real number})x^{(\text{whole number})}$$

For example, $4x^2 - 3x^1 + 6x^0$ is a polynomial, as is the simplified form, $4x^2 - 3x + 6$. Also, since $6x^0 = 6$, 6 itself is a polynomial.

The function $f(x) = 7x^5 + 2.5x^3 - \frac{1}{2}x + 7$ is a polynomial function.

A **binomial** is a polynomial with only two terms, for example, $x^3 - 0.5x$ and $2x + 5$.

The following expressions are *not* polynomials: $2^x - 3$, $\frac{1}{x^2-2}$, and $\sqrt{x-2}$.

An expression that can be written as the quotient of two polynomials is a **rational expression**. For example, $\frac{1}{x^2-2}$ is a rational expression.

3-45.   Rewrite each equation below. Then solve your new equation. Be sure to check your solution using the original equation.

a. $(n+4) + n(n+2) + n = 0$ b. $\frac{4}{x} = x + 3$

3-46.   Decide whether each of the following pairs of expressions or equations are equivalent. If they are, show how you can be sure. If they are not, justify your reasoning completely.

      a. $(ab)^2$ and a^2b^2 b. $3x - 4y = 12$ and $y = \frac{3}{4}x - 3$

      c. $y = 2(x - 1) + 3$ and $y = 2x + 1$ d. $(a + b)^2$ and $a^2 + b^2$

      e. $\frac{x^6}{x^2}$ and x^3 f. $y = 3(x - 5) + 2$ and $y = 2x - 8$

3-47.   Look back at the expressions in problem 3-46 that are not equivalent. Are there any values of the variables that would make them equal? Justify your reasoning.

3-48.   Find the formula for $t(n)$ for the arithmetic sequence in which $t(15) = 10$ and $t(63) = 106$.

3-49.   Jillian's parents bought a house for $450,000, and the value of the house has been increasing steadily by 3% each year.

      a.   Find the formula $t(n)$ that represents the value of the house each year.

      b.   If Jillian's parents sell their house 10 years after they bought it, how much profit will they make? (That is, how much more are they selling it for than they bought it for?) Express your answer as both a dollar amount and a percent of the original purchase price.

3-50.   Factor $5x^3y + 35x^2y + 50xy$ completely. Show every step and explain what you did.

3-51.   While Jenna was solving the equation $150x + 300 = 600$, she wondered if she could first change the equation to $x + 2 = 4$. What do you think?

      a.   Solve both equations and verify that they have the same solution.

      b.   What did Jenna do to the equation $150x + 300 = 600$ to change it to $x + 2 = 4$?

      c.   Use the same method to rewrite and solve $60t - 120 = 300$.

3-52. Consider the sequence $10, 2, \ldots$

     a.   Assuming that the sequence is arithmetic with $t(1)$ as the first term, write the next four terms of the sequence and then write an equation for $t(n)$.

     b.   Assuming that the sequence is geometric with $t(1)$ as the first term, write the next four terms of the sequence and then write an equation for $t(n)$.

     c.   Create a totally different sequence that begins $10, 2, \ldots$ For your sequence, write the next four terms and an equation for $t(n)$.

3-53. Rewrite each radical below as an equivalent expression using fractional exponents.

     a. $\sqrt[2]{5}$ b. $\sqrt[3]{9}$ c. $\sqrt[8]{17^x}$ d. $7\sqrt[4]{x^3}$

3-54. Give the equation of each circle below in graphing form.

     a.   A circle with center $(0, 0)$ and radius 6.

     b.   A circle with center $(2, -3)$ and radius 6.

     c.   A circle with equation $x^2 + y^2 - 8x + 10y + 5 = 0$.

3-55. If the cooling system in a light-water nuclear reactor is shut off, the temperature of the fuel rods will increase. The temperature of the fuel rods during the first hour could be modeled by the equation $T = 680(1.0004)^t - 655$, where t is the time in seconds, and T is the temperature of the fuel rods in degrees Fahrenheit. **Average rate of change** can be calculated by finding the slope between two points. Find the average rate at which the temperature changes for the first 30 minutes.

3-56. In the year 2006, the average cost to rent a car was \$39 for the first day and an additional \$23 for each additional day.

     a.   Graph the relationship between cost and the duration of a car rental in 2006.

     b.   Describe how the graph would be transformed if the current average cost of a car rental has increased to \$50 for the first day.

3.2.1 Where does the graph go?

∙∙∙

Investigating Rational Functions

In your experience with algebra, you have added, subtracted, and multiplied polynomials, but what happens when you divide them? Today you will make some predictions about the graphs that result when two linear functions are combined by adding, subtracting, multiplying, or dividing them. You will further explore division of polynomials in Chapter 8.

3-57.   COMBINING LINEAR FUNCTIONS INVESTIGATION

Your team will be assigned a pair of linear functions from the list below.

$f_1(x) = x - 2$	$f_2(x) = x + 3$	$f_3(x) = x - 4$
$g_1(x) = 2x + 3$	$g_2(x) = 5x - 9$	$g_3(x) = 5x + 8$
$f_4(x) = x - 1$	$f_5(x) = x - 3$	$f_6(x) = x + 4$
$g_4(x) = 2x + 5$	$g_5(x) = 5x - 9$	$g_6(x) = 5x + 6$
$f_7(x) = x - 3$	$f_8(x) = x + 3$	$f_9(x) = x + 2$
$g_7(x) = 2x + 5$	$g_8(x) = 5x + 7$	$g_9(x) = 5x + 3$

Your Task: With your team, find out as much as you can about what happens when you combine the two linear functions using each of the operations of addition, subtraction, multiplication, and division. Use the following steps to guide your investigation.

1. Make your own prediction of the shape of each new graph and draw a quick, rough sketch on your paper.

2. Discuss your prediction with your teammates.

3. Use a graphing calculator to check your team's prediction.

4. Summarize your findings.

Be sure to carefully record all of your work and be prepared to share your summary statements about the results for each operation with the class.

Note: When entering operations into the graphing calculator, you may need to insert extra parentheses so the calculator will follow your intended Order of Operations.

Discussion Points

What does the new graph look like?

What happens when we use the expressions in a different order? Why?

What are the domains and ranges of the new graphs?

Further Guidance

3-58.   First investigate the graphs for the sum and difference of your two functions. Does the order of subtraction matter? What do you think would happen if you added or subtracted any two linear functions $f(x)$ and $g(x)$. Can you think of any exceptions?

3-59.   Now multiply the functions and graph the product $f(x) \cdot g(x)$. How well did your team predict the result? What do you think the resulting graph would look like if you multiplied any two linear functions?

3-60.   Divide the two functions, $\frac{f(x)}{g(x)}$, and graph the result. Check the table of values or use the [TRACE] function on your calculator to find the x-values that are "holes" in your graph. (Your teacher will check if the graph in the standard window of your graphing calculator has extra lines that obscure the picture. If that is the case, the teacher will make some suggestions.)

——————   *Further Guidance*   ——————
                 section ends here.

3-61.   **CLOSED SETS**

Whole numbers (positive integers and zero) are said to be a **closed set** under addition: if you add two whole numbers, you always get a whole number. Whole numbers are not a closed set under subtraction: if you subtract two whole numbers, you do not always get a whole number. For example, $2 - 5 = -3$ and -3 is not a whole number.

a.   Investigate with your team whether the set of integers is a closed set under addition and under subtraction. Then investigate whether the integers are a closed set under multiplication and under division. Give examples. If you think the set is closed, explain why. If, not, give counterexamples.

b.   Are single-variable polynomials closed under addition, subtraction, and multiplication? In other words, if you add, subtract, or multiply two polynomials that have the same variable, will you always get a polynomial as your answer? If you think the set is closed, explain why. If, not, give counterexamples.

3-62. With your team describe the graphs of $p(x)$ and $q(x)$ and then make an estimate of their sum, difference, product, and quotient functions *before* using a graphing tool.

$$p(x) = x^3 - 3x - 1 \qquad\qquad q(x) = x - 1$$

a. $p(x) + q(x)$ b. $p(x) - q(x)$ c. $p(x) \cdot q(x)$ d. $\frac{p(x)}{q(x)}$

e. For parts (a) through (d) above, sketch a careful graph and make a note of the shape, the domain and range, and any other characteristics you notice. Your team should be prepared to share their observations with the class.

3-63. Given that n is the length of the bottom edge of the backward L-shaped figures below, what sequence is generated by the total number of dots in each figure? What is the 46th term, or $t(46)$, of this sequence? The nth term?

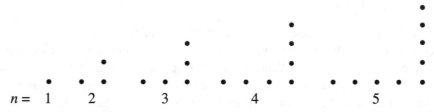

$n =$ 1   2   3   4   5

3-64. A piece of metal at 20°C is warmed at a steady rate of 2 degrees per minute. At the same time, another piece of metal at 240°C is cooled at a steady rate of 3 degrees per minute. After how many minutes is the temperature of each piece of metal the same? Explain how you found your answer.

3-65. The price of a movie ticket averages $10.25 and is increasing by 3% per year. Use that information to complete parts (a) through (c) below.

a. What is the multiplier in this situation?

b. Write a function that represents the cost of a movie ticket n years from now.

c. If tickets continue to increase at the same rate, what will they cost 10 years from now?

3-66. Use the meaning of an exponent to rewrite the expression $(y - 2)^3$.

3-67.   This problem is a checkpoint for rewriting and simplifying expressions with integral and rational exponents. It will be referred to as Checkpoint 3A.

For parts (a) through (d), rewrite each expression. For parts (e) through (h), simplify each expression.

a. $\sqrt[5]{x}$ b. $\frac{1}{x^3}$ c. $x^{2/3}$ d. $\frac{1}{\sqrt{x}}$

e. $x^{-1}y^{-8}$ f. $(m^2)^{-3/2}$ g. $(x^3y^6)^{1/2}$ h. $(9x^3y^6)^{-2}$

Check your answers by referring to the Checkpoint 3A materials located at the back of your book.

If you needed help solving these problems correctly, then you need more practice. Review the Checkpoint 3A materials and try the practice problems. Also, consider getting help outside of class time. From this point on, you will be expected to do problems like these quickly and easily.

3-68.   While David was solving the equation $100x + 300 = 500$, he wondered if he could first change the equation to $x + 3 = 5$. What do you think?

a.   Solve both equations and verify that they have the same solution.

b.   What could you do to the equation $100x + 300 = 500$ to change it into $x + 3 = 5$?

3-69.   Multiply the expressions below using generic rectangles.

a. $(5m - 1)(m + 2)$ b. $(6 - x)(2 + x)$

c. $(5x - y)^2$ d. $3x(2x - 5y + 4)$

3.2.2 How can "1" be useful?

Simplifying Rational Expressions

In this chapter, you will focus on an important number: the number 1. What is special about 1? What can you do with the number 1 that you cannot do with any other number? You will use your understanding of the number 1 to simplify algebraic fractions, which are also known as **rational expressions**.

3-70. What do you know about the number 1? With your team, brainstorm ideas and be ready to report your ideas to the class. Create examples to help show what you mean.

3-71. Mr. Wonder claims that anything divided by itself equals 1 (as long as you do not divide by zero).

a. Mr. Wonder states that $\frac{16x}{16x} = 1$ if x is not zero. What is his hypothesis and his conclusion?

b. Is Mr. Wonder correct? That is, is his statement true? Justify your conclusion.

c. Why can't x be zero?

d. Next he considers $\frac{x-3}{x-3}$. Does this equal 1? What value of x must be excluded in this fraction?

e. Create your own rational expression (algebraic fraction) that equals 1.

f. Mr. Wonder also says that when you multiply any number by 1, the number stays the same. For example, he says that the product below equals $\frac{x}{y}$. Is he correct?

$$\frac{\frac{z}{z}} \cdot \frac{x}{y} = \frac{x}{y}$$

3-72. Use a calculator to graph the function $f(x) = \frac{16x}{16x}$. Use the trace button to trace along the line and notice what happens at $x = 0$. Is the expression $\frac{16x}{16x}$ equivalent to 1? Explain.

Core Connections Algebra 2

3-73.   With your team, compare and contrast the graphs of each of the following functions:

$$f_1(x) = \frac{2x-3}{2x-3} \qquad\qquad f_2(x) = \frac{2x-3}{3-2x}$$

$$f_3(x) = \frac{2x-3}{2x+3} \qquad\qquad f_4(x) = \frac{1}{2x-3}$$

a.   First visualize and make a quick sketch of what you imagine the graph of each will look like.

b.   Discuss your sketches with the rest of your team.

c.   Use calculators to graph each rational function, and adjust your sketches if needed.

d.   Use the [TRACE] function or the table on your graphing calculator to find the location of the "hole" in each of the graphs, and describe their similarities and differences. Include their domains and ranges in the descriptions.

3-74.   Use what you know about the number 1 to simplify each expression below, if possible. State any value(s) of the variable that would make the denominator zero.

a. $\frac{x^2}{x^2}$

b. $\frac{x}{x} \cdot \frac{x}{x} \cdot \frac{x}{3}$

c. $\frac{x-2}{x-2} \cdot \frac{x+5}{x-1}$

d. $\frac{9}{x} \cdot \frac{x}{9}$

e. $\frac{h \cdot h \cdot k}{h}$

f. $\frac{(2m-5)(m+6)}{(m+6)(3m+1)}$

g. $\frac{6(n-2)^2}{3(n-2)}$

h. $\frac{3-2x}{(4x-1)(3-2x)}$

3-75.   Mr. Wonder now tries to simplify $\frac{4x}{x}$ and $\frac{4+x}{x}$.

a.   Mr. Wonder thinks that since $\frac{x}{x} = 1$, then $\frac{4x}{x} = 4$. Is he correct? Substitute three values of x to justify your answer.

b.   He also wonders if $\frac{4+x}{x} = 5$. Is this simplification correct? Substitute three values of x or use your calculator to compare the graphs of $g(x) = \frac{4+x}{x}$ with $h(x) = 5$ to justify your answer. Remember that $\frac{4+x}{x}$ is the same as $(4 + x) \div x$.

c.   Compare the results of parts (a) and (b). When can a rational expression be simplified in this manner?

d.   Which of the following expressions below is simplified correctly? Explain how you know.

    i. $\frac{x^2 + x + 3}{x+3} = x^2$ ii. $\frac{(x+2)(x+3)}{x+3} = x + 2$

3-76.   In problem 3-75, you may have noticed that *both* the numerator and denominator of an algebraic fraction must be written as a product before you can use any of the terms to create a **Giant One** (a form of the number 1). Examine the expressions below. Factor the numerator and denominator of each fraction, if necessary. That is, rewrite each one as a product. Then look for "Giant Ones" and simplify. For each expression, assume the denominator is not zero.

    a. $\frac{x^2 + 6x + 9}{x^2 - 9}$ b. $\frac{2x^2 - x - 10}{3x^2 + 7x + 2}$ c. $\frac{28x^2 - x - 15}{28x^2 - x - 15}$ d. $\frac{x^2 + 4x}{2x + 8}$

3-77.   LEARNING LOG

In your Learning Log, explain how to simplify rational expressions such as those in problem 3-76. Be sure to include an example. Title this entry "Simplifying Rational Expressions" and include today's date.

3-78.   Simplify the expressions below.

   a. $\frac{x^2-8x+16}{3x^2-10x-8}$ for $x \neq -\frac{2}{3}$ or 4

   b. $\frac{10x+25}{2x^2-x-15}$ for $x \neq -\frac{5}{2}$ or 3

   c. $\frac{(k-4)(2k+1)}{5(2k+1)} \div \frac{(k-3)(k-4)}{10(k-3)}$ for $k \neq 3, 4,$ or $-\frac{1}{2}$

3-79.   How many solutions does each equation below have?

   a. $4x + 3 = 3x + 3$ b. $3(x-4) - x = 5 + 2x$

   c. $(5x - 2)(x + 4) = 0$ d. $x^2 - 4x + 4 = 0$

3-80.   Now David wants to solve the equation $4000x - 8000 = 16,000$.

   a.   What easier equation could he solve instead that would give him the same solution? (In other words, what equivalent equation has easier numbers to work with?)

   b.   Justify that your equation in part (a) is equivalent to $4000x - 8000 = 16,000$ by showing that they have the same solution.

   c.   David's last equation to solve is $\frac{x}{100} + \frac{3}{100} = \frac{8}{100}$. Write and solve an equivalent equation with easier numbers that would give him the same answer.

3-81.   Solve each of the following inequalities for the given variable. Represent your solutions on a number line.

   a. $5 + 3x < 5$ b. $-3x \geq 8 - x$

3-82.   In Lesson 3.2.3 you will focus on multiplying and dividing
         rational expressions. Recall what you learned about
         multiplying and dividing fractions in a previous course as you
         answer the questions below. To help you, the following
         examples have been provided.

$$\frac{9}{16} \cdot \frac{4}{6} = \frac{36}{96} = \frac{3}{8}$$

$$\frac{5}{6} \div \frac{20}{12} = \frac{5}{6} \cdot \frac{12}{20} = \frac{60}{120} = \frac{1}{2}$$

a.   Without a calculator, multiply $\frac{2}{3} \cdot \frac{9}{14}$ and reduce the result. Then use a
      calculator to check your answer. Describe your method for multiplying
      fractions.

b.   Without a calculator, divide $\frac{3}{5} \div \frac{12}{25}$ and reduce the result. Then use a
      calculator to check your answer. Describe your method for dividing
      fractions.

3-83.   Sketch the graph of $y = (x + 2)^3 + 4$.

a.   What is the parent graph of this function? How has the graph of this
      function been transformed from the parent graph?

b.   Rewrite the equation $y = (x + 2)^3 + 4$ without parentheses. Remember the
      Order of Operations.

c.   How would the graph in part (a) differ from the graph of the original
      equation?

3-84.   Sketch the graph of the function
         $f(x) = 3 \cdot 5^x$.

a.   What is the domain of $f(x)$?

b.   Sketch the graph of the geometric sequence $t(n) = 3 \cdot 5^n$.

c.   What is the difference between $f(x)$ and $t(n)$? Explain completely.

3.2.3 How can I rewrite it?

Multiplying and Dividing Rational Expressions

You know how to multiply and divide fractions. But what if the fractions have variables in them? That is, what if they are rational expressions? Is the process the same? Today you will learn how to multiply and divide rational expressions and will continue to practice simplifying rational expressions.

3-85. Review your work from yesterday by simplifying the rational expression below using a "Giant One." What are the excluded values of x? (That is, what values can x *not* be?)

$$\frac{3x^2+11x-4}{2x^2+11x+12}$$

3-86. With your team, review your responses to homework problem 3-82. Verify that everyone obtained the same answers and be prepared to share with the class how you multiplied and divided the fractions below.

$$\frac{2}{3} \cdot \frac{9}{14} \qquad\qquad \frac{3}{5} \div \frac{12}{25}$$

3-87. Use your understanding of multiplying and dividing fractions to rewrite the expressions below. Then look for "Giant Ones" and simplify. For each rational expression, also state any values of the variables that would make the denominator zero.

a. $\frac{4x+3}{x-5} \cdot \frac{x-5}{x+3}$

b. $\frac{x+2}{9x-1} \div \frac{2x+1}{9x-1}$

c. $\frac{2m+3}{3m-2} \cdot \frac{7+4m}{3+2m}$

d. $\frac{(y-2)^3}{3y} \cdot \frac{y+5}{(y+2)(y-2)}$

e. $\frac{15x^3}{3y} \div \frac{10x^2y}{4y^2}$

f. $\frac{(5x-2)(3x+1)}{(2x-3)^2} \div \frac{(5x-2)(x-4)}{(x-4)(2x-3)}$

3-88.   PUTTING IT ALL TOGETHER

Multiply or divide the expressions below. Leave your answers as simplified as possible. For each rational expression, assume the denominator is not zero.

a. $\frac{20}{22} \cdot \frac{14}{35}$

b. $\frac{12}{40} \div \frac{15}{6}$

c. $\frac{5x-15}{3x^2+10x-8} \div \frac{x^2+x-12}{3x^2-8x+4}$

d. $\frac{12x-18}{x^2-2x-15} \cdot \frac{x^2-x-12}{3x^2-9x-12}$

e. $\frac{5x^2+34x-7}{10x} \cdot \frac{5x}{x^2+4x-21}$

f. $\frac{2x^2+x-10}{x^2+2x-8} \div \frac{4x^2+20x+25}{x+4}$

3-89.   LEARNING LOG

In your Learning Log, explain how to multiply and divide rational expressions. Be sure to include an example of each. Title this entry "Multiplying and Dividing Rational Expressions" and include today's date.

3-90.   Multiply or divide the expressions below. Simplify your results.

a. $\frac{x-7}{9(2x-1)} \div \frac{(x+5)(x-7)}{6x(x+5)}$

b. $\frac{6x^2-x-1}{3x^2+25x+8} \cdot \frac{x^2+4x-32}{2x^2+7x-4}$

3-91.   For each rational expression below, state any values of the variables that would make the denominator zero. Then complete each part.

a. Use the fact that $(x+4)^2 = (x+4)(x+4)$ to rewrite $\frac{(x+4)^2}{(x+4)(x-2)}$. Then look for "ones" and simplify.

b. Use the strategy you used in part (a) to simplify the expression $\frac{8(x+2)^3(x-3)^3}{4(x+2)^2(x-3)^5}$.

3-92.   Monica's younger sister is just learning how to add fractions, and she is confused. She has to add $\frac{1}{3}+\frac{2}{5}$.

Help Monica explain to her by writing a detailed step-by-step explanation of exactly what she needs to do.

3-93.   Solve the systems of equations below using any method.

a. $3x - 3 = y$
      $6x - 5y = 12$

b. $3x - 2y = 30$
      $2x + 3y = -19$

3-94.   Janelle conducted an experiment by mistake when she left her bologna sandwich at school over winter break. When she got back, her sandwich was much larger than it was when she left it. Her science teacher explained that the sandwich had produced large quantities of a rare bacterium, *Bolognicus sandwichae*. Based on a sample taken from the sandwich, Janelle determined that there were approximately 72 million bacteria present. Her
science teacher explained that this is not very surprising, since the number of this bacteria triples every 24 hours. Since the sandwich had been made only 15 days ago, Janelle was sure that she could sue the meat company. The food-industry standard for the most bacteria a sandwich-sized portion can have at the time of production is 100. Find out how many of the bacteria were present when the sandwich was made to determine if Janelle has a case.

3-95.   Determine if the function shown on the graph at right is odd or even or neither? Explain how you decided.

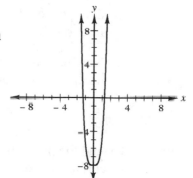

3-96.   Solve the equations below. Check your solutions.

a. $\frac{m}{6} = \frac{m+1}{5}$

b. $\frac{3x-5}{2} = \frac{4x+1}{4}$

c. $\frac{8}{k} = \frac{14}{k+3}$

d. $\frac{x}{9} = 10$

3.2.4 How can I rewrite it?

Adding and Subtracting Rational Expressions

So far in this course you have learned quite a bit about rational expressions. You have learned how to simplify complex algebraic fractions by factoring the numerators and denominators. You have also learned how to multiply and divide rational expressions. What else is there? Today you will develop a method to add and subtract algebraic fractions.

3-97. With your team, read your directions for Monica's sister from homework problem 3-92. Verify that everyone obtained the same answer and be prepared to share how you added the fractions with the class.

$$\tfrac{1}{3} + \tfrac{2}{5}$$

a. Now Monica's sister wants to know *why*? Why does she have to do all of those steps with the common denominator? What is a fraction anyway, and why does adding them have to be so complicated? Draw some pictures or diagrams or make up some situations that will help her to know what fractions like $\tfrac{1}{3}$ and $\tfrac{2}{5}$ mean.

b. Now use your ideas from part (a) to show Monica *why* she needs a common denominator to add the two fractions.

3-98. Extend the procedures your class developed for numerical fractions to add these algebraic fractions.

$$\frac{2x}{x-1} + \frac{3}{x+5}$$

3-99. Now add the fractions below. After you have added them, be sure to check to see if the numerator can be factored. You may be able get a simpler answer.

a. $\dfrac{x}{3x+1} + \dfrac{2x^2-2}{(x-5)(3x+1)}$

b. $\dfrac{9-3x}{(x+3)(x-3)} + \dfrac{2x}{x+3}$

3-100.   Examine the expression below.

$$\frac{2x-1}{3x^2+13x+4} + \frac{x+3}{x^2-3x-28}$$

a.   With your team, decide how you can alter the expression so that the fractions have a common denominator. Be ready to share your idea with the class.

b.   If you have not already do so, add the fractions. Then simplify the result, if possible.

c.   Repeat the process to subtract the expressions below. Simplify the result, if possible.

$$\frac{2}{x+4} - \frac{4x-x^2}{x^2-16}$$

3-101.   LEARNING LOG

In your Learning Log, explain how to add and subtract rational expressions. Be sure to include an example. Title this entry "Adding and Subtracting Rational Expressions" and include today's date.

METHODS AND MEANINGS

Rewriting Rational Expressions

To simplify a rational expression, both the numerator and denominator must be written in factored form. Then, look for factors that make a "Giant One" (a form of the number 1) and simplify. Study the examples below.

Example 1: $\dfrac{x^2+5x+4}{x^2+x-12} = \dfrac{(x+4)(x+1)}{(x+4)(x-3)} = 1 \cdot \dfrac{x+1}{x-3} = \dfrac{x+1}{x-3}$ for $x \neq -4$ or 3

Example 2: $\dfrac{2x-7}{2x^2+3x-35} = \dfrac{(2x-7)(1)}{(2x-7)(x+5)} = 1 \cdot \dfrac{1}{x+5} = \dfrac{1}{x+5}$ for $x \neq -5$ or $\frac{7}{2}$

Just as you can multiply and divide fractions, you can multiply and divide rational expressions.

Example 3: Multiply $\dfrac{x^2+6x}{(x+6)^2} \cdot \dfrac{x^2+7x+6}{x^2-1}$ and simplify for $x \neq -6$ or 1.

After factoring, this expression becomes: $\dfrac{x(x+6)}{(x+6)(x+6)} \cdot \dfrac{(x+1)(x+6)}{(x+1)(x-1)}$

After multiplying, reorder the factors: $\dfrac{(x+6)}{(x+6)} \cdot \dfrac{(x+6)}{(x+6)} \cdot \dfrac{x}{(x-1)} \cdot \dfrac{(x+1)}{(x+1)}$

Since $\dfrac{(x+6)}{(x+6)} = 1$ and $\dfrac{(x+1)}{(x+1)} = 1$, simplify: $1 \cdot 1 \cdot \dfrac{x}{(x-1)} \cdot 1 \Rightarrow \dfrac{x}{(x-1)}$

Example 4: Divide $\dfrac{x^2-4x-5}{x^2-4x+4} \div \dfrac{x^2-2x-15}{x^2+4x-12}$ and simplify for $x \neq 2, 5, -3$, or -6.

First, change to a multiplication expression: $\dfrac{x^2-4x-5}{x^2-4x+4} \cdot \dfrac{x^2+4x-12}{x^2-2x-15}$

Then factor each expression: $\dfrac{(x-5)(x+1)}{(x-2)(x-2)} \cdot \dfrac{(x-2)(x+6)}{(x-5)(x+3)}$

After multiplying, reorder the factors: $\dfrac{(x-5)}{(x-5)} \cdot \dfrac{(x-2)}{(x-2)} \cdot \dfrac{(x+1)}{(x-2)} \cdot \dfrac{(x+6)}{(x+3)}$

Since $\dfrac{(x-5)}{(x-5)} = 1$ and $\dfrac{(x-2)}{(x-2)} = 1$, simplify to get: $\dfrac{(x+1)(x+6)}{(x-2)(x+3)} \Rightarrow \dfrac{x^2+7x+6}{x^2+x-6}$

Note: From this point forward in the course, unless specifically asked, you may assume that all values of x that would make a denominator zero are excluded.

3-102.   Estacia wants to learn more about excluded values.

    a.   Explain to Estacia why x cannot be 4 in the expression $\frac{x+2}{x-4}$.

    b.   Find the excluded values of x in each of the expressions of problem 3-99.

    c.   Create an expression that has the excluded values of $x \neq -6$ and $x \neq \frac{1}{3}$.
       Be prepared to share your expression to the class.

3-103.   Use the methods developed in class to add or subtract the following rational
       expressions. Be sure to look for factors before trying to determine a common
       denominator, and simplify your answers, if possible.

    a. $\frac{4x}{x^2-2x-8}+\frac{4}{x-4}$
                            b. $\frac{16x-12}{4x^2+5x-6}-\frac{3}{x+2}$

3-104.   Solve the equations and inequalities below. Check your solutions, if possible.

    a. $|5x+8|\geq -4$
                                 b. $x^2+x-20<0$

    c. $2x^2-6x=-5$
                                 d. $\frac{5}{9}-\frac{x}{3}=\frac{4}{9}$

3-105.   Simplify the rational expressions below as much as possible.

    a. $\frac{(x-4)^3(2x-1)}{(2x-1)(x-4)^2}$
                            b. $\frac{7m^2-22m+3}{3m^2-7m-6}$

    c. $\frac{(z+2)^9(4z-1)^7}{(z+2)^{10}(4z-1)^5}$
                          d. $\frac{(x+2)(x^2-6x+9)}{(x-3)(x^2-4)}$

3-106.   Lexington High School has an annual growth rate of 4.7%. Three years ago
       there were 1500 students at the school.

    a.   How many students are there now?

    b.   How many students were there 5 years ago?

    c.   How many students will there be n years from now?

3-107. Multiply or divide the expressions below. Leave your answers as simplified as possible.

a. $\dfrac{(3x-1)(x+7)}{4(2x-5)} \cdot \dfrac{10(2x-5)}{(4x+1)(x+7)}$

b. $\dfrac{(m-3)(m+11)}{(2m+5)(m-3)} \div \dfrac{(4m-3)(m+11)}{(4m-3)(2m+5)}$

c. $\dfrac{2p^2+5p-12}{2p^2-5p+3} \cdot \dfrac{p^2+8p-9}{3p^2+10p-8}$

d. $\dfrac{4x-12}{x^2+3x-10} \div \dfrac{2x^2-13x+21}{2x^2+3x-35}$

3-108. Graph the function $g(x)=\frac{x+2}{x-1}$ on graph paper and name all x- and y-intercepts. What happens at $x=1$?

3-109. If $f(x)=3x-9$ and $g(x)=-x^2$, find:

a. $f(-2)$ b. $g(-2)$ c. x if $f(x)=0$ d. $g(m)$

3.2.5 Pulling it all together

Creating New Functions

In this lesson you will use all four operations of arithmetic to combine rational expressions. As you work with your team on the problems consider the following questions:

What operation are we using here and what steps will we need to take?

Is it possible to factor the numerators or denominators of the expressions?

How can we use the multiplication property of the "Giant One"?

What values of x must be excluded? How will that affect the graph?

Is our answer a rational expression?

3-110. PULLING IT ALL TOGETHER

You now know how to add, subtract, multiply, and divide rational expressions. Pull this all together by simplifying the following expressions.

a. $\dfrac{2x^2+x}{(2x+1)^2} - \dfrac{3}{2x+1}$

b. $\dfrac{x^2-3x-10}{x^2-4x-5} \div \dfrac{x^2-7x-18}{2x^2-5x-7}$

c. $\dfrac{15x-20}{x-5} \cdot \dfrac{x^2-2x-15}{3x^2+5x-12}$

d. $\dfrac{4}{2x+3} + \dfrac{x^2-x-2}{2x^2+5x+3}$

e. $\dfrac{6x-4}{3x^2-17x+10} - \dfrac{1}{x^2-2x-15}$

f. $\dfrac{x^2-x-2}{4x^2-7x-2} \div \dfrac{x^2-2x-3}{3x^2-8x-3}$

3-111. EXPLORING OPERATIONS WITH RATIONAL FUNCTIONS

What will the graphs of the sum, difference, product or quotient of
two rational functions look like? Graphs of rational functions can
be very complicated and difficult to interpret using a graphing
calculator, so you will work to get a glimpse of some of the
simpler outcomes by using two fairly simple rational functions.

$$f(x) = \frac{1}{x-2} \text{ and } g(x) = \frac{1}{x+1}$$

a. Algebraically find $f(x) \cdot g(x)$ and write this as a single function without
    any parentheses.

b. Graph the simplified function from part (a), and simultaneously graph the
    function $f(x) \cdot g(x)$. Are the graphs the same? How can you be sure the
    graphs are the same, and one graph is not just "hiding" out of the window
    you chose?

c. The graphs should be the same. If they are not, check your algebra (and
    your input) to see what happened.

d. Algebraically find $f(x) + g(x)$, $f(x) - g(x)$, and $\frac{f(x)}{g(x)}$, and simplify the
    function.

e. Graph each of your simplified algebraic functions from part (d)
    simultaneously with the original operation on two functions. Check that
    the graphs are the same and correct any mistakes if necessary.

f. Along with exploring the shape of the various function operations, you
    have discovered a way to check you work when simplifying rational
    expressions. Check you answer to part (a) of problem 3-110.

3-112. Based on your limited experience with rational expressions so far, do you think
        that the set of all rational expressions is closed for each of the four operations,
        addition, subtraction, multiplication, and division? If so, what are some reasons
        you think so, and if not, why not? Discuss this question with your team and be
        prepared to defend your conjecture.

METHODS AND MEANINGS

MATH NOTES

Adding and Subtracting Rational Expressions

In order to add and subtract fractions, the fractions must have a common denominator. One way to do this is to change each fraction so that the denominator is the **least common multiple** of the denominators. For the example at right, the least common multiple of $(x+3)(x+2)$ and $x+2$ is $(x+3)(x+2)$.

$$\frac{4}{(x+2)(x+3)} + \frac{2x}{x+2}$$

The denominator of the first fraction already is the least common multiple. To get a common denominator in the second fraction, multiply the fraction by $\frac{(x+3)}{(x+3)}$, a "Giant One" (a form of the number 1).

$$= \frac{4}{(x+2)(x+3)} + \frac{2x}{x+2} \cdot \frac{(x+3)}{(x+3)}$$

Multiply the numerator and denominator of the second term.

$$= \frac{4}{(x+2)(x+3)} + \frac{2x(x+3)}{(x+2)(x+3)}$$

Distribute the numerator, if necessary.

$$= \frac{4}{(x+2)(x+3)} + \frac{2x^2+6x}{(x+2)(x+3)}$$

Add, factor, and simplify the result.

$$= \frac{2x^2+6x+4}{(x+2)(x+3)} = \frac{2(x+1)(x+2)}{(x+2)(x+3)} = \frac{2(x+1)}{(x+3)}$$

3-113. Add, subtract, multiply, or divide the following rational expressions. Simplify your answers, if possible.

a. $\frac{2x}{3x^2+16x+5} + \frac{10}{3x^2+16x+5}$

b. $\frac{x^2-x-12}{3x^2-11x-4} \cdot \frac{3x^2-20x-7}{x^2-9}$

c. $\frac{2x^2+8x-10}{2x^2+15x+25} \div \frac{4x^2+20x-24}{2x^2+x-10}$

d. $\frac{7}{x+5} - \frac{4-6x}{x^2+10x+25}$

3-114. Examine the graph of $f(x)=|x-3|+1$ at right. Use the graph to find the values listed below.

a. $f(3)$

b. $f(0)$

c. $f(4)$

d. $f(-1)$

3-115. Use the graph of $f(x)=|x-3|+1$ in problem 3-114 to solve the equations and inequalities below. It may be helpful to copy the graph onto graph paper first.

a. $|x-3|+1=1$

b. $|x-3|+1\le 4$

c. $|x-3|+1=3$

d. $|x-3|+1>2$

3-116. This problem is a checkpoint for using function notation and identifying domain and range. It will be referred to as Checkpoint 3B.

Given $g(x)=2(x+3)^2$, state the domain and range, calculate $g(-5)$ and $g(a+1)$, and then find the value of x when $g(x)=32$ and when $g(x)=0$.

Check your answers by referring to the Checkpoint 3B materials located at the back of your book.

If you needed help solving these problems correctly, then you need more practice. Review the Checkpoint 3B materials and try the practice problems. Also, consider getting help outside of class time. From this point on, you will be expected to do problems like these quickly and easily.

3-117. Solve the quadratic below *twice*: once by factoring and using the Zero Product Property and once by completing the square. Verify that the solutions match.

$$x^2+14x+33=0$$

3-118. Match each graph below with its domain.

a. D: All values of x

b. D: $x>-2$

c. D: $x\le 3$

1)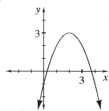

2)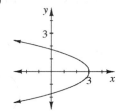

3)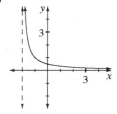

3-119. Graph the two functions below and find all points where they intersect. List all points in the form (x,y).

$$f(x)=x^2-3x-10$$

$$g(x)=-5x-7$$

3-120. Simplify each expression.

    a. $\frac{1}{x+2} + \frac{3}{x^2-4}$ b. $\frac{3}{2x+4} - \frac{x}{x^2+4x+4}$

    c. $\frac{x^2+5x+6}{x^2-9} \cdot \frac{x-3}{x^2+2x}$ d. $\frac{4}{x-2} \div \frac{8}{2-x}$

3-121. Solve $\sqrt{x+2} = 8$ and check your solution.

3-122. Use each pair of points given below to write a system of equations in $y = mx + b$ form to find the equation of a line that passes through the points.

    a.   (20, 2) and (32, –4)   b.   (–3, –17) and (12, –7)

3-123. Phana's garden is 2 meters wide and 5 meters long. She puts a walkway of uniform width around her garden. If the area of the walkway is 30 square meters, what are the outer dimensions of the walkway? Drawing a diagram will help you solve this problem.

3-124. Leadfoot Lilly was driving 80 miles per hour when she passed a parked highway patrol car. By the time she was half a mile past the spot where the patrol car was parked, the officer was driving after her at 100 miles per hour. If these rates remain constant, how long will it take the officer to catch up to Lilly? Write and solve an equation to represent this situation.

3-125. Two congruent overlapping squares are shown at right. If a point inside the figure is chosen at random, what is the probability that it will *not* be in the shaded region?

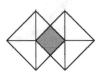

3-126. Factor each expression completely.

    a. $25x^2 - 1$ b. $5x^3 - 125x$

    c. $x^2 + x - 72$ d. $x^3 - 3x^2 - 18x$

Chapter 3 Closure What have I learned?

Reflection and Synthesis

The activities below offer you a chance to reflect about what you have learned during this chapter. As you work, look for concepts that you feel very comfortable with, ideas that you would like to learn more about, and topics you need more help with. Look for connections between ideas as well as connections with material you learned previously.

① **TEAM BRAINSTORM**

What have you studied in this chapter? What ideas were important in what you learned? With your team, brainstorm a list. Be as detailed as you can. To help get you started, a list of Learning Log entries and Math Notes boxes are below.

What topics, ideas, and words that you learned *before* this chapter are connected to the new ideas in this chapter? Again, be as detailed as you can.

How long can you make your list? Challenge yourselves. Be prepared to share your team's ideas with the class.

Learning Log Entries

- Lesson 3.1.1 – Equivalent Expressions
- Lesson 3.2.2 – Simplifying Rational Expressions
  Lesson 3.2.3 – Multiplying and Dividing Rational Expressions
- Lesson 3.2.4 – Adding and Subtracting Rational Expressions

Math Notes

- Lesson 3.1.3 – Vocabulary for Expressions
- Lesson 3.2.4 – Rewriting Rational Expressions
- Lesson 3.2.5 – Adding and Subtracting Rational Expressions

② MAKING CONNECTIONS

Below is a list of the vocabulary used in this chapter. Make sure that you are familiar with all of these words and know what they mean. Refer to the glossary or index for any words that you do not yet understand.

closed set	coefficient	constant term
difference of squares	equivalent	equation
excluded value	exponent	expression
factor	function	Giant One
least common denominator	polynomial	rational expression
rational function	rewrite	simplify
substitution	term	

Make a concept map showing all of the connections you can find among the key words and ideas listed above. To show a connection between two words, draw a line between them and explain the connection. A word can be connected to any other word as long as you can justify the connection.

While you are making your map, your team may think of related words or ideas that are not listed here. Be sure to include these ideas on your concept map.

③ PORTFOLIO: EVIDENCE OF MATHEMATICAL PROFICIENCY

This section gives you an opportunity to show growth in your understanding of key mathematical ideas over time as you complete this course.

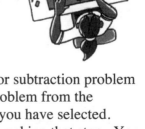

Your team has been assigned the task of preparing a set of directions for future algebra students on how to perform operations with rational expressions. Your assignment is to select one rational expressions addition or subtraction problem and one rational expressions multiplication or division problem from the chapter. Show step-by-step how to do the two problems you have selected. Next to each step, include an explanation of why you are making that step. You want to be sure your result is correct, so use a graphing tool to check your answer by comparing the graph of the original problem and with the graph of your answer.

A student who has just enrolled in an Algebra 2 class needs help understanding why $(x+y)^2 = x^2 + 2xy + y^2$. She thinks that $(x+y)^2 = x^2 + y^2$. Justify why $(x+y)^2 = x^2 + 2xy + y^2$ so that she is convinced that your answer is correct.

④ WHAT HAVE I LEARNED?

Most of the problems in this section represent typical problems found in this chapter. They serve as a gauge for you. You can use them to determine which types of problems you can do well and which types of problems require further study and practice. Even if your teacher does not assign this section, it is a good idea to try these problems and find out for yourself what you know and what you still need to work on.

Solve each problem as completely as you can. The table at the end of the closure section has answers to these problems. It also tells you where you can find additional help and practice with problems like these.

CL 3-127. Solve the following systems algebraically. What does each solution reveal about the graph of the equations in the system?

a. $x + 2y = 17$
   $x - y = 2$

b. $4x + 5y = 11$
   $2x + 6y = 16$

c. $4x - 3y = -10$
   $x = \frac{1}{4}y - 1$

d. $2x + y = -2x + 5$
   $3x + 2y = 2x + 3y$

CL 3-128. Solve each equation after first rewriting it in a simpler equivalent form.

a. $3(2x - 1) + 12 = 4x - 3$

b. $\frac{3x}{7} + \frac{2}{7} = 2$

c. $\frac{3}{4}x^2 = \frac{5}{4}x + \frac{1}{2}$

d. $4x(x - 2) = (2x + 1)(2x - 3)$

CL 3-129. Which of the following pairs of equations or expressions are equivalent? Justify your reasoning either by using algebra to transform the first equation or expression into the second or by demonstrating with a counterexample.

a. $n(2n + 1)(2n - 1)$; $4n^2 - n$

b. $(2x - 1)^2$; $4x^2 - 1$

c. $10x^2 - 55x - 105$; $5(2x + 3)(x - 7)$

d. $\left(\frac{4x^{12}}{-2x^8}\right)^3$; $-8x^{12}$

e. $2x - 3y = 6$; $y = \frac{2}{3}x + 6$

f. $\sqrt{108}$; $6\sqrt{3}$

CL 3-130. Perform the indicated operation on each of the following rational expressions. Be sure to state any values of the excluded variable and that your final answer is simplified. If a graphing tool is available, check the graph of the original problem to see if it coincides with the graph of your answer.

a. $\dfrac{x^2-x-6}{x^2-9} \cdot \dfrac{x^2+5x+6}{x^2+4x+4}$

b. $\dfrac{\dfrac{x^2-1}{x}}{\dfrac{x^2-2x+1}{2x^2+x}}$

CL 3-131. Evan spent the summer earning money so he could buy the classic car of his dreams. He purchased the car for $2295 from Fast Deal Freddie, the local used car salesman. Freddie told Evan that the car would increase by half its value after five years. Evan knows that this model appreciates 8% annually. Did Freddie try to trick Evan, or was his claim accurate?

CL 3-132. Decide whether each function below is even, odd or neither, and explain your reasoning.

a. $y=x^3+x$

b. $y=x^2+x$

c. $y=x^4+x^2$

CL 3-133. First, identify the parent graphs of the following equations. Then, describe how their graphs would be transformed from the parent graphs.

a. $y=0.25(x-8)^3+2$

b. $(x+3)^2+y^2=25$

c. $y=|x-5|+3$

CL 3-134. Last year, Jennifer paid the following for her electricity based on the number of kWh (kilowatt-hours) that she used each month.

kWh used	0 – 20,000	20,000 +
Cost per kWh (cents)	9.1225	6.5714

a. Make a graph of Jennifer's electrical rates.

b. Describe the domain of each of the pieces of this function. Then write an equation for each part of the domain.

c. This year the electrical company has said it is going to raise its rates by 3%. Describe how this will transform the graph and then write new equations for each part of the domain.

CL 3-135. Describe the domain and range of each function or sequence below.

a. The function $f(x) = (x-2)^2$.   b. The sequence $t(n) = 3n - 5$.

CL 3-136. Find the x- and y-intercepts of $y = x^2 - 3x - 3$.

CL 3-137. Check your answers using the table at the end of this section. Which problems do you feel confident about? Which problems were hard? Have you worked on problems like these in math classes you have taken before? Use the table to make a list of topics you need help on and a list of topics you need to practice more.

Answers and Support for Closure Activity #4
What Have I Learned?

Note: MN = Math Note, LL = Learning Log

Problem	Solutions	Need Help?	More Practice
CL 3-127.	a. $(7, 5)$ b. $(-1, 3)$ c. $(-\frac{1}{4}, 3)$ d. $(1, 1)$	Lesson 1.1.3 Checkpoint 2B	Problems 3-9, 3-64, and 3-93
CL 3-128.	a. -6 b. 4 c. $(-\frac{1}{3}, 2)$ d. $\frac{3}{4}$	Lesson 2.2.3	Problems 3-25, 3-38, 3-43, 3-45, 3-51, 3-68, and 3-80
CL 3-129.	Methods vary. Sample answers below. a. $n(2n+1)(2n-1) = (2n^2+n)(2n-1)$ $= 4n^3 - 2n^2 + 2n^2 - n = 4n^3 - n$ Not equivalent b. $(2x-1)^2 = (2x-1)(2x-1)$ $= 4x^2 - 2x - 2x + 1 = 4x^2 - 4x + 1$ Not equivalent c. $10x^2 - 55x - 105 = 5(2x^2 - 11x - 21)$ $= 5(2x+3)(x-7)$ Equivalent d. $(\frac{4x^{12}}{-2x^8})^3 = \frac{4^3 x^{36}}{(-2)^3 x^{24}} = \frac{64x^{(36-24)}}{-8}$ $= -8x^{12}$ Equivalent e. $2x - 3y = 6$, $-3y = -2x + 6$, $y = \frac{2}{3}x - 2$ Not equivalent f. $\sqrt{108} = \sqrt{36 \cdot 3} = \sqrt{6^2 \cdot 3} = 6\sqrt{3}$ Equivalent	Lessons 2.2.1 and 2.2.2	Problems 3-2, 3-3, 3-5, 3-6, 3-15, 3-16, 3-41, and 3-46
CL 3-130.	a. 1 b. $\frac{(x+1)(2x+1)}{(x-1)} = \frac{2x^2+3x+1}{x-1}$	Lessons 3.2.2 and 3.2.3	Problems 3-78, 3-90, 3-91, and 3-113
CL 3-131.	$y = (1.08)^t$ so when $t = 5$, $y \approx 1.46$ which is about 1.5, so Freddie's claim was fairly accurate.	Lessons A.3.2 and B.2.3	Problems 3-49, 3-65, and 3-94

Problem	Solutions	Need Help?	More Practice
CL 3-132.	a. odd, $f(-x) = -f(x)$ b. neither, $f(-x)$ does not equal $f(x)$ or $-f(x)$ c. even, $f(-x) = f(x)$	Lesson 2.2.3 MN: 2.2.5 LL: 2.2.3	Problems 3-9, 3-29, 3-33, and 3-51
CL 3-133.	a. parent: $y = x^3$; cubic shifted up 2 and right 8 and compressed by a factor of 0.25 b. parent: $x^2 + y^2 = r^2$; circle with center at $(-3,0)$ and radius of 5 c. parent: $y = |x|$; absolute value shifted up 3 and right 5	Lessons 2.2.1, 2.2.2, 2.2.3, and 2.2.4	Problems 3-4, 3-5, 3-35, 3-54, and 3-83
CL 3-134.	a. b. $0 \le x \le 20{,}000$ and $x > 20{,}000$; $f_1(x) = 9.1225x$ and $f_2(x) = 6.5714x$ c. The slope of the lines will change. $f_1(x) = 9.3962x$ and $f_2(x) = 6.7685x$	Lesson 2.2.5	Problems 3-34, 3-56, 3-116, and 3-118
CL 3-135.	a. Domain: all real numbers Range: $y \ge 0$ b. Domain: all positive whole numbers; Range: all numbers of the form $3n - 5$	Lesson 1.1.3 Checkpoint 3B MN: 1.1.3	Problems 1-34, 1-62, 1-109, 2-4, 2-108, 3-8, 3-31, and 3-84
CL 3-136.	x-intercepts: $(\frac{3+\sqrt{21}}{2}, 0)$ and $(\frac{3-\sqrt{21}}{2}, 0)$ y-intercept: $(0, -3)$	MN: 1.1.4	Problems 1-48, 1-106, and 3-28

Chapter 4   Solving and Intersections

This chapter begins with a focus on two ways to solve equations and systems of equations: algebraically and graphically. You will build on your understanding of solving and solutions from previous courses to gain a broader and stronger understanding of the meaning of solutions.

In Section 4.2, you will expand your understanding of solving and solutions to include inequalities. You will solve problems designed to illustrate how inequalities might be used for more complicated applications.

Guiding Question

Mathematically proficient students use appropriate tools strategically.

As you work through this chapter, ask yourself:

Which tools can I use to solve the problems and verify my solutions?

Chapter Outline

Section 4.1 In this section, you will write and solve equations and systems of equations. You will develop algebraic and graphical methods for solving and you will gain a broader understanding of the meaning of solutions. You will learn multiple ways to understand the meaning of solutions.

Section 4.2 Here you will extend your understanding of solving and solutions to include inequalities and systems of inequalities.

4.1.1 How can I solve?

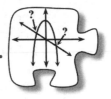

Strategies for Solving Equations

Today you will have the opportunity to solve challenging equations. As you work with your team, the goal of this section is for you to apply your strategies for solving equations to other types of equations. You will be challenged to use multiple approaches and to write clear explanations to show your understanding.

4-1.   SOLVING GRAPHICALLY

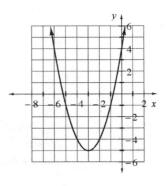

One of the big questions of Chapter 2 was how to the find special points of a function. For example, you now have the skills to look at an equation of a parabola written in graphing form and name its vertex quickly. But what about the locations of other points on the parabola? Consider the graph of $y = (x+3)^2 - 5$ at right.

a.   How many solutions does the equation $y = (x+3)^2 - 5$ have? How is this shown on the graph?

b.   Use the graph to solve the equation $(x+3)^2 - 5 = 4$. How did the graph help you solve the equation?

4-2.   ALGEBRAIC STRATEGIES

The graph in problem 4-1 was useful to solve an equation like $(x+3)^2 - 5 = 4$. But what if you do not have an accurate graph? And what can you do when the solution is not on a grid point or is off your graph?

Your Task: Solve the equation below algebraically (that is, using the equation only and without a graph) in at least three different ways. The "Discussion Points" below are provided to help you get started. Be ready to share your strategies with the class.

$$(x+3)^2 - 5 = 4$$

Discussion Points

What algebraic strategies might be useful?

What makes this equation look challenging? How can we make the equation simpler?

How can we be sure that our strategy helps us find *all* possible solutions?

4-3.   Three strategies your class or team may have used in problem 4-2 are **Rewriting** (using algebra to write a new equivalent equation that is easier to solve), **Looking Inside** (reasoning about the value of the expression inside the function or parentheses), and **Undoing** (reversing or doing the opposite of an operation; for example, taking the square root to eliminate squaring). These strategies and others will be useful throughout the rest of this course. Examine how each of these strategies can be used to solve the equation below by completing parts (a) through (f).

$$\tfrac{x-5}{4} + \tfrac{2}{5} = \tfrac{9}{10}$$

a.   Ernie decided to multiply both sides of the equation by 20 so that his equation becomes $5(x-5)+8 = 18$. Which strategy did Ernie use? How can you tell?

b.   Elle took Ernie's equation and decided to subtract 8 from both sides to get $5(x-5) = 10$. Which strategy did Elle use?

c.   Eric looked at Elle's equation and said, "*I can tell that (x – 5) must equal 2 because 5 • 2 = 10. Therefore, if x – 5 = 2, then x must be 7.*" What strategy did Eric use?

d.   How many solutions does the function $y = \tfrac{x-5}{4} + \tfrac{2}{5}$ have? How can you use the graph of $y = \tfrac{x-5}{4} + \tfrac{2}{5}$ on your graphing calculator to check your solution to $\tfrac{x-5}{4} + \tfrac{2}{5} = \tfrac{9}{10}$? Where did you look on the graph?

e.   How can you use the table for $y = \tfrac{x-5}{4} + \tfrac{2}{5}$ on your graphing calculator to check your answer? Where did you look on the table?

f.   Use the strategies from parts (a) through (c) in a different way to solve $\tfrac{x-5}{4} + \tfrac{2}{5} = \tfrac{9}{10}$. Did you get the same result?

4-4.   Solve each equation below, if possible, using any strategy. Check with your teammates to see what strategies they chose. Be sure to check your solutions.

a. $4|8x-2| = 8$

b. $3\sqrt{4x-8} + 9 = 15$

c. $(x-3)^2 - 2 = -5$

d. $(2y-3)(y-2) = -12y + 18$

e. $\tfrac{5}{x} + \tfrac{1}{3x} = \tfrac{4x}{3}$

f. $|3-7x| = -6$

g. $\tfrac{6w-1}{5} - 3w = \tfrac{12w-16}{15}$

h. $(x+2)^2 + 4(x+2) - 5 = 0$

4-5. Some of the solutions from the previous problem can quickly be checked with a graph or table on the graphing calculator. Check the answers for those problems with your graphing calculator.

4-6. **LEARNING LOG**

Create a Learning Log entry about all of the solving strategies you saw today. For each strategy, provide an example and explain which types of equations work best with that strategy. Title this entry "Strategies for Solving Equations" and label it with today's date.

4-7. Solve $(x-2)^2 - 3 = 1$ graphically. That is, graph $y = (x-2)^2 - 3$ and $y = 1$ on the same set of axes and find the x-value(s) of any points of intersection. Then use algebraic strategies to solve the equation and verify that your graphical solutions are correct.

4-8. Solve each equation below. Think about Rewriting, Looking Inside, or Undoing to simplify the process.

   a. $2(x-1)^2 + 7 = 39$

   b. $7(\sqrt{m+1} - 3) = 21$

   c. $\frac{x}{2} + \frac{x}{3} = \frac{5x+2}{6}$

   d. $-7 + (\frac{4x+2}{2}) = 8$

4-9. Find the equation of the line that passes through $(0, 2)$ and $(5, 2)$. Then complete parts (a) and (b) below.

   a. What is the equation of the x-axis?

   b. What is the equation of the y-axis?

4-10. Solve the system of equations shown at right.

$$2x + 6y = 10$$
$$x = 8 - 3y$$

   a. Describe what happened when you tried to solve the system.

   b. Draw the graph of the system.

   c. How does the graph of the system explain what happened with the equations? Make your answer as clear and thorough as possible.

4-11.   Classify the triangle with vertices $A(3, 2)$, $B(-2, 0)$, and $C(-1, 4)$ by finding the length of each side. Be sure to consider all possible triangle types. Include sufficient evidence to support your conclusion.

4-12.   Examine the figures at right, and then visualize the figure for $n = 4$.

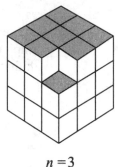

   a.   How many cubes are in the figure for $n = 4$?

   b.   How many cubes are in the figure for $n = 1$?

   c.   Find the general equation for the number of cubes for any n. Verify your formula with the cases of $n = 1$ and $n = 5$.

$n = 2$ $n = 3$

   d.   Is the sequence arithmetic, geometric, or neither? Explain your reasoning.

4-13.   Simplify each of the expressions below. Express your answers as simply as possible.

   a. $\frac{5x^2-11x+2}{x^2+8x+16} \cdot \frac{x^2+10x+24}{10x^2+13x-3}$

   b. $\frac{6x+3}{2x-3} \div \frac{3x^2-12x-15}{2x^2-x-3}$

   c. $\frac{5m + 18}{m + 3} + \frac{4m + 9}{m + 3}$

   d. $\frac{3a^2+a-1}{a^2-2a+1} - \frac{2a^2-a+2}{a^2-2a+1}$

4-14.   The graph of a line and an exponential can intersect twice, once, or not at all. Describe the possible number of intersections for each of the following pairs of graphs. Your solution to each part should include all of the possibilities and a quickly sketched example of each one.

   a.   A line and a parabola

   b.   Two different parabolas

   c.   A parabola and a circle

   d.   A parabola and the hyperbola $y = \frac{1}{x}$

4.1.2 How can I use a graph to solve?

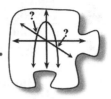

Solving Equations and Systems Graphically

In the previous lesson, you used and named three algebraic methods to solve different kinds of equations. In today's lesson, you will again solve equations, but this time you will use your understanding of graphs, as well as your algebra skills, to solve the equations and to verify your results.

4-15.   In problem 4-1, you used a graph to solve an equation. In what other ways can a graph be a useful solution tool? Consider this question as you solve the equation $\sqrt{2x+3} = x$ by completing parts (a) through (d) below.

   a.   Use algebraic strategies to solve $\sqrt{2x+3} = x$. How many solutions did you find? Which strategies did you use?

   b.   In thinking about $\sqrt{2x+3} = x$, Miranda wrote down $y = \sqrt{2x+3}$ and $y = x$. How many solutions does $y = \sqrt{2x+3}$ have? How many solutions does $y = x$ have?

   c.   Miranda said, *"I'll graph both the functions* $y = \sqrt{2x+3}$ *and* $y = x$ *to check the solutions from part (a)."* How will graphing help her find the solution?

   d.   Miranda looked at the graph on her graphing calculator and said *"I think something is wrong."* What happened? Graph the system on your graphing calculator and find the intersection(s) of the functions. How many solutions does this equation have?

4-16.   When a result from an equation-solving process does not make the original equation true, it is called an **extraneous solution**. It is not a solution of the equation, even though it is a result when solving algebraically.

   Check your two solutions from part (a) of problem 4-15 algebraically.

4-17. The fact that extraneous solutions can arise after following straightforward solving techniques makes it especially important to check your solutions!

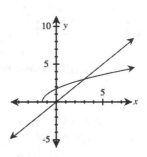

But why did the extraneous solution appear in this problem? Examine the graph of the system of equations $y = \sqrt{2x+3}$ and $y = x$, shown at right. Where would an extraneous solution $x = -1$ appear on the graph? Why do the graphs not intersect at that point? Explain.

4-18. After solving the equation $2x^2 + 5x - 3 = x^2 + 4x + 3$, Gustav got called to the office and left his team. When his teammates examined his graphing calculator to try to find out how he found his solution, they only saw the graph of $y = x^2 + x - 6$. Consider this situation as you answer the questions below.

a. How many solutions do you predict $2x^2 + 5x - 3 = x^2 + 4x + 3$ will have?

b. Solve $2x^2 + 5x - 3 = x^2 + 4x + 3$ algebraically.

c. Where did Gustav get the equation $y = x^2 + x - 6$? How many solutions will $y = x^2 + x - 6$ have?

d. How can you see the solutions to $2x^2 + 5x - 3 = x^2 + 4x + 3$ in the graph of $y = x^2 + x - 6$? Explain why this makes sense.

e. Maiya solved $2x^2 + 5x - 3 = x^2 + 4x + 3$ by graphing a system of equations and looking for the points of intersection. What equations do you think she used? Graph these equations on your graphing calculator and explain where the solutions to the equation exist on the graph.

4-19.   Karen could not figure out how to solve $20x+1 = 3^x$ algebraically, so she decided to use her graphing calculator. However, after she finished entering the equations $y = 20x + 1$ and $y = 3^x$, she got the graph shown at right. After studying the graph, Karen suspects there are no solutions to $20x + 1 = 3^x$.

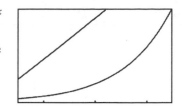

   a.   What do you think? If there are solutions, find them and prove that they are solutions. If there are no solutions, demonstrate that there cannot be a solution.

   b.   What should solutions to the equation, $20x + 1 = 3^x$, look like? In other words, will solutions be a single number, or should they be the coordinates of a point? Explain.

   c.   Elana started to solve first by subtracting 1 from both sides of her equation. So when she graphed her system later, she used the equations $y = 20x$ and $y = 3^x - 1$. Should she get the same solutions? Test your conclusion with your graphing calculator.

   d.   Discuss with your team why Karen could not solve the system algebraically. What do you think?

4-20.   Jack was working on solving an equation and he graphed the functions $f(x) = \frac{12}{x}$ and $g(x) = -(x-3)^2 + 4$, as shown at right.

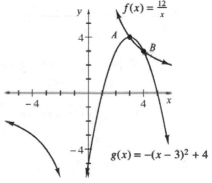

   a.   What equation was Jack solving?

   b.   Use points A and B to solve the equation you wrote in part (a).

   c.   Are there any other solutions to this same equation that are represented by neither point A nor point B? If so, show that these other solutions make your equation true.

4-21.   LEARNING LOG

What does the solution to an equation mean? Do you have any new ideas about solutions that you did not have before? Create a Learning Log entry that explains the meaning of a solution in as many ways as possible. Title this entry "The Meaning of a Solution, Part 1" (Parts 2 and 3 will be coming later) and label it with today's date.

4-22.　Solve $(x-3)^2 - 2 = x + 1$ graphically. Is there more than one way to do this? Explain.

4-23.　Graph a system of equations to solve $2|x-4| - 3 = \frac{2}{3}x - 3$. Show your solutions clearly on your graph.

4-24.　Solve each of the following equations using any method. Be sure to check your solutions.

　　a.　$-3\sqrt{2x-5} + 7 = -8$　　　　　　　b.　$2|3x+4| - 10 = 12$

4-25.　Ted needs to find the point of intersection for the lines $y = 18x - 30$ and $y = -22x + 50$. He takes out a piece of graph paper and then realizes that he can solve this problem without graphing. Explain how Ted is going to accomplish this, and then find the point of intersection.

4-26.　Consider the arithmetic sequence $2, a - b, a + b, 35, \ldots$. Find a and b.

4-27.　Solve the following equations. Be sure to check your answers for any extraneous solutions.

　　a.　$\sqrt{2x-1} - x = -8$　　　　　　　b.　$\sqrt{2x-1} - x = 0$

4-28.　Find the value of x.

　　a.
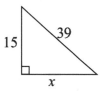

　　b.
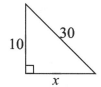

4-29.　Solve $3x - 1 = 2^x$ graphically. Could you solve this equation algebraically? Explain.

4-30.   Consider the graphs of $f(x) = \frac{1}{2}(x-2)^3 + 1$ and
        $g(x) = 2x^2 - 6x - 3$ at right.

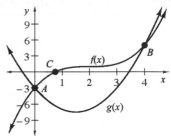

a.   Write an equation that you could solve using
      points A and B. What are the solutions to
      your equation? Substitute them into your
      equation to show that they work.

b.   Are there any solutions to the equation in
      part (a) that do not appear on the graph? Explain.

c.   Write an equation that you could solve using point C. What does the
      solution to your equation appear to be? Again, substitute your solution
      into the equation. How close was your estimate?

d.   What are the domains and ranges of $f(x)$ and $g(x)$?

4-31.   Solve each of the following equations using any method.

a. $2(x+3)^2 - 5 = -5$ b. $3(x-2)^2 + 6 = 9$

c. $|2x-5| - 6 = 15$ d. $3\sqrt{5x-2} + 1 = 7$

4-32.   Solve each of the following equations for the indicated variable.

a. $5x - 3y = 12$ for y b. $F = \frac{Gm_1m_2}{r^2}$ for m_2

c. $E = \frac{1}{2}mv^2$ for m d. $(x-4)^2 + (y-1)^2 = 10$ for y

4-33.   Paul states that $(a+b)^2$ is equivalent to $a^2 + b^2$. Joyce thinks that
        something is missing. Help Joyce show Paul that the two
        expressions are not equivalent. Explain using at least two
        different approaches: diagrams, algebra, numbers, or words.

4-34.   Graph each of the following equations. (Keep the graphs handy, because you
        will need them for your homework for Lesson 4.1.3.)

a. $y = |x|$ b. $|y| = x$

c.   How are the two graphs similar? How are they different?

d.   What are the domain and range of each relation?

4-35.   Find the value of x.

a.

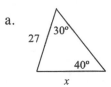

b.

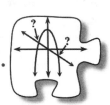

4.1.3 How many solutions are there?

Finding Multiple Solutions to Systems of Equations

You have used many different solving strategies to find solutions of equations with one variable both algebraically and graphically. You have also worked with systems of two equations with two variables. In this lesson, you will use your algebraic and graphing tools to determine the number of solutions that various systems have and to determine the meaning of those solutions.

4-36.   Solve each system of equations below without graphing. For each one, explain what the solution (or lack thereof) tells you about the graph of the system.

a. $y = -3x + 5$
       $y = -3x - 1$

b. $y = \frac{1}{2}x^2 + 1$
       $y = 2x - 1$

c. $y^2 = x$
       $y = x - 2$

d. $4x - 2y = 10$
       $y = 2x - 5$

Core Connections Algebra 2

4-37.   Now consider the system shown at right.

$$x^2 + y^2 = 25$$
$$y = x^2 - 13$$

      a.   How many solutions do you expect this system to have? Explain how you made your prediction.

      b.   Solve this system by graphing. How many solutions did you find? Was your prediction in part (a) correct?

      c.   Find a way to combine these equations to create a new equation so that the only variable is x. Then find another way to combine $x^2 + y^2 = 25$ and $y = x^2 - 13$ to form a different equation that contains only the variable y. Which of these equations would be easier to solve? Why?

      d.   If you have not already done so, solve one of the combined equations from part (c). If solving becomes too difficult, you may want to switch to the other combined equation.

4-38.   In problem 4-37, you analyzed the system shown at right.

$$x^2 + y^2 = 25$$
$$y = x^2 - 13$$

      a.   What minor adjustments can you make to an equation (or both equations) in this system so that the new system has no solutions? Have each member of your team find a different way to alter the system. Justify that your system has no solution algebraically. Also, be ready to share your strategies for changing the system along with your justification with the class.

      b.   Work with your team to alter the system three more times so that the new systems have 3, 2, or 1 solution. For each new system that your team creates, solve the system algebraically to study how the algebraic solution helps indicate how many solutions will be possible. Be prepared to explain what different situations occur during solving that result in a different number of solutions.

4-39.   LEARNING LOG

Look over your work from today. Name all of the strategies you used to solve systems of equations. Which strategies were most useful for solving linear systems? What about non-linear systems? Write a Learning Log entry describing your ideas about solving systems. Title this entry "Finding Solutions to Systems" and label it with today's date.

4-40. Solve each of the following systems algebraically. What do the solutions tell you about each system? Visualizing the graphs may help with your description.

a. $y = 3x - 5$
$y = -2x - 15$

b. $y - 7 = -2x$
$4x + 2y = 14$

c. $y = 2(x + 3)^2 - 5$
$y = 14x + 17$

d. $y = 3(x - 2)^2 + 3$
$y = 6x - 12$

4-41. Solve each equation below. Think about rewriting, looking inside, or undoing to simplify the process.

a. $3(y + 1)^2 - 5 = 43$

b. $\sqrt{1 - 4x} = 10$

c. $\frac{6y-1}{y} - 3 = 2$

d. $\sqrt[3]{1 - 2x} = 3$

4-42. This problem is a checkpoint for writing equations for arithmetic and geometric sequences. It will be referred to as Checkpoint 4A.

a. Write an explicit and recursive rule for $t(n) = 1, 4, 7, 10, \ldots$

b. Write an explicit and recursive rule for $t(n) = 3, \frac{3}{2}, \frac{3}{4}, \frac{3}{8}, \ldots$

In parts (c) and (d), write an explicit rule for the sequence given in the $n \to t(n)$ tables.

c. An arithmetic sequence

n	$t(n)$
0	
1	17
2	
3	3
4	

d. A geometric sequence

n	$t(n)$
0	
1	
2	7.2
3	8.64
4	

e. If an arithmetic sequence has $t(7) = 1056$ and $t(12) = 116$, what is $t(4)$?

Check your answers by referring to the Checkpoint 4A materials located at the back of your book.

If you needed help solving these problems correctly, then you need more practice. Review the Checkpoint 4A materials and try the practice problems. Also, consider getting help outside of class time. From this point on, you will be expected to do problems like these quickly and easily.

4-43.   Wet World has an 18-foot-long water slide. The angle of elevation of the slide (the angle it forms with a horizontal line) is 50°. At the end of the slide, there is a 6-foot drop into a pool. After you climb the ladder to the top of the slide, how many feet above the water level are you? Draw a diagram.

4-44.   Find the slope and y-intercept of each line below.

   a. $y = -\frac{6}{5}x - 7$ b. $3x - 2y = 10$

   c.   The line that goes through the points $(5, -2)$ and $(8, 4)$.

4-45.   Examine the graph of each relation below. For each part below, decide if the relation is a function and then state the domain and range.

   a.   b.

   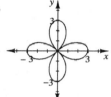   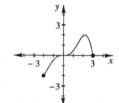

4-46.   Solve the system of equations at right.

$$2^{(x+y)} = 16$$
$$2^{(2x+y)} = \frac{1}{8}$$

4.1.4 How can I use systems?

· ·

Using Systems of Equations to Solve Problems

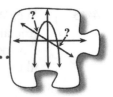

You have developed several strategies for solving equations and systems of equations. You have also focused on the meaning of a solution. In this lesson, you will have the opportunity to see how your strategies can be used in everyday contexts. You will expand your understanding of solutions by applying them to these situations. As you work today, use the questions below to help stimulate mathematical conversations:

How can we model this situation with equations?

What does this solution tell us?

How can we solve it?

Are there any other strategies that could be useful?

4-47.   HOW TALL IS HAROLD?

Jamal and Dinah were still eating lunch as they came into Algebra 2 class. Someone had left a book on the floor and they both tripped. As they each hit the floor, the food they were carrying went flying across the room directly toward Harold, who was showing off his latest dance moves.

As Jamal and Dinah watched in horror, Jamal's cupcake and Dinah's sandwich splatted right on top of Harold's head! Jamal's cupcake flew on a path that would have landed on the floor 20 feet away from him if it had not hit Harold. Dinah's sandwich flew on a path that would have landed on the floor 24 feet away from her if it had not hit Harold. Jamal's cupcake flew 9 feet high, while Dinah's sandwich reached a height of 6 feet, before hitting Harold.

How tall is Harold? Show your solution in as many ways as you can.

4-48.   Write a system of equations to fit the
         situation below. Then solve the system
         using as many strategies as you can. How
         many solutions are possible?

Your math class wants to collect money for
a field trip, so it decides to sell two kinds of
bags of candy. The Chocolate Lover's Bag
costs $4.25 for five chocolate truffles and two caramel turtle candies. The
Combusting Caramel Bag costs $3.50 for eight caramel turtle candies and two
chocolate truffles. How much does each chocolate truffle and caramel turtle
candy cost?

4-49.   Lucky you! You are a new college graduate and you have already been offered
         two jobs. Each job involves exactly the same tasks, but the salary plans differ,
         as shown below.

         • Job A offers a starting salary of $52,000 per year with an annual
           increase of $3,000.

         • Job B starts at $36,000 per year with a raise of 11% each year.

    a.   Under what conditions would Job A be the better choice? When would
         Job B be the better choice? Use graphs, tables, and equations to help you
         justify your answer.

    b.   How could you change this problem slightly so that Job B is always the
         better choice? How could you change it so that Job A is always better?
         If it is not possible for Job A or Job B always to be a better choice, explain
         why not.

4-50.   LEARNING LOG

         Earlier you completed a Learning Log entry about the
         meaning of the solution of an equation. Now think about,
         "What does the solution to a *system of equations* mean?"
         Can you find more than one way to answer that question?
         Create a Learning Log entry that expands on your thinking
         about the meaning of solutions. Title this entry "The Meaning of
         a Solution, Part 2" and label it with today's date.

4-51.   Gloria is weighing combinations of geometric solids. She found that 4 cylinders and 5 prisms weigh 32 ounces and that 1 cylinder and 8 prisms weigh 35 ounces. Write and solve a system of equations to determine the weight of each cylinder and prism.

4-52.   Is $x = -1$ a solution to the inequality $2x^2 + 5x - 3 \le x^2 + 4x + 3$? What about $x = 5$? Show how you know. Then find three more solutions.

4-53.   Solve each equation below algebraically. Think about Rewriting, Looking Inside, or Undoing to simplify the process.

   a. $5 - 3(\frac{1}{2}x + 2) = -7$ b. $5(\sqrt{x-2} + 1) = 15$

   c. $12 - (\frac{2x}{3} + x) = 2$ d. $-3(2x+1)^3 = -192$

4-54.   Given the parabola $y = x^2 - 8x + 10$, complete parts (a) through (c) below.

   a.   Find the vertex by averaging the x-intercepts.

   b.   Find the vertex by completing the square.

   c.   Find the vertex of $y = x^2 - 3x$ using your method of choice.

4-55.   Refer back to the graphs you made for problem 4-34. (It was a homework problem from Lesson 4.1.2.) Use those graphs to help you graph each of the following inequalities.

   a. $y \le |x|$ b. $|y| \ge x$

4-56.   **Multiple Choice:** Which of the points below is a solution to $y < |x - 3|$?

   a. $(2, 1)$ b. $(-4, 5)$ c. $(-2, 8)$ d. $(0, 3)$

4-57.   For the equation $y = -(x+1)^3 + 2$:

   a.   Draw a graph.

   b.   Use your graph to estimate the solution to $-3 = -(x+1)^3 + 2$.

4.2.1 How can I solve inequalities?

Solving Inequalities with One or Two Variables

In this chapter, you developed many strategies for solving equations with one variable and systems of equations with two variables. But what if you want to solve an inequality or system of inequalities instead? Today you will explore how to use familiar strategies to find solutions for an inequality. As you work, the questions below can help focus team discussions:

What strategy should we use?

How do we know if this solution is correct?

How can we be sure we have found all of the solutions?

4-58. In the previous section, you learned how to use the graph of a system to solve an equation. How can the graphs of $y = 2x^2 + 5x - 3$ and $y = x^2 + 4x + 3$ (shown at right) help you solve an *inequality*? Consider this as you answer the questions below.

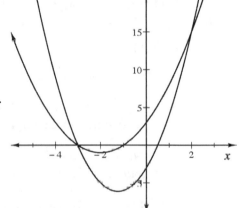

a. How are the solutions of $2x^2 + 5x - 3 = x^2 + 4x + 3$ represented on this graph? What are the solutions?

b. Obtain a Lesson 4.2.1A Resource Page from your teacher. On the resource page, label each graph with its equation and highlight each function with a different color. How did you decide which graph matches which function?

c. On the graph, identify the *x*-values for which $2x^2 + 5x - 3 \le x^2 + 4x + 3$. How did you locate the solutions? How many solutions are there? Find a way to describe all of the solutions.

d. How can these solutions be represented on a number line? Locate the number line labeled with $2x^2 + 5x - 3 \le x^2 + 4x + 3$ below the graph on your resource page. Use a colored marker to highlight the solutions to the inequality on the number line.

e. What about the inequality $2x^2 + 5x - 3 > x^2 + 4x + 3$? What are the solutions to this inequality? Represent your solutions algebraically and on a number line.

4-59.   Consider the inequality $4|x+1|-2>6$.

      a.   How many boundary points are there? Remember that, in this case, a **boundary point** would be the smallest number that will make the inequality *not* true. What are the boundary points? Should they be marked with filled or unfilled circles? Make the appropriate markings on a number line.

      b.   Which portion(s) of the number line contain the solutions for this inequality? How many regions do you need to test? Represent the solutions algebraically and on a number line.

4-60.   Burt and Ernie were solving the inequality $2x^2+5x-3<x^2+4x+3$. They were looking at the graph in problem 4-58 when Burt had an idea. *"Can't we change this into one parabola and solve our inequality that way?"* he said.

Ernie asked, *"What do you mean?"*

"Can't we find the solutions by looking at the graph of $f(x)=x^2+x-6$?" Burt replied.

      a.   Where did Burt get the equation $y=x^2+x-6$?

      b.   Try Burt's idea. Graph the parabola and show how it can be used to solve the original inequality.

      c.   *"Just a minute!"* mumbled Ernie, *"I think I have a short cut. Instead of graphing the parabola, can't we just rewrite the original inequality as $x^2+x-6<0$ and then solve the equation $x^2+x-6=0$? This would give us the boundary points and then we could test numbers to find the regions that contain the solutions."* Check Ernie's short cut. Does it give the same solution?

      d.   Use any method to solve the inequality $x^2-3x-10\geq0$.

4-61.   Next, Burt and Ernie were working on solving the inequality $4|x+1|-2>6$ from problem 4-59. This time, Ernie had an idea. *"Why don't we find the solutions to this by graphing a system of equations like we did in problem 4-58?"*

      a.   What system of equations should they graph?

      b.   Graph the system and explain how you can use it to find the solutions to $4|x+1|-2>6$.

                                                                Core Connections Algebra 2

4-62.   In problem 4-58 you looked at solutions to an inequality with one variable (x). Now consider the system of inequalities with two variables (x and y) below.

$$y \geq 2x^2 + 5x - 3$$
$$y < x^2 + 4x + 3$$

a.   Which points make both inequalities true? For example, does the point $(-3,0)$ make both inequalities true? What about $(-1,1)$? $(1,5)$? Refer back to your Lesson 4.2.1A Resource Page to help you think about these questions.

b.   What is the difference between a solution to the *system* of inequalities above and a solution to the inequality found in problem 4-58?

c.   How are the graphs of the equations $y = 2x^2 + 5x - 3$ and $y = x^2 + 4x + 3$ related to the graph of the system of inequalities?

d.   With your team, find a way to represent all of the solutions to the system of inequalities on the Lesson 4.2.1A Resource Page graph.

4-63.   For each of the following graphs, find an equation, inequality, or system that could have the solution shown. Note that the equations for the line and the parabola are given.

a.
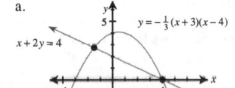

b.
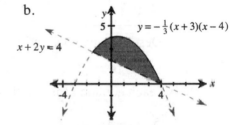

c.
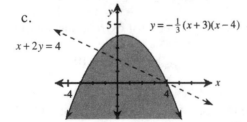

d.
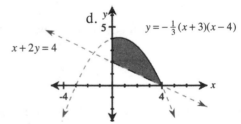

4-64.   LEARNING LOG

Now you will reflect for a third time about the meaning of
solutions. What does the solution to an *inequality* or a
system of inequalities mean? Does it matter if the
inequality has one variable or two? Create a Learning Log
entry that expands on your thinking about the meaning of a solution. Title this
entry "The Meaning of a Solution, Part 3" and label it with today's date.

4-65.   Find boundary points for each of the following inequalities. Draw the
boundaries on a number line and shade the solution regions.

a. $3x + 2 \geq x - 6$

b. $2x^2 - 5x < 12$

4-66.   Solve the following inequalities and draw a number line graph to represent each
solution.

a. $|2x + 3| < 5$

b. $|2x + 3| \geq 5$

c. $|2x - 3| < 5$

d. $|2x - 3| \geq 5$

e. $|3 - 2x| < 5$

f. $|3 - 2x| \geq 5$

g.   Describe any relationships you see among these six problems.

4-67.   Solve each equation for y so that it could be entered into a graphing calculator.

a. $5 - (y - 3) = 3x$

b. $4(x + y) = -2$

4-68.   Solve each equation below. Remember to check for extraneous solutions.

a. $(y - 3)^2 = 2y - 10$

b. $|y - 3| = 2y - 10$

4-69.   Add, subtract, multiply, or divide the following rational expressions. Then
simplify your expression, if possible.

a. $\dfrac{x-4}{2x^2+9x-5} + \dfrac{x+3}{x^2+5x}$

b. $\dfrac{4x^2-11x+6}{2x^2-x-6} - \dfrac{x+2}{2x+3}$

c. $\dfrac{(x+4)(2x-1)(x-7)}{(x+8)(2x-1)(3x-4)} \div \dfrac{(4x-3)(x-7)}{(x+8)(3x-4)}$

d. $\dfrac{2m^2+7m-15}{m^2-16} \cdot \dfrac{m^2-6m+8}{2m^2-7m+6}$

4-70.   Using the technique of completing the square, solve $x^2 + 12x + 15 = 75$ for x.

4-71.   Factor each expression in parts (a) and (b). Then, in parts (c) and (d), factor and simplify each expression.

   a. $bx + ax$ b. $x + ax$ c. $\dfrac{ax+a}{x^2+2x+1}$ d. $\dfrac{x^2-b^2}{ax+ab}$

4-72.   Graph the four inequalities below on the same set of axes.

   i. $2y \geq x - 3$ ii. $x - 2y \geq -7$

   iii. $y \leq -2x + 6$ iv. $-9 \leq 2x + y$

   a.   What type of polygon is formed by the solution of this set of inequalities? Write a convincing argument to justify your answer.

   b.   Find the vertices of the polygon. If your graph is very accurately drawn you will be able to determine the points from the graph. If it is not, you will need to solve the systems (pairs) of equations that represent the corners of your graphs.

4-73.   Solve the following absolute value inequalities.

   a. $|x - 4| < 9$ b. $\left|\frac{1}{2}x - 45\right| \geq 80$ c. $|2x - 5| \leq 2$

4-74.   Your family plans to buy a new air conditioner. They can buy the Super Cool X1400 for $800, or they can buy the Efficient Energy X2000 for $1200. Both models will cool your home equally well, but the Efficient Energy model is less expensive to operate. The Super Cool X1400 will cost $60 per month to operate, while the Efficient Energy X2000 costs only $40 per month to operate.

   a.   Write an equation to represent the cost of buying and operating the Super Cool X1400 where C = cost and m = months.

   b.   Write an equation to represent the cost of buying and operating the Efficient Energy X2000.

   c.   How many months would your family have to use the Efficient Energy model to compensate for the additional cost of the original purchase?

   d.   Figuring your family will only use the air conditioner for 4 months each year, how many years will you have to wait to start saving money overall?

4-75.   MARVELOUS MARK'S FUNCTION MACHINES

Mark has set up a series of three function
machines that he claims will surprise you.

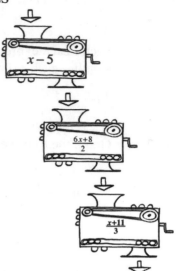

a.   Try a few numbers. Are you surprised by
your results?

b.   Carrie claims that she was not surprised by
her results. She also says that she can show
why the sequence of machines does what it
does by simply dropping in a variable and
writing out step-by-step what happens inside
each machine. Try it. (Use something like c
or m.) Be sure to show all of the steps.

4-76.   Multiply or divide the rational expressions below. Write each answer in
simplified form.

a. $\dfrac{(x-3)^2}{2x-1} \cdot \dfrac{2x-1}{(3x-14)(x+6)} \cdot \dfrac{x+6}{x-3}$

b. $\dfrac{4x^2+5x-6}{3x^2+5x-2} \div \dfrac{4x^2+x-3}{6x^2-5x+1}$

4-77.   Find all of the points at which the parabolas below intersect. Write your
solution(s) in (x, y) form.

$$y = x^2 - x + 12$$
$$y = 2x^2 + 3x + 7$$

4-78.   Find the equation (in $y = mx + b$ form) of each line described below.

a.   A line with slope $\frac{1}{2}$ passing through the point $(6, 1)$.

b.   The line $y = 2x + b$ passing through the point $(1, 4)$.

4.2.2 How can I organize the possibilities?

• •

Using Systems to Solve a Problem

Businesses and industries often use equations and inequalities to model their services and production. Creating a system of equations and inequalities allows them to mathematically optimize their operation and maximize profits. Today you will investigate this technique.

4-79.   THE TOY FACTORY

Otto Toyom builds toy cars and trucks. To make each car, he needs 4 wheels, 2 seats, and 1 gas tank. To make each truck, he needs 6 wheels, 1 seat, and 3 gas tanks. His storeroom has 36 wheels, 14 seats, and 15 gas tanks. He is trying to decide how many cars and trucks to build so he can make the largest possible amount of money when he sells them. Help Otto figure out what his options are. What are all of the choices he could make about how many cars and how many trucks he will build? Make a list of all possible combinations. Then plot the number of possible cars and trucks in the first quadrant of a graph.

4-80.   Otto wants to make as much profit as possible. Use your list from problem 4-79 to find which combination of cars and trucks will make the most profit based on the information below.

a.   Which of Otto's options gives him the greatest profit if he makes $1 on each car and $1 on each truck he sells? How do you know?

b.   The market has changed, and Otto can now make $2 for each truck but only $1 for each car. What is his best choice for the number of cars and the number of trucks to make in this situation? How can you be sure? Explain.

4-81.   To convince Otto that your recommendation was a good one, you probably had to show many calculations in problem 4-80. Now, you will take another look at Otto's business using algebra and graphing tools.

   a.   Write three inequalities to represent the relationship between the number of cars (x), the number of trucks (y), and the number of:

   i.   wheels   ii.   seats   iii.   gas tanks

   b.   Graph this system of inequalities on the same set of axes you used for problem 4-79. Shade the solution region lightly. Why is it okay to assume that $x \geq 0$ and $y \geq 0$?

   c.   What are the vertices of the polygon that outlines your region? Explain how you could find the exact coordinates of those points if you could not read them easily from the graph.

   d.   Are there any points in the solution region that represent choices that seem more likely to give Otto the maximum profit? Where are they? Why do you think they show the best choices?

   e.   Write an equation to represent Otto's total profit (P) if he makes $1 on each car and $2 on each truck. What if Otto ended up with a profit of only $8? Show how to use the graph of the profit equation when $P = 8$ to figure out how many cars and trucks he made.

   f.   Which points do you need to test in the profit equation to get the maximum profit? Is it necessary to try all of the points? Why or why not?

   g.   What if Otto got greedy and wanted to make a profit of $14? How could you use a profit line to show Otto that this would be impossible based on his current pricing?

4-82.   Find Otto's highest possible profit if he gets $3 per car and $2 per truck. Find the profit expression and find the best combinations of cars and trucks to maximize the profit.

Review & Preview

4-83. Solve the system of equations at right. What sub-problems did you need to solve?

$$x + 2y = 4$$
$$2x - y = -7$$
$$x + y + z = -4$$

4-84. Solve each of the following inequalities. Express the solutions algebraically and on a number line.

a. $3x - 5 \leq 7$

b. $x^2 + 6 > 42$

4-85. Three red rods are 2 cm longer than two blue rods. Three blue rods are 2 cm longer than four red rods. How long is each rod?

4-86. Simone has been absent and does not know the difference between the graph of $y \leq 2x - 2$ and the graph of $y < 2x - 2$. Explain thoroughly so that she completely understands what points are excluded from the second graph and why.

4-87. This problem is a checkpoint for solving for one variable in an equation with two or more variables. It will be referred to as Checkpoint 4B.

Rewrite the following equations so that you could enter them into a graphing calculator. In other words, solve for y.

a. $x - 3(y + 2) = 6$

b. $\frac{6x-1}{y} - 3 = 2$

c. $\sqrt{y-4} = x+1$

d. $\sqrt{y+4} = x+2$

Check your answers by referring to the Checkpoint 4B materials located at the back of your book.

If you needed help solving these problems correctly, then you need more practice. Review the Checkpoint 4B materials and try the practice problems. Also, consider getting help outside of class time. From this point on, you will be expected to do problems like these quickly and easily.

4-88. Think about the axis system in the two-dimensional coordinate plane. What is the equation of the x-axis? What is the equation of the y-axis?

4-89. Sammy has a 10-foot wooden ladder, which he needs to climb to reach the roof of his house. The roof is 12 feet above the ground. The base of the ladder must be at least 1.5 feet from the base of the house. How far is it from the top step of the ladder to the edge of the roof? Draw a sketch.

4.2.3 How can I find the best combination?

Application of Systems of Linear Inequalities

The process of using linear systems to find the optimal solution to a problem with multiple constraints is called **linear programming**. You used this process while solving "The Toy Factory." Now you will work on a problem using this technique, only this time you can use a system of inequalities and will not need to list all of the possible outcomes.

4-90. SANDY DANDY DUNE BUGGIES

Jacklyn Toyom, CEO of the Sandy Dandy Dune Buggy Company and Otto's sister, has discovered that your team has found a way to optimize the profit for the Toy Factory. She would like to hire your team to help her company. Here is her letter:

> Dear Study Team,
>
> I was so impressed to hear about how you helped Otto maximize his profits at his Toy Factory! I think your team could help my company as well.
>
> Here at the Sandy Dandy Dune Buggy Company we make two popular models of off-road vehicles: the Crawler and the Rover. Each week, we receive enough parts to build at most 15 Crawlers and 12 Rovers. The only exceptions to the supply of parts are the colored night lamps and high-definition speakers, which have to be specially manufactured for our off-road vehicles. Each of the Crawlers requires 5 of the lamps and 2 of the speakers. The Rover requires 3 lamps and 6 speakers. Our supplier is a small company that can only manufacture 81 of the lamps and 78 of the speakers for us each week.
>
> Since we are also a small company, we have only 12 employees. By contract, the maximum number of hours each employee can work is 37.5 hours per week. It takes our employees 20 hours to assemble one Crawler and 30 hours to assemble one Rover.
>
> Each Crawler sold brings in a profit of $500. The Rover, that is less expensive to manufacture than the Crawler, is very popular and sells for a profit of $1000 each.
>
> I need a detailed proposal of how to maximize our profit that I can submit to our Board of Trustees. I look forward to a profitable business relationship!
>
> Sincerely,
> Ms. Jacklyn Toyom
> CEO, Sandy Dandy Dune Buggy Company

Problem continues on next page →

4-90.   *Problem continued from previous page.*

Your Task: Find the best combination of Crawlers and Rovers to produce each week to maximize the company's profit. Create a detailed proposal to submit to Ms. Toyom that includes:

- The number of Crawlers and Rovers to manufacture each week.
- The maximum profit the company can expect to make.
- Calculations and graphs to justify your recommendation.

Constraints to keep in mind are the number of:
(1)   speakers available
(2)   lamps available
(3)   total employee hours each week

Discussion Points

How does this problem compare to "The Toy Factory" from the previous lesson?

What is the maximum number of hours for all of the employees that can be worked in one week?

How can we justify that we have found the most profitable combination of each vehicle to manufacture?

Further Guidance

4-91.   After emailing a few questions to Ms. Toyom, your team received the following email:

From: "Ms. Toyom" <toyom@welovemath.com>
To: <studyteam@thinkingisgood.net>
Subject: Clarifications to your Questions

Dear Study Team,

Thank you for your questions. I am happy to clarify them. Our Board of Trustees requires the following information in your proposal:

1. A list of all of the constraints (to make sure you took them into consideration).
2. An inequality for each of the constraints.
3. A full-page graph showing all inequalities and the resulting solution region (use a different color for each inequality).
4. Calculations for each of the vertices on your solution region. List these points at their vertex.
5. Profit calculations, with maximum profit included on your graph.

Please make sure to include a cover letter summarizing your proposal. Also include a brief explanation for each of the items listed above.

Sincerely, Ms. Toyom

Further Guidance
section ends here.

Core Connections Algebra 2

METHODS AND MEANINGS

Graphing Inequalities with Two Variables

To graph an inequality with two variables, first graph the boundary line or curve. If the inequality does not include equality (that is, if it is $>$ or $<$ rather than $\geq$ or $\leq$), then the graph of the boundary is dashed to indicate that it is not included in the solution. Otherwise, the boundary is a solid line or curve.

Once the boundary is graphed, choose a point that does not lie on the boundary to test in the inequality. If that point makes the inequality true, then the entire region in which that point lies is a solution. If that point makes the inequality false, then the entire region in which the point lies is not a solution. Examine the two examples below.

Test $(0, 0)$:

$$0 \overset{?}{<} -\tfrac{2}{3}(0) + 2$$

$$0 \overset{?}{<} 2$$

True, so shade below the line.

$$y < -\tfrac{2}{3}x + 2$$

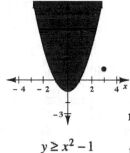

Test $(3, 1)$:

$$1 \overset{?}{\geq} 3^2 - 1$$

$$1 \overset{?}{\geq} 8$$

False, so shade the region that does not contain the test point, that is, shade above the parabola.

$$y \geq x^2 - 1$$

4-92.   Solve the system of equations at right algebraically and explain what the solution tells you about the graphs of the two equations.

$$3x + 2 = y$$
$$-9x + 3y = 11$$

4-93.   Draw the graph of the system of inequalities at right.

$$y \geq |x| - 3$$
$$y \leq -|x| + 5$$

    a.   What polygon does the intersection form? Justify your answer.

    b.   What are its vertices?

    c.   Find the area of the intersection.

4-94.   Solve each of the following inequalities. Express the solutions algebraically and
         on a number line.

    a. $3(x+2) > 4x - 7$ b. $3x^2 - 4x + 2 \le x^2 + x + 6$

4-95.   Solve the equations below.

    a. $\sqrt{x+15} = 5 + \sqrt{x}$ b. $(y-6)^2 + 10 = 3y$

4-96.   Solve the system of equations at right. $x + 3y = 16$

    a.   Now rewrite the system and replace x with x^2. $x - 2y = 31$

    b.   What effect will this have on the solution to the system?
          Solve the new system.

4-97.   A line intersects the graph of $y = x^2$ twice. One point has an x-coordinate of -4,
         and the other point has an x-coordinate of 2.

    a.   Draw a sketch of both graphs, and find the equation of the line.

    b.   Find the measure of the angle that the line makes with the x-axis.

4.2.4 What can I learn from a graph?

Using Graphs to Find Solutions

You have seen that you can find solutions to problems, equations, inequalities and systems using graphs. In this lesson, you will apply this knowledge to a math competition challenge.

4-98. MATH TEAM CHALLENGE

At the annual two-day Math Challenge, teams from various high schools get together for a sometimes not-too-friendly math competition. Your school's biggest rival, Silicon Mountain High School, has won the competition the last five years and is already bragging that they will take first place again. However, your team has worked exceptionally hard this year to understand the Algebra 2 curriculum and its challenging concepts. Everyone on your team feels confident that they can beat Silicon Mountain High.

At the end of the first day of competition, scores for each school are posted, and WOW! Your team and Silicon Mountain's team are tied for first place! Before the teams leave for the day, they are handed a copy of the final problem in the competition (shown below). At first your team is excited, but when your team reads the "Final Challenge," you all realize that everyone has a lot of work to do before tomorrow's event.

> ### Final Challenge
>
> The three math judges will ask your team five questions that can be answered by looking at the graph of the functions at right. Your score for each answer will depend on its accuracy and completeness.
>
>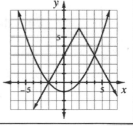

Your Task: Obtain a Lesson 4.2.4 Resource Page from your teacher, which contains a copy of the graph in the "Final Challenge." With your team, discuss the graph and make a list of questions that the judges might ask about it. For each question, form a complete response so that your team is prepared for the "Final Challenge."

Discussion Points

What can a graph tell us about equations? About inequalities?

Can we use the graph to get information about equations and inequalities in one variable and in two variables?

METHODS AND MEANINGS

Solutions to One- and Two-Variable Equations

When an equation has one variable, solutions are single numbers. When an equation contains two variables, solutions are ordered pairs.

For example, the solutions for the system of equations shown at right are the ordered pairs $(4, 44)$ and $(-1, -11)$ because these are the (x, y) pairs that make both equations true. They are also the points at which the graphs of the two equations intersect.

$$y = x^2 + 8x - 4$$
$$y = 2x^2 + 5x - 8$$

The solutions for the one-variable equation $2x^2 + 5x - 8 = x^2 + 8x - 4$ are the numbers 4 and -1, because they are the two x-values that make the equation true.

Review & Preview

4-99. Consider the graph at right as you answer the following questions.

a. Find the equation of the parabola.

b. Find the equation of the line.

c. Use your graph to solve $x + 5 = \frac{1}{2}(x + 3)^2 - 2$.

d. Use your graph to solve the system.

$$y = \frac{1}{2}(x + 3)^2 - 2$$
$$y = x + 5$$

e. Use your graph to solve the inequality $x + 5 < \frac{1}{2}(x + 3)^2 - 2$.

f. Use your graph to solve $\frac{1}{2}(x + 3)^2 - 2 = 0$.

g. Use your graph to solve $x + 5 = 4$.

h. How could you change the equation of the parabola so that the parabola and the line do not intersect? Is there more than one way?

4-100. Write the three inequalities that form the triangle shown at right.

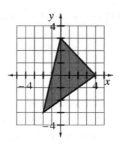

4-101. Solve each of the following inequalities. Represent the solutions algebraically and on a number line.

    a. $2|3x - 5| \geq 4$

    b. $\frac{1}{3}(3x - 6)^3 + 4 < 13$

4-102. On separate pairs of axes, sketch the graph of each equation or inequality below.

    a. $y + 5 = (x - 2)^2$

    b. $y \leq (x + 3)^3$

    c. $y = 4 + \frac{1}{x-3}$

4-103. Find the measure of $\angle CPM$ in the diagram at right.

List any sub-problems that were necessary to solve this problem.

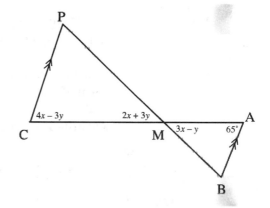

4-104. Graph the solutions to each of the following inequalities on a different set of axes. Label each graph with the inequality as given and with its $y=$ form. Choose a test point and show that it gives the same result in both forms of your inequality.

    a. $3x - 3 < y$

    b. $3 > y$

    c. $3x - 2y \leq 6$

    d. $x^2 - y \leq 9$

4-105. Solve for w in each equation below.

    a. $w^2 + 4w = 0$

    b. $5w^2 - 2w = 0$

    c. $w^2 = 6w$

Chapter 4 Closure   What have I learned?

Reflection and Synthesis

The activities below offer you a chance to reflect about what you have learned during this chapter. As you work, look for concepts that you feel very comfortable with, ideas that you would like to learn more about, and topics you need more help with. Look for connections between ideas as well as connections with material you learned previously.

①   TEAM BRAINSTORM

What have you studied in this chapter? What ideas were important in what you learned? With your team, brainstorm a list. Be as detailed as you can. To help get you started, a list of Learning Log entries and Math Notes boxes are below.

What topics, ideas, and words that you learned *before* this chapter are connected to the new ideas in this chapter? Again, be as detailed as you can.

How long can you make your list? Challenge yourselves. Be prepared to share your team's ideas with the class.

Learning Log Entries

- Lesson 4.1.1 – Strategies for Solving Equations
- Lesson 4.1.2 – The Meaning of a Solution, Part 1
- Lesson 4.1.3 – Finding Solutions to Systems
- Lesson 4.1.4 – The Meaning of a Solution, Part 2
- Lesson 4.2.1 – The Meaning of a Solution, Part 3

Math Notes

- Lesson 4.2.2 – Inequalities with Absolute Value
- Lesson 4.2.3 – Graphing Inequalities with Two Variables
- Lesson 4.2.4 – Solutions to One- and Two-Variable Equations

②   MAKING CONNECTIONS

Below is a list of the vocabulary used in this chapter. Make sure that you are familiar with all of these words and know what they mean. Refer to the glossary or index for any words that you do not yet understand.

solution	boundary curve	boundary line
boundary point	extraneous solution	intercept
intersection	linear programming	Looking Inside
maximize	one-variable equation	one-variable inequality
Rewriting	solution region	system of equations
system of inequalities	two-variable equation	two-variable inequality
Undoing		

Make a concept map showing all of the connections you can find among the key words and ideas listed above. To show a connection between two words, draw a line between them and explain the connection. A word can be connected to any other word as long as you can justify the connection. For each key word or idea, provide an example or sketch that shows the idea.

While you are making your map, your team may think of related words or ideas that are not listed here. Be sure to include these ideas on your concept map.

③   PORTFOLIO: EVIDENCE OF MATHEMATICAL PROFICIENCY

This section gives you an opportunity to show growth in
your understanding of key mathematical ideas over time
as you complete this course.

Explain everything that you know about $f(x) = 2^x - 3$.

Now consider the system below. Describe all of the
strategies you can think of to solve this system of equations. Of all of these
strategies, which would you choose to use to solve this system? Solve the
system using the strategy you have chosen and explain why that choice is best
for you.

$$y = 2x - 1 \qquad\qquad y = -\tfrac{1}{3}x + 6$$

Find a problem from this chapter that can be solved using more than one
strategy. Why did you choose to solve it the way you did? Now solve the
problem again, this time using a different strategy.

Alternatively, your teacher may ask you to showcase your use of inequalities
with your work from "Sandy Dandy Dune Buggies," problem 4-90.

Your teacher may give you the Chapter 4 Closure Resource Page: Solutions
Graphic Organizer page to work on. A "Graphic Organizer" is a tool you can
use to organize your thoughts and communicate your ideas clearly.

④   WHAT HAVE I LEARNED?

Most of the problems in this section
represent typical problems found in this
chapter. They serve as a gauge for
you. You can use them to determine
which types of problems you can do well
and which types of problems require
further study and practice. Even if your
teacher does not assign this section, it is a
good idea to try these problems and find
out for yourself what you know and what
you still need to work on.

Solve each problem as completely as you can. The table at the end of the
closure section has answers to these problems. It also tells you where you can
find additional help and practice with problems like these.

CL 4-106.   Use one of the strategies of Looking Inside, Rewriting, or Undoing to solve each equation.

    a. $2(y-1)^2 + 8 = 80$ b. $\sqrt{1-2x} = 10$

    c. $\frac{6y-1}{y} - 2 = 3$ d. $|2x+1| = 5$

CL 4-107.   Solve each system of equations without graphing. For each case, explain what the solution tells you about the graph of the system.

    a. $y = \frac{1}{3}x^2 + 1$ b. $y = \sqrt{x-3}$ c. $6x - 2y = -4$

           $y = 2x - 2$ $y = x - 5$ $y = 3x + 2$

CL 4-108.   Estelle and Carlos will be hosting a party and will buy 6 pies for their guests. Two lemon meringue pies cost $3 less than 4 blueberry pies. Three lemon meringue pies cost $9 more than 3 blueberry pies. How much does each type of pie cost?

CL 4-109.   Graph the following inequality or systems of inequalities.

    a. $y \le 4x + 16$ b. $y < x^2 - 2x - 3$

           $y > -\frac{4}{3}x - 4$ $y \le \frac{3}{4}x + 2$

    c. $y \ge |x+2| - 3$ d. $y \le \frac{1}{2}x + 3$

                                     $y \ge (x+1)^2 - 2$

CL 4-110.   Solve each inequality and graph the solution on a number line.

    a. $x^2 - 2x - 15 < 0$ b. $|3x - 2| \ge 10$

CL 4-111.   Find the equation of each of the lines described below.

    a.   The line that passes through $(6, 1)$ and $(-10, -7)$.

    b.   The line that is perpendicular to $y = \frac{2}{3}x + 1$ and passes through $(0, 5)$.

CL 4-112. Solve each equation for y.

    a. $2y^2 + 3y = 7$ b. $3(2x - y) + 12 = 4x - 3$

    c. $y(2y+1) + 3(2y+1) = 0$ d. $-4y - 1 = 4y(y - 2)$

CL 4-113. Add, subtract, multiply, or divide the expressions below. Be sure to simplify your answer.

    a. $\dfrac{4x^2-13x+3}{5x^2+23x-10} \cdot \dfrac{5x-2}{x^2+6x-27} \cdot \dfrac{x^2+5x-36}{4x-1}$ b. $\dfrac{x^2-9}{x^2+6x+9} \div \dfrac{x^2-x-6}{x^2+4}$

    c. $6 + \dfrac{3}{x+1}$ d. $\dfrac{5}{x} - \dfrac{10}{x^2+2x}$

CL 4-114. Consider the system of equations at right. $x^2 + y^2 = 25$

                                                   $y = x^2 + 3$

    a.   Solve the system graphically.

    b.   Now solve the system algebraically.

CL 4-115. Check your answers using the table at the end of this section. Which problems do you feel confident about? Which problems were hard? Have you worked on problems like these in math classes you have taken before? Use the table to make a list of topics you need help on and a list of topics you need to practice more.

Answers and Support for Closure Activity #4
What Have I Learned?

Note: MN = Math Note, LL = Learning Log

Problem	Solutions	Need Help?	More Practice
CL 4-106.	a. $y = 7$ or $y = -5$ b. $x = -\frac{99}{2}$ c. $y = 1$ d. $x = 2$ or $x = -3$	Lesson 4.1.1	Problems 4-3, 4-4, 4-8, 4-24, 4-31, 4-41, and 4-53
CL 4-107.	a. $(3, 4)$; a line tangent to parabola b. $(7, 2)$; a line intersecting the positive portion of a parabola, the second algebraic solution, $x = 4$, is extraneous c. infinite solution; lines are coinciding	Lessons 4.1.2 and 4.1.3 Checkpoint 2B MN: 2.1.1, 2.1.3, and 4.2.4	Problems 4-10, 4-36, 4-40, 4-92, and 4-96
CL 4-108.	$2L = 4B - 3$ $3L = 3B + 9$ Lemon meringue pies cost $7.50 each and blueberry pies cost $4.50 each.	Lessons 4.1.3 and 4.1.4 Checkpoint 2B MN: 2.1.1 and 2.1.3	Problems 4-49, 4-51, and 4-85
CL 4-109.	a. b. c. d.	Lesson 4.2.1 MN: 4.2.3	Problems 4-62, 4-63, 4-72, 4-93, 4-100, and 4-104
CL 4-110.	a. $-3 < x < 5$ b. $x \le -\frac{8}{3}$ or $x \ge 4$ 	Lesson 4.2.1 MN: 4.2.2	Problems 4-59, 4-65, 4-66, 4-73, 4-94, and 4-101

Problem	Solutions	Need Help?	More Practice
CL 4-111.	a. $y = \frac{1}{2}x - 2$ b. $y = -\frac{3}{2}x + 5$	Checkpoint 2A	Problems 2-9, 2-10, 2-89, 2-105, and 4-9
CL 4-112.	a. $y = \frac{-3 \pm \sqrt{65}}{4}$ b. $y = \frac{2}{3}x + 5$ c. $y = -\frac{1}{2}, -3$ d. $y = \frac{1}{2}$	Checkpoint 4B MN: 1.1.2 and 1.1.4	Problems 4-32, 4-67, and 4-87
CL 4-113.	a. $\frac{x-4}{x+5}$ b. $\frac{x^2+4}{(x+3)(x+2)}$ c. $\frac{6x+9}{x+1}$ d. $\frac{5}{x+2}$	Lessons 3.2.2, 3.2.3, and 3.2.4	Problems 4-13, 4-69, and 4-76
CL 4-114.	a. See graph at right. Approximately $(1.35, 4.82)$ and $(-1.35, 4.82)$ 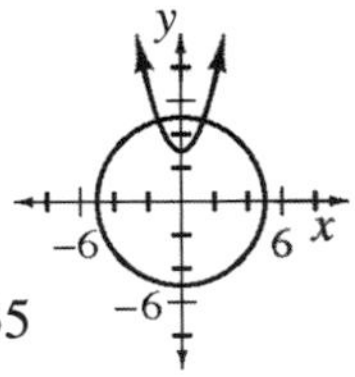 b. $x = \pm\sqrt{\frac{-1+\sqrt{113}}{2} - 3} \approx \pm 1.35$ $y = \frac{-1+\sqrt{113}}{2} \approx 4.82$ 	Lessons 4.1.2 and 4.2.4 MN: 4.2.4 LL: 4.1.2 and 4.1.4	Problems 4-7, 4-22, 4-23, 4-30, and 4-57

Chapter 5

Inverses and Logarithms

In Chapter 4, one of the strategies that you used to solve complicated equations was Undoing. In this chapter you investigate some new functions that "undo" each other. You will learn about inverse relationships and investigate the relationships between functions and their inverses. You will also learn about compositions of functions.

In Section 5.2, you will find the inverses of many parent graphs and add them to the tools you have for working with parent graphs. You will find inverses for exponential functions, which are called logarithmic functions. You will then investigate this family of functions and transform its graphs.

Guiding Question

Mathematically proficient students look for and make use of structure.

As you work through this chapter, ask yourself:

How can I use the reflective nature of inverse graphs to find the equations for inverses?

Chapter Outline

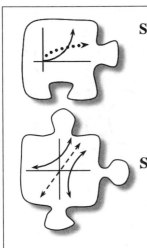

Section 5.1 You will examine relationships, called inverses, that "undo" the actions of functions. You will also learn how to create composite functions by "stacking" function machines, and you will investigate what happens when you compose functions and their inverses.

Section 5.2 You will be introduced to an important new family of functions, called logarithms, which are the inverses of exponential functions. You will investigate this family and learn to transform its graphs.

5.1.1 How can I "undo" a function?

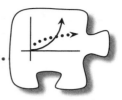

"Undo" Equations

Have you ever heard the expression, "She knows it forward and backward," to describe someone who understands an idea deeply? Often, being able to reverse a process is a way to show how thoroughly you understand it. Today you will reverse mathematical processes, including functions. As you work today, keep these questions in mind:

How can I "undo" it?

How can I justify each step?

5-1.   GUESS MY NUMBER

Today you will play the "Guess My Number" game. Your teacher will think of a number and tell you some information about that number. You will try to determine your teacher's number. (You can use your calculator or paper if it helps.) When you think you know the number, sit silently and do not tell anyone! Be sure to give others a chance to figure it out!

For example your teacher might say: *"When I add 4 to my number and then multiply the sum by 10, I get –70. What is my number?"*

Your task will be to find the number and explain your reasoning.

5-2.   A picture of Anita's function machine is shown at right. When she put 3 into the machine, 7 came out. When she put in 4, 9 came out, and when she put in –3, –5 came out.

a.   Make a table to organize the inputs and outputs from Anita's function machine. Explain in words what this machine is doing to the input to generate an output.

Problem continues on next page →

5-2.   *Problem continued from previous page.*

   b.   Anita's function machine suddenly started working backwards: it began
        pulling outputs back up into the machine, reversing the machine's process,
        and returning the original input. If 7 is pulled back into this machine, what
        value do you think will come out of the top? Anita sets up her new
        backwards function machine and enters the other outputs. What would you
        expect to come out the top if 9 is entered? If –5 is entered? Explain.

   c.   Record the inputs and outputs of the backwards function machine in a
        table. Record the numbers going in as x, and the numbers coming out as y.
        Explain in words what Anita's backwards function machine is doing.

   d.   Write equations for Anita's original function machine and for her
        backwards machine. How are the two equations related?

5-3.   The function machine at right follows the
        equation $h(x) = 5x + 2$.

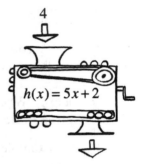

   a.   If the crank is turned backwards, what number
        should be pulled up into the machine in order to
        have a 4 come out of the top?

   b.   Keiko wants to build a new machine that will
        undo what $h(x)$ does to an input. What must
        Keiko's machine do to 17 to undo it and return a
        value of 3?

   c.   An "undo" function is called an **inverse** and has the notation $h^{-1}(x)$. Note
        that the –1 is not a negative exponent. It is the mathematical symbol that
        indicates the inverse function of $h(x)$. Write an equation for $h^{-1}(x)$, the
        "undo" function machine.

   d.   Choose a value for x. Then find a strategy to show that your equation,
        $h^{-1}(x)$, undoes the effects of the function machine $h(x)$.

Core Connections Algebra 2

5-4.   Keiko was working with a new function, $g(x)$. He wrote down the following steps for $g(x)$:

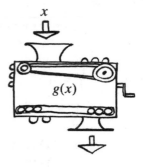

x

$g(x)$

- Add 5.
- Divide by 2.
- Cube it. (Find the third power.)
- Multiply by 6.

a.   What is the equation for $g(x)$? What is the output when 3 is put in?

b.   Help Keiko write down the steps (in words) of the inverse machine, $g^{-1}(x)$, and then write its equation.

c.   Verify that your equation in part (b) correctly "undoes" the output of $g(x)$ in part (a).

5-5.   Find the inverse equations for each of the functions below. Use function notation. Justify that each inverse equation works for its function.

a. $f(x) = 3x - 6$ b. $g(x) = x^3 - 5$

c. $p(x) = 2(x+3)^3$ d. $t(x) = \frac{10(x-4)}{3}$

5-6.   Each team member should choose one function and its inverse from the previous problem. Then they should create a graph and a table for each pair. Be sure to graph the function and its inverse equation on the same set of axes.

When each person in your team has finished, put everyone's work into the middle of the workspace. Describe what relationships you see between the representations of a function and its inverse equation.

5-7.   LEARNING LOG

What strategies did your team use to find inverse equations? How can you be sure that the inverse equations you found are correct? Discuss this idea and then write a Learning Log entry about the strategies you have for finding inverse equations and checking that they work. Title this entry "Finding and Checking Inverse Equations" and label it with today's date.

5-8. Graph $y = \frac{1}{2}x - 3$ and its inverse function on the same set of axes.

    a. What is the equation of the inverse function?

    b. Does this graph, including both lines, have a line of symmetry? If so, what is the equation of the line of symmetry?

5-9. Antonio's function machine is shown at right.

    a. What is $A(2)$?

    b. If 81 came out, what was dropped in?

    c. If 8 came out, what was dropped in? Be accurate to two decimal places.

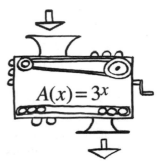

$A(x) = 3^x$

5-10. Nossis has been working on his geometry homework and he is almost finished. His last task is to find a solution of $\sin(x) = 0.75$. Nossis cannot figure out what x could be! Explain how he can find a value for x and show that it works.

5-11. If $10^x = 10^y$, what is true about x and y? Justify your answer.

5-12. Solve each of the following equations for x.

    a. $\frac{x}{3} = \frac{4}{5}$ b. $\frac{x}{x+1} = \frac{5}{7}$ c. $\frac{6}{15} = 2 - \frac{x}{5}$ d. $\frac{2}{3} + \frac{x}{5} = 6$

5-13. Sketch the solution of this system of inequalities.

$$y \geq x^2 - 5$$
$$y \leq -(x-1)^2 + 7$$

5-14.   Jamilla collected data comparing the weight and cost of pieces of sterling silver jewelry. Her data is listed as (weight in ounces, cost in dollars): $(5, 44.00)$, $(8.5, 78.50)$, $(12, 112.00)$, $(10, 93.00)$, $(7, 63.50)$, $(9, 83.20)$.

    a.   Plot the data on a set of axes.

    b.   Use a ruler to draw a line that best approximates the data.

    c.   Determine the equation of the line of best fit drawn in (b).

    d.   Use your equation to predict the cost of a 50-ounce silver bracelet.

5-15.   The angle of elevation of the sun (the angle the rays of sunlight make with the flat ground) at 10:00 a.m. is $29°$. At that point, a tree's shadow is 32 feet long. How tall is the tree?

5.1.2 How can I find an inverse?

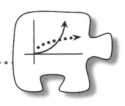

Using a Graph to Find an Inverse

What factors would you consider if you were thinking about buying a car? The first things that come to mind might be color or cost, but increasingly people are considering fuel efficiency (the number of miles a car can drive on a gallon of gas). You can think of the average number of miles per gallon that a car gets as a function that has *gallons* as the input and *miles traveled* as the output. A graph of this function would allow you to use what you know about the number of gallons in your tank to predict how far you could travel.

What would happen if you wanted to look at this situation differently? Imagine you regularly travel a route where there are many miles between gas stations. In this scenario, you would start with the information of the number of miles to the next filling station, and want to determine how many gallons of gas you would need to get there. In this case, you would start with the number of miles and work backwards to find gallons. Your new function would reverse the process.

5-16.   In Lesson 5.1.1 you started with functions and worked backwards to find their inverse equations. Now you will focus on functions and their inverses represented as graphs. Use what you discovered yesterday as a basis for answering the questions below.

$y = 0.5x + 3$ $y = 3(x+2)^2 - 6$ $y = \frac{1}{6}x^3 - \frac{13}{6}x + 2$

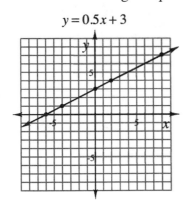   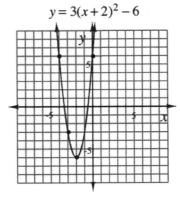   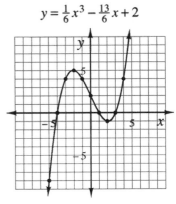

a.   Obtain a Lesson 5.1.2 Resource Page from your teacher and make a careful graph of each inverse equation on the same set of axes as its corresponding function. Look for a way to make the graph without finding the inverse equation first. Be prepared to share your strategy with the class.

b.   Make statements about the relationship between the coordinates of a function and the coordinates of its inverse. Use $x \to y$ tables of the function and its inverse to show what you mean.

5-17.   When you look at the graph of a function and its inverse, you can see a symmetrical relationship between the two graphs demonstrated by a line of symmetry.

   a.   Draw the line of symmetry for each pair of graphs in problem 5-16.

   b.   Find the equation of the line of symmetry for each graph.

   c.   Why do you think this line makes sense as the line of symmetry between the graphs of a function and its inverse relation?

5-18.   The line of symmetry you identified in problem 5-17 can be used to help graph the inverse of a function without creating an $x \rightarrow y$ table.

   a.   Graph $y = (\frac{x}{2})^2$ carefully on a full sheet of graph paper. Scale the x- and y-axes the same way on your graph.

   b.   On the same set of axes, graph the line of symmetry $y = x$.

   c.   Trace over the curve $y = (\frac{x}{2})^2$ with a pencil or crayon until the curve is heavy and dark. Then fold your paper along the line $y = x$, with the graphs on the inside of the fold. Rub the graph to make a "carbon copy" of the parabola.

   d.   When you open the paper you should see the graph of the inverse. Fill in any pieces of the new graph that did not copy completely. Justify that the graphs you see are inverses of each other.

5-19.   Your graphing calculator can also help you to graph the inverse of a function. Check your inverse graph from problem 5-18 by following your teacher's instructions to use the inverse-drawing feature of your graphing calculator. Was the inverse graph that you drew correct?

5-20.   Find the equation of the inverse of $y = (\frac{x}{2})^2$. Is there another way you could write it? If so, show how the two equations are the same. Justify that your inverse equation undoes the original function and use a graphing calculator to check the graphs.

5-21.   Consider your equation for the inverse of $y = (\frac{x}{2})^2$.

     a.   Is the inverse a function? How can you tell?

     b.   Use color to trace over the portion of your graph of $y = (\frac{x}{2})^2$ for which $x \geq 0$. Then use another color to trace the inverse of *only this part* of $y = (\frac{x}{2})^2$. Is the inverse of this part of $y = (\frac{x}{2})^2$ a function?

     c.   Find an equation for the inverse of the restricted graph of $y = (\frac{x}{2})^2$. How is this equation different from the one you found in problem 5-20?

5-22.   Consider the function $f(x) = (x-3)^2$.

     a.   How could you restrict the domain of $f(x)$ so that its inverse will be a function?

     b.   Graph $f(x)$ with its restricted domain and then graph its inverse on the same set of axes.

     c.   Find the equation of the inverse of $f(x)$ with its restricted domain.

5-23.   Is there a way to look at any graph to determine if its inverse will be a function? Explain. Find examples of other functions whose inverses are not functions.

5-24.   Use graphs to find the inverses for the following functions. Label the graph of each function and its inverse with its equation.

     a. $y = 5(x-2)$ b. $y = 1 + \frac{2}{x}$

5-25.   Look at the graph at right of a function and its inverse. If $p(x)$ is a function and $q(x)$ is its inverse, can you tell which is which? Why or why not?

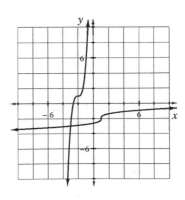

Core Connections Algebra 2

METHODS AND MEANINGS

Notation for Inverses

When given a function $f(x)$, the notation for the inverse of the function is $f^{-1}(x)$. Note that the -1 is not a negative exponent. It is the mathematical symbol that indicates the "undo" or **inverse** function of $f(x)$.

For example, if $f(x) = x^3 - 1$ then $f^{-1}(x) = \sqrt[3]{x+1}$.

This same inverse notation is used to identify the inverse of trigonometric functions. For example the inverse of $\sin(x)$ is written $\sin^{-1}(x)$.

5-26. Make a graph of $f(x) = \frac{1}{2}(x-1)^3$ and then graph its inverse on the same set of axes.

5-27. Write the inverse equation for each of the following equations.

  a. $y = 3x - 8$ b. $y = \frac{1}{2}x + 6$ c. $y = \frac{x+6}{2}$

5-28. Solve the equation $3 = 8^x$ for x, accurate to the nearest hundredth (two decimal places).

5-29. Multiply each expression below.

  a. $(x+2)(x-7)$ b. $(3m+7)(2m-1)$

  c. $(x-3)^2$ d. $(2y+3)(2y-3)$

5-30. Write the equation of a circle with a center at $(-3, 5)$ that is tangent to the y-axis (in other words, it touches the y-axis at only one point). Sketching a picture will help.

5-31. Perform the indicated operation to simplify each of the following expressions. In some cases, factoring may help you simplify.

a. $\dfrac{(x+2)(x-3)}{(x+1)(x-4)} \cdot \dfrac{(x+1)}{x(x+2)}$

b. $\dfrac{x^2+5x+6}{x^2-4} \cdot \dfrac{4}{x+3}$

c. $\dfrac{2x}{x+4} + \dfrac{8}{x+4}$

d. $\dfrac{x}{x+1} - \dfrac{1}{x+1}$

5-32. Barnaby's grandfather is always complaining that back when he was a teenager, he used to be able to buy his girlfriend dinner for only $1.50.

a. If that same dinner that Barnaby's grandfather purchased for $1.50 sixty years ago now costs $25.25, and the price has increased exponentially, write an equation that will give you the costs at different times.

b. How much would you expect the same dinner to cost in 60 years?

5-33. The function $f(x)$ is represented in the graph at right. Draw a graph of its inverse function. Be sure to state the domain and range for both $f(x)$ and $f^{-1}(x)$.

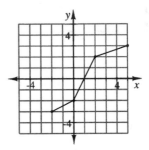

5-34. Lacey and Richens each have their own personal function machines. Lacey's machine, $L(x)$, squares the input and then subtracts one. Richens' function machine, $R(x)$, adds 2 to the input and then multiplies the result by three.

a. Write the equations that represent $L(x)$ and $R(x)$.

b. Lacey and Richens decide to connect their two machines, so that Lacey's output becomes Richens' input. If 3 is the initial input, what is the eventual output?

c. What if the order of the machines was changed? Would it change the output? Justify your answer.

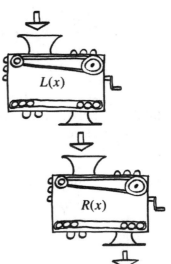

5-35.   Solve the system of equations at right.

$$x - 2y = 7$$
$$6y - 3x = 33$$

a.   What happened? What does this mean?

b.   What does the solution tell you about the graphs?

5-36.   Dana's mother gave her $175 on her sixteenth birthday. *"But you must put it in the bank and leave it there until your eighteenth birthday,"* she told Dana. Dana already had $237.54 in her account, which pays 3.25% annual interest, compounded quarterly. If she adds her birthday money to the account, how much money will she have on her eighteenth birthday if she makes *no* withdrawals before then? Justify your answer.

5-37.   Multiply each expression below.

a. $(x+4)(x-14)$

b. $(2m+5)(2m-1)$

c. $(x-9)(x+9)$

d. $(3y+2)^2$

5-38.   Calculate the x-intercepts for the graph of each function below.

a. $y = (x-2)(x+1)$

b. $y = 2x^2 + 16x + 30$

5-39.   If $2^{x+4} = 2^{3x-1}$, what is the value of x?

5.1.3 What can I do with inverses?

Finding Inverses and Justifying Algebraically

In this chapter you first learned how to find an inverse by undoing a function, and then you learned how to find an inverse graphically. You and your team may also have developed other strategies. In this lesson you will determine how to find an inverse by putting these ideas together and rewriting the equation. You will also learn a new way to combine functions that you can use to decide whether they have an inverse relationship.

x	y
1	−5
3	7
5	19
7	31

5-40.   Consider the table at right.

a.   Write an equation for the relationship represented in the table.

b.   Make a table for the inverse.

c.   How are these two tables related to each other?

d.   Use the relationship between the tables to find a shortcut for changing the equation of the original function into its inverse.

e.   Now solve this new equation for y.

f.   Justify that the equations are inverses of each other.

5-41.   Find the inverse function of the following functions using your new algebraic method, clearly showing all your steps.

a. $y = 2(x-1)^3$

b. $y = \sqrt{x-2} + 3$

c. $y = 3\left(\frac{x-9}{2}\right) + 20$

d. $y = \frac{4}{3}(x-1)^3 + 6$

5-42.   Adriena's strategy for checking that the functions $f(x)$ and $g(x)$ are inverses is to think of them as stacked function machines. She starts by choosing an input to drop into $f(x)$. Then she drops the output from $f(x)$ into $g(x)$. If she gets her original number, she is pretty sure that the two equations are inverses.

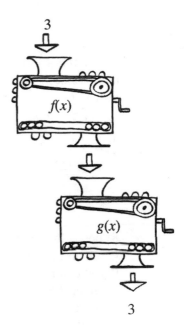

a.   Is Adriena's strategy sufficient? Is there anything else she should test to be sure?

b.   With your team, select a pair of inverse equations from problem 5-41, name them $f(x)$ and $g(x)$, then use Adriena's ideas to test them.

c.   Adriena wants to find a shortcut to show her work. She knows that if she chooses her input for $f(x)$ to be 3, she can write the output as $f(3)$. Next, $f(3)$ becomes the input for $g(x)$, and her output is 3. Since $f(3)$ is the new input for $g(x)$, she thinks that she can write this process as $g(f(3)) = 3$. Does her idea make sense? Why or why not?

d.   Her friend, Cemetra thinks she could also write $f(g(3))$. Is Cemetra correct? Why or why not.

e.   Will this strategy for testing inverses work with any input? Choose a variable to use as an input to test with your team's functions, $f(x)$ and $g(x)$.

5-43.   Statler, Adriena's teammate, is always looking for shortcuts. He thinks he has a way to adapt Adriena's strategy, but wants to check with his team before he tries it. *"If I use her strategy but instead of using a number, I skip a step and put the expression $f(x)$ directly into $g(x)$ to create $g(f(x))$, will I still be able to show that the equations are inverses?"*

a.   What do you think about Statler's changes? What can you expect to get out?

b.   Try Statler's idea on your team's equations, $f(x)$ and $g(x)$.

c.   Describe your results.

d.   Does Statler's strategy show that the two equations are inverses? How?

5-44. Trejo says that if you know the x-intercepts, y-intercepts, domain, and range of an equation then you automatically know the x-intercepts, y-intercepts, domain, and range for the inverse. Hilary disagrees. She says you know the intercepts but that is all you know for sure. Who is correct? Justify your answer.

5-45. Adriena was finding inverses of some equations. Use Statler's strategy from problem 5-43 to check Adriena's work below and test if each pair of equations are inverses of each other. If they are not, explain what went wrong and show how to get the inverse correctly.

a. $f(x) = \frac{3}{5}x - 15$

   $g(x) = \frac{5}{3}x + 25$

b. $f(x) = \frac{2(x+6)}{3} + 10$

   $g(x) = \frac{3}{2}x - 21$

c. $e(x) = \frac{(x-10)^2}{4}$

   $d(x) = 4\sqrt{x} + 10$

5-46. Rebecca thinks that she has found a quick way to graph an inverse of a function. She figures that if you can interchange x and y to find the inverse, she can interchange the x- and y-axes by flipping the paper over so that when she looks through the back the x-axis is vertical and the y-axis is horizontal as shown in the pair of graphs at right. Copy the graph below onto your paper and try her technique. Does it work? If so, do you like this method? Why or why not?

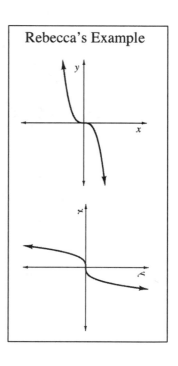

Rebecca's Example

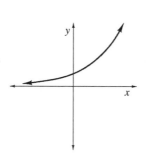

5-47. Make a personal poster that shows what you have learned about inverses so far. Choose an equation and its inverse then justify that your equations are inverses of each other using several representations.

METHODS AND MEANINGS

MATH NOTES

Composition of Functions

When you stack one function machine on top of another so that the output of the first machine becomes the input of the second, you create a new function, which is a **composition** of the two functions. If the first function is $g(x)$ and the second is $f(x)$, the composition of f and g can be written $f(g(x))$. (Note that the notations $f \circ g$ or $f \circ g(x)$ are used in some texts to denote the same composition.)

Note that the order of the composition matters. In general, the compositions $g(f(x))$ and $f(g(x))$ will be different functions.

5-48.   Two function machines, $f(x) = 5x - 3$ and $g(x) = (x-1)^2$, are shown at right.

a.   Suppose $f(3)$, (*not* $x = 3$), is dropped into the $g(x)$ machine. This is written as $g(f(3))$. What is this output?

b.   Using the same function machines, what is $f(g(3))$? Be careful! The result is different from the last one because the *order* in which you use the machines has been switched! With $f(g(3))$, first you find $g(3)$, then you substitute that answer into the machine named $f(x)$.

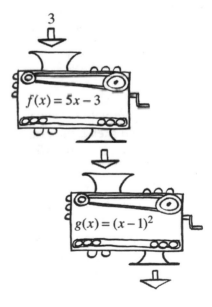

Chapter 5: Inverses and Logarithms

225

5-49.   This problem is a checkpoint for multiplying polynomials. It will be referred to as Checkpoint 5A.

Multiply and simplify each expression below.

a. $(x+1)(2x^2-3)$ b. $(x+1)(x^2-2x+3)$

c. $2(x+3)^2$ d. $(x+1)(2x-3)^2$

Check your answers by referring to the Checkpoint 5A materials located at the back of your book.

If you needed help solving these problems correctly, then you need more practice. Review the Checkpoint 5A materials and try the practice problems. Also, consider getting help outside of class time. From this point on, you will be expected to do problems like these quickly and easily.

5-50.   Solve each of the following equations.

a. $\frac{3x}{5}=\frac{x-2}{4}$ b. $\frac{4x-1}{x}=3x$ c. $\frac{2x}{5}-\frac{1}{3}=\frac{137}{3}$ d. $\frac{4x-1}{x+1}=x-1$

5-51.   Find the inverse of each of the following functions by first switching x and y and then solving for y.

a. $y=x^2+3$ b. $y=\left(\frac{1}{4}x+6\right)^3$ c. $y=\sqrt{5x-6}$

5-52.   Complete the square (for x) to write the equation that follows in graphing form and sketch the graph of $x^2+y^2-4x-16=0$. What is the parent graph and how has it been transformed?

5-53.   Ever eat a maggot? Guess again! The FDA publishes a list, the Food Defect Action Levels list, which indicates limits for "natural or unavoidable" substances in processed food (*Time*, October 1990). So in 100 grams of mushrooms, for instance, the government allows 20 maggots! The average batch of rich and chunky spaghetti sauce has 350 grams of mushrooms. How many maggots does the government allow in a batch?

5-54.   Perform each operation below and simplify your results.

a. $\frac{x^2+4x+3}{x^2+3x}\cdot\frac{3x}{x+1}$ b. $\frac{y^2}{y+4}-\frac{16}{y+4}$

c. $\frac{x^2+x}{x^2-4x-5}\div\frac{3x^2}{x-5}$ d. $\frac{x^2-6x}{x^2-4x+4}+\frac{4x}{x^2-4x+4}$

5.2.1 How can I undo an exponential function?

Finding the Inverse of an Exponential Function

When you first began investigating exponential functions, you looked at how their different representations were interconnected, as in the web at right. So far in this chapter, you have considered how functions and their inverses are related in different representations including equations, $x \rightarrow y$ tables, and graphs. What would the inverse equation for each of the parent functions you worked with in Chapter 2 look like in each representation?

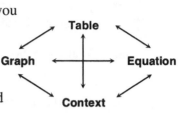

As you work with your team today, ask each other these questions:

What does the parent function look like in this representation?
How can that help us see the inverse relation?

Would another representation be more helpful?

How can we describe the relationship in words?

5-55. So far, you have worked with eight different parent graphs:

i. $y = x^2$ ii. $y = x^3$ iii. $y = x$ iv. $y = |x|$

v. $y = \sqrt{x}$ vi. $y = \frac{1}{x}$ vii. $y = b^x$ viii. $x^2 + y^2 = 1$

a. For each parent, find its inverse, if possible. If you can, write the equation of the inverse in $y =$ form. Include a sketch of each parent graph and its inverse. Remember that you can use the DrawInv function on your graphing calculator to help test your ideas.

b. Are any parent functions their own inverses? Explain how you know.

c. Do any parent functions have inverses that are not functions? If so, which ones?

5-56.   THE INVERSE EXPONENTIAL FUNCTION

There are two parent functions, $y = |x|$ and $y = b^x$, that have inverses that you do not yet know how to write in $y =$ form. You will come back to $y = |x|$ later. Since exponential functions are so useful for modeling situations in the world, the inverse of an exponential function is also important. Use $y = 3^x$ as an example. Even though you may not know how to write the inverse of $y = 3^x$ in $y =$ form, you already know a lot about it.

a.   You know how to make an $x \rightarrow y$ table for the inverse of $y = 3^x$. Make the table.

b.   You also know what the graph of the inverse looks like. Sketch the graph.

c.   You also have one way to write the equation based on your algebraic shortcut that you used in part (d) of problem 5-40. Write an equation for the inverse, even though it may not be in $y =$ form.

d.   If the input for the inverse function is 81, what is the output? If you could write an equation for this function in $y =$ form, or as a function $g(x) =$, and you put in any number for x, how would you describe the outcome?

5-57.   AN ANCIENT PUZZLE

Parts (a) through (f) below are similar to a puzzle that is more than 2100 years old. Mathematicians first created the puzzle in ancient India in the 2nd century BC. More recently, about 700 years ago, Muslim mathematicians created the first tables allowing them to find answers to this type of puzzle quickly. Tables similar to them appeared in school math books until recently.

Here are some clues to help you figure out how the puzzle works:

$$\log_2 8 = 3 \qquad\qquad\qquad \log_3 27 = 3$$

$$\log_5 25 = 2 \qquad\qquad\qquad \log_{10} 10{,}000 = 4$$

Use the clues to find the missing pieces of the puzzles below:

a. $\log_2 16 = ?$ b. $\log_2 32 = ?$ c. $\log_? 100 = 2$

d. $\log_5 ? = 3$ e. $\log_? 81 = 4$ f. $\log_{100} 10 = ?$

5-58.   How is the Ancient Puzzle related to the problem of the inverse function for $y = 3^x$ in problem 5-56? Show how you can use the idea in the Ancient Puzzle to write an equation in $y =$ form or as $g(x) =$ for the inverse function in problem 5-56.

5-59.   THE INVERSE OF ABSOLUTE VALUE

a.   Find the inverse equation and graph of $y = 2|x+1|$.

b.   Although you know how to find the table, graph, and equation for the inverse of absolute value, this is another function whose inverse equation cannot easily be written in $y =$ form. In fact, there is no standard notation for the inverse of the absolute value function. With your team, invent a symbol to represent the inverse, and give examples to show how your symbol works. Be sure to explain how your symbol handles that fact that the inverse of $y = |x|$ is not a function or explain why it is difficult to come up with a reasonable notation.

5-60.   In problem 5-56, you looked at the inverse of $y = 3^x$. Finish investigating this function.

5-61.   Consider the function $f(x) = \frac{2}{7-x}$.

a.   What is $f(7)$?

b.   What is the domain of $f(x)$?

c.   If $g(x) = 2x+5$, what is $g(3)$?

d.   Now use the output of $g(3)$ as the input for f to calculate $f(g(3))$.

5-62.   Amanda wants to showcase her favorite function: $f(x) = 1 + \sqrt{x+5}$. She has built a function machine that performs these operations on the input values. Her brother Eric is always trying to mess up Amanda's stuff, so he created the inverse of $f(x)$, called it $e(x)$, and programmed it into a machine.

a.   What is Eric's equation for his function $e(x)$?

b.   What happens if the two machines are pushed together? What is $e(f(-4))$? Explain why this happens.

c.   If $f(x)$ and $e(x)$ are graphed on the same set of axes, what would be true about the two graphs?

d.   Draw the two graphs on the same set of axes. Be sure to show clearly the restricted domain and range of Amanda's function.

5-63.   Sketch the graph of $y + 3 = 2^x$.

a.   What are the domain and range of this function?

b.   Does this function have a line of symmetry? If so, what is it?

c.   What are the x- and y-intercepts?

d.   Change the equation so that the graph of the new equation has no x-intercepts.

5-64.   Solve for x in the following problems.

a.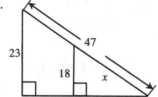

b.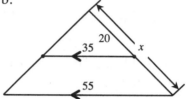

5-65.   A woman plans to invest x dollars. Her investment counselor advises her that a safe plan is to invest 30% of that money in bonds and 70% in low risk stocks. The bonds currently have a simple interest rate of 7% and the stock has a dividend rate (like simple interest) of 9%.

a.   Write an expression for the annual income that will come from the bond investment.

b.   Write an expression for the annual income that will come from the stock investment.

c.   Write an equation and solve it to find out how much the client needs to invest to have an annual income of $5,000.

5-66.   Factor each expression completely.

a. $x^2 - 49$ b. $6x^2 + 48x$ c. $x^2 - x - 72$ d. $2x^3 - 8x$

5-67.   Sketch the solution to this system of inequalities.

$$y \geq (x + 5)^2 - 6$$
$$y \leq -(x + 4)^2 - 1$$

5.2.2 What is a logarithm?

Defining the Inverse of an Exponential Function

You have learned how to "undo" many different functions. However, the exponential function has posed some difficulty. In this lesson, you will learn more about the inverse exponential function. In particular, you will learn how to write an inverse exponential function in $y =$ form.

5-68.   SILENT BOARD GAME

Your teacher will put an $x \rightarrow y$ table on the board or overhead that the whole class will work together to complete. The table will be like the one below. See which values you can fill in.

x	8	32	$\frac{1}{2}$	1	16	4	3	64	2	0	0.25	-1	$\sqrt{2}$	0.2	$\frac{1}{8}$
$g(x)$	3		-1												

a.   Describe an equation that relates x and $g(x)$.

b.   Look back at the Ancient Puzzle in problem 5-57. If you have not already done so, use the idea of the Ancient Puzzle to write an equation for $g(x)$.

c.   Why was it difficult to think of an output for the input of 0 or -1?

d.   Find an output for $x = 25$ to the nearest hundredth.

5-69.   ANOTHER LOGARITHM TABLE

Lynn was supposed to fill in this table for $g(x) = \log_5 x$. She thought she could use the log button on her calculator, but when she tried to enter 5, 25, and 125, she did not get the outputs the table below displays. She was fuming over how long it was going to take to guess and check each one when her sister suggested that she did not have to do that for all of them. She could fill in a few more and then use what she knew about exponents to figure out some of the others.

x	$\frac{1}{25}$	$\frac{1}{5}$	$\frac{1}{2}$	1	2	3	4	5	6	7	8	10	25	100	125	625
$g(x)$		−1		0				1					2		3	

a. Discuss with your team which outputs can be filled in without a calculator. Fill those in and explain how you found these entries.

b. With your team, use your calculator to estimate the remaining values of $g(x)$ to the nearest hundredth. Once you have entered several, use your knowledge of exponent rules to see if you can find any shortcuts.

c. What do you notice about the results for $g(x)$ as x increases?

d. Use your table to draw the graph of $y = \log_5 x$. How does your graph compare to the graph of $y = 5^x$?

5-70.   Find each of the values below, and then justify your answers by writing the equivalent exponential form.

a. $\log_2(32) = ?$ b. $\log_2(\frac{1}{2}) = ?$ c. $\log_2(4) = ?$ d. $\log_2(0) = ?$

e. $\log_2(?) = 3$ f. $\log_2(?) = \frac{1}{2}$ g. $\log_2(\frac{1}{16}) = ?$ h. $\log_2(?) = 0$

5-71.   While the idea behind the Ancient Puzzle is more than 2100 years old, the symbol **log** is more recent. It was created by John Napier, a Scottish mathematician in the 1600's. "log" is short for **logarithm**, and represents the function that is the **inverse of an exponential function**. You can use this idea to find the inverse equations of each of the following functions. Find the inverses and write your answers in $y =$ form.

a. $y = \log_9(x)$ b. $y = 10^x$ c. $y = \log_6(x+1)$ d. $y = 5^{2x}$

5-72.   Practice your logarithm fluency by calculating each of the following, *without changing the expressions to exponential form.* Be ready to explain your thinking.

a. $\log_7 49 = \underline{\quad}$ b. $\log_3 81 = \underline{\quad}$ c. $\log_5 5^7 = \underline{\quad}$

d. $\log_{10} 10^{1.2} = \underline{\quad}$ e. $\log_2 2^{w+3} = \underline{\quad}$

 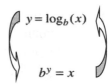

METHODS AND MEANINGS

MATH NOTES

Logarithms and Their Notation

A **logarithm** (called a "log" for short) is an exponent. An expression in logarithmic form, such as $\log_2(32)$, is read, *"the log, base 2, of 32."* To evaluate log expressions, think of the exponent: $\log_2(32) = 5$, because the exponent needed for base 2 to become 32 is 5.

An equation in logarithmic form is equivalent to another equation in exponential form, as shown at right. This conversion helps show why (based on an $x \to y$ interchange) $y = \log_b(x)$ and $y = b^x$ are inverse functions.

$$y = \log_b(x)$$

$$b^y = x$$

Review & Preview

5-73.   Let $y = \log_2(x)$. Rewrite the equation so that it begins with $x =$. Think about how you defined $y = \log_2(x)$ if you get stuck. Put a large box around both equations. Do the two equations look the same? Do the two equations mean the same thing? Are they equivalent? How do you know? This is very important. Think about it, and write a clear explanation.

5-74. Every exponential equation has an equivalent logarithmic form and every logarithmic equation has an equivalent exponential form. For example:

exponent
↓
$$4^3 = 64 \quad \text{is equivalent to} \quad 3 = \log_4 64$$
↑ base   ↑ exponent   ↑ base

Copy the table shown below and fill in the missing form in each row.

	Exponential Form	Logarithmic Form
a.	$y = 5^x$	
b.		$y = \log_7(x)$
c.	$8^x = y$	
d.	$A^K = C$	
e.		$K = \log_A(C)$
f.		$\log_{1/2}(K) = N$

5-75. Suppose you want to buy sugar. Packages of different sizes cost different amounts, but the relationship is not always proportional. That is, a bag twice as big does not usually cost twice as much. The chart shows the prices for various sizes of bags of sugar.

½ lb bag	$0.95
1 lb bag	$1.38
2 lb bag	$1.92
5 lb bag	$4.70
10 lb bag	$9.04
20 lb bag	$17.52

a. Find the rates in cost per pound. (Stores refer to this as unit pricing.)

b. Does the unit price increase or decrease with the size of the bag?

c. Does the unit rate change more drastically for smaller sizes or for larger sizes?

5-76. Although the Quadratic Formula always works as a strategy to solve quadratic equations, for many problems it is not the most efficient method. Sometimes it is faster to factor or complete the square or even just "out-think" the problem. For each equation below, choose the method you think is most efficient to solve the equation and explain your reason. Then solve the problems that can be factored.

    a. $x^2 + 7x - 8 = 0$ b. $(x+2)^2 = 49$

    c. $5x^2 - x - 7 = 0$ d. $x^2 + 4x = -1$

5-77. If $10^{3x} = 10^{(x-8)}$, solve for x. Show that your solution works by checking your answer.

5-78. Find the value of x in each diagram below.

    a.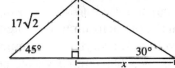

    b.

5-79. Consider the function defined by inputs that are the length of the radii of a circle, and the outputs are the areas of those circles. Write the equation for this function and investigate it completely.

5-80. Consider the equation $y = (x+6)^2 - 7$.

    a.   Explain completely how to get a good sketch of the graph of $y = (x+6)^2 - 7$.

    b.   Explain how to change the graph from part (a) to represent the graph of $y = (x+6)^2 + 2$.

    c.   Given your original graph, how can you get the graph of $y = |(x+6)^2 - 7|$?

    d.   Restrict the domain of the original parabola to $x \geq -6$ and graph its inverse function.

    e.   What would be the equation for the inverse function if you restricted the domain to $x \geq -6$?

5.2.3 What can I learn about logs?

Investigating the Family of Logarithmic Functions

In the last two lessons you have learned what a log is and how to convert an equation in log form to exponential form (and back again). In this lesson, you will explore logs as a family of functions.

5-81.   INVESTIGATING THE FAMILY OF LOGARITHMIC FUNCTIONS

You have learned that a logarithm is the inverse of an exponential function. Since exponential functions can have different bases, so can logarithms. Investigate the family of logarithmic functions $y = \log_b(x)$. The questions below will help you investigate.

Your Task: Generate data with your team and use it to write summary statements about this family of functions. For each summary statement you find, prepare a poster that shows and explains the summary statement and be prepared to present it to the class. Remember that summary statements should always include thorough justification.

Discussion Points

How can we collect data for this family? How much data is enough?

What have we learned about logs and inverses that can help us work with this family? How can "DrawInv" help?

What patterns can we find in our data? Why do they happen?

What are all the possible inputs for our function? Are there some *x*-values that do not make sense? Why or why not? How do these results appear in different mathematical representations?

What are some characteristics that all logarithmic functions have in common?

What happens as the value of *b* changes? What values of *b* make sense?

5-82.   As a team, begin your investigation of $y = \log_b x$ by choosing a positive value for b and work together to generate a table and a graph. Then, have each member of your team choose a different value for b. Since there is no key for a log of base b on your calculator, you will need to find another method to generate data for a table. Several strategies are suggested below.

   • While it may still be hard to make a table for your equation, your knowledge of inverses will help you. Write the inverse of your equation and make an $x \to y$ table for it. Use this table to help you make a table for your original function.

   • Use the calculator to guess and check possible outcomes.

   • Rewrite your log equation as an equivalent exponential equation and reverse your thinking.

   —————   *Further Guidance*   —————
   section ends here.

5-83.   LEARNING LOG

   Write a Learning Log entry about the family of functions $y = \log_b x$. Include the summary statements your team came up with and any others that you think should be added from the class discussion. As you write, think about which statements are very clear to you and which need further clarification. Title this entry "The Family of Logarithmic Functions" and label it with today's date.

5-84.   Write the equation of an increasing exponential function that has a horizontal asymptote at $y = 15$.

5-85.   If $x = 7^y$, how would you write this equation in $y =$ form? Explain.

5-86.   Solve for n: $n^3 = 49$.

5-87.   A circle has the equation $x^2 + (y + 2)^2 = r^2$. If the circle is shifted 2 units to the left, 5 units up, and the radius is doubled, what will its new equation be?

5-88.   On Wednesdays at Tara's Taquería four tacos are the same price as three burritos. Last Wednesday the Lunch Bunch ordered five tacos and six burritos, and their total bill was $8.58 (with no tax or drinks included). Nobody in the Lunch Bunch can remember the cost of one of Tara's tacos. Help them figure it out.

5-89.   Graph the two functions at right on the same set of axes. $y = 3(2^x)$

$$y = 3(2^x) + 10$$

a.   How do the two graphs compare?

b.   Suppose the first equation is $y = km^x$ and the graph is shifted up b units. What is the new equation?

5-90.   Solve each equation or inequality.

a. $|x - 1| = 9$ b. $2|x + 1| + 3 = 9$

c. $|x - 1| < 3$ d. $|x + 5| \geq 8$

5-91.   Factor each expression below.

a. $x^2 + 8x$ b. $x^2 y^2 - 81z^2$

c. $2x^2 + 14x - 16$ d. $3x^2 - 11x - 4$

5-92.   For each of the following rational expressions, add or subtract, then simplify.

a. $\frac{2-x}{x+4} + \frac{3x+6}{x+4}$ b. $\frac{3}{(x+2)(x+3)} + \frac{x}{(x+2)(x+3)}$

c. $\frac{3}{x-1} - \frac{2}{x-2}$ d. $\frac{8}{x} - \frac{4}{x+2}$

Core Connections Algebra 2

5.2.4 How can I transform log functions?

Transformations of Logarithmic Functions

In Lesson 5.2.3, you investigated logarithmic functions with different bases. To do this, you had to convert a log equation into its corresponding exponential form. In this lesson, you will figure out what a calculator can and cannot do with logs. This will help you write a general equation for a log function. As you work with your team, use the following questions to help focus your discussions.

What is a log?

How are logarithms and exponential equations related to each other?

How can we find an equivalent exponential equation for an equation that is in log form?

How can we transform the graphs of log functions?

5-93.   SOLVE THE LOG MYSTERY!

Have you noticed the $\boxed{\text{LOG}}$ key on your calculator? Clearly it is a logarithm, but what is its base? It would have been nice if the designers of your graphing calculator had allowed the $\boxed{\text{LOG}}$ key to work with any base, but they did not!

Your Task: Find the base of the $\boxed{\text{LOG}}$ key on your calculator. With your team, start by gathering some data and making a table for $y = \log x$. Analyze your data, and when you are sure you have figured out the base, write a clear summary statement justifying your conclusion.

Discussion Points

What input values give whole number outputs?
What do those values tell us?

How can we rewrite $y = \log_? x$?

5-94.   Now that you know the base of $f(x) = \log x$, you are ready to use your transformation skills to write a general equation.

   a.   Copy and complete the following table for $f(x) = \log x$.

x								1	2	3	4	5	6
y	−6	−5	−4	−3	−2	−1	0						

   b.   Using a full sheet of graph paper, make an accurate graph of $f(x) = \log(x)$. Remember that, just like the graphs of exponential functions, the graphs of log functions have asymptotes, so make sure any asymptotes on your graph are clearly shown.

   c.   Find all of the possible types of transformations of the graph of $f(x) = \log x$. For each transformation you find, show the graph and its equation. Then, find the general form for this family of logarithm graphs. Be prepared to explain your reasoning to the class.

5-95.   You have learned a lot about logs in a short time. Use what you have learned so far to answer the questions below.

   a.   Why does your calculator say that $\log(6) \approx 0.778$?

   b.   Justify why $\log(6)$ must have a value less than 1 but greater than 0.

   c.   Create a Learning Log entry that includes your answers to the focus questions from today's lesson, reprinted below. Show examples and use color or arrows to help explain your ideas. Title this entry "Working with Logs" and label it with today's date.

What is a log?

How are logarithms and exponential equations related to each other?

How can you find an equivalent exponential equation for an equation that is in log form?

How can you transform the graphs of log functions?

5-96. Last night, while on patrol, Agent 008 came upon a spaceship! He hid behind a tree and watched a group of little space creatures carry all sorts of equipment out of the ship. But suddenly, he sneezed. The creatures jumped back into their ship and sped off into the night. 008 noticed that they had dropped something, so he went to pick it up. It was a calculator! What a great find. He noticed that it had a $\boxed{\text{LOG}}$ button, but he noticed something interesting: $\log 10$ did not equal 1! With this calculator, $\log 10 \approx 0.926628408$. He tried some more: $\log 100 \approx 1.853256816$ and $\log 1000 \approx 2.779885224$.

   a. What base do the space creatures work in? Explain how you can tell.

   b. How many fingers do you think the space creatures have?

5-97. Copy these equations and solve for x. You should be able to do all these problems without a calculator.

   a. $\log_x(25) = 1$ b. $x = \log_3(9)$ c. $3 = \log_7(x)$

   d. $\log_3(x) = \frac{1}{2}$ e. $3 = \log_x(27)$ f. $\log_{10}(10000) = x$

5-98. Is $\log(0.3)$ greater than or less than one? Justify your answer.

5-99. Solve $1.04^x = 2$. Your answer should be accurate to three decimal places.

5-100. This problem is a checkpoint for factoring quadratics. It will be referred to as Checkpoint 5B.

Factor each expression below.

a. $4x^2 - 1$ b. $4x^2 + 4x + 1$

c. $2y^2 + 5y + 2$ d. $3m^2 - 5m - 2$

Check your answers by referring to the Checkpoint 5B materials located at the back of your book.

If you needed help solving these problems correctly, then you need more practice. Review the Checkpoint 5B materials and try the practice problems. Also, consider getting help outside of class time. From this point on, you will be expected to do problems like these quickly and easily.

5-101. Solve the following inequalities.

a. $x^2 - 2x < 3$ b. $3x - x^2 \le 2$

5-102. Is it true that $\log_3(2) = \log_2(3)$? Justify your answer.

5-103. Consider the general form of an exponential function: $y = ab^x$.

a.   Solve for a.   b.   Solve for b.

5-104. Make a sketch of a graph that is a decreasing exponential function with the x-axis as the horizontal asymptote. Then make a similar sketch, but this time with the line $y = 5$ as the horizontal asymptote.

5.2.5 How can I build a new function?

Investigating Compositions of Functions

Today you will work with your team to create and analyze new, interesting functions that are compositions of functions with which you are already familiar.

5-105. Polly Parabola's first corporate venture, Professional Parabola Productions, was so successful that Felix's Famous Functions bought her out in a corporate takeover. With all of the money she made from the transaction, she has decided to start a new company, Creative Compositions. Creative Compositions plans to develop a line of composite functions designed to appeal to the imagination of the next generation of function groupies. She wants to market three new functions and is offering huge contracts to the winners of the competition. Your boss wants your company to enter this competition and has assigned your team to the development department.

> ## CREATIVE COMPOSITIONS
> ### Call for new and visually interesting compositions of functions
>
> The Creative Composition Corporation announces an open competition for contracts to design new products. The products must be a composition of two or more functions whose parent functions are listed below:
>
> $$f(x) = x^2 \quad g(x) = x^3 \quad h(x) = 2^x \quad i(x) = \tfrac{1}{x} \quad j(x) = \sqrt{x} \quad k(x) = |x| \quad l(x) = \log_3 x$$
>
> Competing teams will prepare a poster to display their composite function and respond to questions from a panel of judges. Three contracts will be awarded based on the evaluation of the judges.
>
> The judges will base their review on the following:
>
> Is the graph of the composition a new and interesting shape?
>
> Are multiple representations used effectively to show key features of the new function?
>
> Does the selection of examples show off a variety of ways the function will appear when it is transformed?

Problem continues on next page →

5-105.   *Problem continued from previous page.*

> **Your Task:** With your team, try out different ways to write compositions involving two or more of the given functions and check their graphs. Record everything you try as documentation for the report you will need to give your boss. When your team agrees on a function they like, investigate it thoroughly and prepare a poster for the competition.

Discussion Points

What does the graph of each function look like separately?

How does making the output of one function the input of the other change the original graph?

How do we have to adjust the domains and ranges?

Is the inverse a function?

Further Guidance

5-106.   Consider $h(x) = 2^x$ and $k(x) = |x|$. Write the equation for each composite function $k(h(x))$ and $h(k(x))$. Discuss what each graph will look like and then sketch it. For each graph, explain the effect of one parent function on the other.

5-107.   Choose other pairs of parent functions from the list. Then write the composite functions in both directions. In other words, use one function as the input for the other and then switch. Check the graphs and decide whether either is a good candidate for the competition. Try out at least five different pairs and record your equations and sketches of their graphs.

5-108.   As a team, decide which of the functions you created that you want to enter in the competition. Now do a thorough investigation of that function.

5-109.   Prepare a poster to show off your new function. Be sure to include all of the important details from your investigation on your poster and be prepared to respond to the judges with your arguments for why this function should be selected as one of the new products of Creative Compositions.

──────────   *Further Guidance*   ──────────
                  section ends here.

5-110.   Consider the functions $f(x)$ in parts (a) and (b) below. For each $f(x)$, find two functions $h(x)$ and $g(x)$, so that $h(g(x)) = f(x)$. Use numerical examples to demonstrate that your functions $h(x)$ and $g(x)$ work.

a. $f(x) = \sqrt{3x + 6}$

b. $f(x) = \frac{5}{\sqrt{x}}$

c.   **Additional Challenge:** Work with your team to find another possibility for $h(x)$ and $g(x)$ such that $h(g(x)) = f(x)$ for each function given in parts (a) and (b). Be prepared to share your ideas with the class.

5-111.   LEARNING LOG

Create a Learning Log entry explaining what you have learned about compositions of functions. Use examples to illustrate your ideas. Title this entry "Compositions of Functions" and label it with today's date.

5-112.   If $f(x) = \sqrt{7 - x} - 6$ and $g(x) = -(x + 6)^2 + 7$, find $f(g(x))$ and $g(f(x))$. What do the results tell you about $f(x)$ and $g(x)$?

5-113.   For functions of the form $f(x) = mx$, it is true that $f(a) + f(b) = f(a + b)$? For example, when $f(x) = 5x$, $f(a) + f(b) = 5a + 5b = 5(a + b)$ and $f(a + b) = 5(a + b)$. Is $f(a) + f(b) = f(a + b)$ true for all linear functions? Explain why or show why not.

5-114.   Find the value of x in the equation $2^x = 3$. Make your answer accurate to three decimal places.

5-115. Consider the following three sequences:

$$t(n) = 50 - 7n \qquad\qquad h(n) = 4 \cdot 3^n \qquad\qquad q(n) = n^2 - 6n + 17$$

a. Which, if any, is arithmetic? Geometric? Neither?

b. Are there any terms that all three sequences have in common? Justify how you know for sure.

c. Are there any terms that two of them share? Justify how you know for sure.

5-116. Using the sequences in the previous problem, suppose we define a new sequence, $s(n)$, defined as $s(n) = q(t(n))$, a composition of two sequences. Do you think the new sequence will be arithmetic? Geometric? Neither? Explain. Make a table of values. Does the table support your hypothesis, or do you want to change your guess? Explain.

5-117. Gary has his function $g(x) = 10^x$ and Amy has her function $a(m) = 10^m$.

a. Each person is going to choose a whole number at random from the numbers $1, 2, 3\ldots10$, and substitute it into his or her respective function. After they do this, what is the probability that $g(x) = a(m)$?

b. Find and simplify an expression for $g(x) \cdot a(m)$.

5-118. Sketch the graph of $y = 3\log(x + 4) - 1$.

5-119. Solve the system of equations at right.

$$x + y = -3$$
$$2x - y = -6$$
$$3x - 2y + 5z = 16$$

5-120. Solve for m: $m^5 = 50$.

5-121.   Consider two functions $f(x) = \log x$ and $g(x) = |x|$.

a.   Use these two functions to write an equation for a composite function and sketch its graph.

b.   Use these two functions to write a different composite function and sketch its graph.

c.   What makes the two composite functions so different from each other?

d.   **Challenge:** Now try graphing $g(f(g(x)))$.

5-122.   Sketch square $ABCD$ on your paper, then randomly choose a point on $\overline{AB}$ and label it X. Draw $\overline{XC}$ and $\overline{XD}$ to form $\triangle XCD$. If a dart is thrown and lands inside the square, what is the probability that it landed inside $\triangle XCD$? Does it matter where you place X on $\overline{AB}$?

5-123.   Solve $5^x = 15$ for x. Make your answer accurate to two decimal places.

5-124.   Some of the following algebraic fractions have common denominators and some do not. Add or subtract the expressions and, if possible, simplify.

a. $\frac{3}{(x-4)(x+1)} + \frac{6}{x+1}$

b. $\frac{5}{2(x-5)} + \frac{3x}{x-5}$

c. $\frac{x}{x^2-x-2} - \frac{2}{x^2-x-2}$

d. $\frac{x+2}{x^2-9} - \frac{1}{x+3}$

5-125.   Simplify each of the expressions in parts (a) through (c) below.

a. $ab(\frac{1}{a} + \frac{1}{b})$

b. $cd(\frac{3}{c} + \frac{2c}{d})$

c. $x(1 - \frac{1}{x})$

d.   What expression would go in the box in order to make the equation $\Box(\frac{5}{x} + \frac{8}{y}) = 5y + 8x$ true?

Chapter 5 Closure What have I learned?

Reflection and Synthesis

The activities below offer you a chance to reflect about what you have learned during this chapter. As you work, look for concepts that you feel very comfortable with, ideas that you would like to learn more about, and topics you need more help with. Look for connections between ideas as well as connections with material you learned previously.

①   TEAM BRAINSTORM

What have you studied in this chapter? What ideas were important in what you learned? With your team, brainstorm a list. Be as detailed as you can. To help get you started, a list of Learning Log entries and Math Notes boxes are below.

What topics, ideas, and words that you learned *before* this chapter are connected to the new ideas in this chapter? Again, be as detailed as you can.

How long can you make your list? Challenge yourselves. Be prepared to share your team's ideas with the class.

Learning Log Entries

- Lesson 5.1.1 – Finding and Checking Inverse Equations
- Lesson 5.2.3 – The Family of Logarithmic Functions
- Lesson 5.2.4 – Working with Logs
- Lesson 5.2.5 – Composition of Functions

Math Notes

- Lesson 5.1.2 – Notation for Inverses
- Lesson 5.1.3 – Composition of Functions
- Lesson 5.2.2 – Logarithms and Their Notation

②   MAKING CONNECTIONS

Below is a list of the vocabulary used in this chapter. Make sure that you are familiar with all of these words and know what they mean. Refer to the glossary or index for any words that you do not yet understand.

asymptote	composite function	domain
exponential equation	$f^{-1}(x)$	inverse function
inverse relation	line of symmetry	logarithm
range	undo	$y = x$

Make a concept map showing all of the connections you can find among the key words and ideas listed above. To show a connection between two words, draw a line between them and explain the connection. A word can be connected to any other word as long as you can justify the connection. For each key word or idea, provide an example or sketch that shows the idea.

While you are making your map, your team may think of related words or ideas that are not listed here. Be sure to include these ideas on your concept map.

③   PORTFOLIO: EVIDENCE OF MATHEMATICAL PROFICIENCY

This section gives you an opportunity to show growth in your understanding of key mathematical ideas over time as you complete this course.

Include your investigation from problem 5-81 INVESTIGATING THE FAMILY OF LOGARITHMIC FUNCTIONS in your portfolio. Copy it over neatly and enhance your explanations if necessary.

Then investigate the following problem. (If you completed Appendix B in this course, you may have seen this problem already at the end of that appendix. Now you should have new graphs to add to your list of examples. You should expect to be able to add even more when you revisit this problem again at the end of Chapter 8.)

How many different kinds of graphs can you create that have:

a.   No x-intercepts?   b.   One x-intercept?

c.   Two x-intercepts?   d.   Three or more x-intercepts?

For each type of graph, show a sketch, label the key points, and give its equation. Make sure that each graph you give as an example represents a different family and describe the family in words or with a general equation. Show how to calculate the x-intercepts of each of your sample graphs.

Your teacher may assign you the Chapter 5 Closure Resource Page: Inverses GO to include in your portfolio.

④   WHAT HAVE I LEARNED?

Most of the problems in this section
represent typical problems found in this
chapter. They serve as a gauge for
you. You can use them to determine
which types of problems you can do well
and which types of problems require
further study and practice. Even if your
teacher does not assign this section, it is a
good idea to try these problems and find
out for yourself what you know and what you still need to work on.

Solve each problem as completely as you can. The table at the end of the
closure section has answers to these problems. It also tells you where you
can find additional help and practice with problems like these.

CL 5-126.   Quinten and his sister Kelsey always make a habit of undoing each other's
work. If Kelsey folds the laundry, Quinten unfolds it. If Quinten rakes the
leaves in the yard, Kelsey "unrakes" them! While working on her math
homework, Kelsey wrote the following equations. Help Quinten undo these
equations by finding their inverse equations.

a. $y = 3x - 2$ b. $y = \frac{x+1}{4}$

c. $y = x^3 + 1$ d. $y = 1 + \sqrt{x+5}$

CL 5-127.   Given the function $f(x) = 2 + \sqrt{x-1}$:

a.   Graph $f(x)$ and state the domain and range.

b.   Determine the equation for $f^{-1}(x)$, that is, the inverse of $f(x)$.

c.   Graph $f^{-1}(x)$ using the appropriate new domain and range.

d.   Compute $f^{-1}(f(5))$ and $f(f^{-1}(5))$ to show that your answer is correct.

CL 5-128.   Use the definition of logarithms to compute each of the
following *without using a calculator*.

a. $\log_8(64) = x$ b. $\log_9(x) = \frac{1}{2}$

c. $\log_3(3^4) = x$ d. $10^{\log_{10}(4)} = x$

e.   What do the answers to (c) and (d) demonstrate about logs and
exponents with the same base?

CL 5-129. Use the graph at right to help answer the questions below.

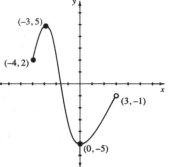

a. State the domain and range of the graph. Is this graph a function?

b. Draw the inverse of the graph. Is the inverse a function? Explain your answer.

c. State the domain and range of the inverse.

CL 5-130. A gallon of milk costs $3.89. Inflation has steadily increased 4% per year.

a. What did a gallon of milk cost ten years ago?

b. How much longer will it be until it costs $10?

CL 5-131. Perform the indicated operation on each of the following rational expressions. Be sure to state any values of the excluded variable and that your final answer is simplified. If a graphing tool is available, check the graph of the original problem to see if it coincides with the graph of your answer.

a. $\dfrac{5x}{x+3} + \dfrac{3+x}{x^2+9}$

b. $\dfrac{x}{x-1} - 1$

c. $\dfrac{x^2+5x+6}{x^2-4x} \cdot \dfrac{4x}{x+2}$

d. $\dfrac{x^2-2x}{x^2-4x+4} \div \dfrac{4x^2}{x-2}$

CL 5-132. Graph the system of $y \geq x^2$ and $y \geq (x-4)^2 + 2$ and shade the inequalities' overlapping region. How is the graph of $y \geq (x-4)^2 + 2$ positioned in relation to the graph of $y \geq x^2$?

CL 5-133.   Write possible equations for the graphs shown below.

a.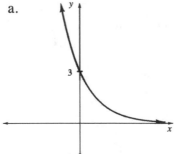

b.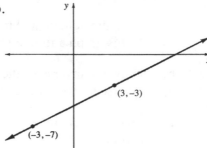

c.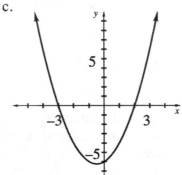

d.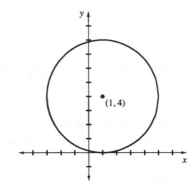

CL 5-134.   Factor the expressions below.

a. $3x^2 + 11x + 10$

b. $6x^3 - 31x^2 + 5x$

c. $6ab^2 + 15ab - 21a$

d. $y^2 + 5y - 24$

CL 5-135.   Check your answers using the table at the end of this section. Which problems do you feel confident about? Which problems were hard? Have you worked on problems like these in previous math classes? Use the table to make a list of topics you need to learn more about and a list of topics you just need to practice more.

Answers and Support for Closure Activity #4
What Have I Learned?

Note: MN = Math Note, LL = Learning Log

Problem	Solutions	Need Help?	More Practice
CL 5-126.	a. $y = \frac{x+2}{3}$ b. $y = 4x - 1$ c. $y = \sqrt[3]{x-1}$ d. $y = (x-1)^2 - 5$	Lessons 5.1.1 and 5.1.3	Problems 5-2, 5-3, 5-5, 5-40, and 5-41
CL 5-127.	a. domain $x \geq 1$; range $y \geq 2$ 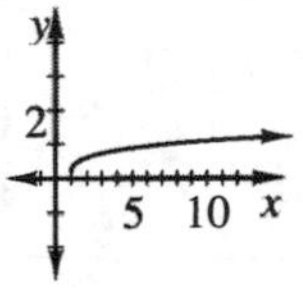 b. $f^{-1}(x) = (x-2)^2 + 1$ c. domain $x \geq 2$; range $y \geq 1$ 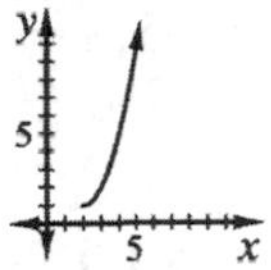 d. $f^{-1}(f(5)) = f(f^{-1}(5)) = 5$	Lessons 5.1.2 and 5.1.3 MN: 5.1.2 and 5.1.3	Problems 5-21, 5-22, 5-24, 5-26, 5-41, 5-42, 5-43, 5-45, 5-44, 5-33, 5-62, and 5-112
CL 5-128.	a. 2 b. 3 c. 4 d. 4	Lesson 5.2.2 MN: 5.2.2	Problems 5-70, 5-72, 5-74, and 5-97
CL 5-129.	a. domain: $-4 \leq x < 3$ range: $-5 \leq y \leq 5$ b. See graph at right. No, there are 2 outputs when $-5 < x < -1$ and $2 < x \leq 5$ 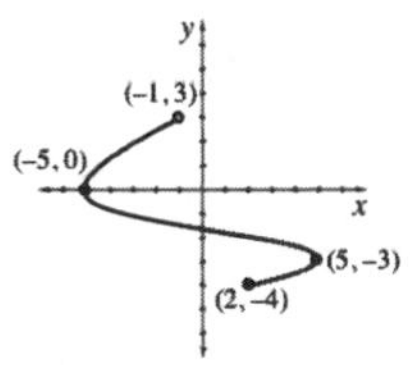 c. domain: $-5 \leq x \leq 5$ range: $-4 \leq y < 3$	Lesson 5.1.2	Problems 5-16, 5-21, 5-24, 5-44, 5-33, and 5-46

Problem	Solutions	Need Help?	More Practice
CL 5-130.	a. $2.63 b. ≈ 24 years (by guess and check)	Lessons A.3.2 and B.2.3	Problems A-116, B-36, and B-46
CL 5-131.	a. $\frac{5x^2-14x+3}{(x-3)(x+3)}$, $x \neq \pm 3$ b. $\frac{1}{x-1}$, $x \neq 1$ c. $\frac{4(x+3)}{x-4}$, $x \neq -2, 0,$ or 4 d. $\frac{1}{4x}$, $x \neq 0, 2$	Lessons 3.2.3, 3.2.4, and 3.25 MN: 3.2.5 LL: 3.2.3 and 3.2.4	Problems 5-31, 5-54, 5-124, and 5-92
CL 5-132.	See graph below. It is shifted to the right 4 units and up 2 units. 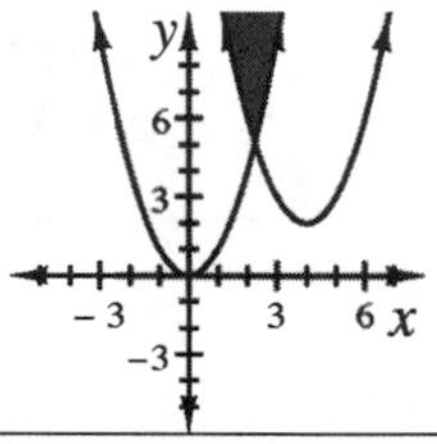	Lesson 4.2.1 MN: 4.2.3 LL: 4.2.1	Problems 4-93, 4-100, CL 4-109, 5-13, and 5-67
CL 5-133.	Possibilities include: a. $y = 3(\frac{1}{2})^x$ or $y = 3(2)^{-x}$ b. $y = \frac{2}{3}x - 5$ c. $y = (x-2)(x+3)$ or $y = x^2 + x - 6$ d. $(x-1)^2 + (y-4)^2 = 16$	Lessons B.1.5, 2.1.3, 2.2.1, and 2.2.2 MN: 1.1.2, 2.1.3, 2.2.2, 2.2.3	Problems B-60, B-89, 2-95, and 2-107
CL 5-134.	a. $(3x+5)(x+2)$ b. $x(6x-1)(x-5)$ c. $3a(2b+7)(b-1)$ d. $(y-3)(y+8)$	MN: 1.1.4 Checkpoint 5B	Problems 1-13, 2-98, 2-169, and CL 2-178

Chapter 6   3-D Graphing and Logarithms

In this chapter, you will learn to extend your mathematical thinking to three dimensions and you will further your understanding of logarithms, which will give you the tools to solve a murder mystery.

In the first section, you will expand your understanding of graphing equations and systems of equations to three dimensions and you will broaden your understanding of solutions to include solutions to systems in three dimensions.

In Section 6.2, you will return to logarithms to learn more about their properties and why they are useful. You will construct an exponential function to model a situation, and you will use logarithms to solve a mathematical murder mystery.

Guiding Question

Mathematically proficient students make sense of problems and persevere in solving them.

As you work through this chapter, ask yourself:

How can I apply what I learned about graphs and equations in two dimensions to three-dimensional situations?

Chapter Outline

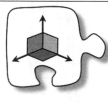

Section 6.1 In this section, you will learn how to graph points, equations, and systems of equations in three dimensions. You will solve three-dimensional systems of equations. You will learn how to use systems of three equations in three variables to solve problems, including finding the equation of a parabola passing through any three points.

Section 6.2 You will learn some important properties of logarithms that will enable you to solve equations. You will then use these skills to solve a murder mystery, "The Mystery of the Cooling Corpse."

6.1.1 How can I plot points in three dimensions?

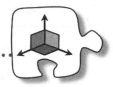

Creating a Three-Dimensional Model

In geometry, you worked with objects that existed in different dimensions. You considered lines and line segments, which have only one dimension: length. You also looked at flat shapes like circles, rectangles, and trapezoids that have two dimensions: length and width. Prisms, cones, and most objects that you encounter in the real world have volume, and therefore have three dimensions: length, width and height.

When you worked with graphs in Algebra 1, you represented points, the number line, and curves on a **two-dimensional** (flat) surface called the xy-plane. So far, you have only been able to represent relationships with at most two unknowns, usually the variables x and y. However, many problems, like some that you may have done in homework problems in Chapter 6, have more than two unknowns. Today, you and your team will build a model that will help you graph in three dimensions. As you work on this lesson, consider the following questions with your team:

How can we plot a point in three dimensions?

How can we write the coordinates of a point in three dimensions?

How can we show three dimensions on flat paper?

6-1.   Consider when it is appropriate to graph a situation in one, two, and/or three dimensions. It may be helpful to think about your experience representing numbers and relationships on a number line or an xy-plane, and how you can adapt your knowledge to work in three dimensions. Discuss each question with your team before writing your response.

    a.   How can you represent the solution to $x = 5$ graphically? Can you think of more than one way?

    b.   How can you represent the solutions to $x + 2y = 5$ graphically?

    c.   How could you represent the solutions to $x + 2y + z = 5$? What would the solutions look like? Discuss these questions with your team and write down any ideas that you have.

6-2.   To graph solutions to equations with three variables, you need to use a three-dimensional coordinate system. Obtain a Lesson 6.1.1A or 6.1.1B Resource Page from your teacher. Use scissors to cut out the region indicated on the page. Then fold along each of the axes and use tape to attach the dashed edge to the z-axis. Be sure that the grid ends up on the *inside* of your model (rather than the outside). The result should look similar to the diagram at right.

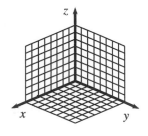

6-3.   Place a penny (or other marker) on the bottom surface of your model at the point where $x = 4$ and $y = 2$. Now lift your marker straight up so that it you are holding it 3 units above the bottom of the model.

   a.   With your team, find a way to write the coordinates of this point.

   b.   In your model, find the point where $x = 3$, $y = 4$, and $z = 2$. Use your team's method to write the coordinates for this point.

   c.   The model you have created is only a portion of the entire coordinate system used to represent three dimensions mathematically. How many of these models would you have to put together to create a model that represents the entire three-dimensional coordinate system? Think about the regions you would need to graph points like $(5, -2, -7)$ or $(-1, -2, -4)$.

6-4.   Use cubes to build each shape described below inside your three-dimensional model. Make sure that one corner of each shape you build lies at the **origin** (at the point $(0, 0, 0)$).

   a.   Build a $2 \times 2 \times 2$ cube. Use coordinates to name the vertex that is farthest from the origin.

   b.   Build a rectangular prism that is 2 units in length along the x-axis, 1 unit in length along the y-axis, and 3 units in length along the z-axis. Use coordinates to name the vertex that is farthest from the origin.

   c.   Draw and label a three-dimensional coordinate system on isometric dot paper, as shown at right. Now add the prism from part (b) to the drawing. On your dot paper, label the coordinates of *all* of the vertices.

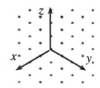

6-5.   Build a rectangular prism that will have vertices in your model at $(1, 0, 0)$, $(0, 0, 4)$, and $(0, 3, 0)$.

   a.   Find the coordinates of the other five vertices.

   b.   Move the rectangular prism so that three vertices are at $(-1, 0, 0)$, $(0, 0, 4)$, and $(0, 3, 0)$. Now where are the other vertices?

   c.   Is it possible to build another rectangular prism that has the same coordinates for the vertex farthest from the origin as the prism in part (b)? Be sure to justify your conclusion.

Core Connections Algebra 2

6-6. On isometric dot paper, draw a three-dimensional coordinate system and plot the following points: $(0,1,-1)$, $(1,2,0)$, and $(2,3,1)$.

    a. What do you notice about the three points?

    b. With your team, find a strategy to make each point clearly different from the others. Be prepared to share your strategy with the class.

    c. Identify the coordinates of two points that appear to be the same as $(-2,0,0)$.

6-7. LEARNING LOG

In your Learning Log, show and explain how to graph points in three dimensions. Include clear pictures to illustrate your method. Title this entry "Plotting Points in xyz-Space" and label it with today's date.

6-8. Make a table like the one below. Choose points in each of the locations listed at the top of the table and write in the coordinates of the points you have chosen.

	Points on the x-axis	Points on the y-axis	Points on the z-axis	Points not on the x-, y-, or z-axes
1st point	(, ,)	(, ,)	(, ,)	(, ,)
2nd point	(, ,)	(, ,)	(, ,)	(, ,)
3rd point	(, ,)	(, ,)	(, ,)	(, ,)
4th point	(, ,)	(, ,)	(, ,)	(, ,)

    a. What do you notice about the coordinates of the points on the x-axis?

    b. Make a conjecture about the coordinates of points that lie on any of the coordinate axes.

6-9. Solve the system of equations at right.

$$3x + 8 = 2$$
$$7x + 3y = 1$$

6-10.   Each cube below is 1 cm on a side.

 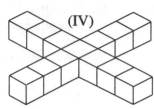

(I)   (II)   (III)   (IV)

?

a.   Based on the pattern, find the volume of Figure III.

b.   If the pattern continues, write an expression to represent the volume of Figure N. What kind of sequence is this?

6-11.   Solve each exponential equation for x.

a. $10^x = 16$ b. $10^x = 41$ c. $3^x = 729$ d. $10^x = 101$

6-12.   Rewrite each expression below as an equivalent expression without negative exponents.

a. 5^{-2} b. xy^{-2} c. $(xy)^{-2}$ d. $a^3b^4a^{-4}b^6$

6-13.   Multiply or divide and simplify each of the following expressions.

a. $\dfrac{3x}{x^2+2x+1} \div \dfrac{3}{x^2+2x+1}$ b. $\dfrac{3}{x-1} \cdot \dfrac{2}{x-2}$

6-14.   Given the two points $(-2, 0)$ and $(0, 1)$, complete parts (a) through (c) below.

a.   Find the slope of the line that passes through these two points.

b.   Find the slope of the line perpendicular to the line that passes through these two points.

c.   Describe the relationship between the slopes of perpendicular lines.

6-15.   The cost of food has been increasing by 4% per year for many years. To find the cost of an item 15 years ago, Heather said, *"Take the current price and divide it by $(1.04)^{15}$."*

Her friend Elissa said, *"No, you should take the current price and multiply it by $(0.96)^{15}$!"*

Explain who is correct and why.

Core Connections Algebra 2

6.1.2 How can I graph an equation in three dimensions?

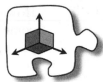

Graphing Equations in Three Dimensions

In the past, you have used the two-dimensional Cartesian coordinate system (x- and y-axes) to graph equations involving two variables. In Lesson 6.1.1, you used a three-dimensional coordinate system to plot points. Today you will use the three-dimensional coordinate system to graph equations that have three variables. As you are working through the lesson, use the following questions to help focus your discussion:

> How can we use what we know about graphing in two dimensions
> to help us graph in three dimensions?

> What does a solution to a three-variable equation represent?

6-16.   Consider the equation $5x + 8y + 10z = 40$.

   a.   Discuss with your team what you think the shape of the graph would be. Explain how you decided.

   b.   Is the point $(4, 5, -2)$ a solution to the equation $5x + 8y + 10z = 40$? Justify your answer.

   c.   Your team will be given a list of points to test in the equation. Plot each point that makes the equation true on the three-dimensional graphing tool your teacher has set up.

   d.   Now examine the solutions displayed on the graphing tool. With your team, discuss the questions below. Be ready to share your discoveries with the class.

   - Are there any points that you suspect are solutions, but do not have a point showing on the graph?

   - How many solutions do you think there are?

   - Are there any points showing that you think are not solutions? Explain.

   - What shape is formed by all of the solutions? That is, what is the shape of the graph of $5x + 8y + 10z = 40$?

6-17.   How can you graph an equation like $12x + 4y + 5z = 60$ in three dimensions? To come up with a strategy to graph a three-variable equation, look at the strategies you can use to graph a two-variable equation in two dimensions. For example, consider $5x + 8y = 40$.

   a.   What is the shape of the graph of $5x + 8y = 40$? How can you tell?

   b.   With your team, brainstorm all of the strategies you could use to graph $5x + 8y = 40$. Which strategy do you prefer? Why?

6-18.   Now you will work with your team to graph $12x + 4y + 5z = 60$.

   a.   What do you think it will look like?

   b.   Which of the strategies you used to graph a two-variable equation in problem 6-17 can be used to graph this three-variable equation? Work with your team to find a strategy and then graph $12x + 4y + 5z = 60$ on your isometric dot paper. Be prepared to share your strategy with the class.

6-19.   Use your new strategy to graph each of the following equations in three dimensions.

   a. $13x + 4y + 5z = 260$ b. $12x - 9y + 108 = 0$

6-20.   Consider the graph of $x = 4$ for each of the following problems.

   a.   Graph the solution to $x = 4$ in one dimension (on a number line).

   b.   Graph the solutions to $x = 4$ in two dimensions (on the xy-plane).

   c.   Graph the solutions to $x = 4$ in three dimensions (in the xyz-space).

METHODS AND MEANINGS

MATH NOTES

Locating Points in Three Dimensions

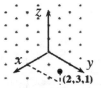

When locating a point on a *number line*, a single number, x, is used.

The location of a point in a *plane* is given by two numbers, (x, y), called an ordered pair.

To locate a point in *space*, three numbers, (x, y, z), are used, which are called an **ordered triple**. The point $(2, 3, 1)$ is shown at right. The dotted lines help clarify which coordinate was graphed.

6-21.   For each of the following equations, find every point where its *three-dimensional* graph intersects one of the coordinate axes. That is, find the x-, y- and z-*intercepts*. Express your answer in (x, y, z) form.

   a. $6y + 15z = 60$ b. $3x + 4y + 2z = 24$

   c. $(x + 3)^2 + z^2 = 25$ d. $z = 6$

6-22.   Answer each of the following questions. Illustrate your answers with a sketch.

   a.   What do you think the intersection of two planes looks like?

   b.   What do you think it means for two planes to be parallel?

   c.   What do you think it means for a line and a plane to be parallel?

6-23.   Find an equation that will generate each graph.

a.
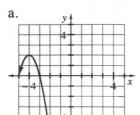

b.
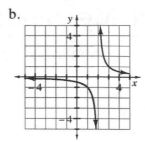

c.
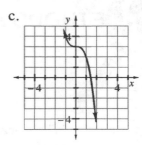

6-24.   Is $y = \frac{1}{x}$ the parent of $y = \frac{1}{x^2 + 7}$? Explain your reasoning.

6-25.   Solve each equation below for x.

a. $2x + x = b$ b. $2ax + 3ax = b$ c. $x + ax = b$

6-26.   Mark claims to have created a sequence of three function machines that always gives him the same number he started with.

a.   Test his machines. Do you think he is right?

b.   Be sure to test negative numbers. What happens for negative numbers?

c.   Mark wants to get his machines patented but has to prove that the set of machines will always do what he says it will, at least for positive numbers. Show Mark how to prove that his machines work for positive numbers by dropping in a variable (for example, n) and writing out each step the machines must take.

d.   Why do the negative numbers come out positive?

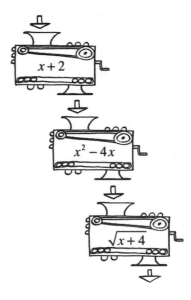

6-27.　Sketch the graph of $y = \log_5(x-2)$ and describe how the graph is transformed from the parent graph.

6-28.　The table at right shows the total population of Mexico for the given years.

a.　What was the average rate of change for the population from 1900 to 1950?

b.　What was the average rate of change from 1960 to 2010?

c.　When was the population growth rate higher?

Year	Population (millions)
1900	13.6
1910	15.2
1920	14.4
1930	16.6
1940	19.8
1950	26.3
1960	35.0
1970	50.7
1980	69.7
1990	87.8
2000	100.3
2010	113.7

6-29.　Given $f(x) = -2x^2 - 4$ and $g(x) = 5x + 3$, calculate:

a.　$g(-2)$　　　　b.　$f(-7)$　　　　c.　$f(g(-2))$　　　　d.　$f(g(1))$

6.1.3 What can I discover about 3-D systems?

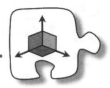

Systems of Three-Variable Equations

You know a lot about systems of two-variable equations, their solutions, and their graphs. Today you will investigate systems of three-variable equations.

6-30.   THREE-DIMENSIONAL SYSTEM INVESTIGATION

Consider the following systems of equations:

System I	*System II*
$20x + 12y + 15z = 60$	$20x + 15y + 12z = 60$
$20x + 12y + 15z = 120$	$10x + 30y + 12z = 60$

Your Task: With your team, find out as much as you can about each of these systems of equations, their graphs, and their solutions. Be sure to record all of your work carefully and be prepared to share your summary statements with the class.

Discussion Points

What does the graph of a three-variable equation look like?

What does it mean to be a solution to a system of equations?

What does a solution to a three-variable system of equations look like on a graph?

Is there always a solution to a system of equations?

Further Guidance

6-31.   Using isometric dot paper, graph both equations in *System I* from problem 6-30 on a single three-dimensional coordinate system. Use different colors to help identify each graph.

a.   Describe the graph of the system in as much detail as you can.

b.   Looking at the graph, can you tell what the solution to this system is? Explain.

6-32.   Using isometric dot paper, graph both equations in *System II* from problem 6-30 on a single three-dimensional coordinate system. Use different colors to help identify each graph.

   a.   Describe the graph of the system in as much detail as you can.

   b.   Looking at the graph, can you tell what the solution to this system is? Explain.

6-33.   Now compare the graphs of the two systems. How are they similar? How are they different?

————— *Further Guidance section ends here.* —————

6-34.   Look closely at your graph of *System II*. Can you see the intersection of the two planes clearly? If not, make a new set of axes and graph the systems carefully.

   a.   What does the intersection of two planes look like?

   b.   Work with your team to find the coordinates of as many points as you can that lie in both planes. Show your work and describe your strategies. Be prepared to share your ideas with the class.

   c.   Can you add a third equation to the system that will share the same intersection with the original two graphs?

6-35.   On isometric dot paper, graph the system of equations at right. What shape is the intersection? Use color to show the intersection clearly on your graph.

$$10x + 6y + 5z = 30$$
$$6x + 15y + 5z = 30$$

6-36.   Verify that $2^7 = 128$. Is it true that $\log 2^7 = \log 128$?

6-37.   If $24 = y$, is it true that $\log 24 = \log y$? Justify your answer.

6-38. Write the system of inequalities that would give the graph at right.

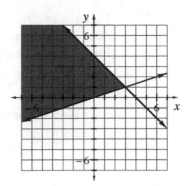

6-39. Simplify each of the following expressions.

    a. $\dfrac{2x^3+5x^2-3x}{4x^3-4x^2+x}$

    b. $\dfrac{3x^2-5x-2}{2x^2-11x+15} \cdot \dfrac{2x^2-5x}{3x^3-5x^2-2x}$

6-40. Solve $\sqrt{3x+1}-x=-3$ and check your solution.

    a.   You should have gotten two values for x when you solved. Did you? If not, rework the problem.

    b.   Did you check *both* solutions? What happened?

6-41. Solve each of the following equations.

    a. $(x+4)(2x-5)=0$

    b. $(x+4)(x^2-5x+6)=0$

    c. $3x(x+1)(2x-7)(3x+4)^2(x-13)(x+7)=0$

    d.   Describe how to solve an equation made up of any number of factors all multiplied to equal zero.

6-42. Determine if each of the following functions is odd, even, or neither.

    a. $f(x)=3x^3+2$ b. $y=x^6+x^4$

6-43. Solve for x, y, and z: $(2^x)(3^y)(5^z)=(2^3)(3^{x-2})(5^{2x-3y})$.

6.1.4 What is a solution in three dimensions?

••

Solving Systems of Three Equations with Three Unknowns

Today you will extend what you know about systems of equations to examine how to solve systems of equations with three variables. As you work with your team, look for connections to previous work. The focus questions below can help generate mathematical discussion.

What does a solution to a system in three variables mean?

What strategies can we use?

What does the intersection look like?

6-44.   Review the strategies for solving systems that you already know as you solve the following two-variable system of equations. Use any method. Do not hesitate to change strategies if your first strategy seems cumbersome. If there is no solution, explain what that indicates about the graph of this system. Leave your solution in (x, y) form.

$$12x - 2y = 16$$
$$30x + 2y = 68$$

6-45.   Solve the following three-variable system of equations by graphing it with your graphing tool or on isometric dot paper. Give your solution in (x, y, z) form. Then test your solution in the equations and describe your results.

$$2x + 3y + 3z = 6$$
$$6x - 3y + 4z = 12$$
$$2x - 3y + 2z = 6$$

6-46.   FINDING AN EASIER WAY

As you saw in problem 6-45, using a graph to solve a system of three equations with three variables can lead to inconclusive results. What other strategies should be considered? Discuss this with your team and be prepared to share your ideas with the class.

6-47. Looking at the equations in problem 6-45, Elissa wanted to see if she could apply some of her solving techniques from two-variable equations to this three-variable system.

    a. Elissa noticed that the first two equations could be combined to form the new equation $8x + 7z = 18$. How did she accomplish this? Explain.

    b. Now that Elissa has an equation with only x and z, she needs to find another equation with only x and z to be able to solve the system. Choose a different pair of equations to combine and find a way to eliminate y so that the new equation only has x and z. Then solve the system to find x and z.

    c. For which variable do you still need to solve? Work with your team to solve for this variable. Then write the solution as a point in (x, y, z) form.

    d. Is your solution reasonable? Does it make sense? Does it agree with your graph?

6-48. Practice using your algebraic strategies by solving the systems below, if possible. If there is no solution or if the solution is different than you expected, use the graphing tool to help you figure out why.

    a.
$$x + y + 3z = 3$$
$$2x + y + 6z = 2$$
$$2x - y + 3z = -7$$

    b.
$$20x + 12y + 15z = 60$$
$$20x + 12y + 15z = 120$$
$$10x + 20z = 30$$

    c.
$$5x - 4y - 6z = -19$$
$$-2x + 2y + z = 5$$
$$3x - 6y - 5z = -16$$

    d.
$$6x + 4y + z = 12$$
$$6x + 4y + 2z = 12$$
$$6x + 4y + 3z = 12$$

6-49. Today you developed a way to solve a system of three equations with three variables. But what do the solutions of a system like those provided in problem 6-48 represent? Consider this as you answer the questions below with your graphing tool.

    a. One of the systems in problem 6-48 had no solution. Graph this system with your graphing tool. Describe how the planes are positioned and why there is no common point on all three planes.

    b. In what other ways could three planes be positioned so that there is no solution? Use paper or cardboard to help you communicate your ideas with others.

    c. Graph the system in part (d) of problem 6-48 with your graphing tool and examine the result. How can you describe the intersection of these planes?

6-50.   LEARNING LOG

In your Learning Log, describe your algebraic strategy to
solve a system of three equations with three variables.
Provide enough detail to allow you to repeat the process
when you refer to it later. Title this entry "Systems of Three
Equations with Three Variables" and include today's date.

METHODS AND MEANINGS

Graphing Planes in Three Dimensions

To graph a plane, it is easiest to use the intercepts to draw the
"trace lines" (the intersections of the plane with the xy-, xz-,
and yz-planes) that will represent the plane.

To find the intercepts, let two of the variables equal zero. Then solve to
find the intercept corresponding to the remaining variable.

For example, for $2x + 3y + 4z = 12$, the x-intercept is found by letting y
and z equal zero, which gives $2x = 12$. Therefore the x-intercept is
$(6, 0, 0)$. Similarly, the y-intercept is $(0, 4, 0)$, and the z-intercept is
$(0, 0, 3)$.

Drawing the line between two intercepts gives one
of the trace line in that coordinate plane. For
example, connecting the x- and y-intercepts, you
would get the equation $2x + 3y = 12$, which is the
trace line in the xy-plane when $z = 0$ in the equation
$2x + 3y + 4z = 12$. Connecting the x- and z-intercepts
gives the trace line in the xz-plane, etc.

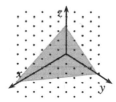

6-51.   Use the algebraic strategies you developed in today's lesson
to solve the system of equations at right. Be sure to check
your solution.

$$2x + y - 3z = -12$$
$$5x - y + z = 11$$
$$x + 3y - 2z = -13$$

6-52. Suppose that a two-bedroom house in Nashville is worth $110,000 and appreciates at a rate of 2.5% each year.

    a. How much will it be worth in 10 years?

    b. When will it be worth $200,000?

    c. In Homewood, houses are depreciating at a rate of 5% each year. If a house is worth $182,500 now, how much will it be worth two years from now?

6-53. Solve $\sqrt{5x-1} = \sqrt{6+4x}$ and check your solution.

6-54. If two quantities are equal, are their logarithms also equal? Consider the questions below.

    a. Is it true that 4^2 is equal to 2^4? Is this a special case, or is a^b equal to b^a for any values of a and b?

    b. Is $\log 4^2$ equal to $\log 2^4$? How can you be sure?

    c. Are the equations $x = 5$ and $\log x = \log 5$ equivalent? Justify your answer.

    d. Is the equation $\log 7 = \log x^2$ equivalent to the equation $7 = x^2$? How can you be sure?

6-55. Use the ideas from problem 6-54 to help you solve the following equations.

    a. $\log 10 = \log(2x - 3)$ b. $\log 25 = \log(4x^2 - 5x - 50)$

6-56. Find an equation for each of the lines described below.

    a. The line with slope $\frac{1}{3}$ that goes through the point $(0, 5)$.

    b. The line parallel to $y = 2x - 5$ that goes through the point $(1, 7)$.

    c. The line perpendicular to $y = 2x - 5$ that goes through the point $(1, 7)$.

    d. The line that goes through the point $(0, 0)$ so that the tangent of the angle it makes with the x-axis is 2.

6-57.   Solve each equation below for y so that it can be entered into the graphing calculator.

    a. $x^2 = x(2x-4)+y$ b. $x = 3+(y-5)^2$

6-58.   Sketch the graph of each equation or inequality below.

    a. $(x-2)^2+(y+3)^2 = 9$ b. $(x-2)^2+(y+3)^2 \geq 9$

6-59.   You are standing 60 feet away from a five-story building in Los Angeles, looking up at its rooftop. In the distance you can see the billboard on top of your hotel, but the building is completely obscured by the one in front of you. If your hotel is 32 stories tall and the average story is 10 feet high, how far away from your hotel are you?

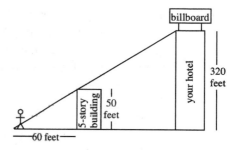

6.1.5 How can I apply systems of equations?

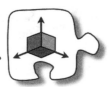

Using Systems of Three Equations for Curve Fitting

In this lesson you will work with your team to find the equation of a quadratic function that passes through three specific points. You will be challenged to extend what you know about writing and solving a system of equations in two variables to solving a system of equations in three variables.

6-60.   In your work with parabolas, you have developed two forms for the general equation of a quadratic function: $y = ax^2 + bx + c$ and $y = a(x - h)^2 + k$. What information does each equation give you about the graph of a parabola? Be as detailed in your explanation as possible. When is each form most useful?

6-61.   Suppose the graph of a quadratic function passes through the points $(1, 0)$, $(2, 5)$, and $(3, 12)$. Sketch its graph. Then work with your team to develop an algebraic method to find the equation $y = ax^2 + bx + c$ of this specific quadratic function.

Discussion Points

What does the graph of any quadratic function look like?

What does it mean for the graph of $y = ax^2 + bx + c$
to pass through the point $(3, 12)$?

What solving method can we use to find a, b, and c?

How can we check our equation?

Would this method allow us to find
the equation of a quadratic using *any* three points?

Would this method work if we only had two points?

6-62. How many points does it take to determine the equation of a linear function $y = ax + b$? Discuss this with your team and include at least one sketch to support your answer.

Now think about the graph of a quadratic function $y = ax^2 + bx + c$. How many points do you think it would take to determine this graph? Why? Does there need to be any restriction on the points you use? Discuss these questions with your team and justify your answers before moving on to part (a).

a. Suppose you wanted the graph of a quadratic function $y = ax^2 + bx + c$ to pass through the points $(1, 0), (2, 5)$, and $(3, 12)$. How would these points be useful in finding the specific equation of this function? If your team has not already done so, include a sketch of the parabola going through these points to support your answer.

b. It is often useful to label points with the variable they represent. For instance, for the point $(3, 12)$, which variable does the 3 represent? Which variable does the 12 represent?

c. Using the general equation of a quadratic, $y = ax^2 + bx + c$, substitute the x- and y-values from your first point into the equation. Then do the same for the other two points to create three equations where the unknowns are a, b, and c.

d. Now use the strategies you developed in Lesson 6.1.4 to solve the system of equations for a, b, and c.

e. Use your results to write the equation of the quadratic function that passes through the points $(1, 0), (2, 5)$, and $(3, 12)$. How can you check your answer? That is, how can you make sure your equation would actually go through the three points? Using the method your team decides on, check your equation.

—————————   *Further Guidance*   —————————
                     section ends here.

6-63. LEARNING LOG

In your Learning Log, summarize the method you used in problem 6-61 (or problem 6-62) to find the equation $y = ax^2 + bx + c$ of the quadratic function whose graph passes through three given points. Title this entry "Finding the Equation of a Parabola Given Three Points" and label it with today's date.

6-64.   Find the equation $y = ax^2 + bx + c$ of the function that passes through the three points given in parts (a) and (b) below. Be sure to check your answers.

   a. $(3, 10), (5, 36)$, and $(-2, 15)$ b. $(2, 2), (-4, 5)$, and $(6, 0)$

6-65.   What happened in part (b) of problem 6-64? Why did this occur? (If you are not sure, plot the points on graph paper.)

6-66.   CPM engineers are considering developing a private space rocket. In a computer simulation, the rocket is approaching a star and is caught in its gravitational pull. When the rocket's engines are fired, the rocket will slow down, stop momentarily, and then pick up speed and move away from the star, avoiding its gravitational field. CPM engaged the rocket engines when it was 750 thousand miles from the star. After  one full minute, the rocket was 635 thousand miles from the star. After two minutes, the ship was 530 thousand miles from the star.

   a.   Name the three points given in the information above if x = the time since the engines were engaged and y = the distance (in thousands of miles) from the star.

   b.   Based on the points in part (a), make a rough sketch of a graph that shows the distance reaching a minimum and then increasing again, over time. What kind of function could follow this pattern?

   c.   Find the equation of a graph that fits the three points you found in part (a).

   d.   If the ship comes within 50 thousand miles of the star, the shields will fail and the ship will burn up. Use your equation to determine whether the space ship has failed to escape the gravity of the star.

6-67. Sickly Sid has contracted a serious infection and has gone to the doctor for help. The doctor takes a blood sample and finds 900 bacteria per cc (cubic centimeter) and gives Sid a shot of a strong antibiotic. The bacteria will continue to grow for a period of time, reach a peak, and then decrease as the medication succeeds in overcoming the infection. After ten days, the infection has grown to 1600 bacteria per cc. After 15 days it has grown to 1875.

a. Name three data points given in the problem statement.

b. Make a rough sketch that will show the number of bacteria per cc over time.

c. Find the equation of the parabola that contains the three data points.

d. Based on the equation, how long will it take until the bacteria are eliminated?

e. Based on the equation, how long had Sid been infected before he went to the doctor?

6-68. THE COMMUTER

Sensible Sally has a job that is 35 miles from her home and needs to be at work by 8:15 a.m. She wants to get as much sleep as she can, leave as late as possible, and still get to work on time. Sally discovered that if she leaves at 7:10, it takes her 40 minutes to get to work. If she leaves at 7:30, it takes her 60 minutes to get work. If she leaves at 7:40, it takes her 50 minutes to get to work. Since her commute time increases and then decreases, Sally decided to use a parabola to model her commute, assuming the time it takes her to get to work varies quadratically with the number of minutes after 7:00 that she leaves her house.

a. If x = the number of minutes after 7:00 that Sally leaves, and y = the number of minutes it takes Sally to get to work, what three ordered pairs can you determine from the problem?

b. Use the three points from part (a) to find the equation of a parabola in standard form that can be used to model Sally's commute.

c. Will Sally make it to work on time if she leaves at 7:20?

6-69.   PAIRS PARABOLA CHALLENGE

Your challenge will be to work with a partner to create a parabola puzzle for another pair of students to solve. Follow the directions below to create a puzzle that will make them think and allow them to show off their algebra skills. When you are ready, you will trade puzzles with another pair and attempt to solve theirs.

a.   With your partner, decide on an equation for a parabola and then identify three points that lie on its graph. Keep track of how you came up with your equation and how you chose your points. Be ready to share strategies.

b.   Write the coordinates of the three points on an index card or small slip of paper to give to another pair of students. Be sure you keep a copy of your equation so you can check their work later.

c.   Trade points with another pair and work with your partner to solve their puzzle. When you are confident of your equation, check your work with the pair that wrote it.

6-70.   Make a conjecture about how you would find the equation of a cubic function that passes through a given set of points when graphed, $y = ax^3 + bx^2 + cx + d$. How many points do you think you would need to be given to be able to determine a unique equation? How could you extend the method you developed for solving a quadratic to solving a cubic?

6-71.   Solve the system of equations at right and then check your solution in each equation. Be sure to keep your work well organized.

$$x - 2y + 3z = 8$$
$$2x + y + z = 6$$
$$x + y + 2z = 12$$

6-72.   Find the equation in $y = ax^2 + bx + c$ form of the parabola that passes through the points $(1, 5)$, $(3, 19)$, and $(-2, 29)$.

6-73. This problem is a checkpoint for multiplying and dividing rational expressions. It will be referred to as Checkpoint 6A.

Multiply or divide each pair of rational expressions. Simplify the result.

a. $\dfrac{x^2-16}{(x-4)^2} \cdot \dfrac{x^2-3x-18}{x^2-2x-24}$

b. $\dfrac{x^2-1}{x^2-6x-7} \div \dfrac{x^3+x^2-2x}{x-7}$

Check your answers by referring to the Checkpoint 6A materials located at the back of your book.

If you needed help solving these problems correctly, then you need more practice. Review the Checkpoint 6A materials and try the practice problems. Also, consider getting help outside of class time. From this point on, you will be expected to do problems like these quickly and easily.

6-74. Simplify each expression in parts (a) through (c) below. Then complete part (d).

a. $xy(\frac{1}{x}+\frac{1}{2y})$

b. $ab(\frac{2}{a}+\frac{4a}{b})$

c. $2x(3-\frac{1}{2x})$

d. What expression would go in the box to make the equation $\square(\frac{2}{x}+\frac{7}{y})=2y+7x$ true?

6-75. Change each of the following equations from logarithmic form to exponential form, or vice versa.

a. $y=\log_{12} x$

b. $x=\log_y 17$

c. $y=1.75^{2x}$

d. $3y=x^7$

6-76. Solve $\sqrt{3x-6}+6=12$ and check your solution.

6-77. The half-life of an isotope is 1000 years. A 50-gram sample of the isotope is sealed in a box.

a. How much is left after 10,000 years?

b. How long will it take to reduce to 1% of the original amount?

c. How long will it take until all of the original sample of the isotope is gone? Support your answer.

6-78.   Graph the following piece-wise defined function.

$$x > 0; \quad y = |x| + 3$$
$$x \le 0; \quad y = x^3 + 3$$

a.   Now shift the function down 3 and to the left 2 and draw the new graph on the same set of axes.

b.   Write the new equations for the shifted function.

6-79.   Rewrite each expression below as an exponential expression with a base of 2.

a.   16   b. $\frac{1}{8}$ c. $\sqrt{2}$ d. $\sqrt[3]{4}$

6-80.   Solve the system of equations at right and then check your solution in each equation. Be sure to keep your work well organized.

$$x + 2y - z = -1$$
$$2x - y + 3z = 13$$
$$x + y + 2z = 14$$

6-81.   Find an equation for the parabola that passes through the points $(-1, 10)$, $(0, 5)$, and $(2, 7)$.

6-82.   Change each of the following equations from logarithmic form to exponential form, or vice versa.

a. $a = \log_b 24$ b. $3x = \log_{2y} 7$

c. $3y = 2^{5x}$ d. $4p = (2q)^6$

6-83.   Add or subtract and simplify each of the following expressions. Justify that each step of your process makes sense.

a. $\frac{3x}{x^2 + 2x + 1} + \frac{3}{x^2 + 2x + 1}$ b. $\frac{3}{x-1} - \frac{2}{x-2}$

6-84.   On their Team Test, Raymond, Sarah, Hannah, and Aidan were
given $y = 4x^2 - 24x + 7$ to change into graphing form. Raymond
noticed that the leading coefficient was a 4 and not a 1. His team
agreed on a way to start rewriting, but then they worked in pairs
and got two different solutions, shown below.

Raymond and Hannah

(1) $y = 4x^2 - 24x + 7$

(2) $y = 4(x^2 - 6x) + 7$

(3) $y = 4(x^2 - 6x + 3^2) + 7 - 36$

(4) $y = 4(x - 3)^2 - 29$

Aidan and Sarah

(1) $y = 4x^2 - 24x + 7$

(2) $y = 4(x^2 - 6x + 9) + 7 - 9$

(3) $y = 4(x - 3)^2 + 7 - 3^2$

(4) $y = 4(x - 3)^2 - 2$

Hannah says, *"Aidan and Sarah made a mistake in Step 3. Because of the
factored 4 they really added 4(9) to complete the square, so they should subtract
36, not just 9."* Is Hannah correct? Justify your answer by showing whether the
results are equivalent to the original equation.

6-85.   Use the correct method from problem 6-84 to change each of the following
equations to graphing form. Then, without graphing, find the vertex and
equation of the line of symmetry for each.

a. $y = 2x^2 - 8x + 7$ b. $y = 5x^2 - 10x - 7$

6-86.   Shift the graph of $\log x$ up 3 units and to the right 6. Graph both the original
and the transformed graph on the same set of axes and write the equation for the
transformed graph.

6-87.   Given $f(x) = 2x^2 - 4$ and $g(x) = 5x + 3$, find the value of each expression below.

a. $f(a)$ b. $f(3a)$ c. $f(a + b)$

d. $f(x + 7)$ e. $f(5x + 3)$ f. $g(f(x))$

6.2.1 How can I solve exponential equations?

Using Logarithms to Solve Exponential Equations

In Chapter 5, you learned what a logarithm was and several important facts about logs. In this lesson, you will learn about a property of logarithms that will be very useful for solving problems that involve exponents.

6-88.   LOGARITHMS SO FAR

There are three important log facts you have learned so far. Discuss these questions with your team to ensure everyone remembers these ideas. For each problem, make up an example to illustrate your ideas.

    a.   What is a logarithm? How can log equations be converted into another form?

    b.   What do you know about the logarithm key on your calculator?

    c.   What does the graph of $y = \log(x)$ look like? Write a general equation for $y = \log(x)$.

6-89.   Marta was convinced that there had to be some way to graph $y = \log_2 x$ on her graphing calculator. She typed in $y = \log(2^x)$ and pressed $\boxed{\text{GRAPH}}$.

"It WORKED!" Marta yelled in triumph.

"Whaaaat?" said Celeste. *"I think $y = \log_2 x$ and $y = \log(2^x)$ are totally different, and I bet we can show it by converting both of them to exponential form."*

"Yeah, I think you're wrong, Marta," said Sophia. *"I think we can show that $y = \log_2 x$ and $y = \log(2^x)$ are totally different by looking at the graphs."*

    a.   Show that the two equations are different by sketching the graph of $y = \log_2 x$. Then sketch what your graphing calculator shows to be the graph of $y = \log(2^x)$.

    b.   Now show that $y = \log_2 x$ and $y = \log(2^x)$ are different by converting both of them to exponential form.

                    Core Connections Algebra 2

6-90.   The work you did in problem 6-89 is a **counterexample**, which shows that in general, the statement $\log_b x = \log(b^x)$ is *false*. For each of the following log statements, use the strategies from problem 6-89 to determine whether they are true or false, and justify your answer. Be ready to present your conclusions and justifications.

a. $\log_5(25) \overset{?}{=} \log_{25}(5)$ b. $\log(x^2) \overset{?}{=} (\log x)^2$

c. $\log(7^x) \overset{?}{=} x \log(7)$ d. $\log(2x) \overset{?}{=} \log_2 x$

6-91.   In the previous problem only *one* of the statements was true.

a.   Use different numbers to make up four more statements that follow the same pattern as the one true statement, and test each one to see whether it appears to be true.

b.   Use your results to complete the following statement, which is known as the **Power Property of Logarithms**: $\log(b^x) = $ _____ .

6-92.   Do you remember solving problems like $1.04^x = 2$ in your homework? What method(s) did you and your teammates use to find x? In tonight's homework there are several more of these problems. (You probably wish there were a more efficient way!)

6-93.   THERE MUST BE AN EASIER WAY

It would certainly be helpful to have an easier method than guess and check to solve equations like $1.04^x = 2$. Complete parts (a) through (c) below to discover an easier way.

a.   What makes the equation $1.04^x = 2$ so hard to solve?

b.   Surprise! In the first part of this lesson, you already found a method for getting rid of inconvenient exponents! Talk with your team about how your results from problems 6-90 and 6-91 can help you rewrite the equation $1.04^x = 2$. Be prepared to share your ideas with the class.

c.   Solve $1.04^x = 2$ using this new method. Be sure to check your answer.

6-94.   Solve the following equations. After checking your answer, round them to three decimal places.

a. $5 = 2.25^x$ b. $3.5^x = 10$

c. $2(8^x) = 128$ d. $2x^8 = 128$

6-95.   Complete the table at right and find its equation.

x	y
	1
	3
2	9
	27
4	
	243
6	
7	
8	

6-96.   Margee thinks she can use logs to solve $56 = x^8$, since logs seem to make exponents disappear. Unfortunately, Margee is wrong. Explain the difference between equations like $2 = 1.04^x$, in which you can use logs, and $56 = x^8$, in which it does not make sense to use logs.

6-97.   What values must x have so that log (x) is greater than 2? Justify your answer.

6-98.   At right is a graph of $y = \log_b x$. Describe the possible values for b.

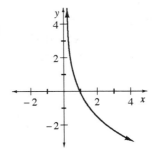

6-99.   Consider the questions below.

   a.   What can you multiply 8 by to get 1?

   b.   What can you multiply x by to get 1?

   c.   Using the rules of exponents, find a way to solve $m^8 = 40$. Remember that logarithms will not be useful here, but the exponent key on your calculator *will* be. (Obtain the answer as a decimal approximation using your calculator. Check your result by raising it to the 8th power.)

   d.   Now solve $n^6 = 300$.

   e.   Describe a method for solving $x^a = b$ for x with a calculator.

6-100.   Adam keeps getting negative exponents and fractional exponents confused. Help him by explaining the difference between $2^{1/2}$ and 2^{-1}.

6-101.   Solve each inequality and graph its solution on a number line.

    a. $|x| < 3$ b. $|2x+1| < 3$ c. $|2x+1| \geq 3$

6-102.   Consider the graph at right.

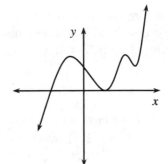

    a.   Is the graph a function? Explain.

    b.   Make a sketch of the inverse of this graph. Is the inverse a function? Justify your answer.

    c.   Must the inverse of a function be a function? Explain.

    d.   Describe what is characteristic about functions that do have inverse functions.

    e.   Could the inverse of a non-function be a function? Explain or give an example.

6-103.   Solve each system of equations below.

    a. $-4x = z - 2y + 12$ b. $3x + y - 2z = 6$
        $y + z = 12 - x$ $x + 2y + z = 7$
        $8x - 3y + 4z = 1$ $6x + 2y - 4z = 12$

    c.   What does the solution in part (b) tell you about the graphs?

6.2.2 How can I rewrite it?

Investigating the Properties of Logarithms

You already know the basic rules for working with exponents. Since logs are the inverses of exponential functions, they also have properties that are similar to the ones you already know. In this lesson, you will explore these properties.

6-104.   Marta now knows that if she wants to find $\log_2(30)$, she cannot just type $\log(2^{30})$ into her calculator, since her calculator's log key cannot directly calculate logs with base 2. But she still wants to be able to find what $\log_2(30)$ equals.

     a.   First, use your knowledge of logs and exponents to estimate $\log_2(30)$.

     b.   Now use what you learned in Lesson 6.2.1 to get a better estimate. Since you want to determine what $\log_2(30)$ equals, you can write $\log_2(30) = x$. When working with a log equation, it is often easier to first convert it to exponential form. Rewrite this equation in exponential form.

     c.   Use the methods you developed in class to solve this equation. Refer back to your work on problem 6-93 if you need help.

6-105.   Congratulations! You are smarter than your calculator. You have just evaluated a log with base 2, even though your calculator does not do that. Now you will practice some more.

     a.   First estimate an answer, then apply the method you have just developed to evaluate $\log_5(200)$.

     b.   Apply the process you used in part (a) to evaluate the expression $\log_a b = x$.

6-106.   Since logs and exponentials are inverses, the properties of exponents (which you already know) also apply to logs. The problems below will help you discover these new log properties.

  a.   Complete the two exponent rules below. In part (b), you will find the equivalent properties for logs.

$$x^a x^b = \underline{\hspace{2cm}} \quad \text{and} \quad \frac{x^b}{x^a} = \underline{\hspace{2cm}}$$

  b.   To help you find the equivalent log properties, use your calculator to solve for x in each problem below. Note that x is a whole number in parts (*i*) through (*v*). Look for patterns that would make your job easier and allow you to generalize in part (*vi*).

   i. $\log(5) + \log(6) = \log(x)$ *ii.* $\log(5) + \log(2) = \log(x)$

   iii. $\log(5) + \log(5) = \log(x)$ *iv.* $\log(10) + \log(100) = \log(x)$

   v. $\log(9) + \log(11) = \log(x)$ *vi.* $\log(a) + \log(b) = \log(\underline{\hspace{1cm}})$

  c.   What if the log expressions are being subtracted instead of added? Solve for x in each problem below. Note that x will not always be a whole number. Again, look for patterns that will allow you to generalize in part (*vi*).

   i. $\log(20) - \log(5) = \log(x)$ *ii.* $\log(30) - \log(3) = \log(x)$

   iii. $\log(5) - \log(2) = \log(x)$ *iv.* $\log(17) - \log(9) = \log(x)$

   v. $\log(375) - \log(17) = \log(x)$ *vi.* $\log(b) - \log(a) = \log(\underline{\hspace{1cm}})$

6-107.   LEARNING LOG

The two properties you found in problem 6-106 work for logs in *any* base, not just base 10. (You will officially prove this later.) You now know three different log properties and you have developed a process for solving log problems that are not in base 10. Write and explain each of these log properties in your Learning Log. Be sure to include examples, with at least one problem where you need to change to base 10. Title this entry "Logarithm Properties" and label it with today's date.

6-108.   LOG PROPERTY PUZZLES

Obtain the Lesson 6.2.2A Resource Page from your teacher or copy the table below. Use the log properties to fill in the missing parts. Be sure to remember that in every row, each expression is equivalent to every other expression.

	Product Property		Quotient Property	
$\log_3 60 =$	$\log_3 6 + \_\_ =$	$\log_3 3 + \_\_ =$	$\log_3 120 - \_\_$	$= \log_3 240 - \_\_$
$\log_7 36 =$	$=$	$=$		$=$
	$= \log_6 9 + \log_6 2 \ =$	$=$		$=$
$=$	$=$		$= \log_{25} 75 - \log_{25} 1.5 \ =$	
$=$	$=$		$= \log 160 - \log 4 \ =$	

6-109.

Use the properties of logs to write each of the following expressions as a single logarithm, if possible.

a. $\log_{1/2}(4) + \log_{1/2}(2) - \log_{1/2}(5)$

b. $\log_2(M) + \log_3(N)$

c. $\log(k) + x\log(m)$

d. $\frac{1}{2}\log_5 x + 2\log_5(x+1)$

e. $\log(4) - \log(3) + \log(\pi) + 3\log(r)$

f. $\log(6) + 23$

6-110.

What values must x have so that $\log(x)$ has a negative value? Justify your answer.

6-111.

The fact that for any base m (when $m > 0$), $\log_m a + \log_m b = \log_m ab$ is called the **Product Property of Logarithms**. To prove that this property is true, follow the directions below.

a.   Since logarithms are the inverses of exponential functions, each of their properties can be derived from a similar property of exponents. Here, you are trying to prove that "logs turn products into sums." First, recall similar properties of exponents. If $a = m^x$ and $b = m^y$, write $a \cdot b$ as a power of m.

b.   Rewrite $a = m^x$, $b = m^y$, and your answer to part (a) in logarithmic form.

c.   In the third equation you wrote for part (b), substitute for x and y to obtain a log equation of base m that involves only the variables a and b.

d.   The property $\log_m a - \log_m b = \log_m \frac{a}{b}$ is called the **Quotient Property of Logarithms**. Use $a = m^x$ and $b = m^y$ to express $\frac{a}{b}$ as a power of m. Then use a similar process to rewrite each into log form and prove the Quotient Property of Logs.

6-112.   The **Power Property of Logarithms**, which you learned in Lesson 6.2.1, is a little trickier to prove. A proof is given below. As you copy each step onto your paper, work with your team to make sense of what was done. Give a reason for each step.

To prove that $\log_m a^n = n \log_m a$,

Let $\log_m a^n = p$ and $n \log_m a = q$

Convert to $m^p = a^n$ First rewrite as $\log_m a = \frac{q}{n}$ and then convert to $m^{q/n} = a$.

Using the two resulting equations, substitute for a and then simplify

$$m^p = (m^{q/n})^n$$

$$m^p = m^q$$

Therefore, $p = q$.

Remember that $p = \log_m a^n$ and $q = n \log_m a$, so $\log_m a^n = n \log_m a$, which was the goal of the proof.

METHODS AND MEANINGS

Logarithm Properties

The following definitions and properties hold true for all positive $m \neq 1$.

Definition of logs: $\log_m(a) = n$ means $m^n = a$

Product Property: $\log_m(a \cdot b) = \log_m(a) + \log_m(b)$

Quotient Property: $\log_m(\frac{a}{b}) = \log_m(a) - \log_m(b)$

Power Property: $\log_m(a^n) = n \cdot \log_m(a)$

Inverse relationship: $\log_m(m)^n = n$ and $m^{\log_m(n)} = n$

6-113. Solve each of the following equations to the nearest 0.001.

a. $(5.825)^{(x-3)} = 120$

b. $18(1.2)^{(2x-1)} = 900$

6-114. Simplify each expression below. If you are stuck, the ideas in problem 6-74 should be helpful.

a. $\dfrac{x}{1-\frac{1}{x}}$

b. $\dfrac{\frac{1}{a}+\frac{1}{b}}{\frac{1}{b}-a}$

6-115. Use the definition of a logarithm to change $\log_2 7$ into a logarithmic expression of base 5.

6-116. Sketch the graph of $y = \log_3(x+4)$ and describe the transformation from its parent graph.

6-117. Due to the worsened economy, merchants in downtown Hollywood cannot afford to replace their outdoor light bulbs when the bulbs burn out. On average, about thirteen percent of the light bulbs burn out every month. Assuming there are now about one million outside store lights in Hollywood, how long will it take until there are only 100,000 bulbs lit? Until there is only one bulb lit?

6-118. Raymond, Hannah, Aidan, and Sarah were working together to change $y = 3x^2 - 15x - 5$ into graphing form. They started by rewriting it as $y = 3(x^2 - 5x) - 5$, when Raymond said, "Will this one work? Look, the perfect square would have to be $(x-2.5)^2$."

After thinking about it for a while, Sarah said, "That's OK. Negative 2.5 squared is 6.25, but because of the 3 we factored out, we are really adding 3(6.25)."

"Yes," Aidan added, "So we have to subtract 18.75 to get an equivalent equation."

Hannah summarized with the work shown at right.

$y = 3x^2 - 15x - 5$
$y = 3(x^2 - 5x) - 5$
$y = 3(x-2.5)^2 - 5 - 18.75$
$y = 3(x-2.5)^2 - 23.75$

What do you think? Did they rewrite the equation correctly? If so, find the vertex and the line of symmetry of the parabola. If not, explain their mistakes and show them how to do it correctly.

6-119.   Use the ideas developed in problem 6-118 to change each of the following quadratic equations into graphing form. Identify the vertex and the line of symmetry for each one.

a. $f(x) = 4x^2 - 12x + 6$

b. $g(x) = 2x^2 + 14x + 4$

6-120.   Consider the function $y = 3(x+2)^2 - 7$ as you complete parts (a) through (c) below.

a.   How could you restrict the domain to show "half" of the graph?

b.   Find the equation for the inverse function for your "half" graph.

c.   What are the domain and range for the inverse function?

6-121.   Add or subtract and simplify each of the following expressions. Justify that each step of your process makes sense.

a. $\frac{3}{(x-4)(x+1)} + \frac{6}{x+1}$

b. $\frac{x+2}{x^2-9} - \frac{1}{x+3}$

6-122.   Eniki has a sequence of numbers given by the formula $t(n) = 4(5^n)$.

a.   What are the first three terms of Eniki's sequence?

b.   Chelita thinks the number 312,500 is a term in Eniki's sequence. Is she correct? Justify your answer by either giving the term number or explaining why it is not in the sequence.

c.   Elisa thinks the number 94,500 is a term in Eniki's sequence. Is she correct? Explain.

6.2.3 How can I find an exponential function?

Writing Equations of Exponential Functions

You have worked with exponential equations throughout this chapter. Today you will look at how you can find the equation for an exponential function using data.

6-123.   DUE DATE

Brad's mother has just learned that she is pregnant! Brad is very excited that he will soon become a big brother. However, he wants to know when his new sibling will arrive and decides to do some research. On the Internet, he finds the following article:

Hormone Levels for Pregnant Women

When a woman becomes pregnant, the hormone HCG (human chorionic gonadotropin) is produced to enable the baby to develop.

During the first few weeks of pregnancy, the level of HCG hormone grows exponentially, starting with the day the embryo is implanted in the womb. However, the rate of growth varies with each pregnancy. Therefore, doctors cannot use just a single test to determine how long a woman has been pregnant. They must test the levels over time. Commonly, the HCG levels are measured two days apart to look for this rate of growth.

Brad's mother says she was tested for HCG during her last two doctor visits. On March 21, her HCG level was 200 mIU/ml (milli-international units per milliliter). Two days later, her HCG level was 392 mIU/ml.

a.   Assuming that the model for HCG levels is of the form $y = ab^x$, find an equation that models the growth of HCG for Brad's mother's pregnancy.

b.   Assuming that Brad's mother's level of HCG on the day of implantation was 5 mIU/ml, on what day did the baby most likely become implanted? How many days after implantation was his mother's first doctor visit?

c.   Brad learned that a baby is born approximately 37 weeks after implantation. When can Brad expect his new sibling to be born?

Core Connections Algebra 2

6-124.   SOLVING STRATEGIES

In problem 6-123, you and your team developed a strategy to find the equation of an exponential equation of the form $y = ab^x$ when given two points on the curve.

a.   What different strategies were generated by the other teams in your class? If no one shares your solving method with the class, be sure to share yours. Take notes on the different strategies that are presented.

b.   Did any team use a system of exponential equations to solve for a and b? If not, examine this strategy as you answer the questions below.

i.   The doctor visits provide two data points that can help you find an exponential model: $(21, 200)$ and $(23, 392)$. Use each of these points to substitute for x and y into $y = ab^x$. You should end up with two equations in terms of a and b.

ii.   Consider the strategies you already have for solving systems of equations. Are any of those strategies useful for this problem? Discuss a way to solve your system from part (i) for a and b with your team. Be ready to share your method with the class.

6-125.   The context in problem 6-123 required you to assume that the exponential model had an asymptote at $y = 0$ to find the equation of the model. But what if the asymptote is not at the x-axis? Consider this situation below.

a.   Assume the graph of an exponential function passes through the points $(3, 12.5)$ and $(4, 11.25)$. Is the exponential function increasing or decreasing? Justify your answer.

b.   If the horizontal asymptote for this function is the line $y = 10$, make a sketch of its graph showing the horizontal asymptote.

c.   If this function has the equation $y = ab^x + c$, what would be the value of c? Use what you know about this function to find its equation. Verify that as x increases, the values of y get closer to $y = 10$.

d.   Find the y-intercept of the function. What is the connection between the y-intercept and the asymptote?

6-126.   Janice would like to have $40,000 to help pay for college in 8 years. Currently, she has $1000. What interest rate, when compounded yearly, would help her reach her goal?

    a.   What type of function would best model this situation? Explain how you know and write the general form of this function.

    b.   If y represents the amount of money and x represents the number of years after today, find an equation that models Janice's financial situation. What interest rate does she need to earn?

    c.   Janice's friend Sarah starts with $7800 and wants to have $18,400 twenty years from now. What interest rate does she need (compounded yearly)?

    d.   Is Janice's goal or Sarah's goal more realistic? Justify your response.

6-127.   Ryan has the chickenpox! He was told that the number of pockmarks on his body would grow exponentially until his body overcomes the illness. He found that he had 60 pockmarks on November 1, and by November 3 the number had grown to 135. To find out when the first pockmark appeared, he will need to find the exponential function that will model the number of pockmarks based on the day.

    a.   Ryan decides to find the exponential function that passes through the points $(3, 135)$ and $(1, 60)$. Use these points to write the equation of his function of the form $f(x) = ab^x$.

    b.   According to your model, what day did Ryan get his first chickenpox pockmark?

6-128.   Give an example of an equation that requires the use of logarithms to solve it.

6-129.   Write three different, but equivalent, expressions for each of the following logs. For example: $\log(7^{3/2})$ can be written as $\frac{3}{2}\log(7)$, $\frac{1}{2}\log(7^3)$, $3\log(\sqrt{7})$, etc.

    a. $\log(8^{2/3})$ b. $-2\log(5)$ c. $\log(na)^{bo}$

6-130.   Kendra just made a cup of hot chocolate that was too hot for her to drink. She set it aside so it could cool off. While she was waiting, her friend Lara called and Kendra forgot about her hot chocolate. Sketch a graph that shows the temperature of the hot chocolate since Kendra first set it aside. How cold will the hot chocolate get?

6-131. Find the equation of the parabola that passes through the points $(-2, 24)$, $(3, -1)$, and $(-1, 15)$.

6-132. Use $f(x) = 3 + \sqrt{2x-1}$ to complete parts (a) through (e) below.

a. What are the domain and range of $f(x)$?

b. What is the inverse of $f(x)$? Call it $g(x)$.

c. What are the domain and range of $g(x)$?

d. Find an expression for $f(g(x))$.

e. Find an expression for $g(f(x))$. What do you notice? Why does this happen?

6-133. Solve each of the following equations for x.

a. $x^3 = 243$

b. $3^x = 243$

6-134. Write the equation of each circle graphed below.

a.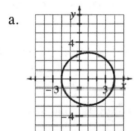

b.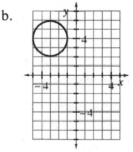

6-135. Add or subtract each expression below. Be sure to simplify.

a. $\dfrac{x^2}{x-5} - \dfrac{25}{x-5}$

b. $\dfrac{a^2}{a+5} + \dfrac{10a+25}{a+5}$

c. $\dfrac{x^2}{x-y} - \dfrac{2xy-y^2}{x-y}$

d. $\dfrac{x}{x+1} + \dfrac{1}{x-1}$

6-136. Find the inverse of each of the functions below. Write your answers in function notation.

a. $p(x) = 3(x^3 + 6)$

b. $k(x) = 3x^3 + 6$

c. $h(x) = \dfrac{x+1}{x-1}$

d. $j(x) = \dfrac{2}{3-x}$

6.2.4 Who killed Dr. Dedman?

An Application of Logarithms

Today you will put together everything that you have learned about logs and exponents to solve a murder mystery!

6-137.   THE CASE OF THE COOLING CORPSE

The coroner's office is kept at a cool 17°C. Agent 008 kept pacing back and forth trying to keep warm as he waited for any new information about his latest case. For more than three hours now, Dr. Dedman had been performing an autopsy on the Sideroad Slasher's latest victim, and Agent 008 could see that the temperature of the room and the deafening silence were beginning to irritate even Dr. Dedman. The Slasher had been creating more work than Dr. Dedman cared to investigate.

"Dr. Dedman, don't you need to take a break?" Agent 008 queried. *"You've been examining this body for hours! Even if there were any clues, you probably wouldn't see them at this point."*

"I don't know," Dr. Dedman replied, *"I just have this feeling something is not quite right. Somehow the Slasher slipped up with this one and left a clue. We just have to find it."*

"Well, I have to check in with headquarters," 008 stated. *"Do you mind if I step out for a couple of hours?"*

"No, that's fine," Dr. Dedman responded. *"Maybe I'll have something by the time you return."*

"Sure," 008 thought to himself. *"Someone always wants to be the hero and solve everything himself. The doctor just does not realize how big this case really is. The Slasher has left a trail of dead bodies through five states!"* Agent 008 left, closing the door quietly. As he walked down the hall, he could hear the doctor's voice describing the victim's gruesome appearance into the tape recorder fade away.

The hallway from the coroner's office to the elevator was long and dark. This was the only way to Dr. Dedman's office. Didn't this frighten most people? Well, it didn't seem to bother old Ajax Boraxo who was busy mopping the floor, thought 008.

Problem continues on next page →

6-137.   *Problem continued from previous page.*

He stopped briefly to use the restroom and bumped into one of the deputy coroners, who asked, *"Dedman still at it?"*

"Sure is, Dr. Quincy. He's totally obsessed. He's certain there is a clue." As usual, when leaving the courthouse, 008 had to sign out.

"How's it going down there, Agent 008?" Sergeant Foust asked. Foust spent most of his shifts monitoring the front door, forcing all visitors to sign in while he recorded the time next to the signature. Agent 008 wondered if Foust longed for a more exciting aspect of law enforcement. He thought if he were doing Foust's job he would get a little stir-crazy sitting behind a desk most of the day. Why would someone become a cop to do this?

"Dr. Dedman is convinced he will find something soon. We'll see!" Agent 008 responded. He noticed the time: ten minutes before 2:00. Would he make it to headquarters before the chief left?

"Well, good luck!" Foust shouted as 008 headed out the door.

Some time later, Agent 008 sighed deeply as he returned to the coroner's office. Foust gave his usual greeting: *"Would the secret guest please sign in?"* he would say, handing a pen to 008 as he walked through the door. *"Sign in again,"* he thought to himself. *"Annoying!"* 5:05 PM. Agent 008 had not planned to be gone so long, but he had been caught up in what the staff at headquarters had discovered about that calculator he had found. For a moment he saw a positive point to having anyone who came in or out of the courthouse sign in: He knew by quickly scanning the list that Dr. Dedman had not left. In fact, the old guy must still be working on the case.

As he approached the coroner's office, he had a strange feeling that something was wrong. He could not hear or see Dr. Dedman. When he opened the door, the sight inside stopped him in his tracks. Evidently, Dr. Dedman was now the *newest* victim of the Slasher. But wait! The other body, the one the doctor had been working on, was gone! Immediately, the security desk with its annoying sign-in sheet came to mind. Yes, there were lots of names on that list, but if he could determine the time of Dr. Dedman's death, he might be able to scan the roster to find the murderer! Quickly, he grabbed the thermometer to measure the Doctor's body temperature. He turned around and hit the security buzzer. The bells were deafening. He knew the building would be sealed off instantly and security would be there within seconds.

"Oh no!" Foust cried as he rushed in, *"How could this happen? I spoke to the Doctor less than an hour ago!"*

As the security officers crowded into the room, Agent 008 explained what he knew, which was almost nothing. He had stopped long enough to check the doctor's body temperature: 27°C. That was 10°C below normal. Then he remembered: the tape recorder! Dr. Dedman had been taping his observations; that was standard procedure. They began looking everywhere.

Problem continues on next page →

6-137.   *Problem continued from previous page.*

The Slasher must have realized that the doctor had been taping and taken the tape recorder as well. Exactly an hour had passed during the search, and Agent 008 noticed that the thermometer still remained in Dr. Dedman's side. The thermometer clearly read 24°C. Agent 008 knew he could now determine the time of death.

Coroner's Office – Please Sign In		
Name	**Time In**	**Time Out**
Lt. Borman	12:08	2:47
Alice Bingham	12:22	1:38
Chuck Miranda	12:30	2:45
Harold Ford	12:51	1:25
Ajax Boraxo	1:00	2:30
D.C. Quincy	1:10	2:45
Agent 008	1:30	1:50
Ronda Ripley	1:43	2:10
Jeff Dangerfield	2:08	2:48
Stacy Simmons	2:14	2:51
Brock Ortiz	2:20	2:43
Pierce Bronson	3:48	4:18
Max Sharp	3:52	5:00
Maren Ezaki	3:57	4:45
Caroline Cress	4:08	4:23
Milly Osborne	4:17	4:39
D.C. Quincy	4:26	4:50
Vinney Gumbatz	4:35	
Cory Delphene	4:48	4:57
Max Crutchfield	5:04	
Agent 008	5:05	
Security	5:12	

a.   Make a sketch showing the relationship between body temperature and time. What type of function is it? Justify your answer.

b.   Is there an asymptote for this relationship? If so, what does it represent? If not, explain why not.

c.   Use your data and the general equation $y = km^x + b$ to find the equation that represents the temperature of the body at any certain time.

d.   At approximately what time did Dr. Dedman die?

e.   Who is the murderer?

6-138.   A rule-of-thumb used by car dealers is that the trade-in value of a car decreases by 20% of its value each year.

   a.   Explain how the phrase "decreases by 20% of its value each year" tells you that the trade-in value varies exponentially with time (i.e., can be represented by an exponential function).

   b.   Suppose the initial value of your car is $23,500. Write an equation expressing the trade-in value of your car as a function of the number of years from now.

   c.   How much will your car be worth in four years?

   d.   In how many years will the trade-in value of your car be $6000?

   e.   If your car is really 2.7 years old now, what was its trade-in value when it was new?

6-139.   Solve for x without using a calculator.

   a. $x = \log_{25}(5)$

   b. $\log_x(1) = 0$

   c. $23 = \log_{10}(x)$

6-140.   Using your calculator, solve the equations below. Round answers to the nearest 0.001.

   a. $x^6 = 125$ b. $x^{3.8} = 240$

   c. $x^{-4} = 100$ d. $(x+2)^3 = 65$

   e. $4(x-2)^{12.5} = 2486$

6-141.   If $f(x) = x^4$ and $g(x) = 3(x + 2)$, find the value of each expression below.

     a. $f(2)$ b. $g(2)$ c. $f(g(2))$ d. $g(f(2))$

     e.   Are $f(x)$ and $g(x)$ inverses of each other? Justify your answer.

6-142.   Kirsta was working with the function machine shown at right, but when she turned her back, her little brother Caleb dropped in a number. She didn't see what he dropped, but she did see what fell out: 9. What operations must she perform on 9 to undo what her machine did? Use this to find out what Caleb dropped in.

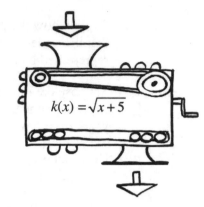

$k(x) = \sqrt{x} + 5$

6-143.   Write an equation for a machine that will undo Kirsta's machine. Call it $c(x)$.

6-144.   What is the equation of the line of symmetry for the graph of $y = (x - 17)^2$? Justify your answer.

6-145.   This problem is a checkpoint for adding and subtracting rational expressions. It will be referred to as Checkpoint 6B.

Add or subtract each pair of rational expressions. Simplify the result.

     a. $\dfrac{4}{x^2+5x+6} + \dfrac{2x}{x+2}$ b. $\dfrac{3x^2+x}{(2x+1)^2} - \dfrac{3}{2x+1}$

Check your answers by referring to the Checkpoint 6B materials located at the back of your book.

If you needed help solving these problems correctly, then you need more practice. Review the Checkpoint 6B materials and try the practice problems. Also, consider getting help outside of class time. From this point on, you will be expected to do problems like these quickly and easily.

6-146.   Find $m\angle C$ in each triangle below.

a.

b.
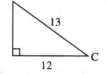

6-147.   Write a system of inequalities that could be represented by the graph at right.

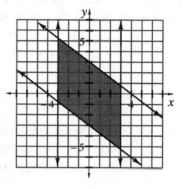

Chapter 6 Closure What have I learned?

Reflection and Synthesis

The activities below offer you a chance to
reflect about what you have learned during this
chapter. As you work, look for concepts that
you feel very comfortable with, ideas that you
would like to learn more about, and topics you
need more help with. Look for connections
between ideas as well as connections with
material you learned previously.

①   TEAM BRAINSTORM

What have you studied in this chapter? What ideas were important in what you
learned? With your team, brainstorm a list. Be as detailed as you can. To help
get you started, a list of Learning Log entries and Math Notes boxes are below.

What topics, ideas, and words that you learned *before* this chapter are connected
to the new ideas in this chapter? Again, be as detailed as you can.

Next consider the Standards for Mathematical Practice that follow
"③ PORTFOLIO". What Mathematical Practices did you use in this chapter?
When did you use them? Give specific examples.

How long can you make your list? Challenge yourselves. Be prepared to share
your team's ideas with the class.

Learning Log Entries

- Lesson 6.1.1 – Plotting Points in *xyz*-Space
- Lesson 6.1.4 – Systems of Three Equations with Three Variables
- Lesson 6.1.5 – Finding the Equation of a Parabola Given Three
Points
- Lesson 6.2.2 – Logarithm Properties

Math Notes

- Lesson 6.1.2 – Locating Points in Three Dimensions
- Lesson 6.1.4 – Graphing Planes in Three Dimensions
- Lesson 6.2.2 – Logarithm Properties

②   MAKING CONNECTIONS

Below is a list of the vocabulary used in this chapter. Make sure that you are familiar with all of these words and know what they mean. Refer to the glossary or index for any words that you do not yet understand.

3-D coordinate system	asymptote
isometric dot paper	logarithm
ordered triple	plane
Power Property of Logarithms	Product Property of Logarithms
Quotient Property of Logarithms	solution

Make a concept map showing all of the connections you can find among the key words and ideas listed above. To show a connection between two words, draw a line between them and explain the connection. A word can be connected to any other word as long as you can justify the connection.

While you are making your map, your team may think of related words or ideas that are not listed here. Be sure to include these ideas on your concept map.

This section gives you an opportunity to show growth in your understanding of key mathematical ideas over time as you complete this course.

Part 1: You may have done this problem before. You have grown mathematically since then. Explain everything that you know about $y = x^2 - 4$ and $y = \sqrt{x+4}$. Be sure to include everything you have learned since the last time you did this problem.

Part 2: Compare your responses to this "Growth Over Time" problem. Consider each of the following questions as you write an evaluation of your mathematical growth. If you only did the problem twice, then answer accordingly.

- What new concepts did you include the second time you did the problem? In what ways was your response better than your first attempt?

- How was your final version different from the first two? What new ideas did you include?

- Did you omit anything in the final version that you used in one of the earlier versions? Why did you omit it?

- Is there anything you want to add to your current version? If so, add it and keep this version for future reference.

- Rate your three attempts by making three bars like the ones below and shading each bar (left to right) to represent how much you knew on each attempt.

First Attempt:	
Second	
Final Attempt:	

Alternatively, your teacher may ask you to showcase your ability to use logarithms to solve a problem involving an exponential function. Copy your work from "The Case of the Cooling Corpse," problem 6-137, and enhance it if needed.

Next consider the Standards for Mathematical Practice that follow. What Mathematical Practices did you use in this chapter? When did you use them? Give specific examples.

Your teacher may give you the Chapter 6 Closure Resource Page: Multiple Representations of Logarithmic Functions Graphic Organizer page to work on.

BECOMING MATHEMATICALLY PROFICIENT
The Common Core State Standards For Mathematical Practice

This book focuses on helping you use some very specific Mathematical Practices. The Mathematical Practices describe ways in which mathematically proficient students engage with mathematics everyday.

Make sense of problems and persevere in solving them:

Making sense of problems and persevering in solving them means that you can solve problems that are full of different kinds of mathematics. These types of problems are not routine, simple, or typical. Instead, they combine lots of math ideas and everyday situations. You have to stick with challenging problems, try different strategies, use multiple representations, and use a different method to check your results.

Reason abstractly and quantitatively:

Throughout this course, everyday situations are used to introduce you to new math ideas. Seeing mathematical ideas within a context helps you make sense of the ideas. Once you learn about a math idea in a practical way, you can "**reason abstractly**" by thinking about the concept more generally, representing it with symbols, and manipulating the symbols. **Reasoning quantitatively** is using numbers and symbols to represent an everyday situation, taking into account the units involved, and considering the meaning of the quantities as you compute them.

Construct viable arguments and critique the reasoning of others:

To **construct a viable argument** is to present your solution steps in a logical sequence and to justify your steps with conclusions, relying on number sense, facts and definitions, and previously established results. You communicate clearly, consider the real-life context, and provide clarification when others ask. In this course, you regularly share information, opinions, and expertise with your study team. You **critique the reasoning of others** when you analyze the approach of others, build on each other's ideas, compare the effectiveness of two strategies, and decide what makes sense and under what conditions.

Model with mathematics:

When you **model with mathematics**, you take a complex situation and use mathematics to represent it, often by making assumptions and approximations to simplify the situation. Modeling allows you to analyze and describe the situation and to make predictions. For example, you model when you use multiple representations, including equations, tables, graphs, or diagrams to describe a situation. In situations involving the variability of data, you model when you describe the data with equations. Although a model may not be perfect, it can still be very useful for describing data and making predictions. When you interpret the results, you may need to go back and improve your model by revising your assumptions and approximations.

Use appropriate tools strategically:

To **use appropriate tools strategically** means that you analyze the task and decide which tools may help you model the situation or find a solution. Some of the tools available to you include diagrams, graph paper, calculators, computer software, databases, and websites. You understand the limitations of various tools. A result can be check or estimated by strategically choosing a different tool.

Attend to precision:

To **attend to precision** means that when solving problems, you need to pay close attention to the details. For example, you need to be aware of the units, or how many digits your answer requires, or how to choose a scale and label your graph. You may need to convert the units to be consistent. At times, you need to go back and check whether a numerical solution makes sense in the context of the problem.

You need to **attend to precision** when you communicate your ideas to others. Using the appropriate vocabulary and mathematical language can help make your ideas and reasoning more understandable to others.

Look for and make use of structure:

To **looking for and making use of structure** is a guiding principal of this course. When you are involved in analyzing the structure and in the actual development of mathematical concepts, you gain a deeper, more conceptual understanding than when you are simply told what the structure is and how to do problems. You often use this practice to bring closure to an investigation.

There are many concepts that you learn by looking at the underlying structure of a mathematical idea and thinking about how it connects to other ideas you have already learned. For example, you understand the underlying structure of an equation such as $y = a(x-h)^2 + b$ which allows you to graph it without a table.

Look for and express regularity in repeated reasoning:

To **look for and express regularity in repeated reasoning** means that when you are investigating a new mathematical concept, you notice if calculations are repeated in a pattern. Then you look for a way to generalize the method for use in other situations, or you look for shortcuts. For example, the pattern of growth you notice in a geometric sequence results in being able to write a general exponential equation that highlights the growth and starting point.

Core Connections Algebra 2

WHAT HAVE I LEARNED?

Most of the problems in this section represent typical problems found in this chapter. They serve as a gauge for you. You can use them to determine which types of problems you can do well and which types of problems require further study and practice. Even if your teacher does not assign this section, it is a good idea to try these problems and find out for yourself what you know and what you still need to work on.

Solve each problem as completely as you can. The table at the end of the closure section has answers to these problems. It also tells you where you can find additional help and practice with problems like these.

CL 6-148.   Graph in three dimensions.

   a. $(2, 3, 1)$ b. $(-2, 3, 0)$ c. $2x + y - z = 6$

CL 6-149.   Determine the point of intersection of the three planes.

   a. $x + y + z = 3$ b. $x + y + 4z = 5$
         $2x - y + 2z = 6$ $-2x\ \ \ +2z = 3$
         $3x + 2y - z = 13$ $3x + y - 2z = 0$

CL 6-150.   The parabola $y = ax^2 + bx + c$ passes through the points $(2, 3), (-1, 6)$, and $(0, 3)$. Determine:

   a.   The equation of the parabola.

   b.   The vertex of the parabola.

   c.   The x-intercepts of the parabola.

CL 6-151.   Solve each equation to the nearest thousandth (0.001).

   a. $2^x = 17$ b. $5x^3 = 75$

   c. $5(3^{x+1}) = 85$ d. $\log_3(x + 1) = -2$

CL 6-152.   A gallon of propane costs \$3.59. Inflation has steadily increased 4% per year.

   a.   What did a gallon of propane cost ten years ago?

   b.   If this trend continues, how much longer will it be until it costs \$10?

CL 6-153.   Find the inverse of this equation: $y = 2 + \sqrt{2x - 4}$.

CL 6-154.   Use your Parent Graph Toolkit or make a table to graph $y = \log_2(x)$.

CL 6-155.   Use your answer to the previous problem to graph $y = 1 + \log_2(x - 3)$. State the equation of the new asymptote and the new x-intercept.

CL 6-156.   Solve each of the following equations. Be sure to check your answers.

   a. $3|2x - 5| - 8 = -5$ b. $\sqrt{3x^2 + 11x} = 2$

CL 6-157.   Graph each of the following systems of inequalities.

   a. $y \geq 3(x - 2)^2 - 4$ b. $y > (x - 1)^2 - 5$
        $y > -2|x - 1| + 3$ $y > 3x - 5$
                                                    $y \leq \frac{1}{2}(x - 1)^2 + 1$

CL 6-158.   Consider the function $f(x) = \sqrt{x + 3}$.

   a.   What are the domain and range of $f(x)$?

   b.   If $g(x) = x - 10$, what is $f(g(x))$?

   c.   What are the domain and range of $f(g(x))$?

   d.   Is $f(g(x)) = g(f(x))$? Justify why or why not.

CL 6-159.   Check your answers using the table at the end of this section. Which problems do you feel confident about? Which problems were hard? Have you worked on problems like these in previous math classes? Sort the problems into three groups: the ones you are confident you can do, the ones you need more practice with, and the ones you need further help to understand.

Answers and Support for Closure Activity #4
What Have I Learned?

Note: MN = Math Note, LL = Learning Log

Problem	Solutions	Need Help?	More Practice
CL 6-148.	a.	Lessons 6.1.1 and 6.1.2	Problems 6-6 and 6-19
		MN: 6.1.2 and 6.1.4	
	b.	LL: 6.1.1	
	c.		
CL 6-149.	a. $(4, 0, -1)$ b. $(-1, 4, 0.5)$	Lesson 6.1.4 LL: 6.1.4	Problems 6-48, 6-51, 6-71, 6-80, and 6-103
CL 6-150.	a. $y = x^2 - 2x + 3$ b. $(1, 2)$ c. No x-intercepts	Lesson 6.1.5 LL: 6.1.5	Problems 6-64, 6-67, 6-68, 6-69, 6-72, 6-81, and 6-131
CL 6-151.	a. 4.087 b. 2.466 c. 1.579 d. −0.889	Lessons 6.2.1 and 6.2.2	Problems 6-11, 6-94, 6-113, 6-133, and 6-140
CL 6-152.	a. $2.43 b. 26.1 years	Lessons A.3.2 and B.2.3	Problems 6-15, 6-52, 6-117, and 6-138
CL 6-153.	$y = \frac{(x-2)^2}{2} + 2$	Lessons 5.1.1 and 5.1.3 LL: 5.1.1	Problems 6-102, 6-120, 6-132, and 6-136

Problem	Solutions	Need Help?	More Practice
CL 6-154.		Lessons 5.2.2 and 5.2.3 LL: 5.2.3	Problems 5-68, 5-69, and 5-94
CL 6-155.	Asymptote $x = 3$ Intercept $(3.5, 0)$	Lesson 5.2.4	Problems 5-94 and 5-118
CL 6-156.	a. $x = 2, 3$ b. $x = \frac{1}{3}, -4$	Lessons 4.1.2 and 4.1.3 LL: 4.1.1 and 4.1.4	Problems 4-22, 4-23, 6-40, 6-53, and 6-76
CL 6-157.	a. b.	Lesson 4.2.1 MN: 4.2.3 and 4.2.4 LL: 4.2.1	Problems 5-13, 5-67, 6-33, 6-58, and 6-147
CL 6-158.	a. domain: $x \geq -3$, range: $y \geq 0$ b. $f(g(x)) = \sqrt{x - 7}$ c. domain: $x \geq 7$, range: $y \geq 0$ d. no, $g(f(x)) = \sqrt{x + 3} - 10$ and $\sqrt{x + 3} - 10 \neq \sqrt{x - 7}$	Lesson 5.1.3 MN: 5.1.3 LL: 5.2.5	Problems 6-87, 6-132, and 6-141

Chapter 7   Trigonometric Functions

This chapter begins with an experiment that will generate a new curve called a cyclic function. You will then explore the relationship between right-triangle trigonometry and this new curve. You will be introduced to a new representation that is useful for the study of cyclic functions: a unit circle. You will also learn how to use radians instead of degrees to describe angles.

In the second section of this chapter, you will transform cyclic functions and find general equations for them. You will also learn about a new property that is characteristic of cyclic functions called a period. Then you will write equations for the curve that you generated in the experiment at the beginning of the chapter.

Guiding Question

Mathematically proficient students look for and make use of structure.

As you work through this chapter, ask yourself:

How can I use what I know about right-triangle trigonometry to describe functions determined by rotations about a circle?

Chapter Outline

Section 7.1 In this section, you will use your understanding of the trigonometric ratios in right triangles to build an understanding of three new functions. You will recognize and create multiple representations of the functions $y = \sin\theta$ and $y = \cos\theta$. You will discover relationships between a unit circle and a graph of a cyclic function. You will also learn to use a new unit, radians, to measure lengths of arcs and angles.

Section 7.2 In this section, you will apply your expertise with transforming parent graphs to graph functions of the family whose parents are $y = \sin x$ and $y = \cos x$. You will develop general equations for cyclic or trigonometric functions. You will also learn about a property particular to cyclic functions called a period.

Core Connections Algebra 2

7.1.1 What cyclic relationships can I model?

Introduction to Cyclic Models

In this chapter, you will learn about a new family of functions that are very useful for describing relationships that are **cyclic** (that is, they have repeating cycles), like the height of the ocean as the tides fluctuate between high and low or the distance of a swinging pendulum from its center point.

7-1.   EMERGENCY!

Nurse Nina rushes through the hospital with one hand on her clipboard and the other pulling a portable blood stand. The bags of blood swinging from the stand are needed in the emergency room *'stat'* for three patients in severe need. She is so intent on delivering the blood in time that she does not notice that one of the bags has a small hole in it and is dripping on the floor behind her. As she reaches the emergency room, she is horrified to see a small pool of blood beginning to form on the floor. Looking down the corridor from where she came, she sees the trail of blood that dripped and notices that it forms a very interesting pattern.

What shape do you think the trail of blood created?

Your Task: Use the materials and instructions provided by your teacher to re-create the pattern that the nurse saw on the hallway floor behind her. Make as many observations as you can about the shape you see and how that shape relates to what was happening to the bag of blood. Be sure to keep track of all the details. Be prepared to explain your observations to the class. Note: Complete directions for conducting this experiment are on the next page.

Directions for the Pendulum Experiment (Problem 7-1)

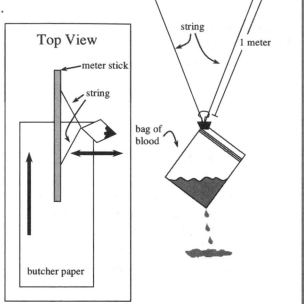

Find a space in the classroom where there is room to work. You may need to move your table or desks out of the way.

Set up your pendulum by attaching your bag of liquid to a meter stick using string, as shown at right.

Assign the following tasks:

- One student holds the meter stick from which the pendulum swings.

- One student holds the bag, releases it when ready, and then stops it when it reaches the end of the paper.

- Two students hold the butcher paper, one at each end, and slide it *at a constant rate* underneath the swinging pendulum. Be sure to slide the paper parallel to the meter stick and perpendicular to the swing of the pendulum, as shown in the diagram at right.

Tips for a successful experiment:

- The student holding the meter stick should hold the places where the string attaches. Otherwise, the string has a tendency to slide toward the center of the meter stick.

- Use as much of the string as you can so that your pendulum is as long as possible.

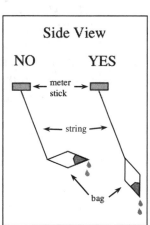

- When you are ready, have your teacher cut a *very* small hole in the corner of the bag. The student holding the bag should pinch this hole closed until the pendulum begins swinging.

- Be sure to slide the butcher paper under the pendulum *at a constant rate*.

- As you pull the bag up to start the pendulum swinging, hold it taut from the bottom corner so that the bag remains in line with the string (see diagram at right).

- Have an extra bag ready to place the dripping bag into when the experiment is complete.

Core Connections Algebra 2

7-2.   Now make predictions about the new curve that you created in problem 7-1.

   a.   With your team, design your own curve similar to the one already created. Decide exactly how you want it to look. How long do you want each cycle? How tall do you want it to be? Where do you want it to be on your paper? Where do you want it to start? Once you have decided on your new curve, make a sketch of it on your paper.

   b.   Predict how you could conduct an experiment to get exactly the curve you have described. How fast should you move the paper? Where would you start it? How high would you start your pendulum? Be prepared to share your predictions and their justifications with the class.

7-3.   Draw a sketch of one of the shapes the class created with the drips from the swinging pendulum in problem 7-1.

   a.   Sketch what the shape would look like if the bag were pulled out farther before it was let go.

   b.   Sketch what the shape would look like if the paper underneath the pendulum traveled faster.

7-4.   Karin was working on graphing the function $f(x) = \frac{2}{x-3}$. She made a table (shown below), but she is not sure how to graph the values in the table. Show Karin how to make her graph and tell her everything you know about her function.

x	−3	−2	−1	0	1	2	3	4	5	6	7	8	9
$f(x)$	$-\frac{1}{3}$	$-\frac{2}{5}$	$-\frac{1}{2}$	$-\frac{2}{3}$	−1	−2	*	2	1	$\frac{2}{3}$	$\frac{1}{2}$	$\frac{2}{5}$	$\frac{1}{3}$

*undefined

7-5.   In each of the following triangles, find the length of the side labeled x.

a.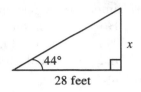

28 feet

b.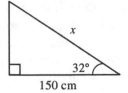

150 cm

c.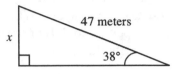

7-6.   Copy the triangles at right and label the missing side lengths.

7-7.   Find the equation of the parabola that passes through the points $(0, 0)$, $(3, 9)$, and $(6, 0)$.

7-8.   Solve and check your solution: $2\sqrt{21-x} - \sqrt{3x-6} = 5$.

7-9.   Consider the function $y = x^2 + 5x + 7$.

   a.   Complete the square to find the vertex.

   b.   Find the y-intercept.

   c.   Use the vertex, the y-intercept, and the symmetry of parabolas to find a third point and sketch the graph.

7-10.   Find the x- and y-intercepts of $y - 7 = 3^{(x+4)}$.

7-11.   Change $x^2 - 2x + y^2 - 29 = 0$ to graphing form, sketch the graph, and label the important points.

7.1.2 How can I graph it?

Graphing the Sine Function

Today you will use what you know about right-triangle relationships and graphing functions to investigate a new function.

7-12.   *"HURRY!!! Let's get there before the line gets too long!"* shouts Antonio to his best friend René as they race to get on *The Screamer*, the newest attraction at the local amusement park.

"It's only been open for one day, and already everyone is saying it's the scariest ride at the park!" exclaims Antonio. *"I hear they really had to rush to get it done in time for summer."*

Antonio whistles as he screeches to a halt in front of the huge sign that says, *"Welcome to The Screamer, the Scariest Ride on Earth."* The picture below it shows an enormous wheel that represents *The Screamer*, with its radius of 100 feet. Half of the wheel is below ground level, in a very dark, murky pit with water at the bottom. As *The Screamer* rotates at dizzying speeds, riders fly up into the air before plunging downward through blasts of freezing air, hair-raising screams, and sticky spider webs into the pit where they splash through the dark, eerie water on their way back above ground.

René and Antonio wait impatiently to get on the ride, watching passengers load and unload. New passengers get on and strap themselves in as others emerge from the pit looking queasy. The ride rotates 15° to load and unload the next set of riders. As René straps himself in, he remembers Antonio's ominous words: *"I hear they really had to rush to get it done in time for summer."*

Sure enough, just as the ride plunges René and Antonio into the greasy water, they hear the piercing scream of metal twisting. Sparks fly and the pit fills with smoke as the ride grinds to a halt. To escape, all of the passengers must climb vertically to ground level from wherever they got stuck, either up from the pit or down from dizzying heights.

Problem continues on next page →

7-12.   *Problem continued from previous page.*

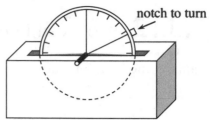

notch to turn

Your Task: Find a function that describes the distance each passenger must climb in order to escape from the broken ride, *The Screamer*.

To help you gather data, your teacher will provide you with materials to build a model of this situation. Layer your transparency circle on top of your cardboard circle and insert a toothpick to act as an axle. Then slide the circles into the slit in your cardboard box, as shown in the diagram at right.

a.   Use the transparent one-unit ruler to measure the escape heights on the model for at least 16 different possible seat positions. The seat could be in the pit, high in the air, or right at ground level. Remember that this position depends on the angle of the ride's rotation when it broke down. The radius of the model wheel will be referred to as one unit. That is, a model height of one unit corresponds to an actual height of 100 feet on the ride, so an actual height of 80 feet on the ride will be represented by a measured height of 0.8 units on the model. Record your data in a table like the one shown below. Leave room for additional columns.

Degree of Rotation from 0° (Platform)	Measured Height $0 \le y \le 1$	Actual Height Above (or Below) Platform	

b.   Graph your data on a large graph.

c.   Suppose you were asked to add 20 more data points to your table. What shortcuts could you use to reduce the amount of work?

7-13.   The function that models the situation in problem 7-12 is a new parent function. To help you figure out what it is, sketch the right triangle shown in the diagram at right.

a.   With your team, write an equation and use it to calculate the height of the triangle. Does the calculated escape height seem reasonable when compared to the data you collected in problem 7-12?

b.   Write an equation representing the escape height $h(\theta)$ for *any* passenger, that is, for any angle of rotation of *The Screamer*. Note that the symbol θ is the angle represented by the Greek letter "theta."

c.   Enter the data from the first two columns of your table into your graphing calculator. Adjust the viewing window so you can see all of the data. Then graph $h(\theta)$ on top of the data. How well does $h(\theta)$ fit your data?

d.   Adjust the viewing window so that you can see more of the graph of $h(\theta)$. Describe the behavior of the graph as θ gets larger. Does this make sense? Why or why not?

e.   Use the 'table' function of your calculator to find the values that it calculated for $h(\theta)$. Add another column to your table from problem 7-12, label it with the equation you found for $h(\theta)$, and enter these values, rounding off to the nearest hundredth. How do the calculated values compare with your measured ones?

7-14.   René and Antonio finally make it home from the amusement park unhurt, but in need of a shower. As soon as they have cleaned up, they go over to a friend's house to share their scary experience on *The Screamer*. They draw a picture of the Ferris wheel and five of the seats, located at 15°, 30°, 45°, 60°, and 75° (shown at right and on the Lesson 7.1.2D Resource Page provided by your teacher).

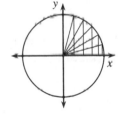

a.   Label each triangle with its *calculated* height. You can use your data from problem 7-12. If you do not have data for all of these angles, return to the 'table' function on your calculator. Plot these heights at their angle location on the coordinate system to the right of the circle. You will be plotting points in the form (x = angle in degrees, y = height).

b.   Draw five new triangles that are congruent to the first five, but that are located in the second quadrant. Label these with their angle measures (from 0°) and heights. Use the angle measures and heights to plot five new points on the graph that correspond to these five new points on the circle.

Problem continues on next page →

7-14.   *Problem continued from previous page.*

    c.   Continue this process by drawing triangles in the third and fourth quadrants. You should have a total of twenty triangles drawn and twenty points plotted. Then label the points where the circle intersects the *x*- and *y*-axes with their angle measures and heights and then add points for them to the graph as well. Sketch a smooth curve through the points.

    d.   With your team, discuss all of the relationships you can find among the points on the circle and between your unit circle and the graph. Be prepared to share your ideas with the class.

METHODS AND MEANINGS

Special Right-Triangle Relationships

MATH NOTES

As you may recall from geometry, there are certain right triangles whose sides have special relationships that make certain calculations easier. One such triangle is half of an equilateral triangle and is known as a **30° – 60° – 90° triangle**, named after the degree measures of its angles.

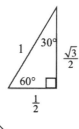

The other special triangle is half of a square and is known as the **45° – 45° – 90° triangle**. Both triangles and the relationships between their side lengths are shown at right.

Review & Preview

7-15.   Copy the triangles at right.

    a.   Label the missing sides with their *exact* lengths. That is, leave your answers in radical form.

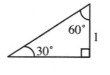

    b.   The 30° – 60° – 90° triangle is sometimes called a half-equilateral. Draw a picture to illustrate this, and explain how that fact can be used to help label the missing sides in part (a).

7-16.   Find the measure of angle A in the diagram at right.

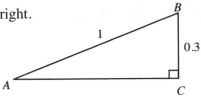

7-17.   Find the x- and y-intercepts of the quadratic function $y = 2x^2 + x - 10$.

7-18.   Evaluate each expression without using a calculator or changing the form of the expression.

  a. $\log(1)$

  b. $\log(10^3)$

  c. $10^{\log(4)}$

  d. $10^{3\log(4)}$

7-19.   Complete the table of values for $f(x) = \frac{x^2 + 4x - 5}{x - 1}$.

x	-2	-1	0	1	2	3
y						

  a.   Graph the points in the table. What kind of function does it appear to be? Why is it not correct to connect all of the dots?

  b.   Look for a simple pattern for the values in the table. What appears to be the relationship between x and y? Calculate $f(0.9)$ and $f(1.1)$ and add the points to your graph. Is there an asymptote at $x = 1$? If you are unsure, calculate $f(0.99)$ and $f(1.01)$ as well.

  c.   Simplify the formula for $f(x)$. What do you think the complete graph looks like?

7-20.   In 1998, Terre Haute, Indiana had a population of 72,000 people. In 2000, the population had dropped to 70,379. City officials expect the population to level off eventually at 60,000.

  a.   What kind of function would best model the population over time?

  b.   Write an equation that would model the changing population over time.

7-21.   A semi-circular tunnel is 26 feet high at its highest point. A road 48 feet wide is centered under the tunnel. Bruce needs to move a house on a trailer through the tunnel. The load is 22 feet wide and 24 feet high. Will he make it? Use a diagram to help justify your reasoning completely.

7-22.   Find the value of x.

a.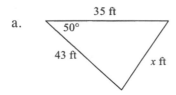

b.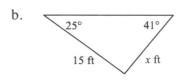

7-23.   Solve the system of equations shown at right.

$$x + y + z = 40$$
$$y = x - 5$$
$$x = 2z$$

7-24.   What is the domain of the entire graph of $h(\theta) = \sin\theta$? Justify your reasoning.

7-25.   Antonio's friend Jessica was also on *The Screamer* when it broke. Her seat was 65 feet above the ground. What was her seat's angle of rotation? Is there more than one possibility?

7-26.   Hilda was working on her homework. She completed the square to change $y = 3x^2 - 24x + 55$ to graphing form in order to identify the vertex of the parabola. She did the work at right and identified the vertex to be $(4, 39)$. When she got back to class and checked her answers, she discovered that the vertex she found is incorrect, but she cannot find her mistake. Examine Hilda's work and explain to her what she did wrong. Then show her how to complete the square correctly and identify the vertex.

$$y = 3x^2 - 24x + 55$$
$$y = 3(x^2 - 8x) + 55$$
$$y = 3(x^2 - 8x + 16) + 55 - 16$$
$$y = 3(x - 4)^2 + 39$$

7-27.   Mr. Keis wrote the following problem on the board and told his class, *"No calculators please. Simplify. You have sixty seconds!"*

$$\left(\frac{13^{12}}{14^{23}}\right)\left(\frac{27^{3}}{13^{11}}\right)\left(\frac{2^{10}}{27^{4}}\right)\left(\frac{14^{22}}{13}\right)\left(\frac{27}{2^{9}}\right)$$

Time yourself and simplify the expression. Did you meet the challenge?

7-28.   Graph the system at right.

$$1 + x - y \geq 3x - 2y - 4$$
$$y < 2x^2 + 1$$

7-29.   Use your knowledge of shifting parent graphs to graph each equation below.

   a. $y = -2(x-3)^2 + 4$ b. $y = \frac{1}{2}(x+2)^3 - 3$

   c. $y = 2|x-5|$ d. $y = \sqrt{x-2} - 3$

7-30.   Find the x- and y-intercepts for the quadratic equation $y + 3 = 8x^2 - 10x$.

7-31.   A function $W(x)$ is sketched at right.

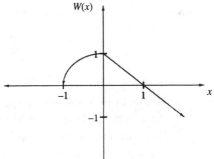

   a.   Make your own copy of the graph,
         and then sketch the graph of the
         inverse of $W(x)$.

   b.   Is the inverse a function? Explain.

7-32.   Mary has an antique marble collection containing 40 marbles. She has five
         more red marbles than blue and twice as many red as green marbles. Write a
         system of equations to find the number of each color of marble.

7.1.3 How are circles and sine graphs connected?

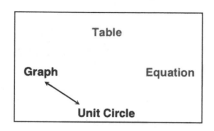

Unit Circle ↔ Graph

Throughout this course, you have used multiple representations (table, graph, equation, and situation) to solve problems, investigate functions, and justify conclusions. In Lesson 7.1.2 you found that a unit circle is one representation of a sine function. Today you will investigate the connections between the unit circle and its graph, as you build a deeper understanding of the sine function.

```
┌─────────────────────────────────┐
│             Table               │
│                                 │
│  Graph              Equation    │
│      ↘                          │
│          Unit Circle            │
└─────────────────────────────────┘
```

7-33.   Draw a circle on your paper. Then draw a triangle that could represent René and Antonio's position on the wheel when *The Screamer* came to a sudden stop. Be sure to choose a different angle position from any of those you drew in problem 7-14.

a.   Label the triangle with its height and its angle measure (from 0°).

b.   Did any other riders have to climb the same distance to get to safety (up *or* down) as René and Antonio did? If so, draw the corresponding triangles and label them completely.

c.   What is the relationship between these triangles? Work with your team to generalize a method for finding all of the other corresponding angles when you are given just one angle.

Core Connections Algebra 2

7-34.   In problem 7-33, you used a unit circle to find the height of a seat on *The Screamer*. Could you use your graph of $y = \sin\theta$ instead to find the height?

  a. Use the Lesson 7.1.3 Resource Page (also called a sine calculator) provided by your teacher to find the height of a seat that has rotated 130° from the starting platform.

  b. Are there any other seats at exactly the same height? If so, indicate them on your resource page.

  c. How can you use the symmetry of the graph to calculate which angles correspond to seats with the same height? Discuss this with your team and be prepared to share your strategies with the class.

  d. For each of the following angles, use the sine calculator from the resource page to find the height at that angle and to find another angle with the same height. Then sketch a small unit circle, draw in each pair of angles, and label the heights.

    i. 80°   *ii.* 200°   *iii.* 310°

7-35.   LEARNING LOG

With your team, discuss the ways in which a unit circle and the graph of $s(\theta) = \sin\theta$ are connected. Be prepared to share your ideas with the class. Then record your ideas in a Learning Log. Use diagrams, arrows, and other math tools to help demonstrate your ideas. Label this entry "Unit Circle ↔ Graph for $s(\theta) = \sin\theta$" and label it with today's date.

7-36.   Sketch a graph of the first two cycles of $s(\theta) = \sin\theta$. Then label your graph to show the following positions of a passenger on *The Screamer*.

  a. The passenger gets on initially.

  b. The passenger reaches the bottom of the water pit.

  c. The passenger is halfway between the highest point of *The Screamer* and the ground level.

7-37.   Each of the points on the graph at right represents
         the position of a rider on *The Screamer*. Draw a
         diagram of each rider's position on a unit circle
         and describe where the rider is located.

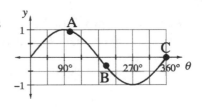

7-38.   While trying to measure the height of a tree, Julie noticed that a 3.5-foot post
         had a 4.25-foot shadow. If the tree's shadow is 100 feet long, how tall is the
         tree?

7-39.   Given that $\log 2 \approx 0.3010$, $\log 3 \approx 0.4771$ and $\log 5 \approx 0.6990$,
         calculate each of the following logarithms without using a
         calculator.

         a. $\log 6$ b. $\log 15$ c. $\log 9$ d. $\log 50$

7-40.   Find the x- and y-intercepts of the quadratic function $y = 3x^2 + 6x + 1$.

7-41.   Write the quadratic function in problem 7-40 in graphing form and sketch
         its graph.

7-42.   Solve $|x+5| = |x| - 5$ by graphing. Express your solution algebraically.

7-43.   Solve $\log_2 x = 2^x$ using any method.

7-44.   Maria Elena is collecting college pennants. She has five fewer pennants from
         Washington campuses than from California campuses and twice as many
         pennants from California campuses as from Pennsylvania campuses. She has
         40 pennants in her collection. Write a system of equations to find the number
         of Pennants from each state.

7.1.4 How can I graph cosine?

Graphing and Interpreting the Cosine Function

In this lesson, you will use your knowledge of right triangles again – this time to develop your understanding of another cyclic function.

7-45. Work with your team to find the coordinates of point P on the unit circle shown at right. Is there more than one way to find point P? Be prepared to share your strategies with the class.

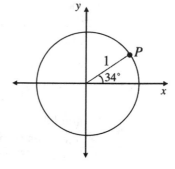

7-46. 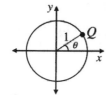 Now generalize what you found in problem 7-45 to write the coordinates of point Q on the unit circle shown at left.

7-47. What can a sine value tell you about a point on a circle? What about a cosine value?

7-48. If you know the sine of an angle in a unit circle, can you find its cosine? How? Work with your team to find a strategy and be prepared to share it with the class.

7-49. An angle θ on the unit circle has a cosine of $\frac{3}{4}$.

   a. Find the exact coordinates of point Q by using the Pythagorean Theorem.

   b. What is the value of $\sin \theta$?

   c. Using what you determined in problems 7-47 and 7-48, how could you rewrite the Pythagorean Theorem using trigonometric functions for the lengths of the sides? When written like this, the Pythagorean Theorem is called the **Pythagorean Identity**.

7-50.   Obtain a copy of the Lesson 7.1.4A Resource Page from your teacher. You will use the same process to graph the cosine function as you did to graph the sine function, but you need to use the base of the triangle instead of the height.

a.   Label the length of the base of each triangle in the unit circle. Plot these lengths at their angle location on the coordinate system to the right of the circle. You will be plotting points in the form (x = angle in degrees, y = base).

b.   Draw five new triangles that are congruent to the first five, but that are located in the second quadrant. Label the angle measure (from 0°) and the base for each triangle. Add five new corresponding points to the graph.

c.   Continue this process by drawing triangles in the third and fourth quadrants. You should have a total of twenty triangles drawn and twenty points plotted. Then find the four points where the circle crosses the axes and label them with both their angle measures and their horizontal distances from the origin. Add points for these to the graph on the right as well. Finally, sketch a smooth curve through the points.

d.   Compare this graph to the sine graph you got from graphing heights in problem 7-14. How are the two graphs similar? How are they different?

7-51.   Remember the scary Ferris wheel, *The Screamer*? LaRasha does! She was riding *The Screamer*, sitting 27 horizontal feet away from the central support pole, when the ride stopped. What was her seat's angle of rotation? Is there more than one possibility? Justify your answer using as many representations as you can.

7-52.   UNIT CIRCLE ↔ GRAPH

In problem 7-51, did you use a graph of $y = \cos\theta$ to find lengths of bases of triangles?

a.   Use the Lesson 7.1.4B Resource Page (a cosine-calculator graph) provided by your teacher to find the length of the base of a triangle formed by a seat on *The Screamer* that had rotated 130° from the starting platform.

b.   Are there any other triangles with the same base? If so, mark their corresponding points on your cosine calculator.

c.   How can you use the symmetry of the cosine-calculator graph to calculate the angle location of seats on *The Screamer* that have the same base? Is your method different than the one you used to find the heights?

328   *Core Connections Algebra 2*

7-53. Use the Pythagorean Identity to find the exact coordinates of a point on the unit circle that has $\sin\theta = \frac{1}{4}$.

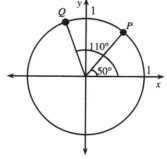

7-54. Find the coordinates of points P and Q on the unit circle at right.

7-55. The measure of $\angle ROS$ in $\triangle ROS$ below is $60°$.

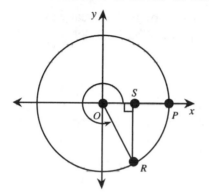

a. The curved arrow represents the rotation of $\overline{OR}$, beginning from the positive x-axis. Through how many degrees has $\overline{OR}$ rotated?

b. If $OR = 1$, what are the *exact* lengths of OS and SR?

c. What are the *exact* coordinates of point R?

7-56. What angle in the first quadrant could you reference to help you find the sine and cosine of each of the following angles?

a. $330°$ b. $120°$ c. $113°$ d. $203°$

7-57. Solve $\left(\frac{1}{8}\right)^{(2x-3)} = \left(\frac{1}{2}\right)^{(x+2)}$ for x.

7-58. Sketch a graph of each equation below.

a. $y = -2(x-2)^2 + 3$ b. $y = (x-1)^3 + 3$

7-59. Solve $3^x + 5 = x^2 - 5$ using any method.

7-60.   Rip-Off Rentals charges $25 per day plus 50¢ per mile to rent a mid-sized car. Your teacher will rent you his or her family sedan and charge you only 3¢ if you drive one mile, 6¢ if you drive two miles, 12¢ if you drive three, 24¢ for four, and so on.

    a.   Write an equation that will give you the cost to rent each car.

    b.   If you plan to rent the car for a two-day road trip, which is the better deal if you drive 10 miles? 20 miles? 100 miles?

7-61.   Refer back to your solutions from problems 7-23, 7-32, and 7-44. Explain how these problems are related.

7-62.   Shinna was riding *The Screamer* when it broke down. Her seat was 53 horizontal feet from the central support pole. What was her seat's angle of rotation? How can you tell?

7-63.   Sketch a unit circle. In your circle, sketch in an angle that has:

    a.   A positive cosine and a negative sine.

    b.   A sine of −1.

    c.   A negative cosine and a negative sine.

    d.   A cosine of about −0.9 and a sine of about 0.4.

    e.   Could an angle have a sine equal to 0.9 and cosine equal to 0.8? Give an angle or explain why not.

7-64.   A 70° angle is drawn for you in the unit circle at right.

    a.   Approximate the coordinates of point *R*.

    b.   How could you represent the *exact* coordinates of point *R*?

    c.   Show that the Pythagorean Identity works for this angle.

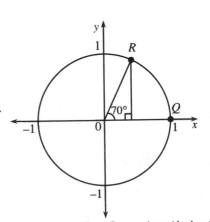

7-65.   Daniel sketched the graphs at right for $y = \sin\theta$ and $y = \cos\theta$.

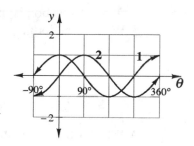

Unfortunately, he forgot to label the graphs, and now he cannot remember which graph goes with which equation. Explain to Daniel how he can tell (and remember!) which graph is $y = \sin\theta$ and which is $y = \cos\theta$.

7-66.   Consider the system of equations $y = \cos x$ and $y = -1$.

a.   Is it possible to solve this system by substitution? By the Elimination Method? By graphing?

b.   List at least five possible solutions.

c.   Consider the list of solutions you wrote in part (b) as a sequence and write an equation to represent *all* possible solutions.

7-67.   This problem is a checkpoint for finding the x- and y-intercepts of a quadratic function. It will be referred to as Checkpoint 7A.

Find the x- and y-intercepts for the graph of $y = x^2 + 4x - 17$ without using a graphing calculator.

Check your answers by referring to the Checkpoint 7A materials located at the back of your book.

If you needed help solving these problems correctly, then you need more practice. Review the Checkpoint 7A materials and try the practice problems. Also, consider getting help outside of class time. From this point on, you will be expected to do problems like these quickly and easily.

7-68.   Solve each equation.

a. $\frac{3}{x+1} = \frac{4}{x}$

b. $\frac{3}{x+1} + \frac{4}{x} = 2$

c. $\frac{3}{x+2} + 5 = \frac{3}{x+2}$

d.   Explain why part (c) has no solution.

7-69.   A $5' \times 4' \times 3'$ box is made for the purpose of storage. What is the longest pole that can fit inside the box?

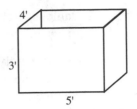

7-70.   While working on their homework on sequences, Davis was suddenly stumped!

"This problem doesn't make sense!" he exclaimed. Tess was working on her homework as well.

"What's the problem?" she asked.

"This problem is about a SEQUENCE, $t(n) = 9n - 2$, but it is asking whether or not it is a function. How can a sequence be a function?"

"Well of course a sequence is a function!" said Tess.

Who is right? Should Davis be confused, or is Tess correct? What is the difference between a sequence and a function? Explain completely.

7.1.5   How else can I measure angles?

Defining a Radian

Whose idea was it to measure angles in degrees? And why are there 360° in a full turn? This decision actually dates back almost 4000 years! Degrees were created by the Babylonians, an ancient people who lived in the region that is now Iraq. The Babylonians also based their number system, called a sexigesimal system, on sixty.

Although you are familiar with measuring angles in degrees, this is not the only way to measure angles, nor is it necessarily the most useful. Today you will learn a different unit for measuring angles called a **radian**. Using radians instead of degrees is actually the standard across mathematics! When you take calculus, you will learn why radians are used in math more often than degrees.

7-71.   What word are you reminded of when you hear the word radian? Discuss this with your team and make a conjecture about how this might relate to a way to measure angles. Be prepared to share your ideas with the class.

7-72.   HOW TO MAKE A RADIAN

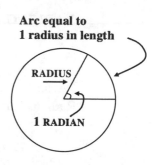

Arc equal to
1 radius in length

Imagine wrapping the radius of a circle around the circle. The angle formed at the center of the circle that corresponds to the arc that is one radius long has a measure of exactly one **radian**.

Your teacher will provide each member of your team with a different-sized circular object and some scissors.

a.   Trace your circular object onto a sheet of paper and carefully cut out the circle. Fold the paper circle in half and then in half again so that it is in the shape of a quarter circle, as in the diagram at right. How can you see the radius of your circular object in this new folded shape?

b.   Place your circular object onto another sheet of paper and trace it again, only this time leave the circular object in place. Roll (or wrap) a straight edge of your folded circle around your circular object and mark one radius length on the traced circle. Then mark another radius length that begins where the first one ended. Continue marking radius lengths until you have gone around the entire circle.

c.   Remove the circular object from your paper. On your traced circle, connect each radius mark to the center, creating central angles. Each angle you see, formed by an arc with a length of one radius, measures one **radian**. Label each of the radius lengths and each angle that measures one full radian. Write a short description of how you constructed an angle with measure one radian.

7-73.   Assume the radius of a circle is one unit.

a.   What is the area of the circle? What is its circumference?

b.   How many radii would it take to wrap completely around the circle? Express your answer as a decimal approximation *and* as an exact value.

c.   Does the size of the circle matter? That is, does the number of radii it takes to wrap around the circle change as the radius of the circle gets larger or smaller? Why does this make sense?

d.   Exactly how many radians are in 360°? In 90°?

7-74. LEARNING LOG

How is a radian related to a radius? Explain your understanding of this relationship in your Learning Log. Use diagrams to support your explanation. Title this entry "Radians" and label it with today's date.

7-75. Parts (a) through (g) below describe angles. Draw each angle on its own unit circle.

a. 1 degree   b. 1 radian   c. π radians   d. $\frac{\pi}{2}$ radians

e. $\frac{\pi}{4}$ radians   f. $\frac{\pi}{3}$ radians   g. $\frac{\pi}{6}$ radians

7-76. Find your sine-calculator (the Lesson 7.1.3 Resource Page). Use your new understanding of radians to convert the units on the θ axis from degrees to radians. Be prepared to share your conversion strategies with the class.

 **M**ETHODS AND **M**EANINGS

Radians

A **radian** is defined as an angular measure such that an arc length of one radius on a circle of radius one produces an angle with measure one radian. It can also be thought of as the ratio of an arc length to the radius of the corresponding circle.

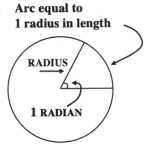

The circumference of any complete circle is $2\pi r$ units, so the corresponding radian measure is $\frac{2\pi r}{r} = 2\pi$. Thus, there are 2π radians in a complete circle.

7-77.   Your scientific or graphing calculator can function in both degrees
        and radians. See if you can determine how to put your calculator in
        radian mode and then how to switch it back to degree mode. On
        most scientific calculators, a small "DEG" or "RAD" shows on the
        screen to let you know in which mode you are working.

    a. With your calculator in degree mode, find sin 60° and record your answer.
        Then switch to radian mode and find $\sin \frac{\pi}{3}$. Did you get the same answer?
        Explain why your answers should be the same or different.

    b. Find $\sin \frac{\pi}{4}$. Which angles, measured in degrees, would have the same sine
        as $\sin \frac{\pi}{4}$?

7-78.   Calculate each of the following values. Express your answers both exactly and
        as decimal approximations.

    a. $\sin(\frac{\pi}{4})$

    b. $\sin(\frac{2\pi}{3})$

7-79.   Show how the Zero Product Property can be used to solve each of the following
        equations.

    a. $x(2x-1)(x-3)=0$

    b. $2x^3 + x^2 - 3x = 0$

7-80.   Solve each of the following equations.

    a. $5^x = 72$

    b. $2^{3x} = 7$

    c. $3^{(2x+4)} = 17$

7-81.   Greg was working on his homework.
        He completed the square to change
        $y = 2x^2 - 6x + 2$ to graphing form and
        identify the vertex of the parabola.
        He did the work at right and
        identified the vertex to be $(\frac{3}{2}, -\frac{1}{4})$.

$y = 2x^2 - 6x + 2$
$y = 2(x^2 - 3x) + 2$
$y = 2(x^2 - 3x + \frac{9}{4}) + 2 - \frac{9}{4}$
$y = 2(x - \frac{3}{2})^2 - \frac{1}{4}$

        When he got back to class and checked his answers, he discovered that his
        vertex was wrong, but he cannot find his mistake. Examine Greg's work and
        explain to him where the mistake occurred. Then show him how to correct the
        mistake and state the vertex.

7-82.　Change each of the following equations to graphing form and then, without graphing, identify the vertex and axis of symmetry for each.

    a.　$y = 3x^2 - 18x + 26$　　　　　　　　b.　$y = 3x^2 - 4x - 11$

7-83.　Solve each of the following equations for x.

    a.　$171 = 3(5^x)$　　　　　　　　　　b.　$171y = 3(x^5)$

7-84.　Sketch a graph of $x^2 + y^2 = 100$.

    a.　Is it a function?

    b.　What are its domain and range?

    c.　Draw a central angle that measures $\frac{2\pi}{3}$ radians. If you remove this wedge of the circle, how much area remains?

7-85.　Find the equation for the inverse of the function $f(x) = 2\sqrt{\frac{(x-3)}{4}} + 1$. Sketch the graph of both the original and the inverse.

7.1.6 What do I know about a unit circle?

Building a Unit Circle

In this lesson, you will further develop your understanding of the unit circle and how useful it can be. By the end of the lesson, you should be able to answer the questions below.

What can the unit circle help me understand about an angle?

What does my information about angles in the first quadrant tell me about angles in other quadrants?

7-86. There are some angles for which you know the *exact values* of sine and cosine. In other words, you can find the exact sine and cosine without using a calculator. Work with your team to find as many such angles (expressed in radians) as you can.

7-87. Now you will build a unit circle. Obtain the Lesson 7.1.6 Resource Page from your teacher. There are points shown at $\frac{\pi}{12}, \frac{\pi}{6}, \frac{\pi}{4}, \frac{\pi}{3}, \frac{5\pi}{12}, \frac{7\pi}{12}, \frac{2\pi}{3}, \frac{3\pi}{4}, \frac{5\pi}{6}$, and $\frac{11\pi}{12}$ units along the circle, starting from the positive *x*-axis.

   a. Find and label the exact coordinates, in (x,y) form, for three of the points shown in the *first quadrant*.

   b. Mark *all* other points in the unit circle for which you can find *exact* coordinates. Not all of them are shown. Label each of these points with its angle of rotation (in radians) and its coordinates.

   c. If you have not done so already, label each angle with its corresponding radian measure.

7-88. Draw a new unit circle, label a point that corresponds to a rotation of $\frac{\pi}{12}$, and put your calculator in radian mode.

a. What are the coordinates of this point, correct to two decimal places?

b. Use the information you found in part (a) to determine each of the following values: (Hint: Drawing each angle on the unit circle will be very helpful.)

    i. $\sin(-\frac{\pi}{12})$ *ii.* $\cos\frac{13\pi}{12}$ *iii.* Challenge: $\cos\frac{7\pi}{12}$

7-89. For angle α in the first quadrant, $\cos\alpha = \frac{8}{17}$. Use that information to find each of the following values without using a calculator. Be prepared to share your strategies with the class.

    a. $\sin\alpha$ b. $\sin(\pi+\alpha)$ c. $\cos(2\pi-\alpha)$

METHODS AND MEANINGS

Reference Angle

For every angle of rotation, there is an angle in the first quadrant ($0 \le \theta \le 90°$) whose cosine and sine have the same absolute values as the cosine and sine of the original angle. This first-quadrant angle is called the **reference angle**.

For example, the angles 51°, 129°, 231°, and 309° (pictured at right) all share the reference angle of 51°.

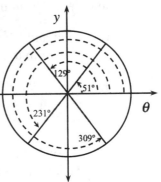

7-90.   Calculate the value of each expression below. Give an exact measurement, if possible. Each measure is given in radians.

a. $\sin(4)$

b. $\sin(\frac{4\pi}{3})$

7-91.   Find the exact values of the angles that are solutions to the equation $\sin(\theta) = 0.5$. Express your solutions in radians.

7-92.   You have seen that you can calculate values of the sine function using right triangles formed by a radius of the unit circle. Values of θ that result in $30° - 60° - 90°$ or $45° - 45° - 90°$ triangles are used frequently on exercises and tests because their sine and cosine values can be found exactly, without using a calculator. You should learn to recognize these values quickly and easily. The same is true for values of $\cos\theta$ and $\sin\theta$ that correspond to the x- and y-intercepts of the unit circle.

The central angles that correspond to these "special" values of x are 30°, 45°, 60°, 90°, 120°, 135°, 150°, 180°, 210°, 225°, 240°, 270°, 300°, 315°, and 330°. What these angles have in common is that they are all multiples of 30° or 45°, and some of them are also multiples of 60° or 90°.

Copy and complete a table like the one below for all special angles between 0° and 360°.

Degrees	0	30	45	60	90	120		
Radians	0	$\frac{\pi}{6}$						

7-93.   Draw a picture of an angle that measures 6 radians.

a.   Approximately how many degrees is this?

b.   Using only your picture, estimate the sine of 6 radians.

7-94. Evaluate each expression without using a calculator or changing the form of the expression.

    a. $\log(10)$

    b. $\log(\sqrt{10})$

    c. $\log(0)$

    d. $10^{(2/3)\log(27)}$

7-95. What interest rate (compounded annually) would you need to earn in order to double your investment in 15 years?

7-96. Angle A is an obtuse angle with a sine of $\frac{3}{10}$. What is the tangent of angle A?

7-97. Find the inverse functions for the functions given below.

    a. $f(x) = \sqrt[3]{4x-1}$

    b. $g(x) = \log_7 x$

7-98. Solve each of the following equations.

    a. $2(x-1)^2 = 18$

    b. $2^x + 3 = 10$

7.1.7 What is tangent?

The Tangent Function

In the past several lessons, you have used your understanding of the sine and cosine ratios to develop and interpret the functions $s(\theta) = \sin\theta$ and $c(\theta) = \cos\theta$. In this lesson, you will expand your understanding by exploring the tangent ratio and graphing the function $t(\theta) = \tan\theta$.

7-99. Jamal was working on his homework when he had a brilliant realization. He was drawing a triangle in a unit circle to estimate the sine of $\frac{\pi}{10}$, when he realized that this triangle is the same kind of triangle that he draws when he wants to find the slope of a line.

    a.   How could you express the slope of the radius in terms of sine and cosine?

    b.   Is there any other way you can use a trigonometric ratio to represent the slope? Discuss this with your team.

7-100. THE TANGENT FUNCTION

Obtain the Lesson 7.1.7 Resource Page from your teacher. Use your knowledge of sine, cosine, and tangent to create a graph of the tangent function. Conduct a full investigation of the tangent function. Be prepared to share your summary statements with the class.

Discussion Points

Does every angle have a tangent value?

How is the tangent graph similar to or different from the sine and cosine graphs?

Why does the tangent graph have asymptotes?

Further Guidance

7-101.   For each triangle in the first quadrant of the unit circle on your resource page, label the sine and cosine.

   a.   Use your knowledge of tangent to complete a table like the one below. Start with the exact values for the sine and cosine.

θ	$\sin\theta$	$\cos\theta$	$\tan\theta$ (exact)	$\tan\theta$ (approximate to nearest 0.01)
$\frac{\pi}{6}$	$\frac{1}{2}$	$\frac{\sqrt{3}}{2}$	$\frac{1}{\sqrt{3}}$	
$\frac{\pi}{4}$	$\frac{\sqrt{2}}{2}$	$\frac{\sqrt{2}}{2}$		
$\frac{\pi}{3}$	$\frac{\sqrt{3}}{2}$	$\frac{1}{2}$		

   b.   Plot the tangent values on the graph to the right of the unit circle.

   c.   Draw five new triangles that are congruent to the first five, but that are located in the second quadrant. Add values for these new angles to your table and your graph.

   d.   Continue this process by drawing triangles in the third and fourth quadrants. You should have a total of twenty triangles drawn and twenty angle values on your graph. If you have not done so already, add data to your table and points to your graph corresponding to the intercepts of the unit circle.

7-102.   Investigate the tangent graph by analyzing the following questions:

   a.   Describe the domain and range of the tangent function.

   b.   Describe any special points or asymptotes.

   c.   Does it have symmetry? Describe any symmetry you see in the graph.

   d.   How is the graph of $t(\theta) = \tan\theta$ different from the graphs of $s(\theta) = \sin\theta$ and $c(\theta) = \cos\theta$?

―――――――――   *Further Guidance*   ―――――――――
section ends here.

7-103.   Draw a new unit circle and label a point that corresponds to a rotation of $\frac{\pi}{6}$ radians.

   a.   What are the coordinates of this point? Use exact values.

   b.   Use this information to find each of the following values without a calculator. (Hint: Drawing each angle on the unit circle will be very helpful.)

   i: $\tan\left(\frac{7\pi}{6}\right)$ *ii:* $\cos\left(\frac{13\pi}{6}\right)$ *iii:* $\tan\left(\frac{2\pi}{3}\right)$

Core Connections Algebra 2

MᴇᴛHODS AND Mᴇᴀɴɪɴɢꜱ

Sine, Cosine, and Tangent

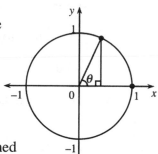

For any real number θ, the **sine of** θ, denoted $\sin \theta$, is the y-coordinate of the point on the unit circle reached by a rotation of θ radians from **standard position** (counter-clockwise starting from the positive x-axis).

The **cosine of** θ, denoted $\cos \theta$, is the x-coordinate of the point on the unit circle reached by a rotation of θ radians from standard position.

The **tangent of** θ, denoted by $\tan \theta$, is the slope of the terminal ray of an angle (the radius) formed by a rotation of θ radians in standard position.

The **Pythagorean Identity**, $\sin^2 \theta + \cos^2 \theta = 1$, describes the relationship between the side lengths of a right triangle formed in a unit circle with the radius as the hypotenuse.

7-104.   What central angle, measured in degrees, corresponds to a distance around the unit circle of $\frac{7\pi}{3}$?

   a.   What other angles will take you to the same point on the circle?

   b.   Make a sketch of the unit circle showing the resulting right triangle.

   c.   Find $\sin\left(\frac{7\pi}{3}\right)$, $\cos\left(\frac{7\pi}{3}\right)$, and $\tan\left(\frac{7\pi}{3}\right)$ exactly.

7-105.   Evaluate each of the following trig expressions without using a calculator.

   a. $\sin(180°)$ b. $\sin(360°)$ c. $\sin(-90°)$

   d. $\sin(510°)$ e. $\cos(90°)$ f. $\tan(-90°)$

7-106.   How do you convert from degrees to radians and from radians to degrees? Explain and justify your method completely. Add some examples to your Toolkit.

7-107.   Convert each of the following angle measures. Give exact answers.

a. $\frac{7\pi}{6}$ radians to degrees

b. $\frac{5\pi}{3}$ radians to degrees

c. 45 degrees to radians

d. 100° to radians

e. 810° to radians

f. $\frac{7\pi}{2}$ radians to degrees

7-108.   Sketch a graph of $f(x) = \frac{1}{2}(x+1)^3$. Then sketch its inverse and write the equation of the inverse.

7-109.   Rewrite $f(x) = 2x^2 - 16x + 34$ in graphing form.

7-110.   For angle θ in the third quadrant, $\cos\theta = -\frac{12}{13}$. Use this information to find each of the following values without using a calculator.

a. $\sin\theta$

b. $\tan\theta$

7-111.   Given that $\log_x 2 = a$, $\log_x 5 = b$, and $\log_x 7 = c$, write expressions using $a, b,$ and/or c for each log expression below.

a. $\log_x 10$ b. $\log_x 49$ c. $\log_x 50$ d. $\log_x 56$

7-112.   The temperature of a pizza after it has been delivered depends on how long it has been sitting on the family-room table.

a. Sketch a reasonable graph of this situation. Be sure to label the axes.

b. Should your graph have an asymptote? Why or why not?

7.2.1 How can I transform a sine graph?

Transformations of $y = \sin x$

In Chapter 2, you developed expertise in investigating functions and transforming parent graphs. In this section, you will investigate families of cyclic functions and their transformations. By the end of this section, you will be able to graph any sine or cosine equation and write the equation of any sine or cosine graph.

7-113.   As you have seen with many functions in this and other courses, x is generally used to represent an input and y is used to represent the corresponding output. By this convention, sinusoidal functions should be written $y = \sin x$, $y = \cos x$, and $y = \tan x$. But beware! Something funny is happening.

With your team, examine the unit circle and the three graphs below. What do x and y represent in the unit circle? What do they represent in each of the graphs? Discuss this with your team and be prepared to share your ideas with the class.

a.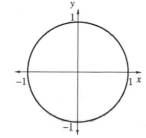

b.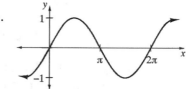

c.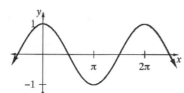

d.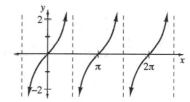

7-114.   With your team, you will apply your knowledge about transforming graphs of functions to transform the graphs of $y = \sin x$ and $y = \cos x$ and find their general equations.

Your Task: As a team, investigate $y = \sin x$ and $y = \cos x$ completely. You should make graphs, find the domain and range, and label any important points or asymptotes. Then make a sketch and write an equation to demonstrate each transformation of the sine or cosine function you can find. Finally, find a general equation for a sine and a cosine function. Be prepared to share your summary statements with the class.

Discussion Points

What can we change in a cyclic graph?

Which points are important to label?

How can we apply the transformations we use with other functions?

Are there any new transformations that are special to the sine function?

Further Guidance

7-115.   Sketch a graph of at least one cycle of $y = \sin x$. Label the intercepts. Then work with your team to complete parts (a) through (c) below.

a.   Write an equation for each part below and sketch a graph of a function that has a parent graph of $y = \sin x$, but is:

   i.   Shifted 3 units up.   ii.   Reflected across the x-axis.

   iii. Shifted 2 units to the right.   iv.   Vertically stretched.

b.   Which points are most important to label in a periodic function? Why?

c.   Write a general equation for the family of functions with a parent graph of $y = \sin x$.

_____   *Further Guidance*   _____
                section ends here.

7-116. Imagine the graph $y = \sin(x)$ shifted up one unit.

 a. Sketch what it would look like.

 b. What do you have to change in the equation $y = \sin x$ to move the graph *up* one unit? Write the new equation.

 c. What are the intercepts of your new equation? Label them with their coordinates on the graph.

 d. When you listed intercepts in part (c), did you list more than one x-intercept? Should you have?

7-117. The graph at right was made by shifting the first cycle of $y = \sin x$ to the left.

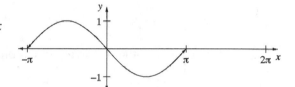

 a. How many units to the left was it shifted?

 b. Figure out how to change the equation of $y = \sin x$ so that the graph of the new equation will look like the one in part (a). If you do not have a graphing calculator at home, sketch the graph and check your answer when you get to class.

7-118. Which of the situations below (if any) is best modeled by a cyclic function? Explain your reasoning.

 a. The number of students in each year's graduating class.

 b. Your hunger level throughout the day.

 c. The high-tide level at a point along the coast.

7-119.   The CPM Amusement Park has decided to imitate *The Screamer* but wants to make it even better. Their ride will consist of a circular track with a radius of 100 feet, and the center of the circle will be 50 feet under ground. Passengers will board at the highest point, so they will begin with a blood-curdling drop. Write a function that relates the angle traveled *from the starting point* to the height of the rider above or below the ground.

7-120.   Should $y = \sin x$ and $y = \cos x$ both be parent graphs, or is one the parent of the other? Give reasons for your decision.

7-121.   Find the equation of the exponential function of the form $y = ab^x$ that passes through each of the following pairs of points.

   a. $(1, 18)$ and $(4, 3888)$ b. $(-2, -8)$ and $(3, -0.25)$

7-122.   Solve each of the following equations. Be sure to check your solutions.

   a. $\frac{3}{x} + \frac{2}{x+1} = 5$

   b. $x^2 + 6x + 9 = 2x^2 + 3x + 5$

   c. $8 - \sqrt{9 - 2x} = x + 3$

7-123.   Evaluate each of the following expressions exactly.

   a. $\tan \frac{2\pi}{3}$ b. $\tan \frac{7\pi}{6}$

7-124.   David Longshot is known for his long golf drives. Today he hit the ball 250 yards and estimated that the ball reached a maximum height of 15 yards. Find a quadratic equation that would model the path of the golf ball.

7.2.2 What is missing?

One More Parameter for a Cyclic Function

In this lesson, you will study one more transformation that is unique to cyclic functions. You will also extend your understanding of these functions to include those with input values that do not correspond to angles.

7-125.   Does the general equation $y = a\sin(x-h)+k$ allow for every possible transformation of the graph of $y = \sin x$? Are there any transformations possible *other than* the ones produced by varying values of a, h, and k? Look back at the graphs you made for the swinging bag of blood in the first lesson of this chapter. Discuss this with your team and be prepared to share your conjectures with the class.

7-126.   **THE RADAR SCREEN**

Brianna is an air traffic controller. Every day she watches the radar line (like a radius of a circle) go around her screen time after time. On one particularly slow travel day, Brianna noticed that it takes 2 seconds for the radar line to travel through an angle of $\frac{\pi}{6}$ radians. She decided to make a graph in which the *input* is time and the *output* is the distance from the outward end of the radar line to the horizontal axis.

Your Task: Following the input and output specifications above, make a table and graph for Brianna's radar.

Discussion Points

How can we calculate the outputs?

How is this graph different from other similar graphs we have made?

How long does it take to complete one full cycle on the radar screen?
How can we see that on the graph?

7-127.   Now that you have seen that it is possible to have a sine graph with a cycle length other than 2π, work with your team to make conjectures about how you could change your general equation to allow for this new transformation.

    a.   In the general equation $y = a\sin(x - h) + k$, the quantities a, h, and k are called **parameters**. Where could a new parameter fit into the equation?

    b.   Use your graphing calculator to test the result of putting this new parameter into your general equation. Once you have found the place for the new parameter, investigate how it works. What happens when it gets larger? What happens when it gets smaller?

    c.   Write a general equation for a sine function that includes the new parameter you discovered.

7-128.   Another word for cycle length is **period**. Which of the following have a period of 2π? Which do not? How can you tell? If the period is not 2π, what is it?

    a.
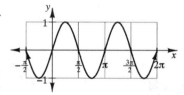

    b.   A pendulum takes 3 seconds to complete one cycle.

    c. $y = \sin\theta$

    d.   A radar line takes 1 second to travel through 1 radian.

7-129. Find an equation for each graph below.

a.

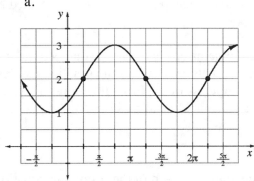

b.

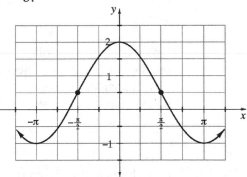

c.

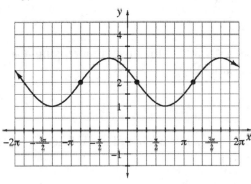

d.

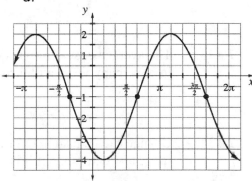

7-130. Claudia graphed $y = \cos\theta$ and $y = \cos(\theta + 360°)$ on the same set of axes. She did not see any difference in their graphs at all. Why not?

7-131. This problem is a checkpoint for completing the square to find the vertex of a parabola. It will be referred to as Checkpoint 7B.

Complete the square to change the equation $y = 2x^2 - 4x + 5$ into graphing form. Identify the vertex of the parabola and sketch the graph.

Check your answers by referring to the Checkpoint 7B materials located at the back of your book.

If you needed help solving these problems correctly, then you need more practice. Review the Checkpoint 7B materials and try the practice problems. Also, consider getting help outside of class time. From this point on, you will be expected to do problems like these quickly and easily.

7-132. Find the x- and y-intercepts of the graphs of each of the following equations.

a. $y = 2x^3 - 10x^2 - x$

b. $y + 2 = \log_3(x - 1)$

7-133. The average cost of movie tickets is \$9.50. If the cost is increasing 4% per year, in how many years will the cost double?

7-134. Change each equation to graphing form. For each equation, find the domain and range and determine if it is a function.

a. $y = -2x^2 - x + 13$

b. $y = -3x^2 - 6x + 12$

7-135. Too Tall Thomas has put Rodney's book bag on the snack-shack roof. Rodney goes to borrow a ladder from the school custodian. The tallest ladder available is 10 feet long and the roof is 9 feet from the ground. Rodney places the ladder's tip at the edge of the roof. The ladder is unsafe if the angle it makes with the ground is more than 60°. Is this a safe situation? Justify your conclusion.

7-136.   Deniz's computer is infected with a virus that will erase information from her hard drive. It will erase information quickly at first, but as time goes on, the rate at which information is erased will decrease. In t minutes after the virus starts erasing information, $5{,}000{,}000(\frac{1}{2})^t$ bytes of information remain on the hard drive.

   a.   Before the virus starts erasing, how many bytes of information are on Deniz's hard drive?

   b.   After how many minutes will there be 1000 bytes of information left on the drive?

   c.   When will the hard drive be completely erased?

7-137.   Graph $f(x) = |x - 6| - 4$.

   a.   Explain how you can graph this without making an $x \to y$ table, but using parent graphs.

   b.   Graph $g(x) = \big||x - 6| - 4\big|$. Explain how you can graph $g(x)$ without making an $x \to y$ table by using your earlier graph.

7.2.3 What is the period of a function?

· ·

Period of a Cyclic Function

In Lesson 7.2.2, you found a place for a new parameter in the general form of a trigonometric equation and discovered that it must have something to do with the period. By the end of this lesson, you will have the tools you need to find the equation for any sine or cosine graph and will be able to graph any sine or cosine equation. In other words, you will learn the graph $\leftrightarrow$ equation connection. The following questions can help your team stay focused on the purpose of this lesson.

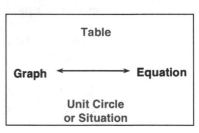

How can we write the equation for any sine or cosine graph?

How can we graph any sine or cosine function?

7-138.   Find the period for each of the following situations:

    a.   The input is the angle θ in the unit circle and the output is the cosine of θ.

    b.   The input is time and the output is the average daily temperature in New York.

    c.   The input is the distance Nurse Nina has traveled along the hallway and the output is the distance of bloody drips from the midline of the hallway.

7-139.   Make sure your graphing calculator is in radian mode.

    a.   Set the domain and range of the viewing window so that you would see just one complete cycle of $y = \sin x$. What is the domain for one cycle? What is the range?

    b.   Graph $y = \sin x$, $y = \sin(0.5x)$, $y = \sin(2x)$, $y = \sin(3x)$, and $y = \sin(5x)$. Make a sketch and answer the following questions for each equation.

        i.   How many cycles of each graph appear on the screen?

        ii.   The **midline** is the horizontal axis that goes through the center of the graph. What is the equation for the midline of these graphs?

        iii.   What is the **amplitude** (height above the midline) of each graph?

        iv.   What is the period (cycle length) of each graph?

        v.   Is each equation a function?

    c.   Make a conjecture about the graph of $y = \sin(bx)$ with respect to each of the questions (*i*) through (*v*) above. If you cannot make a conjecture yet, try more examples.

    d.   Create at least three of your own examples to check your conjectures. Be sure to include sketches of your graphs.

    e.   What is the relationship between the period of a sine graph and the value of b in its equation?

7-140.   Refer to the graph you made by swinging a pendulum in Lesson 7.1.1. Decide where to draw x- and y-axes and find the equation of your graph. Is there more than one possible equation? Be prepared to share your strategies with the class.

7-141. *Without* using a graphing calculator, describe each of the following functions by stating the amplitude, period, horizontal shift, and midline (vertical shift). Using this information, sketch the graph of each function. *After* you have completed each graph, check your sketch with a graphing calculator and correct and explain any errors.

a. $y = \sin 2(x - \frac{\pi}{6})$

b. $y = 3 + \sin(\frac{1}{3}x)$

c. $y = 3\sin(4x)$

d. $y = \sin\frac{1}{2}(x + 1)$

e. $y = -\sin 3(x - \frac{\pi}{3})$

f. $y = -1 + \sin(2x - \frac{\pi}{2})$

7-142. Farah and Thu were working on writing the equation of a sine function for the graph at right. They figured out that the amplitude is 3, the horizontal shift is $\frac{\pi}{4}$ and the midline is $y = -2$. They can see that the period is π, but they disagree on the equation. Farah has written $f(x) = 3\sin 2(x - \frac{\pi}{4}) - 2$ and Thu has written $f(x) = 3\sin(2x - \frac{\pi}{4}) - 2$.

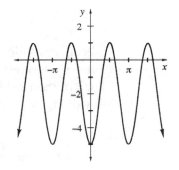

a. Whose equation is correct? How can you be sure?

b. Graph the incorrect equation and explain how it is different from the original graph.

7-143. Look back at the general equation you wrote for the family of sine functions in problem 7-114. Now that you have learned how the period affects the equation, work with your team to add a new parameter (call it *b*) that allows your general equation to account for any transformation of the sine function, including changes in the length of each cycle. Be prepared to share your general equation with the class.

7-144.   Use what you learned in class to complete parts (a) through (c) below.

    a.   Describe what the graph of $y = 3\sin(\frac{1}{2}x)$ will look like compared to the graph of $y = \sin x$.

    b.   Sketch both graphs on the same set of axes.

    c.   Explain the similarities and differences between the two graphs.

7-145.   What is the period of $y = \sin(2\pi x)$? How do you know?

7-146.   Colleen and Jolleen both used their calculators to find $\sin 30°$. Colleen got $\sin 30° = -0.9880316241$, but Jolleen got $\sin 30° = 0.5$. Is one of their calculators broken, or is something else going on? Why did they get different answers?

7-147.   Ceirin's teacher promised a quiz for the next day, so Ceirin called Adel to review what they had done in class. *"Suppose I have $y = \sin 2x$,"* said Ceirin, *"what will its graph look like?"*

"It will be horizontally compressed by a factor of 2," replied Adel, *"so the period must be π ."*

"Okay, now let's say I want to shift it one unit to the right. Do I just subtract 1 from x, like always?"

"I think so," said Adel, *"but let's check on the graphing calculator."* They proceeded to check on their calculators. After a few moments they both spoke at the same time.

"Rats," said Ceirin, *"it isn't right."*

"Cool," said Adel, *"it works."*

When they arrived at school the next morning, they compared the equations they had put in their graphing calculators while they talked on the phone. One had $y = \sin 2x - 1$, while the other had $y = \sin 2(x-1)$.

Which equation was correct? Did they both subtract 1 from x? Explain. Describe the rule for shifting a graph one unit to the right in a way that avoids this confusion.

7-148. George was solving the equation $(2x-1)(x+3)=4$ and he got the solutions $x=\frac{1}{2}$ and $x=-3$. Jeffrey came along and said, *"You made a big mistake! You set each factor equal to zero, but it's not equal to zero, it's equal to 4. So you have to set each factor equal to 4 and then solve."* Who is correct? Show George and Jeffrey how to solve this equation. To be sure that you are correct, check your solutions.

7-149. Compute the value of each expression without using a calculator.

    a. $\log(8)+\log(125)$ b. $\log_{25}(125)$

    c. $\frac{1}{2}\log(25)+\log(20)$ d. $7^{\log_7(12)}$

7-150. An exponential function $y=km^x+b$ passes through $(3, 7.5)$ and $(4, 6.25)$. It also has an asymptote at $y=5$.

    a.   Find the equation of the function.

    b.   If the equation also passes through $(8, w)$, what is the value of w?

7-151. Consider the equation $f(x)=3(x+4)^2-8$,

    a.   Find an equation of a function $g(x)$ such that $f(x)$ and $g(x)$ intersect in only one point.

    b.   Find an equation of a function $h(x)$ such that $f(x)$ and $h(x)$ intersect in no points.

7.2.4 What are the connections?

Graph $\leftrightarrow$ Equation

In the past few lessons, you have been developing the understanding necessary to graph a cyclic equation without making a table and to write an equation from a cyclic graph. In today's lesson, you will strengthen your understanding of the connections between a cyclic equation and its graph. By the end of this lesson, you will be able to answer the following questions:

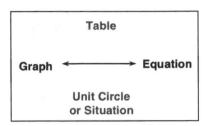

Does it matter if we use sine or cosine?

What do we need to know to make a complete graph or write an equation?

7-152.   What do you need to know about the sine or cosine functions to graph them or write their equations? Talk with your team and write a list of all of the attributes of a sine or cosine function that you need to know to write an equation and graph it.

7-153.   CREATE-A-CURVE

Split your team into pairs. With your partner, you will create your own sine or cosine function, write its equation, and draw its graph. Be sure to keep your equation and graph a secret! Start by choosing whether you will work with a sine or a cosine function.

a.   Half the distance from the highest point to the lowest point is called the **amplitude**. You can also think of amplitude as the vertical stretch. What is the amplitude of your function?

b.   How far to the left or right of the *y*-axis will your graph begin? In other words, what will be the **horizontal shift** of your function?

c.   How much above or below the *x*-axis will the center of your graph be? In other words, what will be the **midline** of your function?

d.   What will the **period** of your function be?

e.   What will the **orientation** of your graph in relation to $y = \sin x$ or $y = \cos x$ be? Is it the same or is it flipped?

f.   Now that you have decided on all of the attributes for your function, write its equation.

7-154.   Copy the equation for your curve from problem 7-153 on a clean sheet of paper. Trade papers with another pair of students.

   a.   Sketch a graph of the equation you received from the other pair of students.

   b.   When you are finished with your graph, give it back to the other pair so they can check the accuracy of your graph.

7-155.   When you look at a graph and prepare to write an equation for it, do you think it matters if you choose sine or cosine? Which do you think will work best?

   With your team, find *at least four* different equations for the graph at right. Be prepared to share your equations with the class.

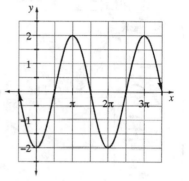

   a.   Did it matter if you choose sine or cosine?

   b.   Which of your equations do you prefer? Why?

7-156.   Brenna's mom, Mrs. Herstone, is watching Brenna playing at the park. Some children are pushing Brenna around the merry-go-round. Mrs. Herstone decides to take some data, so she started her stopwatch. At 0.5 seconds Brenna is farthest from Mrs. Herstone, 26 feet away. When the stopwatch reads 4.2 seconds, Brenna is closest at 12 feet away. Find a cyclic equation that models the distance Brenna is from Mrs. Herstone over time if the merry-go-round is spinning at a constant rate.

7-157.   LEARNING LOG

In your Learning Log, write your ideas about the target
questions for this lesson: *Does it matter if I use sine or
cosine? What do I need to know to make a complete graph
or write an equation?* Title this entry "Cyclic Equations
and Graphs" and label it with today's date.

METHODS AND MEANINGS

MATH NOTES

General Equation for Sine Functions

The general equation for the **sine function** is $y = a\sin[b(x - h)] + k$.

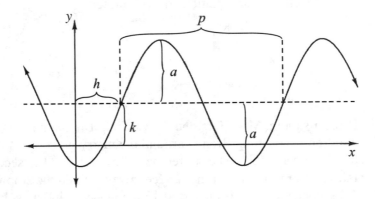

The **amplitude** (half of the distance between the highest and the lowest
points) is a.

The **period** is the length of one cycle. It is labeled p on the graph.

The number of cycles in 2π is b.

The **horizontal shift** is h.

The **vertical shift** is k. The **midline** is $y = k$.

 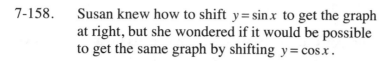

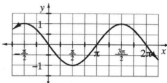

7-158.   Susan knew how to shift $y = \sin x$ to get the graph
at right, but she wondered if it would be possible
to get the same graph by shifting $y = \cos x$.

   a.   Is it possible to write a cosine function for
this graph?

   b.   If you think it is possible, find an equation that does it. If you think it is
impossible, explain why.

   c.   Adlai said, *"I can get that graph without shifting to the right or left."*
What equation did he write?

7-159.   In the function $y = 4\sin(6x)$, how many cycles of sine are there from 0 to 2π?
How long is each cycle (i.e., what is the period)?

7-160.   Write the equation of a cyclic function that has an amplitude of 7 and a period
of 8π. Sketch its graph.

7-161.   Recall the strategies you developed for converting degrees to radians. How
could you reverse that? Convert each of the following angle measures. Be sure
to show all of your work.

   a. π radians to degrees   b. 3π radians to degrees

   c.   30 degrees to radians   d. $\frac{\pi}{4}$ radians to degrees

   e.   225 degrees to radians   f. $\frac{3\pi}{2}$ radians to degrees

7-162.   Find the exact value for each of the following trig expressions. For parts (g) and
(h), assume that $0 \le \theta \le 2\pi$.

   a. $\cos\left(\frac{3\pi}{4}\right) =$ b. $\tan\left(\frac{4\pi}{3}\right) =$

   c. $\sin\left(\frac{11\pi}{6}\right) =$ d. $\sin\left(\frac{3\pi}{4}\right) =$

   e. $\tan\left(\frac{5\pi}{4}\right) =$ f. $\tan\left(\frac{17\pi}{6}\right) =$

   g. $\tan(\theta) = 1$ h. $\tan(\theta) = -1$

7-163.   Solve this system of equations: $5x - 4y - 6z = -19$
$$-2x + 2y + z = 5$$
$$3x - 6y - 5z = -16$$

7-164.   Use the Zero Product Property to solve each equation in parts (a) and (b) below.

a. $x(2x + 1)(3x - 5) = 0$ b. $(x - 3)(x - 2) = 12$

c.   Write an equation and show how you can use the Zero Product Property to solve it.

7-165.   Find a quadratic equation whose graph has each of the following characteristics:

a.   No x-intercepts and a negative y-intercept.

b.   One x-intercept and a positive y-intercept.

c.   Two x-intercepts and a negative y-intercept.

7-166.   A two-bedroom house in Seattle was worth $400,000 in 2005. If it appreciates at a rate of 3.5% each year:

a.   How much will it be worth in 2015?

b.   When will it be worth $800,000?

c.   In Jacksonville, houses are depreciating at 2% per year. If a house is worth $200,000 now, how much value will it have lost in 10 years?

Chapter 7 Closure What have I learned?

Reflection and Synthesis

The activities below offer you a chance to reflect about what you have learned during this chapter. As you work, look for concepts that you feel very comfortable with, ideas that you would like to learn more about, and topics you need more help with. Look for connections between ideas as well as connections with material you learned previously.

①   TEAM BRAINSTORM

What have you studied in this chapter? What ideas were important in what you learned? With your team, brainstorm a list. Be as detailed as you can. To help get you started, a list of Learning Log entries and Math Notes boxes are below.

What topics, ideas, and words that you learned *before* this chapter are connected to the new ideas in this chapter? Again, be as detailed as you can.

How long can you make your list? Challenge yourselves. Be prepared to share your team's ideas with the class.

Learning Log Entries
- Lesson 7.1.3 – Unit Circle ↔ Graph for $s(\theta) = \sin\theta$
- Lesson 7.1.5 – Radians
- Lesson 7.2.4 – Cyclic Equations and Graphs

Math Notes
- Lesson 7.1.2 – Special Right Triangle Relationships
- Lesson 7.1.5 – Radians
- Lesson 7.1.6 – Reference Angle
- Lesson 7.1.7 – Sine, Cosine, and Tangent
- Lesson 7.2.4 – General Equation for Sine Functions

②   MAKING CONNECTIONS

Below is a list of the vocabulary used in this chapter. Make sure that you are familiar with all of these words and know what they mean. Refer to the glossary or index for any words that you do not yet understand.

amplitude	angle	cosine
cyclic function	horizontal shift	midline
orientation	parameter	period
radian	reference angle	sine
special right triangles	tangent	theta (θ)
trigonometric functions	unit circle	vertical shift

Make a concept map showing all of the connections you can find among the key words and ideas listed above. To show a connection between two words, draw a line between them and explain the connection. A word can be connected to any other word as long as you can justify the connection.

While you are making your map, your team may think of related words or ideas that are not listed here. Be sure to include these ideas on your concept map.

PORTFOLIO: EVIDENCE OF MATHEMATICAL PROFICIENCY

This section gives you an opportunity to show growth in
your understanding of key mathematical ideas over time
as you complete this course.

Part 1: You may have done this problem before. You
have grown mathematically since then. Explain
everything that you know about $f(x) = 2^x - 3$. Be
sure to include everything you have learned since
the last time you did this problem.

Part 2: Compare your responses to this "Growth Over Time" problem. Write
an evaluation of your growth based on your responses. Consider each
of the following questions as you write your answer. If you only did the
problem twice, then answer accordingly.

- What new concepts did you include the second time you did the
  problem? In what ways was your response better than your first
  attempt?

- How was your final version different from the first two? What new
  ideas did you include?

- Did you omit anything in the final version that you used in one of the
  earlier versions? Why did you omit it?

- Rate your three attempts by making three bars like the ones below
  and shading each bar (left to right) to represent how much you knew
  on each attempt.

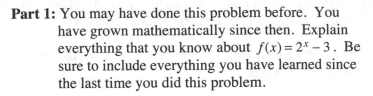

First Attempt:
Second
Final Attempt:

- Is there anything you want to add to your current version? If so, add
  it and keep this version for future reference.

Include a copy of the unit circle you built in Lesson 7.1.6 in your portfolio.
Make enhancements as necessary.

Your teacher may give you the Chapter 7 Closure Resource Page:
Trigonometric Functions and the Unit Circle Graphic Organizer page to
work on.

④　　　　　WHAT HAVE I LEARNED?

Most of the problems in this section represent typical problems found in this chapter. They serve as a gauge for you. You can use them to determine which types of problems you can do well and which types of problems require further study and practice. Even if your teacher does not assign this section, it is a good idea to try these problems and find out for yourself what you know and what you still need to work on.

Solve each problem as completely as you can. The table at the end of the closure section has answers to these problems. It also tells you where you can find additional help and practice with problems like these.

CL 7-167.　Describe how you can tell the difference between the graphs of $y = \sin x$ and $y = \cos x$. Be sure to justify your ideas.

CL 7-168.　Convert the following angles to radians.

　　a.　225°　　　b.　75°　　　　　c.　−15°　　　　d.　330°

CL 7-169.　Sketch each of the following angles in its own unit circle.

　　a.　An angle that has a positive cosine and a negative sine.

　　b.　All angles that have a sine of 0.5.

　　c.　An angle that measures $\frac{4\pi}{3}$ radians. Find its exact sine.

　　d.　An angle with a negative cosine and a positive tangent.

CL 7-170.　Without using a calculator, give the exact value of each expression.

　　a.　$\sin 60°$　　　　b.　$\cos 180°$　　　　c.　$\tan 225°$

　　d.　$\sin \frac{\pi}{4}$　　　　e.　$\cos \frac{2\pi}{3}$　　　　f.　$\tan \frac{3\pi}{2}$

CL 7-171.   If an angle between 0 and 2π radians has a sine of -0.5, what is its cosine? How do you know?

CL 7-172.   Find the exact values of x and y in the drawings below.

a.

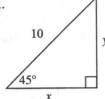

b.

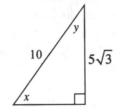

CL 7-173.   Rewrite each equation below in graphing form and sketch its graph. Then state the domain and range and whether or not it is a function.

a. $y = 3x^2 - 30x + 73$

b. $x^2 + y^2 - 6x + 4y + 4 = 0$

CL 7-174.   Solve each equation to the nearest thousandth.

a. $2 \cdot 3^x = 40.8$

b. $3x^4 = 27$

c. $\log_5(2x+1) = 3$

d. $\log(x) + \log(2x) = 5$

CL 7-175.   Find an equation for an exponential function that passes through the points $(1, 22), (3, 20.125)$, and has a horizontal asymptote at $y = 20$.

CL 7-176.   Check your answers using the table at the end of this section. Which problems do you feel confident about? Which problems were hard? Have you worked on problems like these in previous chapters math classes? Sort the problems into three groups: the ones you are confident you can do, the ones you need more practice with, and the ones you need further help to understand.

Note: MN = Math Note, LL = Learning Log

Problem	Solutions	Need Help?	More Practice
CL 7-167.	The graph of $y = \cos x$ has a y-intercept of 1 because $\cos 0 = 1$ and the base of the triangle at 0 degrees in the unit circle is 1 unit long. The graph of $y = \sin x$ has a y-intercept of 0 because $\sin 0 = 0$ and the height of the triangle at 0 degrees in the unit circle is 0 units.	Lessons 7.1.2, 7.1.3, and 7.1.4 MN: 7.1.7 LL: 7.2.4	Problems 7-14, 7-36, 7-47, 7-48, 7-50, 7-51, 7-54, 7-62, 7-63, 7-65, and 7-114
CL 7-168.	a. $\frac{5\pi}{4}$ b. $\frac{5\pi}{12}$ c. $-\frac{\pi}{12}$ d. $\frac{11\pi}{6}$	Lesson 7.1.5	Problems 7-77, 7-92, 7-106, 7-107, and 7-161
CL 7-169.	a. [unit circle diagram] b. [unit circle diagram] c. [unit circle diagram] $\sin\frac{4\pi}{3} = -\frac{\sqrt{3}}{2}$ d. [unit circle diagram]	Lessons 7.1.3 and 7.1.6 MN: 7.1.5	Problems 7-63, 7-75, and 7-104
CL 7-170.	a. $\frac{\sqrt{3}}{2}$ b. -1 c. 1 d. $\frac{\sqrt{2}}{2}$ e. $-\frac{1}{2}$ f. undefined	Lessons 7.1.5 and 7.1.6	Problems 7-78, 7-90, 7-104, 7-105, 7-123, and 7-162
CL 7-171.	$\frac{\sqrt{3}}{2}$ or $-\frac{\sqrt{3}}{2}$; If the sine is negative, the angle must lie in the 3rd or 4th quadrant and 0.5 is one leg of a 30°-60°-90° triangle.	Lessons 7.1.3, 7.1.4, and 7.1.6 MN: 7.1.7	Problem 7-34, 7-52, 7-63, 7-77, and 7-104

Problem	Solutions	Need Help?	More Practice
CL 7-172.	a. $x = 5\sqrt{2}$, $y = 5\sqrt{2}$ b. $x = 60°$, $y = 30°$	MN: 7.1.2	Problems 7-6 and 7-15
CL 7-173.	a. $y = 3(x-5)^2 - 2$, $-\infty < x < \infty$, $y \geq -2$; it is a function. b. $(x-3)^2 + (y+2)^2 = 9$, $0 \leq x \leq 6$, $-5 \leq y \leq 1$; it is not a function. 	Lessons 2.1.3, 2.1.4, and 2.2.3 Checkpoint 7B MN: 2.1.4 and 2.2.3	Problems 7-41, 7-109, 7-131, and 7-134
CL 7-174.	a. $x = 2.745$ b. $x \approx 1.732$ c. $x = 62$ d. $x = 223.607$	Lessons 6.2.1 and 6.2.2	Problems 7-18, 7-39, 7-83 part (a), 7-94, and 7-149
CL 7-175.	$y = 8(\frac{1}{4})^x + 20$	Lesson 6.2.3	Problems 7-20 and 7-136

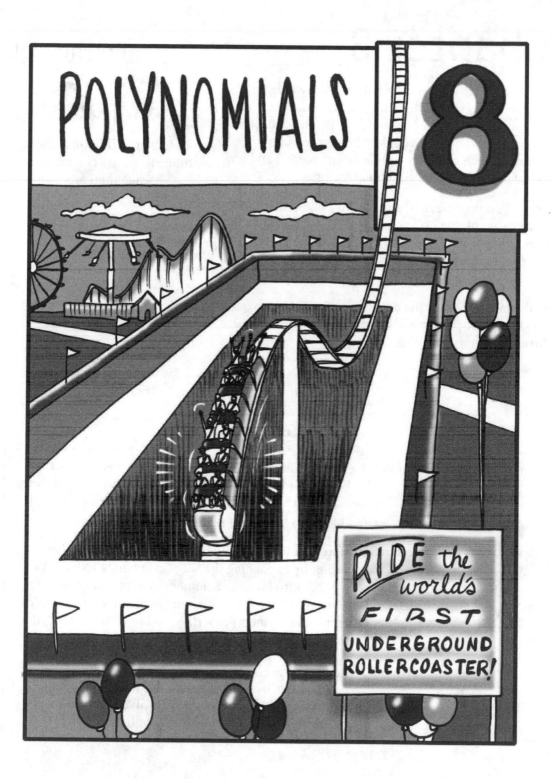

Chapter 8

In this chapter you will expand your knowledge of families of functions to include polynomial functions. As you investigate the equation ↔ graph connection for polynomials, you will learn how to search for factors (which can help you find *x*-intercepts) and how to use division to find additional factors.

When you investigate the graphs of polynomials and systems involving polynomials, you will see many that appear not to intersect. As you investigate these systems further, you will learn about imaginary and complex numbers.

In the last section of the chapter, you will apply your knowledge of polynomials to model some of the attractions at a county fair.

Guiding Question

Mathematically proficient students reason abstractly and quantitatively.

As you work through this chapter, ask yourself:

How can the degree of a polynomial help me determine the nature of its graph or a possible equation?

Chapter Outline

Section 8.1 You will investigate polynomial functions and learn how to sketch graphs of them without using a graphing calculator. You will also learn how to find polynomial equations from their graphs.

Section 8.2 Here you will solve equations you could not solve earlier by expanding the set of numbers you use. You will be introduced to a number system called *complex numbers*. You will learn what imaginary and complex numbers are, their properties, and how they are used to represent solutions when graphs do not intersect.

Section 8.3 In this section, you will learn how to divide polynomials by applying your knowledge of area models and factoring. You will solve equations using polynomial division to factor polynomials.

Core Connections Algebra 2

8.1.1   How can I describe the graph?

Sketching Graphs of Polynomial Functions

In previous courses and chapters, you learned how to graph many types of functions, including lines and parabolas. Today you will work with your team to apply what you know to more complicated **polynomial** equations. Just as quadratic polynomial equations can be written in standard or factored form, other polynomial equations can be written in standard or factored form. For example, $y = x^4 - 4x^3 - 3x^2 + 10x + 8$ is in standard form, but it can be written in factored form as $y = (x+1)^2(x-2)(x-4)$.

During this lesson, you will develop techniques for sketching the graph of a polynomial function from its equation, and you will justify why those techniques work.

8-1.   The Mathamericaland Carnival Company has decided to build a new roller coaster to use at this year's county fair. The new coaster will have a very special feature: part of the ride will be underground. The designers will use polynomial functions to describe different pieces of the track. Part of the design is shown at right. Your task is to guess a possible equation to represent the track and test it on your graphing calculator. To help get an idea of what to try, start by checking the graphs of the equations given below. Think about how the graphs are the same and how they are different.

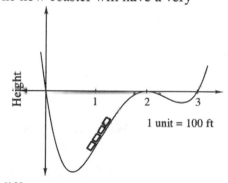

$$y = x(x-2)$$
$$y = (x-2)^2$$
$$y = x(x-2)(x-3)$$

Your Task: Use the information you found by graphing the above equations to help you make guesses about the equation that would produce the graph of the roller coaster. Once you have found a graph that has a shape close to this one, try zooming in or changing the viewing window on your graphing calculator to see the details better. Keep track of what you tried and the equations you find that fit most accurately.

8-2.   POLYNOMIAL FUNCTION INVESTIGATION

In this investigation, you will determine which information in a
polynomial equation can help you sketch its graph.

Your Task: With your team, create summary statements explaining the
relationship between a polynomial equation and its graph. To accomplish this
task, first divide up the equations listed below so each team member is
responsible for two or three of them. Make a complete graph of each of your
functions. Whenever possible, start by making a sketch of your graph without
using your graphing calculator. Then, as a team, share your observations
including your responses to the Discussion Points. Choose two or three
equations that can be used to represent all of your findings. You can choose
them from the list below, or you can create new ones as a team.

The form of your presentation to the class can be on a poster, a display to be
projected onto the board or as a PowerPoint™ presentation. Whichever format
your teacher decides, make sure you include complete graphs and summary
statements that are well justified.

$P_1(x) = (x-2)(x+5)^2$ $P_2(x) = 2(x-2)(x+2)(x-3)$

$P_3(x) = x^4 - 21x^2 + 20x$ $P_4(x) = (x+3)^2(x+1)(x-1)(x-5)$

$P_5(x) = -0.1x(x+4)^3$ $P_6(x) = x^4 - 9x^2$

$P_7(x) = 0.2x(x+1)(x-3)(x+4)$ $P_8(x) = x^4 - 4x^3 - 3x^2 + 10x + 8$

Discussion Points

What can we predict from looking at the equation of a polynomial?
Why does this make sense?

Which form of a polynomial equation is most useful for making a graph?
What information does it give?

How can we use the equation to help predict what a useful window might be?

Which examples are most helpful in finding the connections between the
equation and the graph?

How does changing the exponent on one of the factors change the graph?

8-3.   As a team, examine the first polynomial $P_1(x) = (x-2)(x+5)^2$.

a.   To which family of functions does it belong? How do you know? Based on its equation, sketch the shape of its graph.

b.   Now use your graphing calculator to graph $P_1(x)$. Label the x-intercepts. How are the x-intercepts related to the equation? "Reading" from left to right along the x-axis, describe the graph before the first x-intercept, between x-intercepts, and after the last x-intercept.

8-4.   Continuing your work as a team, examine the equation $P_2(x) = 2(x-2)(x+2)(x-3)$.

a.   How many distinct (different) factors are there? How many x-intercepts would you predict it would have on its graph? Draw the graph and label the x-intercepts. How is this graph similar to or different from the graph of $P_1(x)$?

b.   Does the factor 2 have any effect on the x-intercepts? On the shape of the graph? On the y-intercepts? How would the graph change if the factor 2 were changed to be a factor –2?

8-5.   What is different about $P_3(x) = x^4 - 21x^2 + 20x$? What x-intercept(s) can you determine from the equation, before graphing with the calculator? Explain how you know. Use the graph to figure out exactly what the other intercepts are. Explain how you can prove that your answers are exact.

8-6.   With your team, divide up the work to investigate $P_4(x)$ through $P_8(x)$ and continue your investigation, referring back to the "Your Task" statement and the discussion points in problem 8-2.

———————   *Further Guidance*   ———————
section ends here.

8-7.   LEARNING LOG

Based on what your team learned and on the class discussion that followed, record a list of useful strategies for graphing polynomial functions. Use as many of the new vocabulary words as you can and write down the ones you are not sure of yet. You will add to and refine this list over the next several lessons. Title this entry "Graphing Polynomials" and label it with today's date.

METHODS AND MEANINGS

Polynomials, Degree, Coefficients

Refer to the Math Notes box in Lesson 3.1.3 for an explanation of a **polynomial** in one variable.

Polynomials with one variable (often x) are usually arranged with powers of x in order, starting with the highest, left to right.

The highest power of the variable in a polynomial of one variable is called the **degree** of the polynomial. The numbers that multiply each term are called **coefficients**. See the examples below.

Example 1: $f(x) = 7x^5 + 2.5x^3 - \frac{1}{2}x + 7$ is a polynomial function of degree 5 with coefficients $7, 0, 2.5, 0, -\frac{1}{2}$, and 7. Note that the last term, 7, is called the **constant term** but represents the variable expression $7x^0$, since $x^0 = 1$.

Example 2: $y = 2(x+2)(x+5)$ is a polynomial in factored form with degree 2 because it can be written in standard form as $y = 2x^2 + 14x + 20$. It has coefficients 2, 14, and 20.

8-8. For each equation below, make tables that include x-values from -2 to 2 and draw each graph.

a. $y = (x-1)^2(x+1)$

b. $y = (x-1)^2(x+1)^2$

c. $y = x^3 - 4x$

d. What are the parent functions for these equations?

8-9.   **Polynomials** are expressions that can be written as a sum of terms of the form:

$$(\text{any number}) \cdot x^{(\text{whole number})}$$

Which of the following equations are polynomial equations? For those that are not polynomials, explain why not. Check the lesson 8.1.1 Math Notes box for further details about polynomials.

a. $f(x) = 8x^5 + x^2 + 6.5x^4 + 6$ b. $y = \frac{3}{5}x^6 + 19x^2$

c. $y = 2^x + 8$ d. $f(x) = 9 + \sqrt{x} - 3$

e. $P(x) = 7(x-3)(x+5)^2$ f. $y = x^2 + \frac{1}{x^2+5}$

g.   Write an equation for a new polynomial function and then write an equation for a new function that is not a polynomial.

8-10.   Describe the possible numbers of intersections for each of the following pairs of graphs. Sketch a graph for each possibility. For example, a circle could intersect a line twice, once, or not at all. Your solution to each part should include all of the possibilities and a sketched example of each one.

a.   Two different lines.   b.   A line and a parabola.

c.   Two different parabolas.   d.   A parabola and a circle.

8-11.   Solve the following system: $y = x^2 - 5$
$y = x + 1$

8-12. A table can be used as a useful tool for finding some inverse functions. When the function has only one x in it, the function can be described with a sequence of operations, each applied to the previous result. Consider the following table for $f(x) = 2\sqrt{x-1} + 3$.

	1st	2nd	3rd	4th
What f does to x:	subtracts 1	$\sqrt{}$	multiplies by 2	adds 3

Since the inverse must undo these operations, in the opposite order, the table for $f^{-1}(x)$ would look like the one below.

	1st	2nd	3rd	4th
What does f^{-1} to x:	subtracts 3	divides by 2	$(\ \ )^2$	adds 1

a. Copy and complete the following table for $g^{-1}(x)$ if $g(x) = \frac{1}{3}(x+1)^2 - 2$

	1st	2nd	3rd	4th
What g does to x:	adds 1	$(\ \ )^2$	divides by 3	subtracts 2
What g^{-1} does to x:			$\sqrt{}$	

b. Write the equations for $f^{-1}(x)$ and $g^{-1}(x)$.

8-13. Describe the difference between the graphs of $y = x^3 - x$ and $y = x^3 - x + 5$.

8-14. Sketch the graph of each equation below.

a. $y = \sin(2\pi x)$ b. $y = 3\sin(\pi x)$ c. $y = 2\sin(2\pi x) + 1$

8-15. An arithmetic sequence starts out $-23, -19, -15 \ldots$

a. What is the equation?

b. How many times must the generator be applied so that the result is greater than 10,000?

8-16. Without a calculator, find two solutions $0° \le \theta < 360°$ that make each of the following equations true.

a. $\cos\theta = \frac{1}{2}$ b. $\tan\theta = -1$ c. $\sin\theta = \frac{\sqrt{3}}{2}$ d. $\cos\theta = -\frac{\sqrt{3}}{2}$

8-17.   Which of the following equations are polynomial functions? For each one that is not, justify why not.

a. $y = 3x^2 + 2x^2 + x$ b. $y = (x-1)^2(x-2)^2$

c. $y = x^2 + 2^x$ d. $y = 3x - 1$

e. $y = (x-2)^2 - 1$ f. $y^2 = (x-2)^2 - 1$

g. $y = \frac{1}{x^2} + \frac{1}{x} + \frac{1}{2}$ h. $y = \frac{1}{2}x + \frac{1}{3}$

i. $y = x$ j. $y = -7$

8-18.   Samantha thinks that the equation $(x-4)^2 + (y-3)^2 = 25$ is equivalent to the equation $(x-4)+(y-3)=5$. Is she correct? Are the two equations equivalent? Explain how you know. If they are not equivalent, explain Samantha's mistake.

8-19.   Find the **roots** (the solutions when $y = 0$) of each of the following polynomial functions.

a. $y = x^2 - 6x + 8$ b. $f(x) = x^2 - 6x + 9$ c. $y = x^3 - 4x$

8-20.   Sketch a graph of $y = x^2 - 7$.

a.   How many roots does this graph have?

b.   What are the roots of the function?

8-21.   Solve $x^2 + 2x - 5 = 0$.

a.   How many x-intercepts does $y = x^2 + 2x - 5$ have?

b.   Approximately where does the graph of $y = x^2 + 2x - 5$ cross the x-axis?

8-22.   Graph the inequality $x^2 + y^2 \le 25$, and then describe its graph in words.

8-23.   Find x if $2^{p(x)} = 4$ and $p(x) = x^2 - 4x - 3$.

8-24.   Start with the graph of $y = 3^x$, then write new equations that will shift the graph as described below.

    a.   Down 4 units.   b.   Right 7 units.

8-25.   THE COUNTY FAIR FERRIS WHEEL

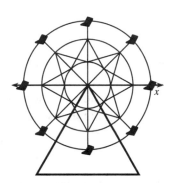

Consider this picture of a Ferris wheel. The wheel has a 60-foot diameter and is drawn on a set of axes with the Ferris wheel's hub (center) at the origin. Use a table like the one below and draw a graph that relates the angle (in standard position) of the spoke leading to your seat to the approximate height of the top of your seat above or below the height of the central hub. The table below starts at $-90°$, your starting position before you ride around the wheel.

x (angle)	$-90°$	$-45°$	$0°$	$45°$	$90°$	$135°$	$180°$	....	$270°$
y (height)	$-30'$								

    a.   The wheel goes around (counter-clockwise) several times during a ride. How could you reflect this fact in your graph? Update your graph.

    b.   What is the maximum distance above or below the center that the top of your seat attains during the ride?

    c.   Find an equation to fit the County Fair Ferris wheel ride.

8.1.2 How can I predict the graph?

. . . .

More Graphs of Polynomials

Today you will use what you learned in the Polynomial Function Investigation in Lesson 8.1.1 to respond to some questions. Thinking about how to answer these questions should help you clarify and expand on some of your ideas as well as help you learn how to use the polynomial vocabulary.

8-26.   As directed by your teacher, use your finger to trace an approximate graph of polynomial functions in the air. Alternatively, you may sketch each of the polynomial functions below quickly on paper. Just sketch the graph without the x- and y-axes.

   a. $P(x) = (x+10)(x+7)(x-12)$

   b. $Q(x) = (x+6)(x+3)(x-5)(x-8)$

   c. $R(x) = -(x+4)(x+2)(x-6)(x-10)$

   d. $W(x) = (x+7)^2(x-7)^2$

   e. $S(x) = (x+6)(x+3)(x-5)(x-8)(x-12)$

8-27.   Look back at the work you did in Lesson 8.1.1 problem 8-2, Polynomial Function Investigation. Then answer the following questions.

   a.   What is the maximum number of roots a polynomial of degree 3 can have? Sketch an example.

   b.   What do you think is the maximum number of roots a polynomial of degree n can have?

   c.   Can a polynomial of degree n have fewer than n roots? Under what conditions?

8-28.   For each polynomial function shown below, state the minimum degree its equation could have.

i.   ii.   iii.   iv.

a.   Which of the graphs above show that as the x-values get very large, the y-values continue to get larger and larger?

b.   How would you describe the other graphs for very large x-values?

c.   When the y-values of a graph get very large as the x-values get large, the graph has **positive orientation**. When the y-values of a graph get very small as the x-values get large, the graph has **negative orientation**. How is each of the above graphs oriented?

8-29.   For each graph in problem 8-28, you decided what the minimum degree of its equation could be. Under what circumstances could graphs that look the same as these have polynomial equations of a *higher* degree?

Consider the graphs of $y = (x-1)^2$ and $y = (x-1)^4$.

a.   How are these graphs similar? How are they different?

b.   Could the equation for graph (*ii*) from the previous problem be degree 4?

c.   Could it have degree 5? Explain.

d.   How is the graph of $y = x^3$ similar to or different from the graph of $y = x^5$?

e.   How do the shapes of graphs of $y = (x-2)^3$ and $y = (x+1)^5$ with repeated factors differ from the shapes of graphs of equations that have three or five factors that are different from one another?

8-30.   In the first example from the Polynomial Function Investigation, $P_1(x) = (x-2)(x+5)^2$, $(x+5)^2$ is a factor. This squared factor produces what is called a **double root** of the function.

a.   What effect does this have on the graph?

b.   Check your equations for a **triple root**. What effect does a triple root have on the graph?

8-31.   You can use a number line to represent the x-values for which a polynomial graph is above or below the x-axis. The bold parts of each number line below show where the output values of a polynomial function are positive. That is, where the graph is above the x-axis. The open circles show locations of the x-intercepts or roots of the function. Where there is no shading, the value of the function is negative. Sketch a possible graph to fit each number line, and then write a possible equation. Each number line represents the x-axis for a different polynomial.

a.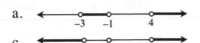

b.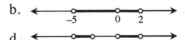

c.

d.

8-32.   What can you say about the graphs of polynomial functions with an even degree compared to the graphs of polynomial functions with an odd degree? Use graphs from the Polynomial Functions Investigation (and maybe some others) to justify your response.

8-33.   Choose three of the polynomials you graphed in the Polynomial Functions Investigation (problem 8-2) and create number lines for their graphs similar to the ones in problem 8-31.

$P_1(x) = (x-2)(x+5)^2$ $P_2(x) = 2(x-2)(x+2)(x-3)$

$P_3(x) = x^4 - 21x^2 + 20x$ $P_4(x) = (x+3)^2(x+1)(x-1)(x-5)$

$P_5(x) = -0.1x(x+4)^3$ $P_6(x) = x^4 - 9x^2$

$P_7(x) = 0.2x(x+1)(x-3)(x+4)$ $P_8(x) = x^4 - 4x^3 - 3x^2 + 10x + 8$

8-34.   Create a new number-line description (like the ones in problem 8-31) and then trade with a partner. (Each team member should create a different number line.) After you have traded, find a possible graph and equation for a polynomial function to fit the description you have received. Then justify your results to your team and check your team members' results.

8-35.   Without using a calculator, sketch rough graphs of the following functions.

a. $P(x) = -x(x+1)(x-3)$

b. $P(x) = (x-1)^2(x+2)(x-4)$

c. $P(x) = (x+2)^3(x-4)$

METHODS AND MEANINGS

Roots and Zeros

MATH NOTES

The **roots** of a polynomial function, $p(x)$, are the **solutions** of the equation $p(x)=0$. Another name for the roots of a function is **zeros of the function** because at each root, the value of the function is zero. The real roots (or zeros) of a function have the same value as the x-values of the x-intercepts of its graph because the x-intercepts are the points where the y-value of the function is zero.

Sometimes roots can be found by factoring and solving for $p(x)=0$.

In the Parabola Lab investigation (Lesson 2.1.2), you discovered how to make a parabola "sit" on the x-axis (the polynomial has one root), and you looked at ways of making parabolas intersect the x-axis in two specific places (two roots).

8-36.   Where does the graph $y=(x+3)^2-5$ cross the x-axis?

8-37.   If you were to graph the function $f(x)=(x-74)^2(x+29)$, where would the graph intersect the x-axis?

8-38.   For each pair of intercepts given below, write an equation for a quadratic function in standard form.

   a. $(-3,0)$ and $(2,0)$ b. $(-3,0)$ and $(\frac{1}{2},0)$

8-39.   What is the degree of each polynomial function below?

   a. $P(x)=0.08x^2+28x$ b. $y=8x^2-\frac{1}{7}x^5+9$

   c. $f(x)=5(x+3)(x-2)(x+7)$ d. $y=(x-3)^2(x+1)(x^3+1)$

8-40.   Consider the graphs of the following types of functions. Which functions are polynomial functions? Explain your reasoning.

    a.   Parabolas   b.   Exponentials

    c.   Cubics   d.   Lines

    e.   Circles

8-41.   Graph each system below and shade the solution region.

    a. $y \geq x^2 - 4$ b. $y < 2x + 5$
         $y < -3x + 1$ $y \geq |x + 1|$

8-42.   A circle with its center on the line $y = 3x$ in the 1st quadrant is tangent to the y-axis.

    a.   If the radius is 2, what is the equation of the circle?

    b.   If the radius is 3, what is the equation of the circle?

8-43.   Sketch the graph of each function below on the same set of axes.

    a. $y = 2^x$ b. $y = 2^x + 5$ c. $y = 2^x - 5$

8-44.   For each equation, find two solutions $0° \leq \theta < 360°$, which make the equation true. You should not need a calculator.

    a. $\sin\theta = \frac{1}{2}$ b. $\tan\theta = \sqrt{3}$

    c. $\cos\theta = \frac{\sqrt{3}}{2}$ d. $\sin\theta = -\frac{\sqrt{2}}{2}$

8.1.3 How can I find the equation?

Stretch Factors for Polynomial Functions

In Lesson 8.1.2 you found possible equations for the graphs of polynomial functions based on their x-intercepts. Many of the sketches you used did not even include the scale on the y-axis. In this lesson, you will focus on figuring out equations that represent *all* of the points on the graphs.

8-45.   Find reasonable equations for each of the following polynomial functions. Without using a graphing calculator, how can you check the accuracy of your equations? Were each of your equations accurate? If not, why do you think your equation(s) were not accurate?

a.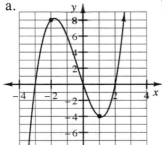

b.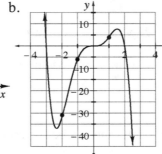

c.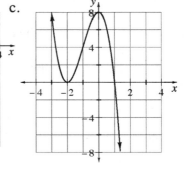

8-46.   What is the difference between the graphs of the functions $y = x^2(x-3)(x+1)$ and $y = 3x^2(x-3)(x+1)$?

8-47.   ARE THE INTERCEPTS ENOUGH?

Melvin wrote the equation
$y = (x+3)(x+1)(x-2)^2$ to represent the graph
at right.

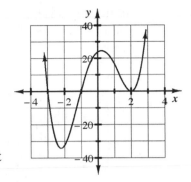

a.   Explain how you can decide whether the
equation represents the graph. What can
you do to the equation to make it a better
fit for the graph? What equation would fit
better?

b.   Before you figured it out, you could have written the polynomial for this
graph as $P(x) = a(x+3)(x+1)(x-2)^2$. What if you did not have a graphing
calculator, but you were told that the graph goes through the point $(1, 16)$?
How could you use that information to determine the exact equation?
Once you have decided on a method with your team, try it. How can you
test the accuracy of your equation?

8-48.   THE COUNTY FAIR COASTER RIDE

Now that you have more expertise with
polynomial equations and their graphs,
the Mathamericaland Carnival Company
has hired your team to find the *exact*
equation to represent its roller-coaster
track.

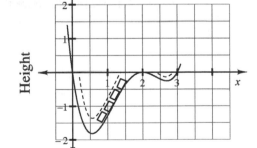

The numbers along the x-axis are in
hundreds of feet. At 250 feet from the
starting point, the track will be 20 feet
below the surface. This gives the
point $(2.5, -0.2)$.

a.   What degree polynomial
represents the portion of the
roller coaster represented by the
graph at right?

b.   What are the roots?

c.   Find an exact equation for the polynomial that will generate the curve of
the track.

d.   What is the deepest point of the roller coaster's tunnel?

8-49.   Some polynomials have a stretch factor, just like the a in parabolas and other parent functions. Write an exact equation, including the stretch factor, for each graph below.

a.

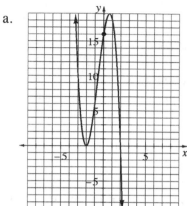

b.

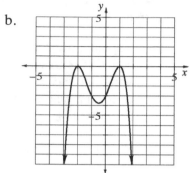

8-50.   Write a polynomial equation for a function with a graph that bounces off the x-axis at $(-1,0)$, crosses it at $(4,0)$, and goes through the point $(-2,-18)$.

8-51.   Armando came up with the equation $y = 3(x+1)^4(x-4)$ for problem 8-50. Does his equation fit all of the given criteria? Why or why not? Is it the same as the equation you came up with?

8-52.   What if problem 8-50 also had said that the graph went through the point $(1,-36)$? Is there still more than one possible equation? Explain.

8-53.   What information about the graph of a polynomial function is necessary to determine exactly one correct equation? Discuss this with your team.

METHODS AND MEANINGS

Notation for Polynomials

The **general equation** of a second-degree (quadratic) polynomial is often written in the form $f(x) = ax^2 + bx + c$, and the general equation of a third-degree (cubic) polynomial is often written in the form $f(x) = ax^3 + bx^2 + cx + d$.

For a polynomial with an undetermined degree n, it is unknown how many letters will be needed for the coefficients. Instead of using a, b, c, d, e, etc., mathematicians use only the letter a, and they used subscripts, as shown below.

$$f(x) = (a_n)x^n + (a_{n-1})x^{(n-1)} + \ldots + (a_1)x^1 + a_0$$

This general polynomial has degree n and coefficients a_n, a_{n-1}, ..., a_1, a_0.

For example, for $7x^4 - 5x^3 + 3x^2 + 7x + 8$, the degree is 4. In this specific case, a_n is a_4 and $a_4 = 7$, a_{n-1} is $a_3 = -5$, a_{n-2} is $a_2 = 3$, $a_1 = 7$, and $a_0 = 8$.

8-54. What is the stretch factor for the equation of the graph in part (c) of problem 8-45? Write the exact equation of the function.

8-55. For each of the following polynomial expressions, find the degree, list the coefficients, and then label them a_0 through a_n. Refer to the example in the Math Notes box above about polynomial notation.

    a. $6x^4 - 3x^3 + 5x^2 + x + 8$ b. $-5x^3 + 10x^2 + 8$ c. $-x^2 + x$

    d. $x(x-3)(x-5)$ e. x f.   10

8-56. Write a polynomial equation for a graph that passes through the point $(-1, 60)$ and has three x-intercepts: $(-4, 0), (1, 0)$, and $(3, 0)$.

8-57. The x-intercepts of a quadratic polynomial are given below. Find a possible quadratic equation in standard form.

    a. $x = \frac{3}{4}, x = -2$ b. $x = -\sqrt{5}, x = \sqrt{5}$

8-58. Solve the equation $\sqrt{5 - 2x} + 7 = 4$ and check your solution.

8-59. Find the center and radius of each circle below.

    a. $(y - 7)^2 = 25 - (x - 3)^2$ b. $x^2 + y^2 + 10y = -9$

    c. $x^2 + y^2 + 18x - 8y + 47 = 0$ d. $y^2 + (x - 3)^2 = 1$

8-60. Without using a calculator, find the solution to each equation.

    a. $2^x = 17$ b. $\log_3(x + 1) = 5$

    c. $\log_3(3^x) = 4$ d. $4^{\log_4(x)} = 7$

8-61. Solve each absolute value inequality.

    a. $|2x + 1| < 5$ b. $2|3x - 2| \geq 10$

8-62. Write a possible equation for the graph at right.

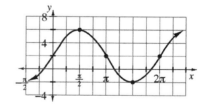

8.2.1 What are imaginary numbers?

· ·

Introducing Imaginary Numbers

In the past, you have not been able to solve some quadratic equations like $x^2 + 4 = 0$ and $x^2 + 1 = 0$, because there are no real numbers you can square to get a negative answer. To solve this issue, mathematicians created a new, expanded number system based on one new number. However, this was not the first time mathematicians had invented new numbers! To read about other such inventions, refer to the Historical Note that follows problem 8-63.

In this lesson, you will learn about imaginary numbers and how you can use them to solve equations you were previously unable to solve.

8-63.   Consider the equation $x^2 = 2$.

    a.   How do you "undo" squaring a number?

    b.   When you solve $x^2 = 2$, how many solutions should you get?

    c.   How many x-intercepts does the graph of $y = x^2 - 2$ have?

    d.   Solve the equation $x^2 = 2$. Write your solutions both as radicals and as decimal approximations.

Historical Note: Irrational Numbers

In Ancient Greece, people believed that all numbers could be written as fractions of whole numbers (what are now called **rational numbers**). Many individuals realized later that some numbers could not be written as fractions (such as $\sqrt{2}$), and these individuals challenged the accepted beliefs. Some of the people who challenged the beliefs were exiled or outright killed over these challenges!

The Greeks knew that for a one-unit square, the length of the diagonal, squared, yielded 2. When it was shown that no rational number could do that, the existence of what are called **irrational numbers** was accepted and symbols like $\sqrt{2}$ were invented to represent them.

The problem $x^2 = 3$ also has no rational solutions; fractions can never work exactly. The rational (i.e., decimal) solutions that calculators and computers provide are only approximations; the exact answer can only be represented in radical form, namely, $\pm\sqrt{3}$.

8-64.   Mathematicians throughout history have resisted the idea that some equations may not be solvable. Still, it makes sense that $x^2 + 1 = 0$ cannot be solved because the graph of $y = x^2 + 1$ has no x-intercepts. What happens when you try to solve $x^2 + 1 = 0$?

Historical Note: Imaginary Numbers

In some ways, each person's math education parallels the history of mathematical discovery. When you were much younger, if you were asked, *"How many times does 3 go into 8?"* or *"What is 8 divided by 3?"* You might have said, *"3 doesn't go into 8."* Then you learned about numbers other than whole numbers, and the question had an answer. Later, if you were asked, *"What number squared makes 5?"* you might have said, *"No number squared makes 5."* Then you learned about numbers other than rational numbers, and you could answer that question.

Similarly, until about 500 years ago, the answer to the question, *"What number squared makes –1?"* was, *"No number squared makes –1."* Then something remarkable happened. An Italian mathematician named Bombelli used a formula for finding the roots of third-degree polynomials. Within the formula was a square root, and when he applied the formula to a particular equation, the number under the square root came out negative. Instead of giving up, he had a brilliant idea. He had already figured out that the equation had a solution, so he decided to see what would happen if he pretended that there *was* a number he could square to make a negative. Remarkably, he was able to continue the calculation, and eventually the "imaginary" number disappeared from the solution. More importantly, the resulting answer worked; it solved his original equation. This led to the acceptance of these so-called **imaginary numbers**. The name stuck, and mathematicians became convinced that all quadratic equations do have solutions. Of course, in some situations you will only be interested in real number solutions (that is, solutions not having an imaginary part).

8-65.   In the 1500s, an Italian mathematician named Rafael Bombelli invented the imaginary number $\sqrt{-1}$, which is now called i. $\sqrt{-1} = i$ implies that $i^2 = -1$. After this invention, it became possible to find solutions for $x^2 + 1 = 0$; they are i and $-i$. The value of $\sqrt{-16} = \sqrt{16(-1)} = \sqrt{16i^2} = 4i$. Use the definition of i to rewrite each of the following expressions.

a. $\sqrt{-4}$ b. $(2i)(3i)$ c. $(2i)^2(-5i)$ d. $\sqrt{-25}$

Core Connections Algebra 2

8-66.   Graph the function $y = x^2 - 4x + 5$.

     a.   Does the graph cross the x-axis? Should the equation $x^2 - 4x + 5 = 0$ have real solutions?

     b.   Use the Quadratic Formula to solve $x^2 - 4x + 5 = 0$. Use your new understanding of imaginary numbers to simplify your results as much as possible.

     c.   A real number plus (or minus) a multiple of i, like each of the solutions to $x^2 - 4x + 5 = 0$, is called a **complex number**. Check one of your solutions from part (b) by substituting it into the equation for x and simplifying the result.

8-67.   When a graph crosses the x-axis, the x-intercepts are often referred to as the **real roots** of the equation that results when $y = 0$. You have seen that solutions to equations can be real or complex, so it follows that roots can also be real or complex. Compare and contrast what happens with the graphs and equations for the three cases in parts (a) through (c) below.

     a.   Sketch the graph of $y = (x + 3)^2 - 4$. What are the roots?

     b.   Sketch the graph of $y = (x + 3)^2$. What are the roots?

     c.   Sketch the graph of $y = (x + 3)^2 + 4$. Can you find the roots by looking at the graph? Why or why not? Find the roots by solving $(x + 3)^2 + 4 = 0$.

     d.   Make general statements about the relationship between graphs of parabolas and the kinds of roots their equations have.

8-68.   Consider the equations $y = x^2$ and $y = 2x - 5$.

     a.   On one set of axes, sketch the graphs and label the intersection.

     b.   Use algebra to solve the system of equations.

     c.   Discuss your results with your team. What could these solutions mean?

8-69.   Do the graphs of $y = \frac{1}{x}$ and $y = -x + 1$ intersect? What kind of algebraic solutions will this system have? Verify your answer by solving the system.

METHODS AND MEANINGS

Imaginary and Complex Numbers

MATH NOTES

The **imaginary number** that solves the equation $x^2 = -1$ is i, so $i^2 = -1$, and the two solutions of the equation are i and $-i$.

In general, i follows the rules of real number arithmetic. The sum of two imaginary numbers is imaginary (unless it is 0). Multiplying the imaginary number i by every possible real number would yield the set of all the imaginary numbers.

The set of numbers that solve equations of the form $x^2 =$ (a negative real number) is called the set of **imaginary numbers**. Imaginary numbers are not positive, negative, or zero. The collection (set) of positive and negative numbers (integers, rational numbers (fractions), and irrational numbers), are referred to as the **real numbers**.

The sum of a real number (other than zero) and an imaginary number, such as $2 + i$, is generally neither real nor imaginary. Numbers such as these, which can be written in the form $a + bi$, where a and b are real numbers, are called **complex numbers**. Each complex number has a real component, a, and an imaginary component, bi. The real numbers are considered to be complex numbers with $b = 0$, and the imaginary numbers are complex numbers with $a = 0$.

8-70.   Write each of the following expressions in the form $a + bi$.

    a. $-18 - \sqrt{-25}$ b. $\frac{2 \pm \sqrt{-16}}{2}$ c. $5 + \sqrt{-6}$

8-71.   Explain why $i^3 = -i$. What does i^4 equal?

8-72.   If $f(x) = x^2 + 7x - 9$, calculate the values in parts (a) through (c) below.

    a. $f(-3)$ b. $f(i)$ c. $f(-3 + i)$

8-73.   Is $5 + 2i$ a solution to $x^2 - 10x = -29$? How can you be sure?

8-74.   Solve $16^{(x+2)} = 8^x$.

8-75.   Is $(x-5)^2$ equivalent to $(5-x)^2$? Explain why or why not.

8-76.   Calculate the value of each expression below.

      a. $\sqrt{-49}$ b. $\sqrt{-2}$ c. $(4i)^2$ d. $(3i)^3$

8-77.   Find the inverse functions below.

      a.   If $f(x) = 2x - 3$, then what does $f^{-1}(x)$ equal?

      b.   If $h(x) = (x-3)^2 + 2$, then what does $h^{-1}(x)$ equal?

8-78.   Solve each equation.

      a. $5.2(3.75)^x = 100$ b. $4 + 3x^4 = 81$

8.2.2 What are complex roots?

Complex Roots

In this lesson, you will solve equations as well as reverse your thinking to investigate the relationship between the complex solutions to a quadratic equation and the equation from which these solutions came.

8-79.   Find the roots of each of the following quadratic functions by solving for x when $y = 0$. Does the graph of either of these functions intersect the x-axis?

a. $y = (x+5)^2 + 9$

b. $y = x^2 - 4x + 9$

8-80.   What do you notice about the complex solutions in problem 8-79? Describe any patterns you see. Discuss these patterns with your team and write all of your observations.

8-81.   In parts (a) through (d) below, look for patterns as you calculate the sum and the product for each pair of complex numbers. Use what you find to answer parts (e) through (g).

a. $2 + i,\ 2 - i$

b. $3 - 5i,\ 3 + 5i$

c. $-4 + i,\ -4 - i$

d. $1 + i\sqrt{3}, 1 - i\sqrt{3}$

e.   What complex number can you multiply $3 + 2i$ by to get a real number?

f.   What happens when you multiply $(-4 + 5i)(-4 + 3i)$?

g.   What complex number can you multiply $a + bi$ by to get a real number?

8-82.   WHAT EQUATION HAS THESE SOLUTIONS?

Each of the four pairs of complex numbers in problem 8-81 could be the roots of a quadratic function.

Your Task: With your team, create a quadratic equation for each pair of complex numbers in parts (a) through (d) of problem 8-81 such that those numbers are the roots. Discuss the methods you use for writing the equations and write summary statements describing your methods.

Discussion Points

How can we reverse the process of solving?

How can we use what we know about factors and zeros?

How are the solutions related to the standard form of the equation?

Further Guidance

8-83.   Problem 8-81 made Mariposa curious about sums and products. She decided to solve the equation $x^2 - 6x + 25 = 0$ and look at the sums and products of its solutions. What patterns can you help her find that might give her ideas about the equation once she knows the solutions?

8-84.   Austin had another idea. He knew that if 3 and –5 were solutions of a quadratic equation then $(x - 3)$ and $(x + 5)$ would be factors that could be multiplied to get a quadratic polynomial. How could his idea be used with the pairs of complex solutions in problem 8-81? Choose one pair and show how to use your idea.

8-85.   Melvin had still another idea. "Why not just let $x = -4 \pm i$ and work backwards?" He asked. Would his idea work?

─────────   *Further Guidance*   ─────────
                 section ends here.

8-86.   For each pair of numbers below, find a quadratic equation that has these numbers as solutions.

a. $\frac{3}{4}$ and –5   b. $3i$ and $-3i$

c. $5 + 2i$ and $5 - 2i$ d. $-3 + \sqrt{2}$ and $-3 - \sqrt{2}$

Review & Preview

8-87.   For each of the following sets of numbers, find the equation of a function that has these numbers as roots.

a. $-3 + i$ and $-3 - i$

b. $5 + \sqrt{3}$ and $5 - \sqrt{3}$

c. $-2, \sqrt{7}$, and $-\sqrt{7}$

d. $4, -3 + i$, and $-3 - i$

8-88. Raul claims that he has a shortcut for deciding what kind of roots a function has. Jolene thinks that a shortcut is not possible. She says you just have to solve the quadratic equation to find out. They are working on $y = x^2 - 5x - 14$.

Jolene says, *"See, I just start out by trying to factor. This one can be factored $(x - 7)(x + 2) = 0$, so the equation will have two real solutions and the function will have two real roots."*

"But what if it can't be factored?" Raul asked. *"What about $x^2 + 2x + 2 = 0$?"*

"That's easy! I just use the Quadratic Formula," says Jolene. *"And I get... let's see... negative two plus or minus the square root of... two squared... that's 4... minus... eight..."*

"Wait!" Raul interrupted. *"Right there, see, you don't have to finish. 2^2 minus $4 \cdot 2$, that gives you -4. That's all you need to know. You'll be taking the square root of a negative number so you will get a complex result."*

"Oh, I see," said Jolene. *"I only have to consider part of the solution, the inside of the square root."*

Use Raul's method to tell whether each of the following functions has real or complex roots without completely solving the equation. Note: Raul's method is also summarized in the Math Notes box for this lesson.

a. $y = 2x^2 + 5x + 4$
b. $y = 2x^2 + 5x - 3$

8-89. Sketch the graphs and find the area of the intersection of the inequalities below.

$$y > |x + 3|$$
$$y \le 5$$

8-90. Consider this geometric sequence: $i^0, i^1, i^2, i^3, i^4, i^5, ..., i^{15}$.

a. You know that $i^0 = 1$, $i^1 = i$, and $i^2 = -1$. Calculate the result for each term up to i^{15}, and describe the pattern.

b. Use the pattern you found in part (a) to calculate i^{16}, i^{25}, i^{39}, and i^{100}.

c. What is i^{4n}, where n is a positive whole number?

d. Based on your answer to part (c), simplify i^{4n+1}, i^{4n+2}, and i^{4n+3}.

e. Calculate i^{396}, i^{397}, i^{398}, and i^{399}.

8-91.   Use the pattern from the previous problem to help you to evaluate the following expressions.

a. i^{592} b. i^{797} c. $i^{10,648,202}$

8-92.   Describe how you would evaluate i^n where n could be any integer.

8-93.   Show how to solve the equations below *without* using your calculator. You will have radicals or logarithms in your answers.

a. $3^x = 17$ b. $x^3 = 17$

8-94.   Match each equation with the appropriate graph. Do this without using a graphing calculator.

a. $y = \sin(x + \frac{\pi}{2})$ b. $y = \sin(2x)$ c. $y = 2\sin(\frac{x}{2})$

d. $y = \sin(x) - 3$ e. $y = -\sin[2(x - \frac{\pi}{8})]$

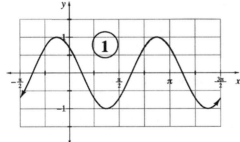

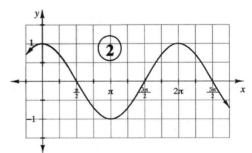

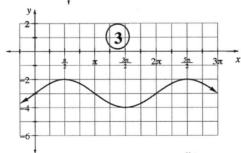

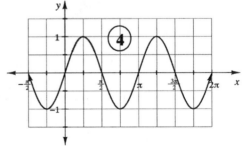

8-95.　The La Quebrada Cliff Divers perform shows for the public by jumping into the sea off the cliffs at Acapulco, Mexico. The height (in feet) of a diver at a certain time (in seconds) is given by $h = -16t^2 + 16t + 400$.

    a.　Use the vertex and y-intercept to make a sketch that represents the dive. What form of the quadratic function helps you determine the y-intercept efficiently? What form helps you determine the vertex easily?

    b.　At what height did the diver start his jump? What is the maximum height he achieved?

8-96.　Consider the graph at right.

    a.　What is the parent for this function?

    b.　What is the equation of the vertical asymptote?

    c.　Write a possible equation for this graph.

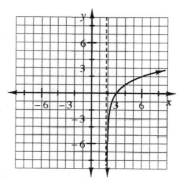

8.2.3 Where are the complex numbers?

More Complex Numbers and Equations

If the number line is filled with real numbers, how can imaginary and complex numbers be represented geometrically? In this lesson, you will learn a way to graph complex numbers and interpret the graphical meaning of complex solutions.

8-97.   Avi and Tran were trying to figure out how they could represent complex numbers geometrically. Avi decided to make a number line horizontal like the x-axis to represent the real part as well as a vertical line like the y-axis to represent the imaginary part.

   a.   Draw a set of axes and label them as Avi described.

   b.   How could Avi and Tran graph a point to represent the complex number $3 + 4i$? Be prepared to share your strategies with the class.

   c.   Use the method from part (b) to plot points to represent the six numbers below.

   i. $2 + 5i$ *ii.* $6 - i$ *iii.* $-5 - 3i$

   iv. 4 *v.* $7i$ *vi.* $-4 + 2i$

8-98.   On a new set of **complex axes** (like those drawn by Avi and Tran in problem 8-97), locate points representing all of the following complex numbers.

   a. $3 + 4i$, $3 - 4i$, $-3 + 4i$, and $-3 - 4i$.

   b.   The four complex numbers represented by $\pm 4 \pm 3i$.

   c. 5, -5, $5i$, and $-5i$

   d.   What do you notice about your graph? How far from $(0, 0)$ is each point?

8-99.   On the real number line, the distance from 0 to a point on the line is defined as the absolute value of the number. Similarly, in the **complex plane** (the plane defined by a set of complex axes), the **absolute value** of a complex number is its distance from zero or the origin $(0,0)$. In the previous problem, the absolute value of all of those complex numbers was 5. For each of the following questions, a sketch in the complex plane will help in visualizing the result.

   a.   What is the absolute value of $-8 + 6i$?

   b.   What is the absolute value of $7 - 2i$?

   c.   What is $|4 + i|$?

   d.   What is the absolute value of $a + bi$?

8-100.   Based on the following graphs, how many *real* roots does each polynomial function have?

a. 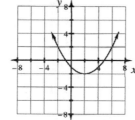   b.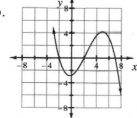

Graphs (a) and (b) above have been vertically shifted to create graphs (c) and (d) shown below. How many *real* roots does each of these new polynomial functions have?

c. 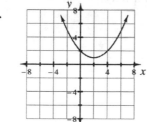   d.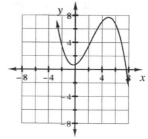

The polynomials in parts (c) and (d) do not have fewer roots. Polynomial (c) still has *two* roots, but now the roots are complex. Polynomial (d) has *three* roots: two are complex, and only one is real.

8-101.   Recall that a polynomial function with degree n crosses the x-axis at most n times. For instance, $y = (x+1)^2$ intersects the x-axis once, while $y = x^2 + 1$ does not intersect it at all. The function $y = x^2 - 1$ intersects it twice. These graphs are shown below.

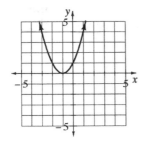   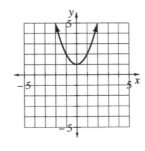   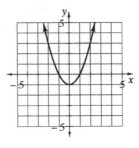

$y = (x+1)^2$ $y = x^2 + 1$ $y = x^2 - 1$

a.   The graph of a third-degree equation might intersect the x-axis one, two, or three times. Make sketches of all these possibilities.

b.   Can a third-degree equation have zero real roots? Explain why or why not.

8-102.   Now consider the graph of $y = x^3 - 3x^2 + 3x - 2$.

a.   How many real solutions could $x^3 - 3x^2 + 3x - 2 = 0$ have?

b.   Check to verify that $x^3 - 3x^2 + 3x - 2 = (x-2)(x^2 - x + 1)$.

c.   Find all of the solutions of $x^3 - 3x^2 + 3x - 2 = 0$.

d.   How many x-intercepts does $y = x^3 - 3x^2 + 3x - 2$ have? How many real roots and how many non-real roots (complex)?

Core Connections Algebra 2

8-103.   Sketch the graph of $f(x) = x^2 + 4$ and solve the equation $x^2 + 4 = 0$ to find its roots.

a.   Describe the parabola. Be sure to include the vertex and the equation of its axis of symmetry.

b.   With a partner, obtain a copy of the Lesson 8.2.3 Resource Page from your teacher, and follow the directions below to make a 3-D model that will show the location of the complex roots in a complex plane that is perpendicular to the real plane in which you drew the graph of the parabola.

i.   Fold the paper on the line marked **bi** and **–bi**. This is a "mountain" fold, so the printing is on the outside.

ii.   Cut the paper exactly along the dotted line. Do not cut beyond the dotted portion.

iii.   Now make "valley" folds on the two lines parallel to the first fold.

iv.   Hold the two ends of the paper and push them toward the center so the center pops up, and then fold the top and bottom of the paper back on the line marked "center."

You should have a three-dimensional coordinate system with the xy-plane facing you and the i-axis coming out toward you. The equation $f(x) = x^2 + 4$ should be in the lower right corner. Now locate the roots of the function on your 3-D model.

MATH NOTES

Graphing Complex Numbers

To represent imaginary numbers, an imaginary axis and a real axis are needed. Real numbers are on the horizontal axis and imaginary numbers are on the vertical axis, as shown in the examples below. This representation is called the **complex plane**.

In the complex plane, $a + bi$ is located at the point (a, b). The number $2 + 3i$ is located at the point $(2, 3)$. The number i or $0 + 1i$ is located at $(0, 1)$. The number -2 or $-2 + 0i$ is located at $(-2, 0)$.

The **absolute value** of a complex number is its distance from the origin. To find the absolute value, calculate the distance from $(0, 0)$ to (a, b):

$$|a + bi| = \sqrt{a^2 + b^2}$$

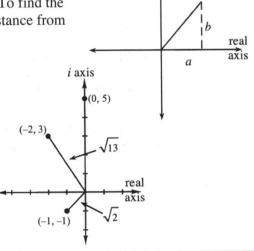

Examples:

$$|-2 + 3i| = \sqrt{(-2)^2 + 3^2} = \sqrt{13}$$

$$|-1 - i| = \sqrt{(-1)^2 + (-1)^2} = \sqrt{2}$$

$$|5i| = 5$$

8-104.   In parts (a) through (d) below, for each polynomial function $f(x)$, the graph of
$f(x)$ is shown. Based on this information, state the numbers of linear and
quadratic factors the factored form of its equation should
have and how many real and complex (non-real) solutions
$f(x) = 0$ might have. (Assume a polynomial function of
the lowest possible degree for each one.)

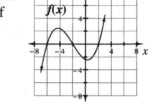

Example: $f(x)$ at right will have three linear factors,
therefore three real roots and no complex roots.

a.
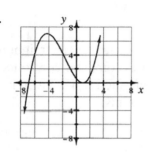

b.
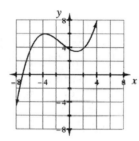

c.
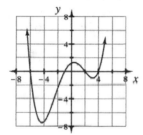

d.
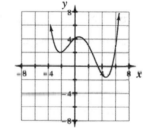

8-105.   Make a sketch of a graph $p(x)$ so that $p(x) = 0$ would have the indicated
number and type of solutions.

a.   5 real solutions

b.   3 real and 2 complex

c.   4 complex

d.   4 complex and 2 real

e.   For parts (a) through (d), what is the lowest degree each function
could have?

8-106.   Consider the function $y = x^3 - 9x$.

      a.   What are the roots of the function? (Factoring will help!)

      b.   Sketch a graph of the function.

8-107.   Make rough sketches of the graphs of each of the following polynomial functions. Be sure to label the x- and y- intercepts.

      a. $y = x(2x + 5)(2x - 7)$ b. $y = (15 - 2x)^2(x + 3)$

8-108.   Graph $y \geq |x + 2| - 3$ and $y \leq 2$ on the same set of axes.

8-109.   Fireworks for the annual Fourth of July show are launched straight up from a steel platform. The launch of the entire show is computer controlled. The height of a particular firework in meters off ground level is given by $h = -4.9t^2 + 49t + 11.27$, where time, t, is in seconds.

      a.   What was the height of the platform? What is the maximum height the firework reached? How many seconds until it hit the ground?

      b.   Rewrite the equation in factored form. Why might factored form of the equation be useful?

8-110.   You are given the equation $5x^2 + bx + 20 = 0$. For what values of b does this equation have real solutions?

8-111.   Show that each of the following equations is true.

      a. $(i - 3)^2 = 8 - 6i$ b. $(2i - 1)(3i + 1) = -7 - i$

      c. $(3 - 2i)(2i + 3) = 13$

8-112.   Consider the functions $y = \frac{1}{2}$ and $y = \frac{16}{x^2 - 4}$. Find the coordinates where the graphs of the functions intersect.

8.3.1 How can I divide polynomials?

. . . .

Polynomial Division

When you graphed polynomial functions in the first section of this chapter, you learned that the factored form of a polynomial is very useful for finding the roots of the function or the x-intercepts of the graph. But what happens when you do not have the factored form and you need to find all of the roots? You will investigate the answer to this question in this lesson.

8-113. Andre needs to find the exact roots of the function $f(x) = x^3 + 2x^2 - 7x - 2$. When he uses his graphing calculator, he can see that one of the x-intercepts is 2, but there are two other intercepts that he cannot identify exactly.

Andre remembers that he learned how to multiply binomials and other polynomials using area models. He figures that since division is the inverse (or undo) operation for multiplication, he should be able to reverse the multiplication process to divide. As he thinks about that idea, he comes across the following news article.

Polydoku Craze Sweeping Nation!

(CPM) – Math enthusiasts around the nation have entered a new puzzle craze involving the multiplication of polynomials. The goal of the game, which enthusiasts have named Polydoku, is to fill in squares so that the multiplication of two polynomials will be completed.

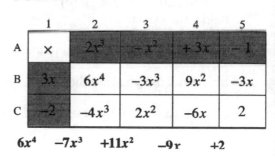

The game shown at right, for example, represents the multiplication of $(3x - 2)(2x^3 - x^2 + 3x - 1) = 6x^4 - 7x^3 + 11x^2 - 9x + 2$.

Most of the squares are blank at the start of the game. While the beginner level provides the factors (in the gray squares), some of the factors are missing in the more advanced levels.

What do you think Andre needs to be able to do to find the other roots?

8-114. Andre decided to join the craze and try some Polydoku puzzles, but he is not sure how to fill in some of the squares. Help him by answering parts (a) and (b) below about the Polydoku puzzle in the news article he read (found in problem 8-113), then complete part (c).

a. Explain how the term $2x^2$ in cell C3 of the news article was generated.

b. What values were combined to get $-7x^3$ in the news article answer?

c. Copy and complete the Polydoku puzzle at right.

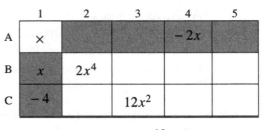

	1	2	3	4	5
A	$\times$	$4x^3$	$+6x^2$	$-2x$	-5
B	$2x$				
C	-3				

8-115. POLYDOKU TEAM CHALLENGE

Work with your team to complete the puzzle at right. Find the factors and the product for the puzzle. If you get stuck, you can consult parts (a) through (c) below for ideas.

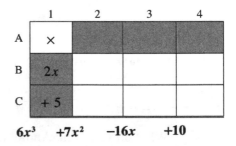

	1	2	3	4	5
A	$\times$			$-2x$	
B	x	$2x^4$			
C	-4		$12x^2$		

$$12x$$

a. How is cell B2 related to the answer?

b. How did you find the third term in the answer?

c. What cells did you use to get the value in cell B5?

8-116. Jessica is about to start the intermediate-level Polydoku puzzle shown at right. Show Jessica how to complete the puzzle. Make sure you can justify your solution.

	1	2	3	4
A	$\times$			
B	$2x$			
C	$+5$			

$$6x^3 \quad +7x^2 \quad -16x \quad +10$$

Use your results to complete the statements below.

$$\frac{6x^3 + 7x^2 - 16x + 10}{2x + 5} = \underline{\hspace{1.5cm}} \text{ and } (2x+5)\cdot\underline{\hspace{1.5cm}} = \underline{\hspace{1.5cm}}$$

8-117.   Unfortunately, Jessica made a mistake when she copied the problem. The constant term of the original polynomial was supposed to have the value $+18$ (not $+10$). She does not want to start all over again to solve the puzzle.

    a.   Jessica realizes that she would now have 8 remaining from the original expression. What is the significance of this 8?

    b.   Jessica writes her work as shown below:

$$\frac{6x^3 + 7x^2 - 16x + 18}{2x+5} = \frac{(6x^3 + 7x^2 - 16x + 10) + 8}{2x+5} = 3x^2 - 4x + 2 \text{, remainder 8.}$$

Gina thinks that there is a way to write the answer without using the word "remainder." Discuss this with your team and find another way to write the result. Be prepared to share your results and your reasoning with the class.

    c.   Use Jessica and Gina's method to divide $(6x^3 + 11x^2 - 12x - 1) \div (3x + 1)$.

8-118.   Create your own Polydoku puzzles that can be used to solve each of the polynomial-division problems below. Express any remainders as fractions and use your results to write a multiplication and a division statement like those in problem 8-117.

    a. $\dfrac{6x^4 - 5x^3 + 10x^2 - 18x + 5}{3x - 1}$ b. $(x^4 - 6x^3 + 18x - 4) \div (x - 2)$

    c. $x - 3 \overline{) x^3 + x^2 - 14x + 3}$ d. $\dfrac{x^5 - 1}{x - 1}$

8-119.   Now work with your team to help Andre solve his original problem (problem 8-113). Find all of the roots (exact zeros) of the polynomial.

Ⓜ️ETHODS AND MEANINGS

Polynomial Division

The examples below show two methods for dividing $x^4 - 6x^3 + 18x - 1$ by $x - 2$. In both cases, the remainder is written as a fraction.

Using long division:

$$
\begin{array}{r}
x^3 - 4x^2 - 8x + 2 \\
x - 2 \overline{\smash{)}\, x^4 \div 6x^3 + 0x^2 + 18x - 1} \\
\underline{x^4 - 2x^3} \\
-4x^3 + 0x^2 \\
\underline{-4x^3 + 8x^2} \\
-8x^2 + 18x \\
\underline{-8x^2 + 16x} \\
2x - 1 \\
\underline{2x - 4} \\
3
\end{array}
$$

Answer: $x^3 - 4x^2 - 8x + 2 + \frac{3}{x-2}$

Using area models:

Remainder

	x^3	$-4x^2$	$-8x$	$+2$	
x	x^4	$-4x^3$	$-8x^2$	$+2x$	3
-2	$-2x^3$	$+8x^2$	$+16x$	-4	

$$x^4 - 6x^3 \quad +0x^2 \quad +18x \quad -1$$

Answer: $x^3 - 4x^2 - 8x + 2 + \frac{3}{x-2}$

Therefore, $(x^4 - 6x^3 + 18x - 1) \div (x - 2) = x^3 - 4x^2 - 8x + 2 + \frac{3}{x-2}$ and
$(x - 2)(x^3 - 4x^2 - 8x + 2 + \frac{3}{x+2}) = x^4 - 6x^3 + 18x - 1$.

8-120. Carlos is always playing games with his graphing calculator, but now his calculator has contracted a virus. The $\boxed{\text{TRACE}}$, $\boxed{\text{ZOOM}}$, and $\boxed{\text{WINDOW}}$ functions on his calculator are not working. He needs to solve $x^3 + 5x^2 - 16x - 14 = 0$, so he graphs $y = x^3 + 5x^2 - 16x - 14$ and sees the graph at right in the standard window.

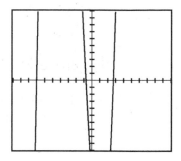

a. From the graph, what appears to be an integer solution to the equation?

b. Check your answer from part (a) in the equation.

c. Since $x = -7$ is a solution to the equation, what is the factor associated with this solution?

d. Use polynomial division to find the other factor.

e. Use your new factor to complete this equation:

$$x^3 + 5x^2 - 16x - 14 = (x + 7)(\textit{other factor}) = 0$$

f. The "other factor" leads to two other solutions to the equation. Find these two new solutions and give all three solutions to the original equation.

8-121. Now Carlos needs to solve $2x^3 + 3x^2 - 8x + 3 = 0$, but his calculator will still only create a standard graph. He sees that the graph of $y = 2x^3 + 3x^2 - 8x + 3$ crosses the x-axis at $x = 1$. Find all three solutions to the equation.

8-122. Without actually multiplying, decide which of the following polynomials could be the product of $(x - 2)(x + 3)(x - 5)$. Justify your choice.

a. $x^3 - 4x^2 - 11x - 5$ b. $2x^3 - 4x^2 - 11x + 30$

c. $x^3 - 4x^2 - 11x + 30$ d. $2x^3 - 4x^2 - 11x - 5$

8-123.　Which of the following binomials could be a factor of $x^3 - 9x^2 + 19x + 5$?
Explain your reasoning.

a.　　$x - 2$　　　　b.　　$x - 5$　　　　c.　　$x + 3$　　　　d.　　$x + 2$

8-124.　Now divide $x^3 - 9x^2 + 19x + 5$ by the factor that you chose in the preceding
problem. If it is a factor, use it and the resulting factor to find all the zeros of
the polynomial. If it is not a factor, reconsider your answer to the preceding
problem and try a different factor.

8-125.　Consider the equation $5x^2 - 7x - 6 = 0$ as you answer the questions in parts (a)
through (d) below.

a.　　What are the factors of $5x^2 - 7x - 6$?

b.　　What are the solutions to the equation?

c.　　Explain the relationship between the factors of the polynomial expression
and the solutions to the equation.

d.　　How are the solutions to the equation related to the lead coefficient and
constant term in the original polynomial?

8-126.　The city of Waynesboro is trying to decide
whether to initiate a composting project
where each residence would be provided
with a dumpster for garden and yard waste.
The city manager needs some measure of
assurance that the citizens will participate
before launching the project, so he chooses a
random sample of 25 homes and provides
them with the new dumpster for yard and
garden waste. After one week the contents of
each dumpster is weighed (in pounds) before processing. The sorted data is
shown below:

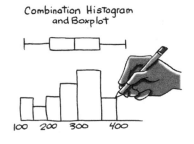

0	0	0	0	1.7	2.6	2.9	4.2	4.4
5.1	5.6	6.4	8.0	8.9	9.7	10.1	11.2	13.5
15.1	16.3	17.7	21.4	22.0	22.2	36.5		

Checksum 245.5

Problem continues on next page →

8-126. *Problem continued from previous page.*

    a.   Create a combination boxplot and histogram. Use an interval of 0 to 42 pounds on the x-axis and a bin width of 6 pounds.

    b.   Describe the center, shape, spread and outliers.

    c.   What is a better measure of center for this distribution the mean or median and why?

    d.   What is a better measure of spread the standard deviation or IQR and why?

    e.   The city can sell the compost, and engineers estimate the program will be profitable if each home averages at least 9 pounds of material. The city manager sees the mean is nearly 10 pounds and is ready to order dumpsters for every residence. What advice would you give him?

8-127.   This problem is a checkpoint for solving and graphing inequalities. It will be referred to as Checkpoint 8A.

Graph the inequality in part (a) and the system of inequalities in part (b).

    a. $|x+1| \geq 3$ b. $y \leq -2x+3$

                                                           $y \geq x$

                                                           $x \geq -1$

Check your answers by referring to the Checkpoint 8A materials located at the back of your book.

If you needed help solving these problems correctly, then you need more practice. Review the Checkpoint 8A materials and try the practice problems. Also, consider getting help outside of class time. From this point on, you will be expected to do problems like these quickly and easily.

8-128.   Given the equation: $3x + y - z = 6$.

    a.   Draw a graph.

    b.   Is $(1, 2, -1)$ on the graph? Justify your answer.

8.3.2 How can I solve it?

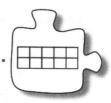

Factors and Integral Roots

You already know several methods for solving quadratic equations, such as factoring, completing the square, and using the Quadratic Formula. Mathematicians have developed formulas for solving third- and fourth-degree polynomial equations, but these formulas are far more complicated and messy than the Quadratic Formula is, and they are rarely used. Furthermore, for polynomials of degree greater than four, there is no single formula to use. For many polynomials, you can develop more useful methods than a formula based on what you already know.

8-129.   SEARCHING FOR ROOTS OF POLYNOMIALS

By combining what you know about graphing, factoring, polynomial division, and solving quadratic equations, you will be able to find the roots of the higher-degree polynomial functions in this lesson.

Your Task: Find all of the zeros of the polynomial below and then write the polynomial in factored form with factors of degree 2 or 1.

$$P(x) = x^4 - x^3 - 5x^2 + 3x + 6$$

Discussion Points

What are some possible linear factors?

How can the graph help us decide which factors to try?

How can we use the known factors to figure out other factors?

What do we need to do to write the polynomial in factored form and find the zeros?

8-130.   Given the polynomial $P(x) = x^4 - x^3 - 5x^2 + 3x + 6$, list all of the possible linear factors $(x \pm a)$ of the polynomial. Use only integer values for a.

a.   Could $x - 5$ be included on your list of possible linear factors? Explain.

b.   Not all of the *possibilities* will actually be factors. Use your graphing calculator to decide which of the factors you listed are the best possibilities.

c.   Now that you have shortened the list of possibilities, which factors on the shortened list really are factors of $P(x)$? Justify your answer.

d.   If you have not already, divide the polynomial by one of the factors from part (c) and write the polynomial as a product of a linear and a cubic factor.

e.   Now divide the cubic factor from part (d) by the other linear factor that worked, and write the original polynomial as a product of two linear factors and one quadratic factor.

f.   From the factored form, you can find all of the solutions to $x^4 - x^3 - 5x^2 + 3x + 6 = 0$ and the exact x-intercepts for the graph of $P(x)$. What are they?

———————   *Further Guidance*   ———————
                section ends here.

8-131.   LEARNING LOG

As a team, look back over the work you did to find the linear factors of $P(x)$ and make a list of steps you can use to find all of the zeros of a given polynomial. Then record your ideas in your Learning Log. Use diagrams, arrows, and other math tools to help demonstrate your ideas. Title this entry "Factors and Roots of Polynomial Functions" and label it with today's date.

8-132.   Your teacher will assign your team one of the following polynomial functions. Use the list of steps your team developed to factor the polynomial and find all of its roots. Then prepare a poster in which you illustrate and justify each of your steps. Be sure to include the graph on your poster and clearly explain the relationship between the solutions of the equation and the x-intercepts.

a. $Q_1(x) = x^3 + 3x^2 + 1x - 5$

b. $Q_2(x) = 6x^4 + 7x^3 - 36x^2 - 7x + 6$

c. $Q_3(x) = x^4 + 2x^3 + 10x^2 + 18x + 9$

d. $Q_4(x) = x^4 - 8x^3 + 18x^2 - 16x + 5$

e. $Q_5(x) = x^5 - 4x^3 - x^2 + 4$

f. $Q_6(x) = x^3 + x^2 - 7x - 7$

8-133.   LEARNING LOG

Make additions and/or adjustments to your Learning Log entry from problem 8-131 to reflect what you leaned from the posters that you and your classmates presented for problem 8-132.

8-134.   Use the procedures you developed to factor each of the following polynomial expressions. Each final answer should be a linear factor times a quadratic factor. Look for patterns in the factors.

a. $x^3 - 1$ b. $x^3 + 8$

c. $x^3 - 27$ d. $x^3 + 125$

8-135.   If you generalize the patterns for the factors in problem 8-134, you will discover a shortcut for factoring cubic polynomials that are described as the sum or difference of two cubes. Write the factors for each polynomial expression below.

a. $x^3 + a^3$ b. $x^3 - b^3$

8-136.   Are there similar patterns for $x^4 + a^4$ and $x^4 - b^4$? Explain.

8-137.   BUILDING POLYNOMIALS

For each of the following descriptions of polynomial functions with integral coefficients, answer each question below.

   i.   What are the possible numbers of real zeros?

   ii.   How many complex zeros are possible?

   iii. For each number of possible real zeros, give an example of a polynomial in factored form.

a.   A third-degree polynomial function.

b.   A fourth-degree polynomial function.

c.   A fifth-degree polynomial function.

MATH NOTES

METHODS AND MEANINGS

Polynomial Theorems

Factor Theorem: If a is a zero of the polynomial $p(x)$, then $(x-a)$ is a factor of the polynomial, and if $(x-a)$ is a factor of the polynomial, then a is a zero of the polynomial.

Example: -3, 2, and $1 \pm i\sqrt{7}$ are zeros of the polynomial $p(x) = x^4 - x^3 + 20x - 48$. According to the Factor Theorem, $(x+3)$, $(x-2)$, $(x-(1+i\sqrt{7}))$, and $(x-(1-i\sqrt{7}))$ are factors of the polynomial.

Fundamental Theorem of Algebra: The Fundamental Theorem of Algebra states that a polynomial of degree n with (real or) complex coefficients has exactly n roots, which may be real or complex. This also means that the polynomial has n linear factors since for every root a, $(x-a)$ is a linear factor. For example, the fourth degree polynomial in the example above has four roots and four linear factors.

Note that the total of n roots might include roots that occur multiple times. For example, the third degree polynomial $p(x) = x^3 - 3x^2 + 4$ has three roots – a root at -1 and a double root at 2. The three linear factors are $(x+1)$, $(x-2)$, and $(x-2)$.

Integral Zero Theorem: For any polynomial with integral coefficients, if an integer is a zero of the polynomial, it must be a factor of the constant term.

Example: Suppose the integers a, b, c, and d are zeros of a polynomial. Then, according to the Factor Theorem, $(x-a)(x-b)(x-c)(x-d)$ are factors of the polynomial. When you multiply these factors together, the constant term will be $abcd$, so a, b, c, and d are factors of the constant term.

Remainder Theorem: For any number c, when a polynomial $p(x)$ is divided by $(x-c)$, the remainder is $p(c)$. For example, if the polynomial $p(x) = x^4 - x^3 + 20x - 48$ is divided by $(x-5)$, the remainder is $p(5) = 552$.

Note that it follows from the Remainder Theorem that if $p(c) = 0$, then $(x-c)$ is a factor. For example, if $p(x) = x^3 - 3x^2 + 4$, one solution to $x^3 - 3x^2 + 4 = 0$ is -1. Since $p(-1) = 0$, then $(x+1)$ is a factor.

8-138.   Carlo was trying to factor the polynomial
$p(x) = x^4 - 4x^3 - 4x^2 + 24x - 9$ to find all of its
roots. He had already found one factor by making
a guess and dividing the polynomial, so he had
$p(x) = (x - 3)(x^3 - x^2 - 7x + 3)$. He was trying to
factor $x^3 - x^2 - 7x + 3$, so he had tried dividing it
by $(x + 3)$, $(x + 1)$, and $(x - 1)$, but none worked
without a remainder. Then Teo came by and said,
"You should look at the graph."

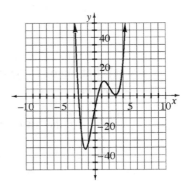

a.   How does the graph help?

b.   Complete the problem.

8-139.   Spud has a problem. He knows that the solutions for a quadratic equation are
$x = 3 + 4i$ and $x = 3 - 4i$, but in order to get credit for the problem he was
supposed to have written down the original equation. Unfortunately, he lost the
paper with the original equation on it. Luckily, his friends are full of advice.

a.   Alexia says, *"Just remember when we made polynomials. If you wanted 7
and 4 to be the answers, you used $(x - 7)(x - 4)$. So you just do x minus the
first one times x minus the other."* Use $(x - (3 + 4i))(x - (3 - 4i))$ to find the
quadratic equation.

b.   Hugo says, *"No, no, no. You can do it that way, but that's too
complicated. I think you just start with $x = 3 + 4i$ and work backward. So
$x - 3 = 4i$, then, hmmm... Yeah, that'll work."* Try Hugo's method.

c.   Whose method do you think Spud should use? Explain your choice.

8-140.   So far you have been able to extend the rules for real numbers to add, subtract, and multiply complex numbers, but what about dividing? Can you use what you know about real numbers to divide one complex number by another? In other words, if a problem looks like this:

$$\frac{3+2i}{-4+7i}$$

What needs to be done to get an answer in the form of a single complex number, $a+bi$?

Natalio had an idea. He said, *"I'll bet we can use the conjugate!"*

"How?" asked Ricki.

"Well, it's a fraction. Can't we multiply the numerator and denominator by the same number?" Natalio replied.

a.   Natalio was not very clear in his explanation. Show Ricki what he meant they should do.

b.   Using Natalio's ideas you probably still came up with a fraction in part (a), but the denominator should be a whole number. To write a complex number such as $\frac{c+di}{m}$ in the form $a+bi$, just use the distributive property to rewrite the result as $\frac{c}{m}+\frac{d}{m}i$. Rewrite your result for part (a) in this form.

8-141.   Use the method developed in problem 8-140 to do the following division problems.

a. $\frac{2-5i}{1-2i}$

b. $(-3+i)\div(2+3i)$

8-142.   Find the inverse of $g(x) = (x + 1)^2 - 3$ with the domain $x \geq -1$. Sketch both graphs and state the domain and range of the inverse function.

8-143.   Sketch the graph of each polynomial function below and find all of the zeros.

a. $y = x^3 + 1$

b. $y = x^3 - 8$

8-144.   Solve the system of equations at right for (x, y, z).

$$x = y + z$$
$$2x + 3y + z = 17$$
$$z + 2y = 7$$

8-145.   Solve $\sqrt{x^2 + 6} = x + 2$.

8-146.   Sketch the graph of each equation below.

a. $y = 3 \sin (x + \frac{\pi}{2})$ b. $y = -2 \sin (4x)$

8-147.   Spud has done it again. He's lost another polynomial function. This one was a cubic, written in standard form. He knows that there were two complex zeros, $-2 \pm 5i$ and one real zero, -1. What could his original function have been?

8-148.   Given the polynomial $p(x) = x^3 - 6x^2 + 7x + 2$.

a.   What is $p(2)$?

b.   Use the Remainder Theorem to find one factor of $x^3 - 6x^2 + 7x + 2$. (See the Math Notes box in Lesson 8.3.2 above.)

c.   Use (b) to find another factor.

d.   What are all the solutions of $x^3 - 6x^2 + 7x + 2 = 0$?

8-149.   Rewrite each of the following division problems as a single complex number.

a. $\frac{5+3i}{5-3i}$ b. $\frac{7+3i}{1-i}$

8-150.   Megan is an industrial engineer for Bowler Cola Company. She takes a random sample of cola cans from the production line each day to determine if the product meets various specifications. One of the measurements she records is the mass (in grams) of the filled cans. The following sorted data are from of a sample of 30 regular and diet cola cans.

Note: The data is sorted so it is easy to work with without a statistical calculator.

Regular

361	362	363	365	366	366	367	367	367	368
368	368	369	369	369	369	370	370	370	371
370	371	371	371	373	375	375	376	376	380

Checksum 11088

Diet

349	349	350	351	353	353	353	354	354	354
354	355	355	355	356	357	358	361	361	361
361	361	361	362	362	363	364	365	366	366

Checksum 10724

a.   Find the five number summary (minimum, third quartile, median, first quartile, maximum) for each soda.

b.   Make a combination histogram and boxplot for each type of soda. Include the five number summary. Use an interval of 348 to 384 grams on the *x*-axis and a bin width of 4 grams.

c.   Describe the center, shape, spread, and any outliers, of each histogram.

d.   Compare the two samples.

e.   Each can is marked as containing 12 fluid ounces. Twelve ounces is about 341 grams. Why is there so much variation from 341 grams in the samples?

8-151.   Sketch both the circle $x^2 + y^2 = 25$ and the parabola $y = x^2 - 13$.

a.   How many points of intersection are there?

b.   Find the coordinates of these points algebraically.

8-152.   Solve each equation. Be sure to check your answers.

a. $\sqrt{x} + 2 = x$

b. $\sqrt{x} + 2 = \sqrt{x+6}$

8-153.   Sketch a graph of each of the following trigonometric functions.

   a. $y = \sin(0.5(x - \pi))$ b. $y = 10\sin(3x) - 2$

   c. $y = 5\cos(x + \frac{\pi}{4})$ d. $y = \cos(2(x - \frac{\pi}{4}))$

8-154.   The graph of $p(x) = x^3 + 4x^2 + x - 26$ is shown at right.

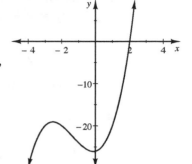

   a.   Use the graph to find one solution to $p(x) = 0$, then use the Remainder Theorem to find a factor of $p(x)$. Read about the Remainder Theorem in the Math Notes box in this lesson.

   b.   Determine all the real and complex factors of $p(x)$.

8-155.   For each equation, find two solutions $0 \le x < 2\pi$, which make the equation true. No calculator should be necessary.

   a. $\cos x = -\frac{1}{2}$ b. $\tan x = \frac{\sqrt{3}}{3}$

   c. $\sin x = 0$ d. $\cos x = \frac{\sqrt{2}}{2}$

8-156.   Rewrite each of the following division problems as a single complex number in simplest form.

   a. $\frac{2 - 6i}{4 + 2i}$ b. $\frac{5}{1 + 2i}$

8-157.   A long lost relative died and left you $15,000! Your parents say that you need to save the money for college, so you put it an account that pays 8% interest compounded annually. How many years will it take until your account is worth $25,000?

8-158.   Solve each equation.

   a. $\log_3(2x - 1) = -2$ b. $5^{\log_5(x)} = 3$

   c. $\log_2(x) - \log_2(3) = 4$ d. $\log_3(5) = x$

8-159.   Verify that the graphs of the equations $x^2 + y^3 = 17$ and $x^4 - 4y^2 - 8xy = 17$ intersect at $(3, 2)$.

8-160.   The graphs of $y = \log_2(x - 1)$ and $y = x^3 - 4x$ intersect at two points: $(2, 0)$ and approximately $(1.1187, -3.075)$. Use that information to solve $\log_2(x - 1) = x^3 - 4x$.

8-161.   Solve each equation below for x.

    a. $1234x + 23456 = 987654$

    b. $\frac{10}{x} + \frac{20}{x} = 5$

    c. $5x^2 - 6x + 1 = 0$

    d. $x^3 - 3x^2 + 2x = 0$

8-162.   Use your knowledge of the unit circle to explain why the graphs of $y = \sin\theta$ and $y = \cos(\theta - \frac{\pi}{2})$ are the same.

8-163.   For homework, Londa was asked to simplify the expression $\sqrt{-7} \cdot \sqrt{-7}$. She got the answer 7, but when she checked, she learned that the correct answer was –7.

    a.   Show Londa the steps she could take to get –7.

    b.   What steps do you think Londa took to get 7 as a result?

    c.   What does she need to consider to avoid making this mistake in the future?

    d.   Londa's example means that it is not always true that $\sqrt{a} \cdot \sqrt{b} = \sqrt{ab}$ for real numbers a and b. What restriction needs to be placed on the numbers a and b?

8-164.   Change each angle from degrees to radians.

    a. $60°$ b. $75°$ c. $210°$ d. $225°$

8.3.3 How can I use it?

An Application of Polynomials

In this lesson, you will have the opportunity to use the equation and graph of a polynomial function to solve a problem involving a game at the County Fair.

8-165.   COUNTY FAIR GAME TANK

The Mathamericaland Carnival Company wants to create a new game. It will consist of a tank filled with Ping-Pong balls of different colors. People will pay for the opportunity to crawl around in the tank blindfolded for 60 seconds, while they collect Ping-Pong balls. Most of the Ping-Pong balls will be white, but there will be a few of different colors. The players will win $100 for each red, $200 for each blue, and $500 for each green Ping-Pong ball they carry out of the tank.

The tank will be rectangular, open at the top, and will be made by cutting squares out of each corner of an 8.5-meter by 11-meter sheet of translucent miracle material that can be bent into shape. The owner of the company thinks that she will make the greatest profit if the tank has maximum volume. She has hired your team to figure out the exact dimensions of the tank that creates the maximum value.

Your Task: Your team will write a report of your findings to the Carnival Company that includes each of the following elements.

- Any data or conjectures your team made based on experimental paper tanks.

- A diagram of the tank with the dimensions clearly labeled with appropriate variables.

- A graph of the volume function that you found with notes on a reasonable domain and range.

- An equation that matches your graph.

- Your conclusions and observations.

Further Guidance

8-166.   Use a full sheet of 8.5" x 11" paper, which is the same shape as the material for the tank. Each member of your team should choose a different sized square to cut out of the corners. Measure the side of the square you cut out and write along the edge of the large piece of paper. Use either inches or centimeters. Your paper should look like the figure at right.

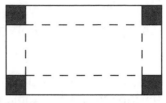

Fold the paper up into an open box (fold on the dotted lines). Then tape the cut parts together so that the box holds its shape. Measure the dimensions of the tank. Record the dimensions directly on the model tank.

8-167.   Make a table like the one below for your team's results. Consider "extreme" tanks, the ones with the largest possible cutout and the smallest possible cutout. For example, imagine cutting a square out of each corner zero inches on a side.

Height of Tank	Width of Tank	Length of Tank	Volume of Tank

a.   Examine the data in the table with your team and make some conjectures about how to find the maximum volume.

b.   Label the height as x. Using x for the height, find expressions for the length and width.

c.   Write an equation to represent the volume of the tank.

d.   Sketch the graph of your function by using the roots and determining the orientation.

e.   What domain and range make sense for your function?

f.   Approximate the maximum volume of the tank and the dimensions of the tank that will generate this volume.

8-168.   Use your graph and your tank model to write your report. Include your answers to the following questions.

    a.   Which points on the graph represent tanks that can actually be made? Explain.

    b.   How are the dimensions of the tank related? In other words, what happens to the length and width as the height increases?

    c.   Make a drawing of your tank. (You may want to use isometric dot paper.) Label your drawing with its dimensions and its volume.

Further Guidance
section ends here.

METHODS AND MEANINGS

Factoring Sums and Differences

The difference of two squares is factored as: $a^2 - b^2 = (a+b)(a-b)$

The sum of two cubes is factored as: $a^3 + b^3 = (a+b)(a^2 - ab + b^2)$

The difference of two cubes is factored as: $a^3 - b^3 = (a-b)(a^2 + ab + b^2)$

8-169.   A polynomial function has the equation $P(x) = x(x-3)^2(2x+1)$. What are the x-intercepts?

8-170.   Sketch a graph of a fourth-degree polynomial that has no real roots.

8-171.   Generally, when you are asked to factor, it is understood that you are only to use integers in your factors. If you are allowed to use irrational or complex numbers, *any* quadratic can be factored.

By setting the polynomial equal to zero and solving the quadratic equation, you can work backwards to "force factor" any quadratic. Use the solutions of the corresponding quadratic equation to write each of the following expressions as a product of two linear factors.

a. $x^2 - 10$ b. $x^2 - 3x - 7$

c. $x^2 + 4$ d. $x^2 - 2x + 2$

8-172.   Decide which of the following equations have real roots, and which have complex roots without completely solving them.

a. $y = x^2 - 6$ b. $y = x^2 + 6$

c. $y = x^2 - 2x + 10$ d. $y = x^2 - 2x - 10$

e. $y = (x - 3)^2 - 4$ f. $y = (x - 3)^2 + 4$

8-173.   Determine whether $x = -2$ is a solution to the equation $x^4 - 4x = 8x^2 - 40$. Show why or why not.

8-174.   This problem is a checkpoint for solving complicated equations. It will be referred to as Checkpoint 8B.

Solve each equation. Check your solutions.

a. $2|x - 3| + 7 = 11$ b. $4(x - 2)^2 = 16$

c. $\sqrt{x + 18} = x - 2$ d. $|2x + 5| = 3x + 4$

Check your answers by referring to the Checkpoint 8B materials located at the back of your book.

If you needed help solving these problems correctly, then you need more practice. Review the Checkpoint 8B materials and try the practice problems. Also, consider getting help outside of class time. From this point on, you will be expected to do problems like these quickly and easily.

8-175.　Let $p(x) = x^3 - 3x^2 - 7x + 9$.

　　a.　Find $p(5)$.

　　b.　Verify the Remainder Theorem. Read about the Remainder Theorem in the Math Notes box in Lesson 8.3.2.

8-176.　The roots of two quadratic polynomials are given below. Write possible quadratic functions in standard form.

　　a.　$x = -i, x = i$　　　　　　　　　b.　$x = 1 + \sqrt{2}, x = 1 - \sqrt{2}$

8-177.　Graph two cycles of each function.

　　a.　$y = -2\cos(x + \frac{\pi}{2})$　　　　　　b.　$y = \sin(x - \frac{\pi}{2})$

Chapter 8 Closure   What have I learned?

Reflection and Synthesis

The activities below offer you a chance to reflect about what you have learned during this chapter. As you work, look for concepts that you feel very comfortable with, ideas that you would like to learn more about, and topics you need more help with. Look for connections between ideas as well as connections with material you learned previously.

① TEAM BRAINSTORM

What have you studied in this chapter? What ideas were important in what you learned? With your team, brainstorm a list. Be as detailed as you can. To help get you started, a list of Learning Log entries and Math Notes boxes are below.

What topics, ideas, and words that you learned *before* this chapter are connected to the new ideas in this chapter? Again, be as detailed as you can.

How long can you make your list? Challenge yourselves. Be prepared to share your team's ideas with the class.

Learning Log Entries
- Lesson 8.1.1 – Graphing Polynomials
- Lesson 8.3.2 – Factors and Roots of Polynomial Functions

Math Notes
- Lesson 8.1.1 – Polynomials, Degree, Coefficients
- Lesson 8.1.2 – Roots and Zeros
- Lesson 8.1.3 – Notation for Polynomials
- Lesson 8.2.1 – Imaginary and Complex Numbers
- Lesson 8.2.2 – The Discriminant and Complex Conjugates
- Lesson 8.2.3 – Graphing Complex Numbers
- Lesson 8.3.1 – Polynomial Division
- Lesson 8.3.2 – Polynomial Theorems
- Lesson 8.3.3 – Factoring Sums and Differences

②   MAKING CONNECTIONS

Below is a list of the vocabulary used in this chapter. Make sure that you are familiar with all of these words and know what they mean. Refer to the glossary or index for any words that you do not yet understand.

coefficient	complex number	conjugate
degree	discriminant	factor
imaginary number	integral roots	polynomial
quotient	real number	remainder
root	solution	x-intercept
zero		

Make a concept map showing all of the connections you can find among the key words and ideas listed above. To show a connection between two words, draw a line between them and explain the connection. A word can be connected to any other word as long as you can justify the connection. For each key word or idea, provide an example or sketch that shows the idea.

While you are making your map, your team may think of related words or ideas that are not listed here. Be sure to include these ideas on your concept map.

③   PORTFOLIO: EVIDENCE OF MATHEMATICAL PROFICIENCY

This section gives you an opportunity to show growth
in your understanding of key mathematical ideas over
time as you complete this course.

Part 1: You may have done this in a previous
chapter. You have grown mathematically since
then. Be sure to include everything you have
learned since the last time you did this problem.

How many different kinds of graphs can you create that have:

i. No *x*-intercepts?   *ii.* One *x*-intercept?

iii. Two *x*-intercepts?   *iv.* Three or more *x*-intercepts?

For each type of graph, show a sketch, label the key points, and give its
equation. Make sure that each graph you give as an example represents a
different family and describe the family in words or with a general
equation. Show how to calculate the *x*-intercepts of each of your sample
graphs.

Part 2: Compare your responses to this "Growth Over Time" problem.
Write an evaluation of your growth based on your responses. Consider
each of the following questions as you write your answer.

- What new concepts did you include the second time you did the
  problem? In what ways was your response better than your first
  attempt?

- If you did the problem three times, how was your final version
  different from the first two? What new ideas did you include?

- Did you omit anything in your later versions that you used in one of
  the earlier versions? Why did you omit it?

- Rate your attempts by making three bars like the ones below and
  shading each bar to represent how much you knew on each attempt.

  First Attempt: [   ]
  Second Attempt: [   ]
  Final Attempt: [   ]

- Is there anything you want to add to your current version? If so, add
  it and keep this version for future reference.

Core Connections Algebra 2

WHAT HAVE I LEARNED?

Most of the problems in this section represent typical problems found in this chapter. They serve as a gauge for you. You can use them to determine which types of problems you can do well and which types of problems require further study and practice. Even if your teacher does not assign this section, it is a good idea to try these problems and find out for yourself what you know and what you still need to work on.

Solve each problem as completely as you can. The table at the end of the closure section has answers to these problems. It also tells you where you can find additional help and practice with problems like these.

CL 8-178. Decide if each of the following equations is a polynomial. If it is, state the degree. If it is not, explain how you know.

a. $f(x) = 3x^3 - 2x + 5$

b. $y = 0.25x^7 - 5x$

c. $y = 3^x - x^2$

d. $f(x) = x^2 - \sqrt{x} + 2$

e. $Q(x) = 3(x-4)^2(x+2)$

f. $y = x^2 - 3x + 5 - \frac{2}{x-2}$

CL 8-179. Where do the graphs of each of the following functions cross the x-axis?

a. $f(x) = (x-2)^2 - 3$

b. $f(x) = (x-19)^2(x+14)$

CL 8-180. Write a polynomial equation for a graph that passes through the point $(1, 56)$ and has three x-intercept: $(-3, 0)$, $(2, 0)$, and $(5, 0)$.

CL 8-181. Decide if each of the following functions has real or complex roots.

a. $y = 3x^2 + 5x + 4$

b. $y = 3x^2 + 5x - 4$

CL 8-182. Make a sketch of a graph $q(x)$ such that $q(x) = 0$ would have the number and type of solutions indicated below.

    a.   7 real solutions   b.   5 real and 2 complex solutions

    c.   4 complex solutions   d.   2 complex and 4 real solutions

CL 8-183. Sketch graphs of each of the following polynomial functions. Be sure to label the x- and the y-intercepts of each graph.

    a. $y = x(2x + 3)(2x - 5)$ b. $y = (11 - 2x)^2(x - 2)$

CL 8-184. Simplify each expression

    a. $(3 + 4i) + (7 - 2i)$ b. $(3 + 5i)^2$

    c. $(7 + i)(7 - i)$ d. $(3i)(2i)^2$

    e. i^3 f. i^{32}

CL 8-185. Divide: $(2x^3 + x^2 - 19x + 36) \div (x + 4)$

CL 8-186. The graph of $f(x) = x^3 + 3x^2 + x - 5$ is shown at right. Use it to determine all real and complex roots.

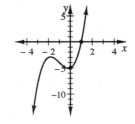

CL 8-187. The roots of a quadratic polynomial are given below. Find a possible quadratic equation in standard form.

    a. $x = 2i,\ x = -2i$ b. $x = 2 + \sqrt{3},\ x = 2 - \sqrt{3}$

CL 8-188. For each equation determine the amplitude, period, locator point, and sketch part of the graph.

    a. $y = 3\cos(2x)$ b. $y = \tan(x - \frac{\pi}{2})$

CL 8-189.   Write an equation for each of the following graphs. If you have a graphing calculator, use it to check your equation (be sure to set your window to match the picture).

a.
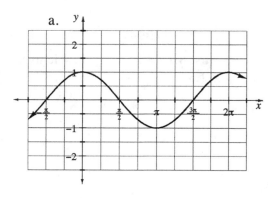

b.
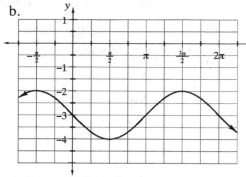

c.
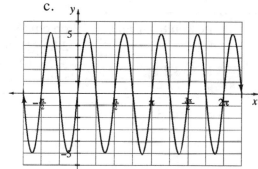

d.
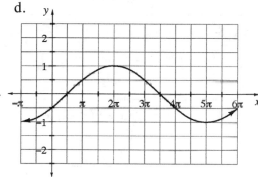

CL 8-190.   Use the system below to answer each question.

$$y = 2x$$
$$y = x^2 + 5$$

a.   Without graphing, what is the solution to the system?

b.   What does the solution to the system tell you about the graphs?

CL 8-191.   Check your answers using the table at the end of this section. Which problems do you feel confident about? Which problems were hard? Have you worked on problems like these in math classes you have taken before? Use the table to make a list of topics you need help on and a list of topics you need to practice more.

Answers and Support for Closure Activity #4
What Have I Learned?

Note: MN = Math Note, LL = Learning Log

Problem	Solutions	Need Help?	More Practice
CL 8-178.	a. Yes; degree 3 b. Yes; degree 7 c. No; it contains a power of x d. No; it contains a power of $\frac{1}{2}$ e. Yes; degree 3 f. No; it contains a negative power of x	MN: 8.1.1 and 8.1.3	Problems 8-9, 8-17, 8-28, 8-39, and 8-55
CL 8-179.	a. $x = \pm\sqrt{3} + 2$ b. $x = 19$ and $x = -14$	Lesson 8.1.1 and 8.1.2 MN: 8.1.2	Problems 8-19, 8-20, 8-21, 8-36, 8-37, 8-106, 8-125, 8-132, and 8-169
CL 8-180.	$y = 3.5(x + 3)(x - 2)(x - 5)$	Section 8.1	Problems 8-38, 8-50, 8-56, and 8-57
CL 8-181.	a. complex roots b. real roots	Lessons 8.2.1 and 8.2.2 MN: 8.2.2 and 8.3.2	Problems 8-88, 8-110, and 8-172
CL 8-182.	a. b. c. d.	Sections 8.1 and 8.2 LL: 8.1.1	Problems 8-104, 8-105, and 8-170

Problem	Solutions	Need Help?	More Practice
CL 8-183.	a b.	Lessons 8.1.1 and 8.1.2 LL: 8.1.1	Problems 8-8, 8-35, and 8-107
CL 8-184.	a. $10 + 2i$ b. $-16 + 30i$ c. 50 d. $-12i$ e. $-i$ f. 1	Lesson 8.2.1 MN: 8.2.1	Problems 8-76, 8-111, 8-141, 8-149, and 8-156
CL 8-185.	$2x^2 - 7x + 9$	Lesson 8.3.1 MN: 8.3.1	Problem 8-124
CL 8-186.	$x = 1, -2 \pm i$	Lesson 8.3.2 LL: 8.3.2	Problems 8-120, 8-121, 8-124, 8-138, 8-148, and 8-154
CL 8-187.	a. $y = x^2 + 4$ b. $y = x^2 - 4x + 1$	Sections 8.1 and 8.2 MN: 8.1.2 and 8.3.2 LL: 8.3.2	Problems, 8-87, 8-139, 8-147, and 8-176
CL 8-188.	a. Locator: $(0, 3)$ Amplitude: 3 Period: π b. Locator: $(\frac{\pi}{2}, 0)$ Period: π There is no amplitude.	Chapter 7 MN: 7.2.4 LL: 7.2.4	Problems 7-141, 7-144, 7-159, 8-14, 8-94, 8-146, 8-153, and 8-177

Problem	Solutions	Need Help?	More Practice
CL 8-189.	a. $y = \sin x$, $y = \sin(x + \frac{\pi}{2})$ or $y = -\sin(x - \frac{\pi}{2})$ b. $y = -3 - \sin x$ c. $y = 5 \sin 4x$ d. $y = \sin \frac{1}{3}(x - \frac{\pi}{2})$	Chapter 7 MN: 7.2.4 LL: 7.2.4	Problems 7-129, 8-62, and 8-94
CL 8-190.	a. $(1 \pm 2i, 2 \pm 4i)$ b. The graphs do not intersect.	Lesson 8.2.1	Problems 8-11, 8-68, 8-69, and 8-161

RANDOMIZATION AND NORMAL DISTRIBUTIONS

9

CHAPTER 9 Randomization and Normal Distributions

In this chapter you will learn some basic techniques of performing opinion surveys along with their limitations and pitfalls. You will learn why randomness is a cornerstone of statistical studies.

In the last section of the chapter, you will create a histogram with percentages called a relative frequency histogram. You will learn a new way to describe the shape of a distribution, and use it to model certain distributions.

Guiding Question

Mathematically proficient students attend to precision.

As you work through this chapter, ask yourself:

How can I use the appropriate degree of precision for this problem—in my mathematics, in my vocabulary, and in how I ask survey questions?

Chapter Outline

Section 9.1 You will create a survey and learn how to avoid bias in creating survey questions. You will learn the importance of randomness in observational studies.

Section 9.2 You will perform an experiment and contrast other experiments with observational studies such as opinion surveys. You will learn the importance of randomness for experiments.

Section 9.3 You will construct relative frequency histograms. When the conditions are appropriate, you will model the relative frequency histogram with a normal distribution. With the help of a calculator, you will use the model to find the proportion of the sample (or population) with certain characteristics.

9.1.1 What questions will I ask?

Survey Design

Have you heard statements like the ones below?

- "81% of public school students are not satisfied with the food provided by their schools."

- "The President has an approval rating of 72%."

How do news sources get this information? Do they ask every public school student? Do they ask every citizen? What questions do they ask? How reliable are their results? Do you believe them?

In this chapter, you will learn some of the methods used by statisticians to justify claims such as these. You will also apply these methods to investigate your own questions.

9-1.   WHAT DO WE WANT TO KNOW?

Before you can figure out a way to find information, you need to know what information you are looking for! Work with your team to brainstorm research questions that you find interesting. Be clear about the **population** (the entire group) in which you are interested. Here are some examples to get your thinking started:

- What do voters in this town think about raising taxes?

- What percentage of students at your school are vegetarians?

- How many children in this area consider themselves to be multiracial?

a.   Work with your team to brainstorm research questions that might be investigated with a short survey.

b.   Next, as a team, discuss your ideas and decide on one research question that you will investigate together. When you have made a decision, call your teacher over to confirm that your question will work.

c.   Talk with your team about how you might go about gathering information about your question. Write down your ideas and be prepared to share them with the class.

9-2.   BIAS IN SURVEY QUESTIONS

Shortly, you will write survey questions for your own investigation. However, before you do that, it is important to understand how the questions that you ask can influence your results. Influence on a study that favors a certain outcome is called **bias**.

Discuss each of the following survey questions with your team. For each one,

- Look for ways in which the question may contain bias.

- Rewrite the question to reduce the bias you found.

- Be prepared to share your ideas with the class.

a.   Do teenagers worry about getting poor grades?

b.   Do you support the Governor's education plan that ensures that students will be more successful in school?

c.   Does the frequent occurrence of brutal violence in movies and video games have a negative affect on the young people exposed to them?

d.   Do you believe the current movie ratings system is effective?

e.   Should your teachers be paid more?

f.   Moderate exercise is necessary to stay healthy. Do you exercise regularly?

9-3.   Consider the following descriptions of common sources of bias in survey questions. Look back at the survey questions in problem 9-2 to see if you can find any of these types of bias in those questions. Note that some of these questions may refer to bias that you already identified, while some may help you see new sources of bias.

   a. **Question Order:** Sometimes two questions are asked in an order such that the first question suggests an answer to the second. Which of the poll questions uses the biased question order technique? Why would you expect it to influence responses?

   b. **Preface:** Some questions start with statements that can bias the result of the question that follows. Which of the survey questions presented to your class uses this technique? Why would you expect such statements to influence responses?

   c. **Two Questions in One:** This technique involves asking two questions at once. Survey respondents may agree with one part and disagree with another part, but they are only allowed to give one answer. Which of the survey questions presented to your class uses this technique?

   d. **Biased Wording:** By using pleasing or unpleasant words, the surveyor can influence results. Which of the survey questions presented to your class uses this technique?

   e. **Desire To Please:** Research shows that many survey takers will answer in the ways that they perceive will please the surveyor. Which of the survey questions presented to your class are likely to be biased in this way? Are some more severely biased than others?

9-4.   CREATING BIAS

You and your team members have been asked by the U.S. Department of Education to survey people about the President's new proposal to extend the school year from the current length of 180 days to 200 days. A survey question might be, "*Do you think students should attend school for 180 days as they do now, or for 200 days?*"

Work with your team to rewrite this question in as many ways as you can to *introduce* bias. For each new question you write, note in which direction the bias is likely to influence responses.

9-5.   Now you and your team will write your own
        survey.

    a.   Work with your team to write a short survey
        that you could use to investigate the research
        question that you selected in problem 9-1.
        Do your best to minimize bias in your
        questions.

    b.   Trade survey questions with another team. Read their questions and
        decide whether you see bias in any of them. If so, write a brief
        explanation of what type of bias you see and offer suggestions for
        rewording the questions to reduce bias.

    c.   Get your survey questions back from the team that offered you feedback.
        Consider their feedback and make any revisions that you decide will help
        improve your survey.

9-6.   There are many considerations involved when writing a survey. For example
        consider the following two survey questions:

        Question 1: What is your favorite way to exercise?

        Question 2: Which of the following ways to exercise do you prefer?

        Running   Swimming   Team Sports   Dancing   Skiing

    a.   Discuss these two ways of asking people about their exercise preferences.
        What are the possibilities and limitations of each question?

    b.   Question 1 is an example of an **open question**,
        while Question 2 is a **closed question**. Open
        questions allow respondents to offer any
        response they like, while closed questions limit
        them to some set number of responses from
        which to choose. Discuss these question types
        with your team. Is one type likely to give
        more accurate information? Why? Is one type
        likely to be more convenient? Why? When
        might you want to choose to ask an open or a closed question?

    c.   Make changes to your survey questions so that you have *at least one* open
        question and *at least one* closed question. Be careful! Changing the
        format of a question can introduce new kinds of bias.

    d.   Store your survey questions in a safe place. They will be needed later in
        this chapter.

METHODS AND MEANINGS

MATH NOTES

Population Parameters and Sample Statistics

The entire group that you are interested in studying and making conclusions about is called the **population**. Some questions can be investigated by studying every member of the population. For example, you can figure out how many students in your class have siblings by asking every student. This process of measuring every member of a population is called taking a **census**. Numerical summaries, such as mean and standard deviation, computed from a population census are called **parameters** of that population.

The United States government performs a census every ten years. The government uses this data to learn such things as how the population is changing, where people live, what types of families exist, and what languages are spoken. For example, the 2010 U.S Census counted 308,745,538 people and 4,239,587 of them were over the age of 85.

To answer some questions, a census is not possible. It might be too expensive or impractical. For example surveying every math student in your state may be too time consuming. It might be that the object being measured is destroyed during the experiment, as when determining how strong bicycle tires are by filling every single bicycle tire with air until it explodes. When it is not possible or practical to take a census, a portion of the population, called a **sample**, is measured or surveyed. Numerical summaries of a sample are called **statistics**.

For example, if all of the people in this class make up our population, then every fifth member of our class is a sample. The whole-class average on the final exam is a parameter, and the average test score of the students in the sample is a statistic.

9-7. Read the Math Notes box in this lesson. For each question, describe the population of interest. Then state whether a census is practical or whether it makes more sense to take a sample. Justify your response.

a. What is the average time it takes U.S. employees to commute to work?

b. What is the average bedtime for students in your math class?

c. How much Vitamin A is in an average carrot?

d. What is the public approval rating of the Governor?

e. How much weight can an elevator cable support?

f. What are your friends' favorite movies?

9-8. Katelyn owns a 24-hour coffee shop in front of a downtown office building. She recorded the number of cups of coffee sold each hour during a 48-hour time period.

Katelyn sorted the data and made the following histogram:

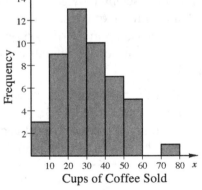

Cups of Coffee Sold		
1	22	37
5	22	38
7	23	38
12	24	40
12	25	41
12	26	41
12	26	42
12	29	47
14	29	47
16	30	49
17	30	51
19	31	52
20	32	55
21	33	55
21	35	59
22	36	76
checksum 1444		

a. Using the sorted data from the table and the histogram, find the five number summary (minimum, first quartile, median, third quartile, maximum) without using your calculator.

b. Describe the distribution of coffee sales per hour.

9-9. Consider the polynomial $x^4 - 6x^3 - 6x^2 + 6x - 7$.

  a. Using only integers, list all the possible linear factors.

  b. Is $(x+1)$ a factor of the polynomial? Is $(x-1)$ a factor? Show how you know without graphing.

9-10. Find all values of a for which the equation $ax^2 + 5x + 6 = 0$ has solutions that are real numbers. Express a in terms of one or more inequalities.

9-11. Solve each equation for $0 \le \theta \le 360$. You may need your calculator, but remember that your calculator only gives *one* answer. Most of these problems have more than one answer. Think about all four quadrants.

  a. $\sin \theta = 0.5$ b. $\cos \theta = -0.5$

  c. $4 \tan \theta - 4 = 0$ d. $3 \sin^2 \theta = 1$

9-12. Verify algebraically that $g(x) = \frac{5x-2}{3}$ is the inverse function of $f(x) = \frac{3x+2}{5}$.

9-13. As you may remember, the magnitude of an earthquake is measured by the amount of energy that is released. Since the amount of energy released from a large earthquake can be millions of times greater than the energy released by a small quake, a scale was created (the **Richter scale**) to give magnitudes in numbers that are easy to use. An earthquake measuring 3.4 on the Richter scale, for example, releases $10^{3.4}$ kilojoules of energy.

  a. How many times more energy is released by an earthquake that measures 6.5 on the Richter scale than an earthquake that measures 5.5?

  b. How many times more energy is released by an earthquake that measures 5.1 than an earthquake that measures 4.3? Give your answer both as a power of 10 and as a decimal. Make sure your answer has the same level of precision as the Richter measurements.

  c. What would be the magnitude of an earthquake that released half as much energy as an earthquake measuring 6.2 on the Richter scale?

9-14.   The roots of a polynomial are given below. Find two linear factors and the
         corresponding quadratic factor.

    a. $x = -2 + \sqrt{3}$, $x = -2 - \sqrt{3}$ b. $x = -2 + i$, $x = -2 - i$

9-15.   Joanne was making repairs to her deck and needed to buy some supplies. She
         purchased two posts, three boards, and four piers for \$52. When she needed
         more materials, she went back to the lumberyard and bought one post and five
         boards for \$13. Realizing she did not need the piers, she made a third trip in
         which she bought three more boards, returned the four piers, and ended up with
         a refund of \$34. What was the cost of each item?

9.1.2 Whom should I survey?

Samples and the Role of Randomness

In order to decide whether you like a particular soup, do you need to eat the whole pot? Usually, you can get a good sense of the flavor of the soup by taking a small taste, or a sample.

When conducting a study, it is usually not possible to survey every person or object in the population in which you are interested (for example, all the residents of the United States, all the students at your school, or all teenage shoppers). However, just as you can learn about the flavor of a soup with a small taste instead of eating the whole pot, you can learn about a population by **sampling** instead of taking a census. Unfortunately, large groups of people are much harder to stir than pots of soup to get a representative mix of their populations.

In this lesson, you will consider ways that statisticians do the equivalent of "stirring" populations in order to take samples that represent the whole population well.

As you work with your team today, consider the following questions.

How should we decide what is "typical" of a group?

How do random selection and intentional selection compare?

9-16.   How should you choose people for your survey to make up a sample that you think represents the population for your research question?

   a.   Discuss this question with your team and write down your ideas. Be sure to justify why your ideas will help you choose a representative sample.

   b.   Do you think your sampling method is better than randomly selecting members of the population? Why or why not?

9-17.   Some astronomers believe that a number of small objects, called Vulcanoid asteroids, exist between Mercury and the Sun. Other scientists, however, do not believe that these asteroids exist. The brightness of the sun has prevented direct observations, so the controversy remains unresolved.

Imagine the following scenario. Scientists invent a special camera that can photograph these asteroids, even though they are so close to the sun. They put the camera on a satellite and send it off. To their joy and amazement, the satellite begins to transmit images back to the earth and the asteroids are visible! Vulcanoids are real!

Unfortunately, in just five seconds, the heat of the sun destroys the camera and the transmission stops. Due to a technical malfunction, the five seconds of video images were not recorded. The scientists who were watching have to rely on their memories of the images.

a.   Help the scientists determine the size of a "typical" Vulcanoid asteroid by modeling this scenario. First, look at your "video" picture (Lesson 6.1.3 Resource Page) for exactly five seconds. Then, *without talking to anyone*, write down your estimate of a typical asteroid diameter in millimeters.

b.   Follow your teacher's instructions to contribute your estimate to the class's histogram. Sketch the histogram on your paper and describe its attributes, including the center, shape, spread, and the presence of any outliers.

9-18.   Now suppose that the camera on the satellite and the recording equipment were repairable and the scientists were able to record a good still photograph of the Vulcanoid asteroids. Now you have much more reliable information with which to determine the size of a typical asteroid.

   a.   Look at your photograph on the Lesson 9.1.2A Resource Page. Again, *without talking to anyone*, pick ten "typical" asteroids and measure the diameter of each in millimeters. Write down each of your measurements and then calculate the mean diameter. Do you think this result is a better estimate of the size of a typical asteroid than the one you estimated in problem 9-17? Why or why not?

   b.   Again, follow your teacher's instructions to contribute your calculated mean to the class's new histogram. Sketch the histogram on your own paper and describe how this histogram compares to the histogram of the class's estimates from problem 9-17.

   c.   In general, which set of estimates is more accurate? How can you tell? Be sure to use your comparison of the histograms to help justify your answer.

9-19.   You will use your calculator's ability to generate random numbers to help you to randomly select 10 asteroid images.

   a.   First, your teacher will give you instructions to make sure that your calculator does not generate the same random numbers as someone else's calculator.

   b.   Your teacher will now give you instructions to use your calculator to randomly select ten asteroids. It is possible that some will be repeated. Each member of your team should generate his or her own set of random numbers.

         Measure the ten asteroids that were randomly chosen by your calculator. If you have repeated numbers, measure those asteroids twice. Calculate the mean diameter of your ten asteroids.

   c.   Again, follow your teacher's instructions to contribute your calculated mean to the class's new histogram of randomly selected asteroids. Sketch the histogram on your own paper and describe how this histogram compares to the histograms of the class's estimates from problems 9-17 and 9-18.

9-20.   HOW SHOULD SAMPLES BE CHOSEN?

Based on the data collected by your class, discuss the following questions with your team. Be prepared to contribute your ideas and questions to a class discussion.

a.   Which selection method produced the most consistent (least variable) results? Why does this result make sense?

b.   Look in particular at the differences in data produced by intentionally-chosen samples and randomly-chosen samples. Why do the differences make sense? Be sure to consider differences in center, shape, spread, and outliers.

c.   Which sampling method seems to produce the best estimate of the size of a "typical" asteroid? How can you tell?

d.   Your teacher will provide you with the actual measures of central tendency of the sizes of the asteroid images. Does your idea about which sampling method is best change?

9-21.   CHOOSING YOUR SAMPLE

Talk with your team about what it would mean to randomly choose a sample from the population in your survey (problems 9-1 and 9-6). How might you do that? Could your calculator help you? Will it be possible to survey a randomly-selected sample? Why or why not?

Store your survey questions in a safe place. They will be needed later in this chapter.

9-22. Consider each of the following survey questions. For each one, explain any bias you find. If you think the question is unbiased (or fair), explain why.

    a. Do you agree that it is important to make ending homelessness a high priority?

    b. Which of the following factors is most important to address in order to slow global climate change?

        A. Car emissions   B. Airplane emissions

        C. Pollutants from private industry   D. Dependence on oil

    c. How important is it to raise teacher salaries?

9-23. Consider each of the following research conditions. For each one, write a research question that would be subject to such conditions.

    a. Sampling must be used because the population is too large to measure.

    b. Sampling must be used because measuring the population would destroy it.

    c. A census can be used because the population is measurable.

    d. A census can be used, even though the population is very large.

9-24.   When vapor under high pressure is released into the air, the resulting noise can severely damage people's hearing. This is a concern for large industrial facilities like power plants and factories. To help control this noise pollution companies install silencers, which work on the same principles as car mufflers. Hector is an engineer for Vapor Kinetics. He is testing two different models of silencers, the Hush Puppy and the Quiet Down, by measuring the sound energy in decibels (dB) each silencer is producing at various temperatures and pressures. The data has been sorted and is shown below:

Hush Puppy

19.7	22.8	26.3	27.4	29.5	38.8	39.3	44.5	46.7	50.0
51.2	52.4	53.4	56.6	58.0	58.6	60.7	62.3	66.4	67.0
68.6	69.6	70.1	70.9	71.3	72.9	76.4	76.5	76.7	79.5

Checksum 1664.1

Quiet Down

14.2	16.3	19.3	24.6	26.0	30.5	35.8	37.4	39.9	40.0
40.1	47.3	52.9	53.5	53.7	56.0	56.6	56.7	59.1	59.8
61.3	62.6	63.3	64.3	66.5	67.1	71.8	95.7	101.2	102.1

Checksum 1575.6

a.   Create a combination boxplot and histogram for each silencer. For the histograms, scale the x-axis from 12 to 108 and use a bin width of 12 dB.

b.   Describe the center, shape, spread and outliers for each silencer. Make sure your results have the same level of precision as the measurements.

c.   Hector needs to recommend one design for production. Which one do you suggest and why?

d.   The decibel scale is logarithmic, not linear. For example, a 105 dB sound is 8 times louder than a 75 dB sound. This is roughly the difference in noise between running a kitchen blender and running a chain saw. Does this information change your answer to part (c)? Why or why not?

9-25.   Rearrange the equation $y = 2x^2 + 8x + 5$ into a more useful form for graphing. State the locator point and draw the graph.

9-26.   Solve this system for y and z: $\frac{z+y}{2} + \frac{z-y}{4} = 3$

$$\frac{4z-y}{2} + \frac{5z+2y}{11} = 3$$

9-27.   Solve each equation.

   a. $\log_2(x) + \log_2(x-2) = 3$ b. $\log(2x) - \log(x^2) = -2$

9-28.   Convert the following angle measurements from degrees to radians.

   a.   30°   b.   15°   c.   −75°   d.   630°

9-29.   Find the exact equation of the graph at right.

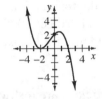

9-30.   A conveyor belt carries grain to the top of a barn, where it drops the grain so that it forms a pile on the ground. The pile is in the shape of a cone. Recall that the volume of a cone is one-third the area of the base times the vertical height.

   a.   Find the volume of the grain when the height of the pile is ten feet and the radius of the base is 4 feet. Use appropriate precision on your results.

   b.   As the pile grows, the cones formed remain similar. If the radius of the base is four feet when the height is ten feet, what is the radius of the base when the height is 15 feet?

   c.   Consider the angle the side of the cone-shaped pile makes with the ground. Is this angle changing? Justify your answer. If not, what is the measure of the angle?

9.1.3 What if random is not possible?

• •

Bias in Convenience Samples

In Lesson 9.1.2, you learned that random samples generally represent populations from which they are selected more closely than intentionally-selected samples. Partly for this reason, randomization is an important part of statistics.

However, it is often the case that it is neither possible nor practical to sample a population randomly. For example, if you wanted to survey voters in the United States about their choice for a presidential candidate, random sampling might not be practical. Even if you designed a method to select 1000 names randomly from the population of American voters, how would you find those 1000 people to survey in a timely and cost effective manner?

Sometimes statisticians are restricted to sampling strategies based on who is available to them, a practice known as **convenience sampling**. When this sampling technique is used, it is often impossible to make responsible claims about the original population. Consider these ideas as you work on the following problems with your team.

9-31.   Delilah is a pollster and she wants to know what American voters think about a possible federal income tax increase to fund education. She stands outside of a grocery store one evening and surveys every adult who is registered to vote. 62% of the voters Delilah surveyed support the tax increase.

a.   Can Delilah claim that this result is representative of American voters in general? Be sure to justify your thinking.

b.   With your team, think about the population that Delilah is actually finding information about. Whom can she responsibly claim her 62%-in-favor result represents?

c.   How might Delilah improve her sampling technique to better represent the population of American voters? Discuss this with your team and be prepared to share your ideas with the class.

9-32.   Sometimes pollsters try to predict the sorts of bias that they are likely to introduce with their sampling methods so that they can report their results appropriately. For example, Delilah might notice that many of the voters she surveyed had school-age children with them, and she might reason that they are more likely than average to support policies that fund public education.

For each of the following sampling methods, consider the actual population it could represent. What sorts of biases might you expect from these groups about Delilah's question from problem 9-31? What biases might you expect them to have about your own team's research question? Be prepared to share your ideas with the class.

a.   A call-in survey on a morning television talk show.

b.   Questionnaires mailed to addresses found in an online phone list.

c.   A survey of every student on the bus to school.

9-33.   Often when it is not possible to use a truly random sample, statisticians try to incorporate as much randomness as they can into their samples. For example, statisticians might divide the population into smaller clusters that each represent the population and randomly choose clusters to sample. They might divide the populations into groups that are each alike  (stratified) for a particular characteristic, then randomly sample from each group. Or they might systematically choose every fifth person or every tenth person, which is just as good as random if there is no order to the subjects.

Consider this idea as you talk with your own team about the survey you have been designing. Make a plan for sampling that considers the following questions. Be prepared to share your plan with your teacher.

- What is the population you are interested in?

- How will you select a sample of your population? How can you incorporate some degree of randomness into your selection process?

- How can you justify claims you will make about how representative this sample is of your population?

Store your survey questions in a safe place. They will be needed later in Chapter 11.

9-34.   In 1988, a committee of the Physicians Health Study Research Group released the results of a five-year experiment conducted on over 22,000 male physicians aged 40 to 84. The research on this sample suggested that the participants who took an aspirin every other day had a lower rate of heart attacks.

   a.   Can you conclude from this experiment that aspirin reduces the risk of heart attacks for all people? Why or why not?

   b.   Can you conclude from this experiment that aspirin reduces heart attacks for all men? Why or why not?

   c.   Can you conclude from this experiment that aspirin is linked to reduced heart attacks for all men aged 40 to 84? Why or why not?

   d.   Can you conclude from this experiment that aspirin reduces heart attacks for male physicians aged 40 to 84? Why or why not?

   e.   Can you conclude from this experiment that male physicians aged 40 to 84 should take aspirin? Why or why not?

9-35.   LEARNING LOG

With your team, discuss what you have learned in Section 9.1 about survey design, sampling strategies and avoiding bias. What are the types of bias that can be present in a survey? How can you avoid them in the questions that you ask? How can you sample the population in which you are interested to best be able to confidently answer your question? Summarize your ideas and include examples in your Learning Log. Title this entry "Survey Design and Bias" and label it with today's date.

9-36.   For each question below, describe a realistic method to collect information to answer the question. Be sure to indicate whether you would use a sample or census and whether your results would be parameters or statistics.

   a.   What percentage of American League baseball players had a batting average above .300 this season?

   b.   How much pressure can be exerted on a chicken egg before it breaks?

   c.   How many hours of television does a high school student watch per day?

9-37.   Label each of the following questions as either "open" or "closed."

   a.   How often do you exercise?

        A.   Every day

        B.   Once a week or more

        C.   Less than once a week

   b.   What is your favorite way to exercise?

   c.   What is your favorite time of year?

   d.   In which country were you born?

9-38.   For each question in problem 9-37 that you decided is open, give examples of
          answers that might be difficult to compare and quantify. For each question that
          you decided is closed, explain how the information you get from an answer may
          not be as accurate as it could be.

9-39.   What is the probability that $x^2 + 7x + k$ is factorable if $0 \le k \le 20$ and k is an
          integer?

9-40.   Victoria is playing with her balance scale and balances 3 blue blocks and 2 red
          blocks on one side with 5 blue blocks and a red block on the other. Later, her
          brother balances 2 red blocks and a blue block with a 40-gram weight. How
          much does each block weigh?

9-41. This problem is a checkpoint for writing and solving exponential equations. It will be referred to as Checkpoint 9A.

When rabbits were first brought to Australia, they had no natural enemies. There were about 80,000 rabbits in 1866. Two years later, in 1868, the population had grown to over 2,400,000!

a. Why would an exponential equation be a better model for this situation than a linear one? Would a sine function be better or worse? Why?

b. Write an exponential equation for the number of rabbits t years after 1866.

c. How many rabbits do you predict were present in 1871?

d. According to your model, in what year was the first pair of rabbits introduced into Australia? Is this reasonable?

e. Actually, 24 rabbits were introduced in 1859, so the model is not perfect, but is close. Is your exponential model useful for predicting how many rabbits there are now? Explain.

Check your answers by referring to the Checkpoint 9A materials located at the back of your book.

If you needed help solving these problems correctly, then you need more practice. Review the Checkpoint 9A materials and try the practice problems. Also, consider getting help outside of class time. From this point on, you will be expected to do problems like these quickly and easily.

9-42. Factor and reduce to simplify $\frac{3x+6}{x^2+7x+10}$. Justify each step.

9-43. Simplify and add $\frac{x-4}{x+2} + \frac{4x+12}{x^2+5x+6}$. Justify each step.

9-44. Change the angle measurements below from radians to degrees or from degrees to radians.

a. $144°$

b. $300°$

c. $\frac{5\pi}{9}$

d. $\frac{17\pi}{12}$

e. $\frac{19\pi}{2}$

f. $220°$

9.2.1 How can an experiment show cause and effect?

Testing Cause and Effect with Experiments

METHODS AND MEANINGS

Observational Studies and Experiments

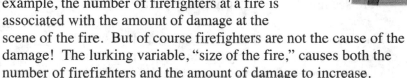

In an **observational study**, data is collected by observing but without imposing any kind of change. A survey is one type of observational study. Observational studies are often plagued by **lurking variables**, that is, hidden variables that are not part of the study, but that are the true cause of an association. For example, the number of firefighters at a fire is associated with the amount of damage at the scene of the fire. But of course firefighters are not the cause of the damage! The lurking variable, "size of the fire," causes both the number of firefighters and the amount of damage to increase.

To determine cause and effect, often a randomized, controlled **experiment is conducted.** In an experiment, subjects are randomly divided between two or more groups, and a **treatment** (a change) is imposed on at least one of the groups. Randomized experiments can be used to determine cause and effect because the influence of lurking variables, even though they are unknown, has mostly been equalized among all the groups. If there is a difference among groups, it is most likely due to the treatment since everything else is mostly the same.

9-45.   Consider this question: *"Does a new type of motor oil improve gas mileage?"*
Assuming this new motor oil was already available to the public, you could
survey some car owners who use the oil and some who do not and compare
their mean gas mileages.

a.   What problems might arise from using
this method? What are some possible
lurking variables that could affect the
outcome of the study?

b.   After reading the Math Notes box in this lesson, design an experiment to
help decide whether the new motor oil improves gas mileage.

c.   Sometimes a group gets no treatment. If people are involved, they may get
a **placebo** (a treatment with no effect) so the psychological effects of
participating in an experiment are the same among the groups. If you have
not already done so, include a no-treatment or placebo group in your
experiment.

9-46.   Testing to see how many drops of water fit on a penny
would be an observational study. You would simply
look to see how much water ordinary pennies can hold.

Today, a treatment has been added to a random sample
of pennies to make it an experiment. Your teacher has
cleaned a sample of pennies using a mild acid. The
research question is, *"Does cleaning pennies cause
them to hold a different amount of water than ordinary
uncleaned pennies?"*

You will be assigned a sample of pennies and a
workstation to test your pennies. Use the test
procedures outlined by your teacher. Make class
histograms and boxplots for the clean pennies and the
regular pennies.

9-47.   As a class, compare the histograms and boxplots, discuss your results, and write
a brief conclusion.

9-48.   Suppose your results from problems 9-46 and 9-47 were seriously biased by a
lurking variable. The effects of this lurking variable can be defeated by using
proper experimental procedures. As a class, discuss improvements that could
be made in the testing procedures.

Core Connections Algebra 2

9-49.   Repeat the experiment using the revised testing procedures. Create the new histograms and box plots. Write a conclusion to the question: "*Do clean pennies hold a different amount of water than regular pennies?*"

9-50.   Statistical results can be affected by psychological issues. Researchers who conduct experiments need to eliminate sources of bias for their statistical analysis to be meaningful. What are some potential causes of bias in the following samples?

   a.   Super Cola paid for a taste test study comparing it to Amazing Cola. Participants were asked to taste both drinks and pick their favorite. Super Cola was labeled "m" and the Amazing Cola was "q." The majority of participants picked the drink labeled "m," which was Super Cola.

   b.   A survey was conducted in the following manner: "The Bill of Rights guarantees the right to bear arms so that we can protect our families and our country. Recently, attempts have been made to enact stricter gun controls. Do you want these restrictions?"

   c.   Another survey was conducted in the following manner: "Last year over 15,000 people were murdered by handguns, which accounted for 68% of all murders. Recently, attempts have been made to enact stricter gun controls. Do you want these restrictions?"

9-51.   As you discovered in the asteroid activity in Lesson 9.1.2, people are not very good at picking representative samples. Similarly, it is actually quite difficult to "fake" randomness.

   In this problem, you will perform a brief survey to get an idea of people's "random" behavior. For this particular survey, you are not concerned with any particular population, so you can choose any sample that is convenient. You should talk with at least 10 people among your friends and family, but try for more to make your results more interesting.

   Use the same survey method for everybody: text messaging, phone call, or personal interview. Carefully record the responses you get.

Problem continues on next page →

9-51.   *Problem continued from previous page.*

    a.   Why would using a mass email or a social networking site not be a good plan?

    b.   Ask each of your respondents to make each of the following choices randomly. Make sure you read the choices exactly the same way to each respondent.

        1. Pick a number between 1 and 4.

        2. Pick a vowel (a, e, i, o, or u).

        3. Choose a color.

    c.   Make a bar graph for the responses to each of the three questions in your survey. Write the precise wording of the question with each bar graph.

    d.   Do your results show that people's choices were truly random? Why or why not?

    e.   Try to explain any trends or interesting patterns that you observe. Were the results similar to what you expected? Why or why not?

9-52.   Because gathering data for entire populations is often impractical, most of the data we analyze are samples. In order to make the sample standard deviation more closely estimate the population standard deviation, statisticians modify the way they calculate the standard deviation for a sample.

Refer to the Math Notes box in Lesson C.1.3 in Appendix C to remind you of how to calculate standard deviation (for a population). The calculation of standard deviation of a *sample* is slightly different. When computing the mean of the distances squared, instead of dividing by the number of values in the data set, divide by *one less* than the number of values in the set.

A non-profit consumer health organization measured the fat content of five low fat raspberry muffins purchased at random Sunbucks coffee shops. Find the mean and standard deviation of the fat content in this sample. Do the computations step by step, without using the "standard deviation" function on your calculator. The fat content follows: 6, 8, 8, 9, 7 grams of fat. (Hint: After showing all of your computations, the correct sample standard deviation is 1.14g.)

9-53.   Solve the system of equations at right.

$$8x - 3y - 2z = -8$$
$$-2x + 8y + 7z = 26$$
$$4x + y - 5z = 23$$

9-54.   Divide $(x^3 - 2x^2 + 25x - 50) \div (x - 2)$.

9-55.   Use your answer from the previous problem to solve $x^3 - 2x^2 + 25x - 50 = 0$.

9-56.   If $\cos\theta = \frac{8}{17}$, find $\sin\theta$.

9-57.   If $a = 2 + 3i$ and $b = 1 - i$, compute each of the following operations:

a. $a + b$ b. $a - b$ c. ab d. $\frac{a}{b}$

9-58.   Solve each equation.

a. $\frac{15}{x-2} = \frac{16}{x}$ b. $\frac{1}{x} + \frac{1}{2x} = 9$

9.2.2 How can I answer the question?

Conclusions From Studies

You will often see headlines in everyday life announcing the results of some statistical study. Today you will critically analyze the possible meanings of such headlines.

9-59.   For each question:

- Does a census or sample make more sense in this situation?
- Should an observational study or an experiment be carried out to answer the question?
- If an observational study is possible, explain how you would carry out the study. How would you get a representative sample from the population?
- If surveys are necessary, list a potential source of bias in the question(s).
- If the study asks for an association between variables, discuss the effects of at least two possible lurking variables.
- If an experiment would be suitable, outline an experimental design.

a.   Is there a relationship between the amount of physical activity a person gets and his or her perceived level of stress?

b.   What is the mean of the 2009 SAT math scores for the state of Arizona? Is it higher than the corresponding mean score for West Virginia?

c.   What percentage of high school students would be willing to donate $10 or an hour of time to help a local food bank?

d.   What is the mean weight of backpacks carried on college campuses? Is it different than the mean weight of backpacks carried on high school campuses?

e.   Would wearing neckties increase standardized test scores for boys in middle school?

f.   What is the average number of absences for the freshman class at your school?

g.   What proportion of refurbished cell phones are defective?

h.   How much cholesterol is in a chicken egg?

i.   Do the seniors at your school do less homework than the sophomores?

Core Connections Algebra 2

9-60.   Answer some of the same questions posed in problem 9-59 for these actual
         newspaper headlines. If an observational study was done, explain how.
         Explain why an experiment was not possible. If the study shows an association
         between variables, discuss the effects of at least two possible lurking variables.
         If you believe an experiment was done, state so, and outline a possible
         experimental design. If surveys were necessary, list a potential source of bias in
         the question(s), and a potential difficulty in getting a representative sample from
         the population.

     a.   "STUDY STICKS IT TO TRADITIONAL BACK
         CARE. Acupuncture – real and fake – gets better
         results for pain than the usual treatments."

     b.   "MARITAL STRIFE A HEART WRECKER? Bad
         marriage can increase risk of coronary disease,
         researchers say."

     c.   "BREASTFEEDING MAY CUT BREAST
         CANCER RISK. Women with a family history of
         breast cancer who have ever breastfed reduce their
         risk of getting premenopausal breast cancer by
         nearly 60%, according to a new study."

     d.   "STUDY: ORAL DRUG BETTER THAN
         LOTION TO KILL LICE... A new study has
         found that in tough cases, a (new) oral medication
         kills the parasites more effectively than a
         prescription lotion applied to the scalp."

9-61.   LEARNING LOG

         With your team, discuss the similarities and differences
         between observational studies, surveys, and experiments.
         What are the advantages and disadvantages of each? What
         are some of the important things to consider when conducting an observational
         study versus a survey or designing an experiment? How confident can you be
         about your conclusions? Summarize your thoughts in your Learning Log. Title
         this entry "Surveys Versus Experiments" and label it with today's date.

9-62.   Suppose you were conducting a survey to
         determine what portion of voters in your town
         supports a particular candidate for mayor.
         Consider each of the following methods for
         sampling the voting population of your town.
         State whether each is likely to produce a
         representative sample and explain your reasoning.

   a.   Call one number from each page of an online
         phone listing for your town between noon
         and 2 p.m.

   b.   Survey each person leaving a local grocery store.

   c.   Survey each person leaving a local movie theater.

   d.   Walk around downtown and survey every fourth person you see.

   e.   Could you make a representative sample by surveying a few people from
         each of the situations described in parts (a) through (d) above? Explain,
         and consider what problems might still remain.

9-63.   Consider the question: "Does a traditional classroom SAT preparation course
         improve scores more than an online study course?"

         Design an experiment that could help to answer this question. Refer to problem
         9-45 for ideas.

9-64.   Suppose you were asked to find lurking variables that would be associated with
         the news headline: "Study: Kids who were spanked have lower IQs." Certainly,
         there are plenty of lurking variables to cast doubt on cause and effect. Think
         about what it would take to do an experiment to determine if spanking causes
         lower IQs. Design an experiment and point out why it is not ethical.

9-65.   In an effort to determine the amount of food a male yellow-billed
         magpie eats in a day, a sample of 5 birds from pet stores was
         observed. The birds ate the following amount of food: 60, 60, 50,
         40, and 50 grams. Find the mean and standard deviation weight of
         food in this sample. Do the computations step by step, without
         using the "standard deviation" function on your calculator, as in problem 9-52.

9-66.   How many solutions are there to the system of equations at right? Justify your response.

$$y = x^2 - 2x + 2$$
$$y = 2x - 2$$

9-67.   Graph $y = \sqrt{(4 - x^2)}$. Imagine revolving this graph around the x-axis, faster and faster, so that it appears to form a sphere. Sketch the sphere and then find its volume. Note: The volume of a sphere is given by $V = \frac{4}{3}\pi r^3$.

9-68.   What is the probability that $x^2 + kx + 12$ will factor if $0 \le k \le 8$ and k is an integer? Make an organized list (sample space) to help you determine the probability.

9-69.   Graph at least two cycles of the following functions.

a. $f(x) = 3\sin 2(x - \frac{\pi}{4}) + 1$

b. $g(x) = \frac{1}{2}\cos\frac{1}{4}(x + \pi)$

9.3.1 What percent is it?

Relative Frequency Histograms

In this lesson you will learn how to make a new kind of histogram, called a relative frequency histogram. A relative frequency histogram helps you find the proportion of the population with a certain characteristic.

9-70.   In order to make the standard deviation of a sample more closely estimate the population standard deviation, statisticians modify the way they calculate the standard deviation for a sample.

   a.   If the data set contains the entire population, you divide by n, the number of values in the data set, when finding the population standard deviation. If the data set is a sample from the population, you divide by $n-1$ to find the sample standard deviation. Which standard deviation has a larger value?

   b.   One of the reasons the sample standard deviation needs to be increased has to do with outliers. Why might the presence of outliers in the population make the standard deviation of a sample too small compared to the standard deviation of the population?

   c.   Refer to problem 9-65. The amounts the five birds ate were: 60, 60, 50, 40, and 50 grams. Explore the functions on your calculator to find the mean and the sample standard deviation for the five birds.

   d.   What if the five birds were the entire population of birds? What would the mean and population standard deviation be? Use the correct symbols, referring as needed to the Math Notes box at the end of this lesson.

Core Connections Algebra 2

9-71.   VISORS FOR RUNNERS, Part 1

The Style & Comfort Headgear Company makes
printed visors as gifts for women running in
charity marathons. Marathons in different cities
have different numbers of participants. S & C
Headgear needs a method for deciding how many
visors of each size to print for each event. The
company collected the data below for women's
head circumference by measuring 40 randomly
selected runners at charity events.

Head circumference (cm)							
55.5	53.7	53.7	53.4	53.1	55.2	53.9	53.8
53.1	52.2	54.8	54.5	53.2	52.3	55.3	53.2
51.9	53.1	53.1	52.2	51.2	55.4	53.3	51.4
52.6	53.7	52.7	52.8	51.9	54.3	55.4	53.7
53.0	52.7	53.0	54.6	52.5	52.9	53.1	51.9

checksum 2133.3

a.   What are the mean head circumference and standard deviation for these
      women?

b.   On your calculator, make a histogram of the distribution of women's head
      circumferences and sketch it. Use an interval from 50 cm to 57 cm with a
      bin width of 1.

c.   Hat size is determined by the whole-number portion of a woman's head
      circumference. For example, a woman with a head measuring 55.8 cm
      would need a size 55 hat. According to your histogram, how many
      women in this sample need a size 52 hat?

d.   What percent of the women in this sample have a hat size less than 54?

9-72.   Questions about percentages, like those in part (d) of problem 9-71 above, are easier to answer if you make a table of **relative frequencies**. Relative frequency is the **proportion** of hats: the percent of hats in that size out of the total 40 hats, written as a decimal.

a.   Copy and complete the following table.

Women's hat sizes		
size interval	frequency (# of hats)	relative frequency (proportion of hats)
50–51	0	0
51–52	5	0.125
52–53	9	0.225
53–54	17	
54–55		
55–56		
56–57		

b.   Your teacher will show you how to make a **relative frequency histogram** from the table above. Sketch the relative frequency histogram. Label the top of each bar with its relative frequency. What do you notice about the shape of the relative frequency histogram?

c.   Relative frequency histograms make percentages easier to visualize. Use the histogram to compute the percent of hats in this sample between size 52 and 55.

d.   What percent of hats in this sample are below size 56? Show a computation.

9-73.   CHARITY RACE TIMES, Part 1

The 40 women in the sample recorded their race times in various charity 5K races in the table below.

Race time (min)							
22.2	22.6	24.9	23.5	22.8	23.3	23.1	21.6
21.3	22.9	25.7	23.3	23.3	22.5	24.4	22.7
24.1	23	22.5	23.2	24.7	24.4	23.3	23.5
23.1	22.5	22.3	22.6	23.6	23.3	23.3	23.4
23.0	23.1	24.5	23.9	20.6	23.5	22.8	24.4

checksum 928.7

a.   Find the mean and standard deviation of the race times to four decimal places. Justify your choice of standard deviation.

b.   Create a relative frequency histogram with your calculator, and sketch it. Use an interval from 19 to 27 with a bin width of 1. Label the top of each bar with its relative frequency.

c.   Use the relative frequencies on your histogram to calculate the percentage of racers in this sample that had a time faster than 22 minutes. Remember, smaller times are faster.

d.   What percentage of racers in this sample completed a race between 22 and 25 minutes? What is the relationship between the area of the bars and the percentage of the population?

9-74.   LEARNING LOG

With your team, discuss the similarities and differences between a histogram and a relative frequency histogram as a way to represent a distribution of single-variable data. What is the meaning of the *area* of the bars on a relative frequency histogram? Summarize the directions for creating a relative frequency histogram, including examples. Title this entry "Relative Frequency Histograms" and label it with today's date.

MᴇTHODS AND MᴇANINGS

MATH NOTES

Symbols for Standard Deviation

In statistics, standard variables are used to represent the mean and standard deviation.

The number of values in a data set is often represented with n.

The population parameters are written using lower-case Greek letters such as μ (pronounced "myoo") for the mean, and σ (pronounced "sigma") for the population standard deviation.

When the data are a sample, $\bar{x}$ (pronounced "x-bar") represents the sample mean, and s is used to represent the sample standard deviation.

9-75.   Bias can take many forms. Sometimes it is created unintentionally by conditions in an experiment. Other times it is more intentional. For each example below, comment on possible bias.

a.   In a TV commercial an interviewer asks people on the street to name their favorite radio station. All five that he asked claimed the same station as their favorite.

b.   A university campus wants to increase fees in order to build a new recreation hall. It surveys students to determine support. Survey booths are placed outside the university gym. The resulting survey showed overwhelming support.

c.   A study shows that many more accidents occur on I-95 during the day than at night. Is it therefore safer to drive at night?

d.   An active citizens' group claimed that a nuclear facility was operating at below average safety levels and therefore should be shut down.

9-76. Design experiments for the following statistical questions. If it would be unethical to conduct such an experiment, state why.

 a. "Does listening to classical music during a math test improve scores?"

 b. "Do seat belts save lives in car crashes?"

 c. "Does vitamin C help prevent colds?"

9-77. Simplify each expression below.

 a. $3^{-2} \cdot 3^4$

 b. $3^{-4} \cdot 3^4$

 c. $(3^{-1} + 3^{-3}) \cdot 3^4$

 d. $\frac{3^{-2} - 3^{-1}}{3^{-3} + 3^{-4}}$

9-78. John has to graph a set of parabolas of the form $y = x^2 - 4x + 2^n$ where n is an integer and $0 \le n \le 6$. What is the probability that one of these parabolas, chosen at random, will have:

 a. One x-intercept?

 b. Two x-intercepts?

 c. No x-intercepts?

9-79. If $\tan\theta = \frac{1}{2}$ and $\pi \le \theta \le \frac{3\pi}{2}$, what is the value of $\sin\theta$?

9-80.   Denae and Gina were trying to solve $\sqrt{x+5}+\sqrt{x}=5$. They knew they would have to square the equation to get rid of the radicals, but when they tried it, they got $x+5+2\sqrt{x(x+5)}+x=25$, which did not look much easier to deal with. Gina had an idea.

"Let's start by putting the radicals on opposite sides of the equation and then squaring." she said. Her work is shown at right.

$$\sqrt{x+5}+\sqrt{x}=5$$
$$\sqrt{x+5}=5-\sqrt{x}$$
$$x+5=25-10\sqrt{x}+x$$

"But there's still a radical!" she exclaimed, disappointed.

"That's okay," said Denae, *"there's only one now, so we can get the term with the radical by itself and then square everything again."*

a.   Follow Denae's advice and solve this equation.

b.   Use Denae and Gina's method to solve $\sqrt{2x-2}-\sqrt{x}=1$.

9-81.   If you deposit $1000 into an account that pays 6% interest compounded monthly, how long do you have to wait until the account is worth $4000?

9-82.   Graph each of the following trig functions.

a. $y=2\sin(x)$ and $y=\cos(x)$ on the same set of axes.

b.   Use your answer to part (a) to graph $y=2\sin(x)+\cos(x)$.

9-83.   You are given a bag that you are told contains eight marbles. You draw out a marble, record its color, and put it back.

a.   If you repeat this eight times and you do not record any red marbles, can you conclude that there are not any red marbles in the bag? Explain.

b.   If you repeat this 100 times and you do not record any red marbles, can you conclude that there are not any red marbles in the bag? Explain.

c.   How many times do you have to draw marbles (putting them back each time) to be absolutely certain that there are no red marbles in the bag?

9.3.2 How can I make predictions?

The Normal Probability Density Function

By creating a mathematical model of data, you can describe the data to others without giving them a list of all the data, and you can make predictions based on the data. In previous courses you created a model when you drew a line of best fit as a model for data in a scatterplot. Using the line of best fit, you were able to describe the association in the data, and you were able to make predictions from the model.

Much of the real data that is encountered in science, business, and industry can be modeled with a bell-shaped curve, called a **normal probability density function**. This function is given by the following mathematical formula:

$$f(x) = \frac{1}{\sqrt{2\pi\sigma^2}} e^{-\frac{(x-\mu)^2}{2\sigma^2}}$$

Although this looks intimidating, your calculator can draw the graph very easily based on the mean and standard deviation of the data.

9-84. CHARITY RACE TIMES, Part 2

Reread problem 9-73 "Charity Race Times" from Lesson 9.3.1. Recreate the relative frequency histogram on your calculator, and record the mean and standard deviation. Use an interval from 19 to 27 with a bin width of 1.

Your teacher will demonstrate how to model the women's 5K times with a normal probability density function ("**normal distribution**"). Sketch the histogram with your model on top of it.

How well does your model represent the data? What are the strengths and weaknesses of your model?

9-85.   If you wanted to use the relative frequency histogram to find the percent of women in this sample that have run times between 22.5 and 24.5 minutes, you would add up the bars between 22.5 and 24.5. But since your histogram is not drawn conveniently with those bins, you would have to redraw the histogram. However, your model of the data comes to the rescue!

a.   The height of the bars between 22.5 and 24.5 can be modeled with the area under the normal distribution between 22.5 and 24.5, as shaded black in the diagram at right.

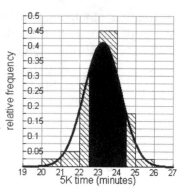

Your teacher will show you how to use the normalcdf function on your calculator to find the area under the curve between 22.5 and 24.5. In general, on a TI83/84+ calculator, you enter 2nd [DISTR] normalcdf(*lower limit, upper limit, mean, standard deviation*) to have your calculator find the proportion for the interval.

What percent of women in this sample have running times between 22.5 and 24.5 minutes?

b.   Your model represents the percentages of women in the sample that have various run times. But it does much more than that – since the sample of 40 randomly selected women represents the whole population of women that run in 5K races, your model can tell you about percentages in the whole population. (You will refine these techniques in more advanced statistics classes.) If your model represented the whole population, what percentage of all women that run 5K races have race times between 20 and 25 minutes?

c.   Even though the fastest (smallest) time in the sample of 40 women was 20.6 minutes, the model that you chose – the normal probability density function – starts at negative infinity and goes all the way to positive infinity. What percentage of all women in the population run faster than 26 minutes according to your model? Since your calculator may not have an infinity key, instead enter -10^{99} for the lower limit.

d.   Using your model, make a prediction for the percentage of women that fall below the mean running time. Does your answer make sense?

9-86.   VISORS FOR RUNNERS, Part 2

The Style and Comfort 5K Race for Charity is coming
up. The Style and Comfort Headwear Company
expects 775 racers. Based on a model for hat size
distributions for all women, they will need to order
hats for the event.

a.   On your calculator, recreate the relative frequency histogram for the 40
      women's hat sizes in problem 9-71. Use an interval from 50 cm to 57 cm
      with a bin width of 1.

b.   Use the mean and standard deviation of hat sizes that you calculated in
      problem 9-71 to make a model of the data using a normal distribution.
      You will need your calculator. Sketch the histogram and the model.

c.   Using your model to represent all women running 5K races, determine
      what percentage of women racers wear a size 51 hat. Shade this
      proportion on a new sketch of the model, and calculate the proportion
      using normalcdf on your calculator. How does the percentage predicted
      by the model compare to the percentage observed in your sample?

d.   How many size 51 hats should Style and Comfort order for the anticipated
      775 racers at the Style and Comfort 5K Race for Charity?

e.   Use the model to predict how many of the racers at the Style and Comfort
      5K Race for Charity are expected to have a hat size below 51. Sketch
      these proportions on a new sketch of the model.

f.   How many racers would you expect to have a hat size over size 56?
      Between 51 and 56?

g.   Does your answer to part (f) make sense
      when compared to the answers from part (e)?

h.   What percentage of racers does your normal
      distribution model predict have hat sizes
      between negative infinity and infinity? Does
      your model make a sensible prediction?

9-87.   LEARNING LOG

With your team, discuss the similarities and differences
between a relative frequency histogram as a way to
represent a sample, and the normal distribution as a model
for the population represented in the random sample. Review the directions and
include some examples for drawing a normal distribution and for finding
percents represented by areas under the normal distribution. Title this entry
"Relative Frequency Histograms and Normal Distributions," and include
today's date.

9-88.   Some students at North City High are abusing the
privilege of being allowed to leave campus for
lunch. The number of students tardy to Mrs.
Greene's period after lunch is too high. In the
last 30 school days, she recorded the number of
tardy students shown in the relative frequency
histogram at right.

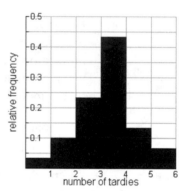

a.   Describe the distribution of tardy students by
estimating the height of each bin.

b.   How many days were 3 or more students tardy?

c.   What percent of the days were no students tardy?

9-89.   Coach Pham claims that his new 6-week agility program will increase an
athletes' vertical leap by 10 centimeters more than traditional workouts.

a.   Design an experiment to test the coach's claim.

b.   If the group using Coach Pham's techniques improved their leaping
significantly more than the group using traditional methods, would this
provide evidence that the new agility program is the cause?

9-90.   A properly randomized and controlled experiment can determine cause and
effect, unlike an observational study, which can be plagued by lurking variables.
Why do we not conduct an experiment for every study? Why do observational
studies at all?

9-91.   Graph the inequalities $y \geq |x-2|$ and $y \leq 4-|x|$, then find the area of the enclosed region.

9-92.   Use the equation $f(x) = (x+3)^3 - 1$ to complete each of the following tasks.

   a.   Find the inverse equation.

   b.   Graph the inverse equation.

   c.   Is the inverse a function? Explain.

9-93.   Make a sketch of the graph of each of the following functions. Describe the graphs.

   a. $y = (x+1)^2(x-2)^2(x-5)^2$ b. $y = -(x+1)^2(x-2)^2(x-5)^2$

9-94.   Given the function $h(x) = -2(x+3)^2 + 2$:

   a.   What are the intercepts?   b.   What are the domain and range?

9-95.   Rewrite each equation in graphing form and identify the key points.

   a. $y = \frac{1}{4}x^2 + \frac{1}{2}x + \frac{5}{8}$ b. $y = \frac{1}{4}x^2 + 5x + 41$

9-96.   Find the distance between the two points.

   a. (x, y) and $(-3, y)$ b. (x, y) and $(-3, 2)$

9-97.   The ACT is a test that colleges use to help make admissions decisions for potential students. Nationwide, the scores are normally distributed, with a mean score of 21 (out of a possible 36) and a standard deviation of 4.7.

    a.   Model the scores of all test takers on your calculator using a normal distribution. An appropriate value for the maximum of the relative frequency axis is 0.1.

    b.   Adèle scored 25 on the ACT. With your team, explore how well she did. Remember your normal distribution is a model for the bars of a histogram. Shade the "bars" (the area under the normal distribution) for all the scores below Adèle's score. What percent of scores are below Adèle's score? Round to the nearest whole number.

    c.   Since 80% of test-takers scored below Adèle, you can say that Adèle scored in the 80th **percentile**. Rémy scored a 16 on the ACT. What was Rémy's percentile?

    d.   Antoinette scored 21 on the ACT. *Without a calculator*, make a sketch of the scores below Antoinette on a normal distribution and indicate what percentile Antoinette fell in.

9-98.   Percentiles are not just for normal distributions. They can be used for any set of data to report the percent of scores that fell below a given score. The following data are the test scores on Mrs. Abraha's Chapter 3 test in Geometry.

Chapter 3 Geometry Test Scores						
75	72	91	90	83	60	89
86	17	71	58	86	81	86
94	94	79	60	53	89	42
89	56	57	93	93	94	76
80	80	94	75	92	69	75

checksum 2679

a.   Make a histogram of the data on your calculator and sketch it. Use a bin width of 5.

b.   Lateefa is modeling the data using a normal distribution, but her partner Farid thinks that it is not a good idea. What advice would you give them about using a normal distribution?

c.   Lateefa scored 86 on the test, and Farid scored 92. What percentile did each score in?

d.   What score is at the 25th percentile? 75th percentile?

e.   Find the five number summary (minimum, first quartile, median, third quartile, maximum) for this data. How does your answer compare to part (d) above?

9-99.   The March 2004 issue of *Ichthyological Research* reported the relative frequencies for the length of 98 larvae of the ayu sweetfish is shown at right.

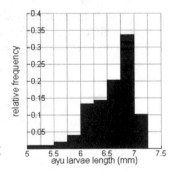

a.   Estimate the 90th percentile for the length of ayu larvae.

b.   Would you recommend making a model using a normal distribution for the data to answer part (a)? Why or why not?

c.   Estimate the 50th percentile. What is another name for the 50th percentile?

9-100.   Rachna's physics class is going out to the football
          field to launch rockets today. The rocket that Rachna
          is launching has historically had a mean flight
          distance of 74 m with a standard deviation of 26 m.
          A rocket's flight distance is modeled with a normal
          distribution.

     a.   Make a graph of the distribution of Rachna's
          rocket flight distances on your calculator, and
          sketch it. An appropriate value for the maximum
          of the relative frequency axis is 0.02.

     b.   From your graph, visually estimate the two flight distances between which
          the rocket will land 90% of the time. Shade this portion of your sketch.

     c.   Use your calculator to check your estimate. How close to 90% did you
          come?

     d.   The middle 90% (or 95% or 99%) of the data is an important computation
          in statistics. It tells you what "typical" data might look like without
          considering the small or large extremes at either end. Statistical
          computations will reveal that the lower bound of the middle 90% of
          normally distributed data is at -1.6449 times the standard deviation, and
          the upper bound is at 1.6449 times the standard deviation. Use this new
          information to make a new, more accurate, determination of the two
          distances between which the rocket will land 90% of the time.

9-101.   Rachna and her sister, Rakhi, were both in the same physics class. They made a
          bet with each other on whose rocket would go farther. The loser would have to
          wash the family dishes for a month! Unfortunately, Rakhi was assigned a very
          different style rocket from the one Rachna got, so it was difficult to make a fair
          comparison. They decided to compare the percentiles. Rakhi's style of rocket
          had a mean flight distance of 30 m with a standard deviation of 6 m.

          Rachna's rocket went 66.74 m, while Rakhi's went 28.17 m. Use percentiles to
          determine who had to wash the dishes for a month.

9-102.   In response to a judging controversy during the 2002 Winter Olympics, a new
          scoring system for ice dancing was implemented in 2006. The new system uses
          a "grade of execution" (GOE) as part of the overall score. The GOE goes from
          -3 to 3, and can be modeled with a normal distribution with mean of 0 and
          standard deviation of 1. Isabella and Tony scored a 2 on the GOE. What
          percentile are they in? What percentage of ice dancers had higher scores?

Core Connections Algebra 2

METHODS AND MEANINGS

Normal Probability Density Function

For many situations in science, business, and industry, data may be represented by a bell-shaped curve. In order to be able to work mathematically with that data – describing it to others, making predictions – an equation called a **normal probability density function** is fitted to the data. This is very similar to how a line of best fit is used to describe and make predictions of data on a scatterplot.

The normal probability density function ("normal distribution") stretches to infinity in both directions. The area under the normal distribution can be thought of as modeling the bars on a relative frequency histogram. However, instead of drawing all the bars, a curve is drawn that represents the tops of all the bars. Like bars on a relative frequency histogram, the area under the normal distribution (shaded in the diagram below) represents the portion of the population within that interval.

The total area under the curve is 1, representing 100% of the population. The mean of the population is at the peak of the normal distribution, resulting in 50% of the population below the mean and 50% above the mean.

The width of the normal distribution is determined by the standard deviation (the variability) of the population under study. The more variability in the data, the wider (and flatter) the normal distribution is.

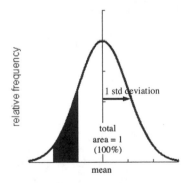

9-103. North City High School has served the following number of lunches since the beginning of the school year. The data has been sorted.

Number of lunches sold per day							
576	605	632	660	671	689	723	774
584	606	636	661	671	695	738	785
594	613	640	663	675	698	745	
595	618	640	665	677	703	755	
603	630	652	666	678	721	774	

checksum 24711

a. What are the mean and standard deviation number of lunches in the sample?

b. What is the five number summary of the distribution?

c. Make a relative frequency histogram of the number of lunches served. Use a scale from 560 to 800 lunches, with a bin width of 40 lunches. Sketch the histogram and label the height of each of the bins.

d. Describe the distribution. Make sure you consider the center, shape, spread, and outliers.

e. Using your histogram, determine the percent of days on which fewer than 600 lunches were sold.

f. Using the histogram, estimate the percent of days on which between 600 and 700 lunches were sold.

9-104.   Do you remember the students tardy to Ms. Greene's class? Now that you have investigated how to create and use a normal distribution, model the number of tardy students Ms. Greene actually recorded using a normal distribution. The data Mrs. Greene gathered for 30 days is shown in the table below.

Number of tardy students per day					
2	4	3	3	4	2
1	3	3	4	3	2
2	3	1	2	3	3
3	0	2	3	2	5
5	3	3	3	4	1
				checksum 82	

a.   On your calculator, recreate the relative frequency histogram for the number of tardy students that is shown in problem 9-88.

b.   Find the mean and standard deviation of the number of tardy students.

c.   On your calculator, model the data with a normal distribution by pressing [Y=] and entering [2nd] [DISTR] normalpdf(X, *mean, standard deviation*). Sketch the model with the histogram.

d.   According to your model, on what percentage of days were 4 people tardy? Shade this proportion on a new sketch of the model, and calculate the proportion using normalcdf(*lower, upper, mean, standard deviation*) on your calculator.

e.   Assume that the last 30 days in Mrs. Greene's class were representative of the 180 days in the whole school year. According to your model, how many days this year can Mrs. Greene expect 4 or more tardy students? Sketch the area representing these days on a new graph of the model.

9-105.   Due to natural variability in manufacturing, a 12-ounce can of soda does not usually hold exactly 12 ounces of soda. The quality control department at a soda factory allows cans to hold a little more or a little less. According to specifications, a soda-can filling machine must fill each can with a mean of 12 ounces of soda and a standard deviation of 0.33 ounces. Filling machines can often be modeled with a normal distribution.

a.   Use your calculator to create a graph of a normal distribution using normalpdf. Sketch the graph. An appropriate value for the maximum of the relative frequency axis is Ymax = 1.5.

b.   How often do you actually get a 12 oz can of soda containing more than 12 oz?

c.   What percent of cans contain between 11.5 and 12.5 ounces of soda? Shade your diagram from part (a) to represent these bottles.

9-106. Use the properties of logarithms to rewrite each expression as an equivalent one using only one logarithm.

    a. $\log_3(5) + \log_3(m)$

    b. $\log_6(p) - \log_6(m)$

    c. $\log_2(r) + 3\log_6(z)$

    d. $\log(90) + \log(4) - \log(36)$

9-107. Simplify each expression.

    a. $\dfrac{x+2}{x^2-2x-3} + \dfrac{x}{x^2-2x}$

    b. $\dfrac{2}{x} - \dfrac{x}{x-2}$

    c. $\dfrac{x^2-x-6}{x^2-x-20} \cdot \dfrac{x^2+6x+8}{x^2-x-6}$

    d. $\dfrac{x^3+8}{x} \div \dfrac{x+2}{x^2}$

9-108. Solve each equation.

    a. $\dfrac{x+1}{5} = \dfrac{5}{x-1}$

    b. $\dfrac{1}{x} + \dfrac{1}{x+2} = 3$

9-109. Graph in three dimensions.

    a. $(2, -1, -3)$

    b. $6x - 3y + 9z = 18$

9-110. Find the distance between each pair of points.

    a. $(17, 29)$ and $(-1, -1)$

    b. (x, y) and $(-1, -1)$

9-111. This problem is a checkpoint for finding the equation for the inverse of a function. It will be referred to as Checkpoint 9B.

Consider the function $f(x) = 2\sqrt{3(x-1)} + 5$.

    a.   Find the equation for the inverse of $f(x)$.

    b.   Sketch the graph of both the original and the inverse.

Check your answers by referring to the Checkpoint 9B materials located at the back of your book.

If you needed help solving these problems correctly, then you need more practice. Review the Checkpoint 9B materials and try the practice problems. Also, consider getting help outside of class time. From this point on, you will be expected to do problems like these quickly and easily.

Chapter 9 Closure What have I learned?

Reflection and Synthesis

The activities below offer you a chance to reflect
about what you have learned during this chapter.
As you work, look for concepts that you feel very
comfortable with, ideas that you would like to learn
more about, and topics you need more help with.
Look for connections between ideas as well as
connections with material you learned previously.

① TEAM BRAINSTORM

What have you studied in this chapter? What ideas were important in what you
learned? With your team, brainstorm a list. Be as detailed as you can. To help
get you started, a list of Learning Log entries and Math Notes boxes are below.

What topics, ideas, and words that you learned *before* this chapter are connected
to the new ideas in this chapter? Again, be as detailed as you can.

Learning Log Entries
- Lesson 9.1.3 – Survey Design and Bias
- Lesson 9.2.2 – Surveys Versus Experiments
- Lesson 9.3.1 – Relative Frequency Histograms
- Lesson 9.3.2 – Normal Probability Density Function

Math Notes
- Lesson 9.1.1 – Population Parameters and Sample Statistics
- Lesson 9.2.1 – Observational Studies and Experiments
- Lesson 9.3.1 – Symbols for Standard Deviation
- Lesson 9.3.3 – Normal Probability Density Function

②   MAKING CONNECTIONS

Below is a list of the vocabulary used in this chapter. Make sure that you are familiar with all of these words and know what they mean. Refer to the glossary or index for any words that you do not yet understand.

5-variable summary	bias	census
convenience sample	experiment	lurking variable
mean	median	normal distribution
observational study	parameter	population
random sample	sample	standard deviation
statistic	survey	treatment
variable		

Make a concept map showing all of the connections you can find among the key words and ideas listed above. To show a connection between two words, draw a line between them and explain the connection. A word can be connected to any other word as long as you can justify the connection.

While you are making your map, your team may think of related words or ideas that are not listed here. Be sure to include these ideas on your concept map.

③   PORTFOLIO: EVIDENCE OF MATHEMATICAL PROFICIENCY

This section gives you an opportunity to show growth in your understanding of key mathematical ideas over time as you complete this course. Several options are presented below. Follow your teacher's directions for which options you should complete.

Part 1: You may have done this problem before in a previous chapter. You have grown mathematically since then. Be sure to include everything you have learned since the last time you did this problem.

Explain everything that you know about $f(x) = 2^x - 3$.

Activity continues on next page. →

Core Connections Algebra 2

③   *Activity continued from previous page.*

Part 2: Compare your responses to this "Growth Over Time" problem. Write an evaluation of your growth based on your responses. Consider each of the following questions as you write your answer. If you only did the problem twice, then answer accordingly.

- What new concepts did you include the second time you did the problem? In what ways was your response better than your first attempt?

- How was your final version different from the first two? What new ideas did you include?

- Did you omit anything in your later versions that you used in one of the earlier versions? Why did you omit it?

- Rate your three attempts by making three bars like the ones below and shading each bar (left to right) to represent how much you knew on each attempt.

First Attempt:
Second Attempt:
Final Attempt:

- Is there anything you want to add to your current version? If so, add it and keep this version for future reference.

Alternatively, your teacher may have you complete the following problem and add it to your portfolio:

Corbin is concerned about the amount of sodium in breakfast cereal. After examining labels from a random sample of cereal brands, he discovers that the amount of sodium in breakfast cereal is approximately normally distributed with a mean of 6.5 milligrams sodium per gram of cereal and a standard deviation of 1.6 mg/g. Corbin has listed his three favorite cereals and their sodium content below and wants to know how they compare to the population of breakfast cereals as a whole. For each cereal listed below, find its sodium content percentile and provide Corbin an explanation of what each percentile means.

a.   Tweeties cereal has 7.3 milligrams sodium per gram of cereal.

b.   Apple Flakes cereal has 4.5 mg/g.

c.   Korn Cripsies cereal has 3.9 mg/g.

④   WHAT HAVE I LEARNED?

Most of the problems in this section
represent typical problems found in this
chapter. They serve as a gauge for
you. You can use them to determine
which types of problems you can do well
and which types of problems require
further study and practice. Even if your
teacher does not assign this section, it is a
good idea to try these problems and find out for yourself what you know and
what you still need to work on.

Solve each problem as completely as you can. The table at the end of the
closure section has answers to these problems. It also tells you where you
can find additional help and practice with problems like these.

CL 9-112.   Stephanie is interested in laws concerning the death penalty. She gives the
following survey question to her government class.

> "The constitution allows individual states the freedom to enact laws
> which are not contradictory to federal laws. For example, capital
> punishment is permissible in some states but not in others. Are you in
> favor of the U.S. Congress passing legislation to override every
> individual state law and ban the practice of capital punishment?"

Thirty-eight percent of the students respond in favor of a federal law
governing the use of capital punishment. Stephanie concludes that there is
insufficient popular support to pass a federal law banning capital
punishment.

a.   Is 38% a parameter or statistic? How do you know? What population
is Stephanie making her conclusion about?

b.   What sources of bias are present in the wording of her question?

c.   What sampling technique did Stephanie use and how might it introduce
bias into her conclusion?

CL 9-113.   Suppose Stephanie wanted to determine whether students in her ceramics
class have a significantly different opinion towards capital punishment
legislation than those in her government class. She finds 55% of the
ceramics students in favor of federal oversight of capital punishment and
concludes that taking ceramics causes opposition to the death penalty. Why
is her conclusion unreasonable? Design an experiment that would test her
conclusion.

CL 9-114.   It is inventory time at the Mathletes Shoe Super Store. To speed up the process, Iris, the storeowner, decided to find the value of the inventory by counting the number of pairs of shoes that belong in $30 intervals. She made the following table:

Value ($)	# of pairs
0 up to 30	47
30 up to 60	67
60 up to 90	60
90 up to 120	46
120 up to 150	18
150 up to 180	6
180 up to 210	4
210 up to 240	2

a.   Make a relative frequency histogram of the distribution of shoes in the store.

b.   Which intervals contain the median, the first quartile and third quartile?

c.   Describe the distribution of shoe values in terms of center, shape, spread and outliers.

d.   What proportion of shoes are valued at least $150?

e.   Calculate an estimated proportion of shoes that cost between $50 and $100.

f.   Calculate an estimated mean price for a pair of shoes. Assume every pair of shoes in each dollar interval is valued at the middle price for that interval.

CL 9-115.   Park rangers study the pellets of hawks to determine their eating habits. Hawks regurgitate the indigestible portion of their diet in a pellet. Pellets are about one or two inches long, and can contain the bones, fur, feathers, and claws of their prey.

In order to determine if hawks were changing their diet to cope with a particularly harsh winter, rangers collected a random sample of ten pellets. The rodent bones in the pellets had mass: 7.3, 12.1, 4.1, 11.9, 6.3, 4.9, 10.7, 6.3, 0.0, 7.0 grams.

From the sample park rangers will make predictions for the population using a normal model. What is the mean and standard deviation they will use in their model? Use an appropriate precision in your response based on the precision of the data.

CL 9-116.   Consider the Integral Zero Theorem.

a.   Using only integers, list all the possible linear factors of $(x^3 + 8)$.

b.   Is $(x+8)$ a factor of $(x^3 + 8)$? Is $(x+2)$ a factor of $(x^3 + 8)$? Show how you know without graphing.

CL 9-117.   Solve the system of equations at right. $\frac{x}{4} + \frac{y}{3} = 1$

$$2x - \frac{y}{3} = 17$$

CL 9-118.   Use the graph at right to solve $2^x + 1 < 3^x$.

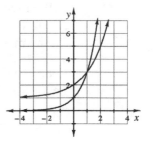

CL 9-119.   Check your answers using the table at the end of this
section. Which problems do you feel confident
about? Which problems were hard? Have you
worked on problems like these in math classes you
have taken before? Use the table to make a list of
topics you need help on and a list of topics you need to
practice more.

Answers and Support for Closure Activity #4
What Have I Learned?

Note: MN = Math Note, LL = Learning Log

Problem	Solution	Need Help?	More Practice
CL 9-112.	a. 38% is a statistic because it represents the opinions of the sample, her government class. Her conclusion is making a statement about the voting U.S. population.	Lessons 9.1.1, 9.1.2, and 9.1.3 MN: 9.1.1	Problems 9-22, 9-23, 9-36, 9-37, 9-38, 9-50, 9-51, 9-62, and 9-75
	b. Stephanie's question has a lead-in statement about the constitution, which may persuade survey-takers that states should be allowed to determine whether or not to use capital punishment.		
	c. Stephanie probably used a convenience sample because it was easy to survey those in her government class. Those students have many things in common like age, location, and level of education, and so do not represent the U.S. population as a whole. Because they are in a government class, they may be more aware of state rights versus federal authority.		

Problem	Solution	Need Help?	More Practice

CL 9-113. Stephanie is using samples from her high school that are not representative of a larger population. Also, it is likely that students choose for themselves whether or not to take ceramics so it is plausible that the kind of student who likes ceramics is already opposed to the death penalty rather than ceramics changing the political opinions of students. To demonstrate cause and effect, Stephanie would need to take a group of student volunteers and randomly assign them to government or ceramics courses. After the course is completed, she could poll them about capital punishment and compare the results.

Lessons 9.2.1 and 9.2.2

MN: 9.2.1

Problems 9-63, 9-76, and 9-89

CL 9-114. a.

Shoe Value ($)

Lesson 9.3.1

Problems 9-72, 9-73, 9-88, 9-103, and 9-104

b. Q1 $30–60, Med $60–90, Q3 $90–120

c. The distribution is positive or right skewed so the median and IQR would describe the center and spread. You would need the actual data points to find these values precisely but the center is approximately $65 and the IQR is about $60. There are no gaps or outliers.

d. $(6 + 4 + 2) / 250 = 0.048$ or 4.8%

e. Using one third of the $30-60 interval and one third of the $90-120 interval $((1/3)67 + 60 + (1/3)46) / 250 = 0.391$ or 39.1%

f. $15(47) + $45(67)+ $75(60) + $105(46) + $135(18) + $165(6) + $195(4) + $225(2) / 250 = $70.8

Problem	Solution	Need Help?	More Practice
CL 9-115.	Mean 7.1 g, sample standard deviation 3.8 g (not population standard deviation 3.6 g).	Problems 9-52 and 9-70	Problems 9-65, 9-73, and 9-103
CL 9-116.	a. $(x\pm1),(x\pm2),(x\pm4),(x\pm8)$ b. $(x+8)$ is not a factor, $(x+2)$ is a factor. Use the Factor Theorem and determine whether -8 and -2 are zeros. Or, divide and see that $(x+8)$ is not a factor because there is a remainder. $(x+2)$ is a factor because there is no remainder.	Lesson 8.3.2 MN: 8.3.2	Problems 8-125, 8-138, 9-9, 9-39, and 9-68
CL 9-117.	$(8,-3)$	Lesson 4.1.1 LL: 4.1.1	Problems 8-11 and 9-26
CL 9-118.	$x>1$	Lesson 4.2.3 MN: 4.2.3 and 4.2.4	Problems 7-28, 8-41, 8-89, and 9-91

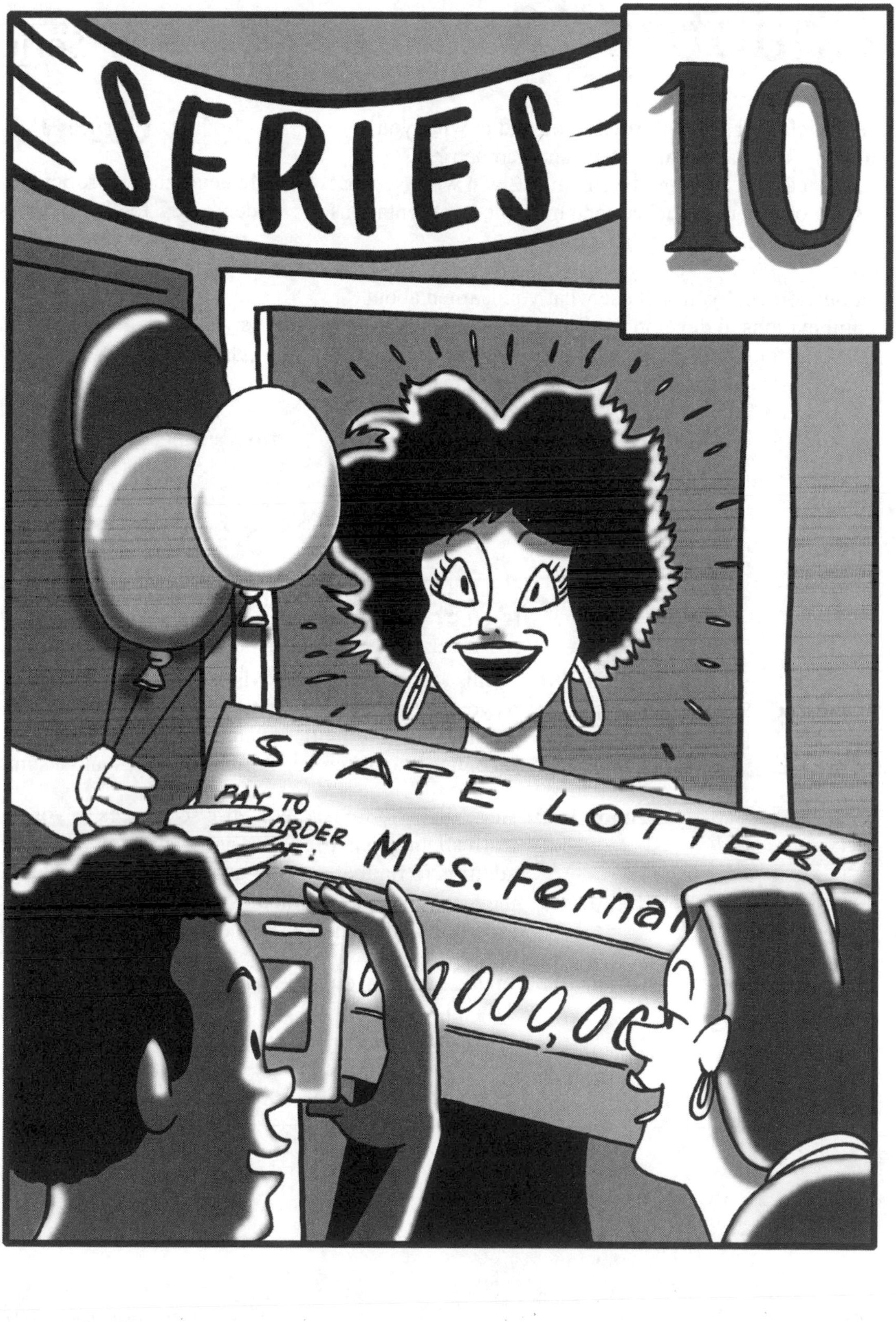
SERIES
10
STATE LOTTERY
PAY TO ORDER OF: Mrs. Ferna

Chapter 10

Series

In this chapter you will revisit and add to what you already know about arithmetic and geometric sequences. In Sections 10.1 and 10.2 you will use what you know about sequences and multiple representations to write series and find their sums.

In Section 10.3 you will use what you learned about combinations to develop the Binomial Theorem, which is useful for simplifying some algebraic manipulations, as well as solving some probability problems.

Guiding Question

Mathematically proficient students look for and express regularity in repeated reasoning.

As you work through this chapter, ask yourself:

How can I extend the pattern from smaller sums to larger sums?

Chapter Outline

Section 10.1 In this section, you will revisit arithmetic sequences as you learn about arithmetic series and devise methods for finding their sums. You will learn to recognize the difference between a series and a sum.

Section 10.2 Here, you will revisit geometric sequences as you learn about geometric series and their sums. In addition to finding sums of geometric series where the last term is determined, you will learn how to represent and calculate sums of some infinite series.

Section 10.3 In this section, you will learn about Pascal's Triangle, and you will connect it to your knowledge of combinations to develop the Binomial Theorem, which can be used to solve some algebraic problems as well as probability problems.

10.1.1 Can I find a sum without adding?

Introduction to Arithmetic Series

Have you ever had to carefully add a long list of numbers? When the numbers are unrelated to each other, there may be no alternative, but if there is a pattern or relationship between the terms in your list, it is often possible to develop strategies to make your calculation much easier.

For example, if ticket sales double each day in the month before a concert, is there a faster method for calculating the total number of tickets sold than by adding the sales for each day one at a time? Similarly, if a mine produces 150 tons more iron each year than in the previous year, how can the amount of iron produced during an entire century can be quickly calculated?

In this section you will explore problems like these and develop new strategies for making these calculations.

Today your team will consider different ways to find the sum of a sequence of terms. As you work, use the following questions to focus and advance your mathematical discussions.

> What do the terms (of the sequence) represent? What does the sum represent?
>
> Is there another way to find the sum?
>
> How can we verify our result?

10-1.   COUNTING ON COLLEGE!

When Angela turned eighteen, her Uncle Zachary explained to her that he had been saving money for her college education since she was born. He told her that when she was one month old, he put $50 into a safe deposit box, and the month following he added $53. He continued adding money like this for the last 18 years, each month putting in $3 more than he had the previous month. The money that had been saved would now pay for Angela to attend any college of her choosing.

a.   Write out the sizes of the deposits for the first few months as an arithmetic sequence. How much was added to Angela's college fund on the 12th month?

b.   Work with your group to find a formula for the arithmetic sequence that determines the amount deposited on the nth month. Check that when n is 1 (representing the first month) your formula gives $50. Using your formula, determine how much was in the final deposit on the last month of the 18th year.

10-2. Angela continued to think about Uncle Zachary's savings.

a. Angela wrote the equation for the sequence as $t(n) = 47 + 3n$. But Uncle Zachary wrote $t(n) = 50 + 3(n-1)$. Which equation gives the correct sequence? What is the advantage of writing the equation like Angela did? What is the advantage of writing it like Uncle Zachary did?

b. Determine the amount of money in Angela's college fund at the time of her first birthday, after her Uncle had made exactly 12 deposits.

c. How much was saved by Angela's 5th birthday? Can you think of ways you might be able to figure this out without having to add the money for every month? Be ready to share your ideas with the class.

10-3. SERIES

In problem 10-1, the total amount of money deposited before Angela's eighteenth birthday is the sum of an arithmetic sequence, where each term in the sequence represents the amount of money added by her uncle in one month. When the terms of a sequence are added instead of listed, the result is called a **series**. When a *sequence* is arithmetic, meaning each term differs from the previous one by some constant amount, then its corresponding *series* is called an **arithmetic series**. The series representing the first year in problem 10-1 could be written:

$$50 + 53 + 56 + \ldots + 80 + 83$$

A matryoshka, a set of Russian nested dolls, can help illustrate the difference between a sequence and its corresponding series. These dolls are special because each doll fills the space inside the doll of the next larger size. When the dolls are placed one inside the other, as in the picture, they are "nested."

a. When the dolls are nested, their diameters steadily increase. (Note: The top half of only the innermost doll is shown in the picture.) If the smallest doll in the diagram has a diameter of 5 cm, and each doll has a diameter that is 1 cm longer than the next-smallest doll, write a sequence that represents the diameters from shortest to longest.

b. In what situation might you want to find the sum of all of the diameters of these dolls? Discuss this with your team, then write the series and calculate its sum.

c. Some matryoshka have as many as 20 dolls! For one such matryoshka, the diameter (in millimeters) of each doll from smallest to largest can be represented with the sequence $t(n) = 8 + 3(n-1)$, where the domain of n is the integers from 1 to 20.

If all 20 dolls were arranged in a line with each doll touching the one next to it, how long would the line of dolls be? Write a series to represent this problem and calculate its sum.

10-4.   FINDING THE SUM

When an arithmetic series has many terms, adding them all one at a time can be tedious. It is useful to have other strategies to calculate the sum. To look for a strategy, consider a new situation:

Flo is preparing to run the 100-meter race at her next track meet. Her coach decides to collect data to learn how well Flo is accelerating (speeding up) at the beginning of the race. The sequence below represents approximately how far Flo travels during each second of the first six seconds of a practice race, in meters.

$$1, 3, 5, 7, 9, 11$$

a.   Find the equation, $t(n)$, in first term form, for this sequence. In the context of Flo's race, explain the meaning of the first term and the common difference. Be sure you include units.

b.   What does the *series* in this situation represent?

c.   Flo decided to use square tiles as shown in the diagram below to represent her distance from the starting line as time passed.

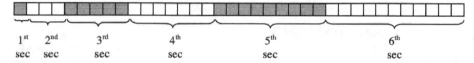

| 1ˢᵗ sec | 2ⁿᵈ sec | 3ʳᵈ sec | 4ᵗʰ sec | 5ᵗʰ sec | 6ᵗʰ sec |

She rearranged her tiles on a graph like the one at right. How are the terms of the sequence (the distance covered in each second) shown in this graph? How is the series (the total distance run) represented?

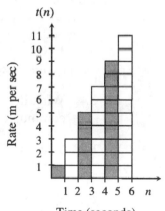

d.   Finding the area of the long rectangle Flo made in part (c) requires adding all the terms. However, if the columns in Flo's graph can be rearranged to form a single rectangle, its area can be found more easily. How might this work? Discuss this with your team and be prepared to share your ideas with the class.

10-5.   Calculate the sum of the arithmetic series represented by the graphs below. Try to do this without adding all of the individual terms of the sequence.

a.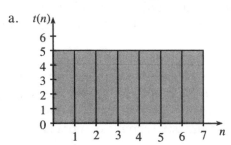

b.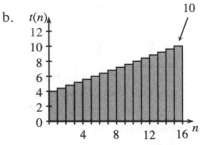

c.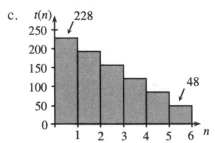

d.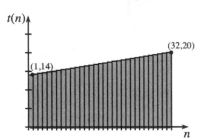

10-6.   TEAM CHALLENGE

How much information do you need to be able to write an arithmetic series and find its sum? For each arithmetic series described below, work with your team to write the series, find its sum, or both. If it is not possible, explain why not.

a.   What if you know that the first term is 18, the last term is 72, and the common difference is 4.5? What is the series? What is the sum?

b.   What if you know that there are 6 terms, the last and smallest term is 21, and the sum is 336? What is the series?

c.   What if you know that the series has 9 terms and the last term is 18? What is the series? What is the sum?

d.   What if the third term of an 18-term series is 29 and the terms are increasing by 10? What is the series? What is the sum?

Ⓜ️ETHODS AND MEANINGS

Permutations and Combinations

MATH NOTES

Eight people are running a race. In how many different ways can they come in first, second, and third?

This is a problem of counting **permutations**, or arrangements, and the result can be represented $_8P_3$, which means the number of ways to choose and arrange three different (not repeated) things from a set of eight, in which *order matters*. There are several ways to write and compute $_8P_3$:

$$_8P_3 = \tfrac{8!}{(8-3)!} = \tfrac{8!}{5!} = \tfrac{8\cdot7\cdot6\cdot5\cdot4\cdot3\cdot2\cdot1}{5\cdot4\cdot3\cdot2\cdot1} = 8 \text{ choices} \cdot 7 \text{ choices} \cdot 6 \text{ choices} = 336$$

In general, $_nP_r = \tfrac{n!}{(n-r)!} = n(n-1)(n-2)...(n-r+1)$ for n items chosen r at a time.

Lists of groups, *without regard to the order* within the group, are called **combinations**. In selecting committees, it matters who is selected but not the order of selection or any arrangement of the groups. Selections such as those with committees are called combinations. Note that combinations do not include repeated elements.

For example: Eight people are eligible to receive $500 scholarships, but only three will be selected. How many different ways are there to select a group of three?

This is a problem of counting combinations. $_8C_3$ represents the number of ways to choose three from a set of eight. This is sometimes read as "eight choose three."

To compute the number of combinations, first calculate the number of permutations and then divide by the number of ways to arrange each permutation.

$$_8C_3 = \tfrac{_8P_3}{3!} = \tfrac{8!}{5!3!} = 56$$

In general:

Number of ways to choose $= \dfrac{\text{\# of ways to choose and arrange}}{\text{\# of ways to arrange}} = {_nC_r} = \tfrac{_nP_r}{r!} = \tfrac{n!}{(n-r)!r!}.$

10-7.   Uncle Zachary decided to increase the amount he was saving for Angela by $5 each month instead of three.

   a.   How much would he deposit on the month of her second birthday?

   b.   Write a formula for the nth term of this sequence.

   c.   How much money is in the account the month of her first birthday, just after he made his 12th deposit?

10-8.   The 300 people who were lined up outside the amusement park had all entered by 8:15 a.m. By 8:30, 550 more had entered. The number who entered each 15 minutes increased steadily by 250 after that. All of the people were planning to stay for the parade at noon.

   a.   How many people entered between 11:45 and noon, just in time for the parade?

   b.   Represent the problem as a series and write a formula for the nth term.

10-9.   Write a formula for the nth term of each of the following series.

   a. $3+10+17+...$ b. $20+11+2+...$

10-10.   If the third term of an arithmetic sequence is 13 and the seventeenth term is –29, what is the eighth term?

10-11.   Graph each of the following functions and label the x- and y-intercepts.

   a. $f(x)=3(x-4)^2-5$ b. $g(x)=2x^2-3x-5$

10-12.   Aurora is starting a fitness program at her school and needs to find an easy
measure of fitness to assign workouts and gauge improvement. She decides
that using resting heart rate would be helpful. Assume that the resting heart rate
of young women is approximately normally distributed with a mean of 74 beats
per minute (bpm) with a standard deviation of 5 bpm.

    a.   Aurora found a chart that said resting heart rates between 70 and 79
(inclusive) are considered average for women her age. What proportion of
her classmates would she expect to find in the average range?

    b.   The chart also claims that resting heart rate of 66 or less indicates excellent
fitness in otherwise healthy young women. What portion of her
classmates would she expect to find in excellent shape?

    c.   If Aurora's fitness program lowers the mean heart rate of her female
classmates by 4 bpm, what will be the *increase* in the proportion of
women now classified as being in excellent shape?

10-13.   Find the distance between each of the following pairs of points.

    a. $(-6,9)$ and $(2,-4)$ b. (x,y) and $(5,2)$

10-14.   If Emily bought three pounds of oranges and four pounds of bananas for $8.53
and Beth bought four pounds of oranges and two pounds of bananas for $7.74,
how much should Jenel expect to pay for nine pounds of oranges and seven
pounds of bananas?

10-15.   How many people were in the amusement park in problem 10-8 to watch the
noontime parade?

10-16.   Chloe wants to place her matryoshka dolls in a row on a windowsill that is
92 cm long. Will her entire set of 20 dolls fit if their diameters in *millimeters*
are given by the formula $t(n)=13+3(n-1)$?

10-17.   Find the sum of $1+6+11+16+21+...$ if the series has 10 terms.

10-18.   A series has 9 terms. The last term is 18 and the fifth term is 6.
What is the series?

10-19.   Is 435 a term in the sequence $3, 11, 19, \ldots$? If so, which term is it? If not, justify why not.

10-20.   Twelve people signed up to play darts during lunch. How many ways can a three-person dart team be chosen? For help, refer to the Math Notes box in this lesson.

10-21.   Andrea has just purchased a five-digit combination lock. It allows her to set up her own combination. She can use the numbers 0 through 9 for her combination, and she must use five digits. For help with this problem, refer to the Math Notes box in this lesson.

   a.   How many five-digit combinations can she make so that no digit is repeated?

   b.   How many five-digit combinations are possible if she *can* repeat the digits?

10-22.   For what values of n does the equation $2x^2 + nx + 9 = 0$ have exactly one root?

10-23.   Without using a calculator, simplify and evaluate each of the following log expressions. Your result should be an expression without logarithms.

   a. $\log(4) + \log(25)$ b. $\dfrac{7^{\log_7(3)}}{\log_5 5^4}$

10-24.   Consider the graph of $f(x) = \sin(x)$.

   a.   Describe the graph.

   b.   Could this graph be an example of any other function? Explain why $f(x) = \sin(x)$ cannot be a polynomial function.

More Arithmetic Series

In Lesson 10.1.1, you explored ways to use a graph of a series to find its sum without adding every term. Can the strategies that you developed help you find the series when you do not have a graph? As you work with your team to answer this question, remember to talk together about how to describe a term or series generally and to ask each other if the answers you find make sense.

10-25.   While trying to find the sum of an arithmetic series, Antonio rearranged the terms so that the last term is combined with the first term, the second-to-last term is combined with the second term, etc. (as shown at right). Use his graph to answer the questions below.

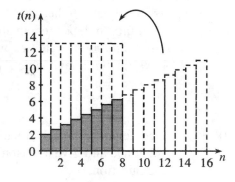

a.   How can Antonio be sure that the result of stacking the terms this way will be a rectangle?

b.   What is the sum of Antonio's series? How do you know?

c.   Which terms of the series form the first column? What is the height of this column?

d.   Write out Antonio's series and find the sum.

10-26.   With your team, create a series that has an odd number of terms. How could you apply Antonio's method to this series? Be prepared to share your ideas with the class.

10-27.   Will Antonio's method work for all arithmetic series? Why or why not? Use an example to explain your conclusion.

10-28.   Do you think that Antonio's method can be altered to find the sum of an arithmetic series without a graph? Work with your team to find the dimensions of the transformed rectangle for each arithmetic series below without graphing the series. Then find the sum.

   a. $11 + 18 + 25 + \ldots + 74$

   b.   14 terms with $t(1) = 8$ and $t(14) = 151$

   c. $t(n) = 4 + 6(n-1)$, for integer values of n starting at 1 and ending at 25

10-29.   Remember Angela from problem 10-1? Her Uncle Zachary has been depositing an increasing amount of money each month to be given to her for college on her 18th birthday. In her first month of life, he started by depositing $50 and then each month deposited an amount that was $3 more than the previous month. Use Anthony's strategies and those that you used in problem 10-28 to determine how much money Uncle Zachary will have for Angela on her 18th birthday.

10-30.   Decide whether each situation below involves a series or a sequence and give a reason for your choice. Then answer the question.

   a.   Hornets build nests by constructing hexagonal cells around a center, as shown at right. As this hexagonal pattern forms, the first ring of cells has 6 cells, the next has 12, and the next has 18. If a colony of hornets builds 10 rings, how many cells will they have?

   b.   Thanks to fundraising, the balance of the math club's savings account grows by $55 each month. The balance during the first month of the school year was $190. At the end of the year, the club's treasurer produced a report showing the balance for each month of the school year. What was the balance after the 8th month?

   c.   Starting after his birthday, Evan's allowance increases $0.25 each week. He decides to save his money in order to buy a new πPod, which costs $180. If his allowance on his birthday is $1.50, will he have enough savings on his next birthday to buy the πPod?

10-31.   JACKPOT FEVER!

While Ms. Fernandez is standing in line to
buy her lottery ticket, she noticed that a
different state has a jackpot that may go even
higher. Then she realizes that because of a
time difference, it has more hours to grow!
She has already predicted that the jackpot in her state will be $50,900,000 when
tickets are drawn, and she has to decide quickly if she should buy tickets in the
other state.

On a nearby television screen, she sees a news report explaining that the other
state started the day with a jackpot of $29,000,000 and that each additional
ticket sold will increase the jackpot by $1.00. The news also mentioned that
1,800,000 tickets were sold in the first hour and hourly ticket sales have steadily
increased by 20,000 tickets per hour throughout the day. If the drawing in that
state occurs 14 hours after stores have opened, which state will have the larger
jackpot? Show how you found your answer.

10-32.   With your team, find the sum of the arithmetic series $t(1) + t(2) + t(3) + ... + t(n)$.

10-33.   LEARNING LOG

Describe how to find the sum of an arithmetic series in your
Learning Log. Be sure to include examples in your
description. Title this entry "Arithmetic Series" and label it
with today's date.

METHODS AND MEANINGS

Series

The sum of the terms of a sequence is called a **series**. If the terms have a constant difference (meaning that they increase or decrease linearly), they form an **arithmetic series**. If the terms instead have a constant ratio or multiplier (meaning that they change exponentially), they form a **geometric series**.

Examples of arithmetic and geometric series are shown below.

arithmetic series: $2 + 6 + 10 + 14 + \ldots + (4n - 2)$

geometric series: $1 + \frac{1}{2} + \frac{1}{4} + \frac{1}{8} + \ldots + \frac{1}{2^n}$

10-34. Examine each of the series below.

> Odd numbers: $1 + 3 + 5 + \ldots + 149$
>
> Even numbers: $2 + 4 + 6 + \ldots + 150$

a. Write an expression for the nth term of each series.

b. What is the sum of each series?

10-35. Consider the series $21 + 17 + 13 + \ldots + -99$ as you answer the questions in parts (a) through (c) below.

a. Write an expression for the nth term.

b. How many terms are in the series? How can you tell?

c. What is the sum of this series?

10-36. On a six-person bowling team, only four players bowl in any game. How many different four-person teams can be made if the order in which they bowl does not matter?

10-37. How many different bowling lineups of four players can be made in the previous problem if order does matter?

10-38. State the degree of $f(x) = (x+4)(x+1)^2(x-2)$ and sketch its graph.

10-39. Find the equation of a third degree polynomial that has the roots 3, 2, and -1 and passes through the point $(1, 1)$.

10-40. Complete the square to convert each of the following quadratic functions to graphing form. State the vertex and sketch the graph.

  a. $f(x) = x^2 + 6x + 7$ 　　　　　　b. $f(x) = x^2 - 10x$

10-41. David and Regina are competitive racers, and they both aim to break 2 minutes in their races. They are trying to figure out which who has the more difficult challenge, since they compete in different sports. David runs the 800-meter race and Regina swims the 200-meter freestyle. They agree to accept the following standards for high school boys and girls: boys' 800-meter mean time is 149 seconds with a standard deviation of 13.6 seconds, girls' 200-meter freestyle mean time is 145 seconds with a standard deviation of 8.2 seconds.

Currently, David's best time is 2:02 minutes and Regina's best time is 2:10 minutes. Assuming times in their respective events are normally distributed, find the percentile in which each David and Regina fall. Which athlete is relatively faster for their sport?

10-42. Convert the following degree measures to radians.

  a. 45°　　　　　b. 75°　　　　　c. −15°　　　　　d. 450°

10.1.3 How else can I see it?

· ·

General Arithmetic Series

So far, you have developed strategies that help find the sum of a given series for a given number of terms. However, what if the number of terms is unknown? For example, in the lottery example from Lessons 10.1.1 and 10.1.2, what if the time of the drawing has not yet been set? How can you find a general expression that would represent the total number of tickets sold after any number of hours?

As you work with your team today, pay attention to the different ways to study a series. Many of the strategies introduced today may be helpful in the future when thinking about the sum of other types of series. When your team finds a new way to "see" the sum of a series, be sure to share the idea with your classmates.

10-43.   Consider the series $1 + 2 + 3 + 4 + ... + n$.

    a.   What is the sum of the first 3 terms? The first 10 terms?

    b.   What is the sum of the first n terms? That is, find $1 + 2 + 3 + 4 + ... + n$. Justify your answer.

    c.   Legend has it that long ago, when famous mathematician Carl Gauss was a young student, his teacher tried to keep his class busy by giving them the task of finding the sum $1 + 2 + 3 + 4 + ... + 99 + 100$. He stunned his teacher and his classmates by finding the sum quickly without assistance. What is the sum?

10-44.   In problem 10-43, you found a general expression that gives the sum of the first n counting numbers, but what about other types of numbers? For example, what is the sum of the first n odd numbers? Or the first n even numbers? Find expressions for both of these cases below. Look for new strategies and justify your answer.

    a.   Sum of the first n even numbers: $2 + 4 + 6 + 8 + ... + 2n$

    b.   Sum of the first n odd numbers: $1 + 3 + 5 + 7 + ... + (2n - 1)$

    c.   Use your expressions from parts (a) and (b) to find the sum of the first 100 even numbers and then the sum of the first 100 odd numbers.

512

10-45.   Terrell noticed that if he adds
          the first terms, second terms,   original series → $\left\{ \begin{array}{l} 1+2+3+4+\ldots+n \\ \underline{2+4+6+8+\ldots+2n} \end{array} \right.$
          third terms, etc. of the two
          arithmetic series at right, he   new series   → $3+6+9+12+\ldots+3n$
          gets a brand new series!

   a.   Describe his new series. Is it arithmetic? How many terms does it have?

   b.   Use the expressions for the sums of the original series to find an
         expression for the sum of the new series.

   c.   Is there another way you could have found the expression for the sum of
         the series $3+6+9+\ldots+3n$? Be prepared to explain your strategy to the
         class.

   d.   If you have not done so already, verify that your strategy in part (c)
         resulted in an expression equivalent to your expression from part (b).

10-46.   In problem 10-45, you used the sums of two different series to find the sum of a
          new series. How else can the sum of one series be used to find the sum of
          another series? Consider this as you work on the problems below.

   a.   How can the sum of $1+2+3+4+\ldots+n$ be used to find the sum of
         $2+4+6+8+\ldots+2n$? Test your idea algebraically using the expressions
         for the sums of these series.

   b.   How can the sum of $2+4+6+8+\ldots+2n$ be used to find the sum of
         $1+3+5+7+\ldots+(2n-1)$? Test your idea algebraically using the
         expressions for the sums of these series.

10-47.   Flo saw the sum of odd numbers from part (b) of problem 10-44 differently. She decided to represent the arithmetic series with the tile pattern below, where the area of each figure is equal to the term of the series.

Fig. 1   Fig. 2   Fig. 3   Fig. 4   Fig. n

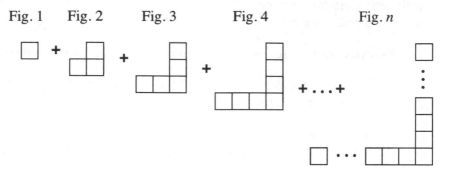

a.   How many tiles are in the nth term? Justify your conclusion.

b.   What is the sum of the first 3 terms? The sum of the first 5 terms? How can you represent this sum with the tiles?

c.   What is the sum of the first n terms? Represent the sum algebraically in terms of n and with a diagram with tiles.

d.   Based on Flo's representation, what is the sum of the first $(n+1)$ odd numbers? Justify your answer.

10-48.   Use one or more of the series below to create a new series you have not summed before. Then use the algebraic expressions for the sums to generate an expression for the sum of your new series. Be ready to share your new series and explain its sum to the class.

$$1+2+3+4+\ldots+n$$

$$2+4+6+8+\ldots+2n$$

$$1+3+5+7+\ldots+(2n-1)$$

METHODS AND MEANINGS

Arithmetic Series

MATH NOTES

An arithmetic sequence can be represented in general by a formula for its nth term:

$$t(n) = a + (n-1)d$$

The first term (when $n = 1$) is a, and the common difference is d.

An arithmetic series is the sum of the terms of an arithmetic sequence.

$$t(1) + t(2) + t(3) + \ldots + t(k)$$

The total sum of this series can be found by adding the first and last terms, multiplying by the number of terms k and dividing by 2:

$$S(k) = \frac{k(t(1) + t(k))}{2}$$

The sum of a series can be represented with the area in the diagram at right, where each column represents a term of the series.

Note that when the diagram is rearranged as shown, the region becomes a rectangle with a height of $t(1) + t(k)$ and a width of $\frac{k}{2}$.

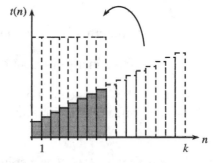

10-49.   Find the sum of the arithmetic series below.

   a. $5 + 10 + 15 + 20 + \ldots + 400$ b. $3 + 8 + 13 + 18 + \ldots + 398$

   c. $80 + 74 + 68 + 62 + \ldots + 14$

10-50.   Consider the sequence of multiples of 11 that are less than 100. Write them as a series and find the sum.

10-51. Lorna is looking at the series $5 + 3 + 10 + 8 + 15 + \ldots + 400 + 398$.

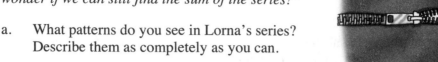

"*The sequence definitely isn't arithmetic, but it does have a pattern,*" Lorna told her team, "*I wonder if we can still find the sum of the series?*"

a. What patterns do you see in Lorna's series? Describe them as completely as you can.

b. Do you agree with Lorna's statement that this sequence is not arithmetic? Justify your conclusion. Do you think it is still possible to find a sum for the series?

c. "*I think I see it!*" Lorna exclaimed. "*I think we can separate the terms into the two different arithmetic series shown below, kind of like unzipping a zipper.*" Her work is shown below.

$$5 + 10 + 15 + \ldots + 395 + 400$$
$$3 + 8 + 13 + \ldots + 393 + 398$$

How can you use Lorna's two series to find the sum of the original series? State the sum and describe your process.

10-52. Your midterm exam contains 12 questions and you must answer any 10.

a. How many different combinations of questions are possible?

b. If everyone must answer questions one, two, and three, how many different combinations are possible?

10-53. Verify that $3 + i\sqrt{2}$ is a solution of $x^2 - 6x + 11 = 0$.

10-54. Show and explain why the equation $2^x = 5 - x$ has only one real solution.

10-55. At McDugal's Golden Parabola, Ramona bought four hamburgers and two milkshakes for $13.50. Inez bought three hamburgers and one milkshake and spent $9.25. What is the cost of a hamburger? A milkshake?

10-56. Solve:

a. $\log_7(3x - 2) = 2$

b. $2^x \cdot 2^{x-2} - 16^2 = 0$

10-57. Sketch a graph of $y = -x^2(x - 2)^2(x + 2)^2$.

10.1.4 How else can I express it?

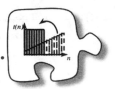

Summation Notation and Combinations of Series

So far in this chapter you have focused your work on arithmetic series represented algebraically, geometrically, and graphically. Today you will be introduced to a new notation for arithmetic series and you will look at methods for writing equations to find sums.

As you work today, keep the following questions in mind to focus your team discussions:

How does this connect to what we have done before?

How can we simplify it?

How can we describe it?

10-58.   Remember Gauss, the mathematician from Lesson 10.1.3, whose teacher tried to keep him busy by asking him to add up the numbers from 1 to 100? Legend has it that Gauss did not show any of his work (shocking!), but he is commonly said to have used a method that starts with the steps below:

$$S = 1 + 2 + 3 + \ldots + 98 + 99 + 100$$
$$\underline{S = 100 + 99 + 98 + \ldots + 3 + 2 + 1}$$
$$2S = 101 + 101 + 101 + \ldots + 101 + 101 + 101$$

a.   Examine his work. What is he doing? Discuss this with your team, and then summarize each step on your paper.

b.   How can you simplify his resulting equation to find the sum of the series $1 + 2 + 3 + \ldots + 100$? Show and explain on your paper.

c.   How is the process from parts (a) and (b) related to how you have used a graph to find the sum of a series? Discuss with your team and write your conclusions.

d.   Show how to use this strategy to find the sum of the series below. Show all of your work.

$$S = 2 + 5 + 8 + 11 + \ldots + 59$$

10-59.   The series in part (d) of problem 10-58 can also be represented using
         summation notation, as shown below:

$$\sum_{c=1}^{20} (2 + 3[c-1])$$

The symbol "Σ" is the Greek letter "sigma," and
indicates that the terms generated as c changes from 1 to
20 are summed. The expression $2 + 3(c-1)$ is the rule for
the terms of the series. As you can see in the table at
right, when $c = 1$, $t(1) = 2 + 3(1-0) = 2$, and so on. So, as
c changes from 1 to 20, the series below is generated:

c	$t(c)$
1	2
2	5
3	8
$\vdots$	$\vdots$
20	59

$$2 + 5 + 8 + \ldots + 59$$

The letter c is used here as an **index**, which temporarily represents the term
number as the series terms are determined. The same series could be written:

$$\sum_{p=1}^{20} (2 + 3[p-1]) \text{ or as } \sum_{p=1}^{20} (-1 + 3p)$$

It is also possible for the series to be written with a different starting value,
such as:

$$\sum_{p=0}^{19} (2 + 3p)$$

a.   Use summation notation to represent the series $15 + 19 + 23 + 27 + 31$.

b.   Expand the series $\sum_{t=1}^{6} t^2$ and find its sum.

10-60.   In problem 10-51 you separated Lorna's complicated series into two different
         arithmetic series, as shown below.

$$5 + 3 + 10 + 8 + 15 + \ldots + 400 + 398 = 5 + 10 + 15 + \ldots + 400$$
$$+ 3 + 8 + 13 + \ldots + 398$$

a.   Write each of the two arithmetic series using summation notation.

b.   How could you use your expressions from part (a) to write an expression
      for Lorna's complicated series using summation notation?

10-61.   Find the sum of each arithmetic series described below.

a. $\displaystyle\sum_{t=1}^{10} -5 + 13t$

b.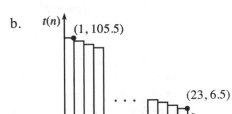

c. $4 + 10 + 16 + 22 + \ldots + (4 + 6(n-1))$

d. $\displaystyle\sum_{t=1}^{30} 10 - 5t$

$\mathbf{M}$ETHODS AND $\mathbf{M}$EANINGS

Summation Notation

MATH NOTES

The capital Greek letter **sigma**, Σ, (equivalent to "S" in English) is used in mathematics as a shorter way to indicate the sum of a series. For example:

$$\sum_{k=1}^{5} (2k - 3) = -1 + 1 + 3 + 5 + 7 = 15$$

Translated, this expression means the sum from $k = 1$ to $k = 5$ of the terms $2k - 3$ equals 15.

Also, the sum of the series $1^2 + 2^2 + 3^2$ can be written $\displaystyle\sum_{k=1}^{3} k^2$.

Note: We call k the **index** and k^2 the **argument** of this summation. The values of the index are consecutive integers only, so the values of k in this example are 1, 2, and 3.

10-62.   Write each series in sigma notation and find the sum or an expression for the sum.

a. $47 + 34 + 21 + \ldots + (-83)$

b. $3 + 10 + 17 + \ldots + (3 + 7(n-1))$

10-63.   Use any method to find the sum of the integers from 100 through 1000.
Describe your strategy.

10-64.   For many years mathematicians have tried to find a formula to generate prime
numbers. One candidate was the expression $n^2 + n + 41$, where n is a positive
integer. Try at least 3 or 4 numbers. What do you think of the formula? Does
it work? Could you prove it?

10-65.   Write each expression in a shorter form.

a. $3(7 \cdot 3^{n-1})$ b. $0.6(10(0.6)^{n-2})$

10-66.   How many different batting orders can be made from the nine starting players
on a baseball team? Write the answer using factorials and as a number.

10-67.   According to the *National Health Statistics Report*, the average height of adult
women in the U.S. is 63.8 inches with a standard deviation of 2.7 inches.
Heights can be modeled with a normal probability density function.

a.   What percent of women are under 4 ft 11 in. tall?

b.   Most girls reach their adult height by their senior year in high school. In
North City High School's class of 324 senior students, how many girls
would you expect to be shorter than 4 ft 11 in.?

c.   How many senior girls do you expect to be taller than 6 ft at North City
High?

10-68.   Graph each plane in three dimensions.

a. $2x - 3y + 4z = 12$ b. $2x - 3y = 12$

10-69.   Use reference angles, the symmetry of a circle, and the knowledge that
$\cos(\frac{\pi}{3}) = \frac{1}{2}$ to write three other true statements using cosine and angles that are
multiples of $\frac{\pi}{3}$.

10-70.   The Flat Building's roof is 32 feet wide and
60 feet long. An antenna rises 25 feet above
the center of the roof, and wires connect the
top of the antenna to each corner of the roof
and to the midpoint of each edge, as shown
in the picture at right.

   a.   What was the total length of wire used
to connect the antenna to the roof
(without counting any extra needed for
attaching it)?

   b.   The wires that attach to the corners of the building form an angle with the
roof. Find the measure of that angle.

   c.   Suppose the height of the antenna is x feet (instead of 25 feet). Represent
the total length of the wires in terms of x.

10.2.1 What if the series is geometric?

Geometric Series

In this lesson you will work with **geometric series** and develop a method for representing and calculating their sums. Being able to find the sum of a geometric series makes it easy to calculate how much a long-term loan will really cost or how much you will end up paying for something when you buy it on credit. As you work with your team on the problems in this lesson, keep the following discussion questions in mind:

> Can we use any of the strategies we already know?
>
> How can we use what we know about systems of equations?
>
> How can we describe what we have done?
>
> How can we generalize what we have done?

10-71. Katelyn was helping her younger sister Janelle with her Algebra 1 homework.

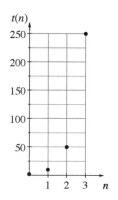

a. Janelle was given the sequence 10, 50, 250, 1250, 6250, … . She wrote the equation $t(n) = 2 \cdot 5^n$ and made the graph at right.

Katelyn cried out, "*No. No. You've written the wrong equation! The correct equation for the sequence is* $t(n) = 10 \cdot 5^{n-1}$."

Is Katelyn correct? Is Janelle wrong?

b. What are the advantages of writing the equation like Katelyn did? What are the advantages of writing the equation like Janelle did?

c. Rewrite the equation $t(n) = 18 \cdot 3^n$ using Katelyn's method.

10-72.   PICKING A PAYOUT, Part 1

With a record-setting lottery jackpot
projected for noon tomorrow, Hank stood in
a very long line to buy a ticket. The man
behind him in line tapped him on the
shoulder to ask, *"Hey, have you thought
about how you'd spend the money if you
won?"* Before he could answer, the woman
in front interrupted to say, *"First, you have to decide whether you want to get
your winnings in one lump sum right away, or if you want to receive them
spread out over time. I'm sure one option must be a better deal, but I haven't
figured out which one!"*

When Hank got home he immediately went on the Internet and learned that
lottery winners do have a choice: receive the winnings in a single payment of
51% of the jackpot right away, or spread payments of the jackpot over 20 years.
He also learned that the jackpot is projected to be $50 million! He knew that if
he took the single payment he could invest it right away and earn 4% interest on
that money.

If he chose to receive the payout over 20 years, the Lottery Commission would
invest the money for him. They guarantee to pay $1,500,000 the first year, and
to increase the amount they pay by 5% each year.

At lunchtime, Hank called his brother and told him that if his class could figure
out the difference between the totals for the two payment methods, he would
give that amount to the class if he won the lottery.

a.   If Hank wins the lottery and takes the payments over time, the amounts he
will receive each year form a geometric sequence. What is the first term?
What is the growth factor? Write an equation to represent any term in this
sequence.

b.   If Hank takes the payments over time, how much will he receive in the
20th year?

c.   When you add up the terms of this sequence to find the total over 20 years,
you are finding the sum for the geometric series. Show the geometric
series.

d.   With your team, discuss a *strategy* for calculating the sum without having
to calculate and add all 20 terms. Consider the graphical method of
creating rectangles that you used with arithmetic series. Would that work
for this kind of series? Explain your thinking. You do not need to actually
sum the series.

10-73.   While working on a strategy to solve the lottery problem, Luann's team decided to try to find a strategy by looking at an easier sequence and using fewer terms:

$$t(n) = 2 \cdot 5^{n-1}$$

They wrote out the series for the first six terms, represented the sum of the series as $S(6)$, and then wrote the series in an equation:

$$2 + 10 + 50 + 250 + 1250 + 6250 = S(6)$$

Then Luann remembered the algebraic strategy for finding the sum of an arithmetic series where she added the sequence to itself, and then manipulated the equations. Is there a similar method you can use for geometric series? Work on this as a team. Is there a way to write the equation down twice and then rewrite the second equation to eliminate some of the terms when the two equations are combined?

10-74.   *"I'm sure that this can be simplified,"* Luann reported to her team. *"But when I try to add the series to itself, like we did with the arithmetic series, it just gets bigger, and there's no clear pattern. If I subtract it from itself I'm left with* $0 = 0$."

a.   What are some techniques for rewriting an equation that you use when solving systems of equations by elimination? Could these techniques be applied in this situation?

b.   *"Aha!"* Luann almost shouted.

"Shhh!" her teammate cautioned. *"What have you got?"*

"Look! I multiplied both sides of the equation by the sequence multiplier." Luann was really excited about the result. How can you use her results and combine the equations to find the sum $S(6)$?

10-75.   Luann wondered if they could use the same method to write an expression for the general sum of any number of terms of the series:

$$2 + 10 + 50 + ... + 2 \cdot 5^{n-1} = S(n)$$

Show how to use her method to write a general expression for the sum. Make a note of what you multiplied by, what was left when you subtracted, and what you finally divided by to get the result.

10-76.   Antonio is working with a new geometric series generated by the equation
$t(n) = 30(1.2)^{n-1}$. His sister has challenged him to find the sum of the first
37 terms. He needs your help.

a.   Show Antonio how he can figure out the sum of *any* number of terms
without adding them all up.

b.   Antonio's sister has challenged him to find the sum of the 38th through the
99th terms of this series. Work with your team to help Antonio meet his
sister's challenge.

10-77.   PICKING A PAYOUT, Part 2

Look back to your work on problem 10-72. For your convenience, the two
payment options are reprinted below. Recall that the jackpot in question is
$50,000,000.

Option 1: Receive a single payment of 51% of the jackpot right away. Invest
the money and earn 4% interest compounded annually.

Option 2: Receive payments once a year for 20 years. The first payment would
be $1,500,000 and the payments would increase by 5% each year.

Your Task: Work with your team to determine which is the best way to collect
the money. Should Hank take his winnings immediately and invest the money
himself? Or should he choose the guaranteed payout each year for 20 years?
With which option would he receive the most money? Be prepared to justify
your decision with explanations and calculations.

Discussion Points

How will the amount increase over time if he invests it himself?

How can we represent the amount he would receive each year
algebraically if he chooses the annual payout?

How much will there be in total after 20 years in each situation?

10-78.   Imagine taking the single payment of 51% of the jackpot.

      a.   How much will you receive?

      b.   If you invest all of the money at a rate of 4% compounded annually, how much can you expect to have after 20 years?

      c.   Is the answer to part (b) the sum of a series?

10-79.   Imagine instead that you choose to take payments spread over 20 years, starting with $1,500,000 in year 1 and growing by 5 percent each year,

      a.   How much money would you receive in year 2? In year 5?

      b.   Write an equation to show how much money you receive in any given year.

      c.   How much money will you have received after 20 years? Be ready to explain your thinking to the class.

10-80.   With which option would you receive more money? How much more? Which option would you choose? Why?

*Further Guidance
section ends here.*

10-81.   Scott and Greg are looking for summer jobs. Their father, who is head of the neighborhood beautification committee, says that if they pick up litter from around the neighborhood for a whole day, he will pay them $0.15 for each piece of trash they collect. Scott realizes that the more litter they pick up, the more difficult it will be to find more pieces, so he proposes a different payment scheme. *"How about you give us $0.10 for the first piece, and increase our pay by 2% for each piece after that? Then we'll get paid more for the pieces we work harder to find."*

   a.   Write an equation to generate the series Scott is proposing.

   b.   With Scott's plan, how much will his dad have to pay him for the 100th piece of litter he finds? For the 200th?

   c.   If Scott collects 150 pieces of litter, how much will he have earned in total? What if he picks up 200 pieces?

   d.   Greg thinks Scott is crazy to propose an increase of just 2% per piece. After all 2% of 10 cents is just $\frac{2}{10}$ of a cent! Instead, he plans to ask for a one-cent increase for every piece. If their father agrees to this, how much would Greg get paid for the 100th piece he collects? For the 200th piece?

   e.   If the boys each collect 150 pieces of litter, which payment scheme will earn them the most money?

   f.   What if they each pick up a total of 200 pieces?

10-82.   Drought-conscious Darcy is collecting rainwater in order to water her garden through the hot, dry summer. During the last big rainstorm she filled 12 buckets full to the brim! Each week of the summer, she used the water from one of the 12 buckets to water her plants.

   However, Darcy had not counted on evaporation. In the sun, each uncovered bucket loses 0.35 gallons of its water volume each week.

   a.   If each bucket starts with 15 gallons in it, how many gallons will be in each of the unused buckets after 2 weeks in the sun? After 7 weeks? How much was in the final bucket when Darcy used it on her garden?

   b.   Is this series arithmetic, geometric, or something else?

   c.   At the end of the 12th week, how many total gallons of water will Darcy have poured on her plants?

10-83. Hannah is very interested in genealogy, the study of family history. She has traced her family back many years and knows the names of her biological parents, grandparents, great-grandparents, great-great-grandparents, and so on.

    a.   If Hannah counts herself as the first generation, how many people are in each of the first three generations on her chart?

    b.   What kind of sequence does the number of people in each generation form? Is it arithmetic, geometric, or something else? Justify your conclusion.

    c.   If Hannah is successful in tracing her true biological ancestors for 12 generations, how many names will she have?

10-84. For each of the problems below, decide if the series is arithmetic, geometric, or something else. Then, find the sum of the series.

    a. $\displaystyle\sum_{t=0}^{15} 5(2)^t$

    b. $\displaystyle\sum_{p=1}^{179} (16 - 4(p-1))$

    c. $4 + 8 + 12 + \ldots + 392$

    d. $\displaystyle\sum_{q=1}^{312} 11q$

    e. $5 + \frac{10}{4} + \frac{10}{8} + \ldots + \frac{10}{4096}$

10-85. Lucy is working with a series whose first term is 12 and that is generated by the expression $t(n) = -9 + 21n$. The sum of her series is 3429. How many terms are in her series?

10-86. Write an entry in your Learning Log that describes what you have learned during this lesson. Include information about the differences between geometric sequences and geometric series, and about how to find the sum of a geometric series. What questions do you have about geometric series? Title this entry "Geometric Series" and label it with today's date.

10-87.   Antonio and Luann were trying to explain their strategy for finding the sum of a geometric series to their homework group. They decided to generate a sequence that would be easy to add up so they could convince the other students that their strategy really worked. They used $t(n) = 3 \cdot 10^{n-1}$.

   a.   The sum of the first six terms of the series is easy to calculate. You can do it in your head. Write out the first six terms and find the sum.

   b.   Now explain Luann and Antonio's strategy for finding the sum and use your answer to part (a) to check your result.

   c.   Represent the first n terms of the series in summation notation and write an expression for the total sum of n terms.

10-88.   According to the school secretary, the size of the graduating class of Gauss High has steadily increased since the school has opened. She claims that the number of graduates each year forms the sequence $t(n) = 42 + 12(n-1)$, where n is the number of years the high school has had students graduate. At the end of the year, the administration mails out invitations to all previous graduates to attend the upcoming graduation ceremony.

   a.   In this situation, what does a sequence represent? What does a series represent?

   b.   After the 10th graduation ceremony, how many total graduates should there be? Explain how you found your answer.

   c.   The total number of Gauss High graduates after n years can be represented by the graph at right. If the alumni relations committee wants to invite all graduates to a party to celebrate the nth anniversary of the school, how may invitations will they need to send?

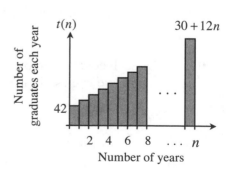

10-89.   Consider the series $8+1+(-6)+(-13)+...+(-90)$.

      a.   How many terms are there?   b.   What is the sum?

10-90.   Evaluate the sum of the series $\sum\limits_{n=3}^{9}(5n)$. Is the series arithmetic or geometric?

10-91.   Connie and Nora went into Ready Scoop to get ice cream cones, but Nora can't make up her mind. They have 23 flavors and she wants 3 scoops.

      a.   Nora is very particular about the order of the scoops. How many choices does she have if all of the scoops are different?

      b.   Nora changes her mind. She wants a dish (in which the order does not matter), not a cone, but she still wants three different flavors. How many ways can she order?

      c.   Connie says, *"I want a cone with dark chocolate on the bottom and then any other flavors for the two scoops on top."* How many cones are possible with dark chocolate on the bottom?

      d.   Vlad came in as they were leaving and saw Connie's cone. He said, *"Oh, that's what I want, a cone with chocolate on the bottom and then two other flavors."* The clerk, said, *"Okay, but we have four kinds of chocolate."* Vlad replied, *"Any kind of chocolate will do."* How many different cones could fill Vlad's order?

10-92.   Using a graph of $y = \sin x$ as a reference, graph $y = |\sin x|$.

10-93.   Factor and simplify each expression below.

      a. $\dfrac{x^2-4}{x^2+4x+4}$ b. $\dfrac{2x^2-5x-3}{4x^2+4x+1}$

      c.   Justify each step in simplifying the expression in part (a).

10-94.   For each equation below, state the amplitude, period, and locator point, and then sketch two cycles of the graph.

      a. $y = \tan(x)$ b. $y = \tan(x - \pi)$

10-95.   Solve each equation.

    a. $\log_5(2x) = 3$ b. $\log_5(x+1) = -1$

    c. $\log(4) - \log(x) = 2$ d. $2\log_3(6) + \log_3(y) = 4$

10-96.   Joe's dad is only 40, but he's already thinking about retiring. If he retires early at age 55, he will receive an annual pension starting at $30,000 and increasing at a rate of 3% each year to account for inflation. If he waits until he is 65, his pension will be a larger percentage of his salary at that time. He figures that it will be about $60,000 to start and the same 3% increase after that for inflation. He wants to know which plan will pay out the largest total by age 80. Show him how to find out the answer to his question.

10-97.   Ms. Fernandez invested $50,000 of her lottery winnings into two different mutual funds. At the end of one year, both funds together were worth $53,550. One of the funds had produced a return of 8% while the second fund had produced a return of 6.5%. How much money was invested in each fund?

10-98.   Eight friends go to the movies. They want to sit together in a row with a student on each aisle. (Assume the row is 8 seats wide including 2 aisle seats.)

    a.   How many ways can they sit in the row?

    b.   If Kristen wants to sit on the far left aisle seat, how many ways can they all sit in the row?

    c.   If Kristen wants either aisle seat, how many ways can the eight students sit?

10-99.   Find the distance between each of the following pairs of points.

    a. $(8, 4)$ and $(12, 20)$ b. (x, y) and $(-3, -5)$

10-100. Solve each of the following equations.

a. $\frac{x}{x+1} = \frac{5}{7}$

b. $\frac{2}{y} = \frac{3}{y+5}$

c. $\frac{x}{x+1} + \frac{2}{x-1} = \frac{8}{x^2-1}$

d. $\frac{2}{y+5} - \frac{3}{y} = \frac{3}{y+5}$

10-101. Solve for x and y in each system below.

a. $2x + y = 12$
   $xy = 16$

b. $2x + y = 12$
   $xy = 20$

c. Explain how the graphs of (a) and (b) relate to the solutions to each system of equations.

10-102. Use reference angles, the symmetry of a circle, and the knowledge that $\tan(20°) \approx 0.3640$ to write three other true statements using tangent.

10-103. Use the properties of logarithms to rewrite each equation and then solve. Check for extraneous roots.

a. $\log(x) + \log(x + 21) = 2$

b. $2\log_4(x) - \log_4(3) = 2$

c. $\log_2(9x + 5) - \log_2(x^2 - 1) = 2$

d. $\log_7(x + 1) + \log_7(x - 5) = 1$

10-104. Calculate $(2 + i)(3 - 5i) - (1 - 4i)^2$.

10.2.2 What if n is very large?

Infinite Series

What is the total distance a ball would travel if you tossed it up and let it bounce? What if a bouncing ball continued to bounce forever? How far would it travel? Today you will discover ways to represent this situation and find the answer to this question.

10-105.   THE BOUNCING BALL

Imagine lying on the ground and tossing a ball straight up 10 meters.

a.   When the ball gets back to you, how far has it travelled?

b.   Instead of catching it, imagine that you let it bounce. The ball has a bounce ratio of 60%, meaning that each time it bounces the ball will bounce to 60% of its previous height. When the ball comes back down to you the second time, how far has it travelled in total?

c.   Imagine that you let the ball bounce until it comes back to you 15 times. Write a geometric series to represent the total distance the ball travels until it comes back to you the 15th time.

d.   What is the total distance the ball will travel up and down?

10-106.   HOW FAR IS IT?

Of course you know that a ball cannot bounce forever, but imagine the ball in the previous problem could. Thinking about this possibility has led to some interesting discoveries. Would the total distance the ball travels up and down continue to grow until it is infinitely large?

Now, imagine starting at 0 on a number line and moving according to the following sequence: move 20 units to the right, and then continue moving right, each time moving 0.6 times the distance you previously moved.

20   12   7.2   • • •

Problem continues on next page →

10-106.   *Problem continued from previous page.*

How far along the number line would you travel if you kept going and going and going ... forever? That is, what is the total distance the ball would travel if it could bounce forever?

Your Task:

*   With your team, investigate the questions above.

*   When your team agrees that you have answered the investigation question, create a new infinite geometric series and generalize your results. As you work with your team, keep the following Discussion Points in mind. Then write a strategy for finding the sum of any infinite geometric series.

Discussion Points

What patterns do we see as n increases?

What happens when the multiplier is smaller than one?

How can we represent this?

Is there a simpler equivalent expression?

*   Prepare a poster to share your team's findings. Include your examples, generalizations, and justifications.

Further Guidance

10-107.   You already calculated the distance for 15 bounces of the ball in problem 10-105. Calculate the distance for 25 moves along the number line, and for several larger values of n.

10-108.   Calculate the sums of each of the following geometric series for $n = 10$ and $n = 30$. What do you notice about the results?

a. $200 + 100 + 50 + ... + 200(\frac{1}{2})^n$

b. $16 + 24 + 36 + ...16(\frac{3}{2})^n$

c.   What makes the difference in the results for the series in parts (a) and (b)?

10-109. What do you notice about the results as you use larger values for n? That is, what happens to the total distance the ball travels? Respond to the investigation questions in problem 10-105.

10-110. Write a strategy for finding the sum of any infinite geometric series. Keep the Discussion Points from problem 10-105 in mind.

Further Guidance section ends here.

10-111. The general formula for the sum of a finite geometric series is

$$S(n) = \frac{r \cdot t(n) - t(1)}{r-1},$$

where $t(n)$ is the formula for each term. Start with this formula and use it to develop a formula for the sum of an infinite geometric series.

a. Since $t(n) = ar^{n-1}$, replace $t(n)$ and $t(1)$ in the formula for $S(n)$ above and simplify.

b. It turns out that $S(n) = \frac{a(1-r^n)}{1-r}$ will be the most useful form for the formula for the sum of a geometric series. If you have not done so already, show that your formula in part (a) is equivalent to:

$$S(n) = \frac{a(1-r^n)}{1-r}.$$

c. In the bouncing ball problem (problem 10-105), $a = 20$ and $r = 0.6$. What happens to the value of r^n as you use larger and larger values for n? What happens to the value of $1-r^n$? Discuss these questions with your team.

d. For infinite series, the formula can be rewritten as shown below. Explain why this is possible.

$$S = \frac{a}{1-r}$$

e. Use this formula for the sum of an infinite series to recalculate the total distance the bouncing ball would travel (in problem 10-105) if it bounced without ending. Compare your results with the results of your investigation in problem 10-106.

10-112. It is believed that the Greek philosopher Zeno of Alea devised this in about 450 BCE: The tortoise challenged Achilles to a race. To be fair, Achilles, who is known for his tremendous speed, gave the tortoise a head start. Zeno proposed that as he ran the race, Achilles would run to the place that the tortoise had started. But by that time, the tortoise would have moved forward some distance. Then by the time Achilles travels that new distance between him and the tortoise, the tortoise will have moved forward again. This would happen over and over again. So, even though the tortoise is much slower than Achilles, it appears Achilles can never catch up to the tortoise!

By this same reasoning, you would not ever be able to cross a street. To cross a street, you must first cross to the halfway point. After you have gone that far, you still have to cross halfway of the remaining distance (which is $\frac{1}{4}$ of the whole distance). When you have crossed that, you still have to cross half of the remaining distance ($\frac{1}{8}$ of the whole distance). You always have halfway of some distance remaining in front of you. It appears you will never be able to cross the street!

Investigate these two paradoxical dilemmas with series.

   a. Represent the distance you have travelled across the street as an infinite geometric series.

   b. What is the sum of the series?

   c. Zeno would point out that crossing the street would mean completing an infinite number of tasks, which would be impossible. What do you think?

10-113. Fannie was helping her younger brother Mac with his math homework when they came to this problem:

   Change the repeating decimal $0.\overline{63}$ into a fraction.

Fannie remembered that they could write the problem as an equation and then create a second equation by multiplying by a useful power of 10.

$$N = 0.636363636363....$$
$$100N = 63.636363636363...$$

Then they could subtract the first equation from the second and divide to find N as follows:

$$99N = 63$$
$$N = \frac{63}{99} = \frac{7}{9}$$

When she returned to her own homework Fannie thought, "*Whoa! I bet I could write $0.\overline{63}$ as an infinite series and use what we just learned about series to get the fraction.*"

   a. Write $0.\overline{63}=0.636363...$ as an infinite series with a multiplier of 0.01.

   b. Find the sum of the series and write the answer as a fraction.

10-114.   Use Fannie's method from problem 10-113 to write $0.\overline{143}$ as an infinite series. Then write the decimal as a fraction.

10-115.   What fraction is $0.\overline{9}$ or 0.9999999…?

10-116.   LEARNING LOG

Write an entry in your Learning Log describing what you learned in this lesson. Include information about infinite geometric series and their sums. What questions do you have about series? Title this entry "Infinite Geometric Series" and label it with today's date.

$\textbf{M}$ETHODS AND $\textbf{M}$EANINGS

Geometric Series

MATH NOTES

A **geometric sequence** can be represented by a formula for its nth term:

$$t(n) = ar^{n-1}$$

The first term is a (for which $n = 1$), and the **common multiplier** (or ratio) is r.

A **geometric series** is the sum of the terms of a geometric sequence:

$$t(1) + t(2) + t(3) + \ldots + t(k)$$

The total sum for a finite series (a series that ends) is:

$$S(k) = \frac{r \cdot t(k) - t(1)}{r - 1} = \frac{a(1 - r^n)}{1 - r}$$

For example, either formula above can be used to find the sum of the series $1000 + 600 + 360 + 216 + 129.6$, which has $a = 1000$ and $r = 0.6$:

$$S(5) = \frac{0.6(129.6) - 1000}{0.6 - 1} = 2305.6 \quad \text{or} \quad S(5) = \frac{1000(1 - 0.6^5)}{1 - 0.6} = 2305.6$$

For an **infinite geometric series** with an initial value of a and a multiplier (or common ratio) r, and $0 < |r| < 1$, the sum of the series can be represented by:

$$S = \sum_{n=1}^{\infty} ar^{n-1} = \frac{a}{1 - r}$$

For example: When $a = 100$ and the multiplier is $r = 0.2$, the sum of the infinite series is: $100 + 20 + 4 + 0.8 + \ldots = \frac{100}{1 - 0.2} = 125$

10-117.   A hiker decided to spend his days walking around the country. On the first day he walked 25 miles, but on the following days he found he could not keep up that pace. On average he traveled a 5% shorter distance each day. If he could walk forever, how far would he go?

10-118.   Given seven points in a plane, no three of which are collinear:

    a.   How many different lines are determined by these points?

    b.   How many distinct triangles can be formed?

    c.   How many distinct quadrilaterals can be formed?

    d.   Explain why the answers to parts (b) and (c) are the same.

10-119.   Solve the following equations.

    a. $\frac{3}{x} + \frac{5}{x-7} = -2$
                       b. $\frac{2x+3}{4} - \frac{x-7}{6} = \frac{2x-3}{12}$

10-120.   Betty's Quick Stop makes a 15% profit on its lunches and a 22% profit on its dinners. If Betty took in $2700 on Tuesday and made $513.01 profit, how much did Betty take in on lunch? Write one or two equations, then solve.

10-121.   For the polynomial function $f(x) = x^3 - 5x^2 + 11x - 15$, which of the following are possible factors?

    a. $(x+1)$ b. $(x-2)$ c. $(x+4)$ d. $(x-3)$

10-122.   Using your answers to the previous problem:

    a.   Factor $f(x) = x^3 - 5x^2 + 11x - 15$.   b.   Solve $f(x) = 0$.

10-123.   What fraction is equivalent to the repeating decimal $0.\overline{27}$?

10-124.   Find the solutions to the system at right. $y = x^2 + 2x + 5$
          The solutions may be real or complex. $y = 2x^2 + 4x + 7$

10-125. Why does the formula for the sum of an infinite geometric series contain the condition that $0 < |r| < 1$?

10-126. Find the sum of the first five terms of this series: $3 + 1 + \frac{1}{3} + \ldots$

10-127. Find the value of each of the following combinations.

a. $_{10}C_8$ b. $_{12}C_7$ c. $_7C_1$

10-128. Without graphing, find where each of the following curves crosses the x-axis. (Find the *exact* points!)

a. $f(x) = x^2 - x - 12$ b. $f(x) = 2x^2 - 3x - 9$

c. $f(x) = 2x^2 + x - 7$ d. $f(x) = 3x^2 - 2x + 7$

e. $f(x) = 3x^3 + 2x^2 - 8x$ f. $f(x) = 2x^3 + 2x^2 + 13x$

10-129. Use properties of exponents to rewrite each expression below so that it involves only multiplication and exponents.

a. $\dfrac{(-2x)^3 yz^2}{2^{-1}\sqrt{x}y^{-3}}$ b. $\dfrac{3x^2 y^3}{\sqrt{3x}\sqrt[3]{y}}$

10-130. For an object shot into the air, its height h in feet above the ground after t seconds is given by the equation $h = 80t - 16t^2$. Use this equation to answer the following questions.

a. At what times is the object on the ground?

b. For what domain is this function reasonable?

c. How long did it take the object to hit the ground?

d. For what times is the height greater than 64 feet?

10-131. Dolores says that the solutions for $x^2 - x + 1 = 0$ are $\frac{1}{2} \pm \frac{i\sqrt{3}}{2}$. Is she correct? Explain your answer.

10-132. The graph of $f(x) = x^2 - 3x - 4$ is shown at right. Use the graph to solve:

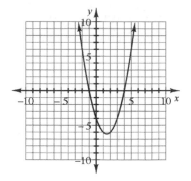

a. $f(x) = 0$

b. $f(x) \geq 0$

c. $f(x) \leq 0$

10.3.1 How fast can I rewrite $(x + y)^6$?

Pascal's Triangle and the Binomial Theorem

In this lesson you will use something you learned when studying probability that may seem, at first, to be totally unrelated to the algebra problems you will be rewriting.

When you learned about probability, you explored several kinds of counting problems. You learned to use **combinations**, $_nC_r$, in situations where order does not matter and results are not repeated. For example, when counting the number of ways to choose a 3-member committee out of five volunteers, you calculated $_5C_3 = \frac{5 \cdot 4 \cdot 3}{3!} = 10$. Then you used **permutations**, $_nP_r$, in situations where the order *does* matter, and results are not repeated. For example, when counting how many ways there are to choose the first, second and third place winners from five finalists, you calculated $_nP_r = 5 \cdot 4 \cdot 3 = 60$.

10-133. Work with your team to complete a table for combinations like the one below. Discuss any patterns you notice as you are working.

r, the number of choices

$_nC_r$	0	1	2	3	4	5	6	7	8
0	1								
1	1	1							
2	1	2	1						
3	1	3	3	1					
4			6						
5									
6									
7									
8							28	8	1

n, the total number

10-134.   The triangular array at right is another arrangement
of the numbers of combinations you entered in the
table in problem 10-133. It is known as Pascal's
Triangle. Copy the triangle and add several more
rows.

n											
0					1						
1				1		1					
2				1	2	1					
3			1	3		3	1				
4		1	4		6		4	1			
5	1	5		10		10		5	1		

a.   There are many patterns in the triangle, which
continues to grow indefinitely. With your team,
find and describe as many patterns as you can.
You should be able to describe at least three.

b.   Discuss with the class the patterns you found. Write down any patterns
your classmates found that your team did not find.

c.   The single number 1 at the top of the triangle is called Row 0. Label the
rows of your triangle to row 10, and describe a rule for writing any new
row in the triangle.

10-135.   Now consider what may appear to be a completely different problem: the
algebraic expansion of the binomial expression $(a+b)^n$. Use what you know
about multiplication to complete parts (a) through (d) below.

a.   Write $(a+b)^2$ in expanded form. In other words, multiply $(a+b)(a+b)$
and combine like terms. How many terms are there in the resulting
polynomial? What are the coefficients of the terms?

b.   Multiply and rewrite $(a+b)^3$ in expanded form. How many terms are
there, and what are their coefficients? What did you do to expand the
polynomial? With your team, discuss possible ways to carry out the
polynomial multiplication quickly.

c.   How many terms do you think $(a+b)^4$ will have when rewritten in
expanded form? Write it in expanded form. What are the coefficients of
these terms?

d.   How could you use Pascal's Triangle to rewrite the binomial expression
$(a+b)^6$ as a sum of monomial terms? Explain your method.

10-136.   Explain how you could use Pascal's Triangle to rewrite $(a+b)^n$ in expanded
form. What problem would use row 1? Row 0?

10-137.   Use Pascal's Triangle to rewrite $(U+V)^3$ in expanded form.

a.   Pascal's Triangle can be used to expand any binomial raised to a power. Use it to expand the expression $(2x+3)^3$, by substituting $2x$ for U and 3 for V.

b.   Now use Pascal's Triangle to expand $(x-1)^5$. What will you need to substitute for U and V?

c.   How many terms are in the answer to part (a)? Part (b)? In general, how many terms would be in the expanded form of the nth power of a binomial?

10-138.   To do problems 10-135 through 10-137 you probably noticed that the pattern in Pascal's Triangle appears to be the same pattern in first four powers of $(a+b)^1, (a+b)^2, (a+b)^3, (a+b)^4$. Patterns are powerful and important tools in mathematics. Some have called mathematics "the science of patterns," but to be sure a pattern fits, you need to justify it. Why are the numbers in Pascal's triangle the same as $(a+b)^n$?

Your Task: Discuss this question with your team, write some examples to illustrate your reasoning, and be prepared to explain your reasoning to the class.

Discussion Points

How are the coefficients of the terms in a binomial expansion of
$a+b$ combinations?

How can we use an example?

How are the factors related to the product?

10-139. Joanna had written $(a+b)^5 = (a+b)(a+b)(a+b)(a+b)(a+b)$ on her paper, when Sareen asked, *"Why did you write that?"*

Joanna replied, *"I thought we could use it as an example. When we did $(a+b)^3$ the variable parts in the expanded form were: a^3, a^2b, ab^2, b^3. What do you think they will be for this one?"*

a. For the fifth power make a list of the variable parts of the expressions that will appear in the expanded form.

b. Garth jumped in and said, *"I've got an idea, maybe we can look at one of the terms like a^3b^2 and look back at the factors to see where it came from!"*

"Wait, I think I see it," James chimed in. *"You just use an 'a' from three of the five factors and a 'b' from the other two."*

What counting formula gives the number of different ways to choose three a's from the five factors? What is the coefficient for a^3b^2 and how could you figure it out without referring to Pascal's Triangle?

———————— *Further Guidance section ends here.* ————————

10-140. For his homework assignment, Andrew had to expand $(a+b)^9$. He just realized that he did not have the coefficient for the term a^3b^6. He started writing out the first nine rows of Pascal's Triangle when his friend Robbie said he could find the value using combinations. What combination should Andrew use, and what is the coefficient?

10-141. Rebecca needs to write the 5th term in the expansion of $(a+b)^{11}$.

a. How many terms are in the expansion?

b. What is the 5th term of the expansion? (The term is of the form $\_\_a^7b^4$.)

c. Now Rebecca needs to know the 5th term of $(x-2)^{11}$. How can you use your result from part (b)?

10-142. **Challenge:** Read the Math Notes box about the Binomial Theorem that follows this lesson. Then, use the general form for the Binomial Theorem to show that the sum of the elements of the nth row of Pascal's Triangle is 2^n.

$$_nC_n +_n C_{n-1} +_n C_{n-2} + ... +_n C_2 +_n C_1 +_n C_0 = 2^n$$

10-143. After doing the above challenge problem and noticing that $_2C_0 + _2C_1 + _2C_2 = 2^2$, Duong noticed that $_1C_0 + _1C_1 = 2^1$. He wondered if this worked for 2^3 also.

a. Does $_3C_0 + _3C_1 + _3C_2 + _3C_3 = 2^3$?

b. Does $_4C_0 + _4C_1 + _4C_2 + _4C_3 + _4C_4 = 2^4$?

c. Explain why $_nC_0 + _nC_1 + _nC_2 + ... + _nC_n = 2^n$.

10-144. LEARNING LOG

Write an entry in your Learning Log explaining Pascal's Triangle and why it is useful. Include several examples. Title this entry "Pascal's Triangle" and label it with today's date.

METHODS AND MEANINGS

MATH NOTES

Binomial Theorem

The **Binomial Theorem** can be used to write the expansion of binomial expressions of the form $(a+b)^n$. For example:

$$(x+3y)^4$$

$$= _4C_4 x^4 (3y)^0 + _4C_3 x^3 (3y)^1 + _4C_2 x^2 (3y)^2 + _4C_1 x^1 (3y)^3 + _4C_0 x^0 (3y)^4$$

$$= 1x^4 + 4x^3(3y) + 6x^2(9y^2) + 4x(27y^3) + 81y^4$$

$$= x^4 + 12x^3 y + 54x^2 y^2 + 108xy^3 + 81y^4$$

In general, $(a+b)^n = _nC_n a^n + _nC_{n-1}a^{n-1}b + _nC_{n-2}a^{n-2}b^2 + \cdots _nC_1 ab^{n-1} + _nC_0 b^n$.

10-145. Use Pascal's Triangle to expand $(x+y)^7$.

10-146. Use the pattern for $(a+b)^5$ to write the fourth term of $(w-4z)^5$.

10-147.   George starts a chain letter by sending it to four friends who then send it to four more friends and so on. If George counts as round one and his four friends as round two, how many people will have received the letter after round six?

10-148.   Find the sum for each of these infinite geometric series if possible. If it is not possible, explain.

   a. $8 + 4 + 2 + ...$ b. $3 + 9 + 27 + 81 + ...$

10-149.   Donna has four bracelets in her jewelry box. They can all be worn together, but each is different from the others. Before she goes to bed at night, she sets out the outfit she will wear the next day, including her accessories. How many different ways can she choose the following: 0 bracelets? 1 bracelet? 2 bracelets? 3 bracelets? 4 bracelets?

   a.   How do these possible combinations compare to the 4th row ($n = 4$) of Pascal's Triangle?

   b.   If Donna bought two new bracelets, how many combinations of four bracelets can she choose for her outfit? How can you figure this out without multiplying or using your calculator?

10-150.   The Spirit Club recently got a call from the school executive council, asking them to make a committee. They now have 10 volunteers and will need to choose a three-person committee. They need to calculate $_{10}C_3$, the number of possible committees, but they have no calculator with them.

   a.   Al had a thought: *"I remember that the number of three-person committees you can select from 9 volunteers is 84. This would be the number of committees the tenth volunteer will NOT be on because he or she would be selected from the other nine members."* How would you calculate this number?

   b.   *"I also know how many committees the new volunteer WILL be on because I can just add his name to each of the two-member committees I had already selected from 9."* How many possible committees would include the tenth volunteer?

   c.   Without using a calculator (and without multiplying or dividing), explain how Al used parts (a) and (b) to calculate $_{10}C_3$.

   d.   How is this related to Pascal's Triangle?

10-151. Sketch a graph of $y = x^3(x-2)(x+2)^2$.

10-152. Parking meters in a beach resort town cost 25¢ for 15 minutes. A normal distribution with a mean $10 and a standard deviation of $2 can be used to model the amount of money one parking meter makes on a busy summer day.

    a.   Make a graph of the distribution of the money made by one meter on your calculator, and sketch it. An appropriate value for the maximum of the relative frequency axis is Ymax = 0.02.

    b.   From your graph, visually estimate where the middle 90% of meter earnings fall. Shade this portion of your sketch.

    c.   Use your calculator to check your estimate. How close to 90% did you come?

10-153. Solve the system at right for (x, y, z).

$$2x + y - 2z = 0$$
$$x - y - 4z = -3$$
$$3x + 2y + 2z = -1$$

10-154. A parabola passes through the points (0, 5), (2, 1), and (6, 17).

    a.   What is its equation?   b.   Where is its vertex?

10-155. What is the third term of $(2x + \frac{1}{4x})^7$?

10-156. Find the sum of the first six terms of the series $2 + 6 + 18 + 54 + \ldots$.

10-157. Use the pattern for $(a+b)^4$ to expand $(3x+1)^4$.

10-158. Complete the square to change the following equations to graphing form. Then sketch the graph of each equation.

    a. $f(x) = x^2 + 4x + 6$ b. $x^2 + 6x + y^2 - 8y = 0$

10-159. Two similar triangles are drawn on a piece of paper. The smaller triangle has an area of 600 square mm and the larger triangle has an area of 960 square mm. If the shortest side of the smaller triangle is 26 mm, how long is the shortest side of the larger triangle?

10-160. Find the equation of the line that is perpendicular to $y = \frac{1}{2}x - 3$ and passes through the point (10, 14).

10-161. For the function $f(x) = \frac{\sqrt{x+4}}{2} - 1$, complete parts (a) through (d) below.

   a.   Sketch the graph and the inverse.

   b.   Find the equation of the inverse function.

   c.   Determine the domain and range of the inverse.

   d.   Compute $f^{-1}(f(5))$.

10-162. Solve each equation below.

   a. $2^{(x-1)} = 64$ b. $9^3 = 27^{(2x-1)}$

   c. $x^6 = 29$ d. $6^x = 29$

10-163. A small rocket is launched from five meters below ground level and reaches a height of 3 meters above the ground after 4 seconds. On the way down it is 3 meters above the ground after a total of 8 seconds.

   a.   What are three data points?

   b.   Draw a rough sketch of the height of the rocket over time.

   c.   Find the equation of the parabola based on the data.

   d.   When will the rocket hit the ground?

   e.   What is the domain for this function?

   f.   For what part of the domain is the rocket below ground?

10.3.2 What is e?

The Number e

So far in this chapter you have learned several things about sums of infinite series and the Binomial Theorem. Now you are going to use this knowledge to look at one particular situation involving an infinite series - compounding interest. This work will reveal a new mathematical constant, another **transcendental number** (like π), which has a decimal representation that continues infinitely and does not form a repetitive pattern. This number is called e. The number e when used as the base of a logarithm is known as a **natural logarithm** and is used widely in the sciences as well as in business and economics.

10-164.   Tabitha's uncle gave her $10,000 on her thirteenth birthday. She wants to invest it in a college savings fund. The banker tells her that interest rates have dropped to 3%, but at their bank they will compound the interest at any time interval– daily, even hourly– so their customers can still get a good deal. Tabitha decided to make a table to see how good a deal she could get.

    a.   Tabitha knows that a one-year compounding period will result in $10000(1+.03)^1 = \$10300$. She also knows that she can get the amount for semiannual periods by dividing the rate by 2 and then squaring to compound, or $10000(1+\frac{0.03}{2})^2 = \$10302.25$. Make a table for shorter compounding periods, including quarterly, monthly, daily, and hourly.

    b.   What do you notice about the amounts? Be prepared to share your observations with the class.

10-165.   Tabitha was disappointed, but she decided the daily compounding would have to do. Her friend Veronica was more of a dreamer. She asked, *"What if you could earn 100% interest and compound that?"*

"Wow, that should grow fast!" said Tabitha. *"I've got my calculator. Let's just start with one dollar to make it easy, and we can multiply by any initial amount later."*

Veronica added, *"Yes, and that makes our formula easier."*

    a.   What is the easier version of the formula Veronica is thinking of?

    b.   With your team, make a table for at least 12 values of n, including some very large ones.

    c.   Did you try 1,000,000? What do you notice as you use larger numbers for n?

10-166.   The Binomial Theorem provides another way to think about the number e. This particular approach turned out to be very useful because later it led to some surprising connections with other areas of mathematics.

The beginning of the binomial expansion for $\left(1+\frac{1}{n}\right)^n$ is written below:

$$\left(1+\tfrac{1}{n}\right)^n = {}_n C_n(1) + {}_n C_{n-1}\left(\tfrac{1}{n}\right) + {}_n C_{n-2}\left(\tfrac{1}{n^2}\right) + {}_n C_{n-3}\left(\tfrac{1}{n^3}\right) + {}_n C_{n-4}\left(\tfrac{1}{n^4}\right) + \dots$$

The combinations can be written in terms of factorials, and algebra can by used to rewrite, so this expression is equivalent to the following expression.

$$1 + 1 + \frac{1-\frac{1}{n}}{2!} + \frac{\left(1-\frac{1}{n}\right)\left(1-\frac{2}{n}\right)}{3!} + \frac{\left(1-\frac{1}{n}\right)\left(1-\frac{2}{n}\right)\left(1-\frac{3}{n}\right)}{4!} + \dots$$

a.   What happens to each factor in the numerators as the value of n gets very large? If n could be infinitely large, what would each numerator equal? Explain your reasoning.

b.   Rewrite the series, changing the numerators to what they would be if n became an infinitely large number.

10-167.   Leonard Euler (pronounced as "oiler") was a preeminent mathematician and physicist in the 1700s. Although he was Swiss, he worked mostly in Russia. You can thank Euler for $f(x)$ notation, and for the symbols i, e, and Σ; he popularized the use of π. Among many other discoveries, he found that when n becomes infinitely large:

$$e = \sum_{n=0}^{\infty} \tfrac{1}{n!} = 1 + 1 + \tfrac{1}{2!} + \tfrac{1}{3!} + \tfrac{1}{4!} + \dots.$$

a.   Is this series arithmetic or geometric? Explain your answer.

b.   Calculate the sum of the first 5 terms and then the sum of the first 7 terms. What do you notice?

10-168.   **Team Challenge:** Investigate the function $f(x) = (1+\tfrac{1}{x})^x$.

METHODS AND MEANINGS

Compound Interest

The formula for **compound interest** is generally written:

$$A = P\left(1+\frac{r}{n}\right)^{nt},$$

where A is the total amount of money at any time, P is the principal or initial value, r is the annual rate of interest, t is the number of years, and n is the number of times per year the interest is compounded.

For example, if you invest $5,000 for 20 years at an annual interest rate of 4.8%, compounded monthly:

$$A = \$5000(1+\tfrac{0.048}{12})^{12\cdot20} = \$5000(1.004)^{240} = \$13,033.50$$

The use of e provides a shortcut for calculation of **continuously compounding interest**. The formula for continuous compounding is

$$A = Pe^{rt},$$

where A is the total amount at any time, P is the original principal, r is the rate of interest, and t is the time period.

MATH NOTES

10-169.   Robin and Teryll each have $8,000 to invest and they disagree about the best place to start a savings account. Teryll found a savings and loan company that will guarantee a rate of 3.9% compounded monthly for the next 10 years. Robin says her bank is much better because they will give her 4% interest compounded semi-annually for the next ten years. In ten years, which account will end up with the greatest amount and how much difference is there?

Core Connections Algebra 2

10-170.   The use of e provides a shortcut for calculation of **continuously compounding interest**. The formula for continuous compounding is $A = Pe^{rt}$, where A is the total amount at any time, P is the original principal, r is the rate of interest, and t is the time period.

      a.   Use this new formula to calculate the amount Tabitha had after investing her $10,000 for one year at 3% annual interest, compounded continuously. How does this compare with her daily compounding result of $10,304.56?

      b.   Suppose a large investment group invested 10 billion dollars at 8% annual interest. Compare the amount they would have in one year if the interest were compounded continuously with the amount they would earn if the interest were compounded daily.

      c.   Which investors might benefit from continuous compounding, rather than daily compounding?

10-171.   Use the Binomial Theorem to write the expansion of each of the following expressions.

      a. $\left(1+\frac{1}{n}\right)^{3}$ b. $\left(1+\frac{1}{n}\right)^{5}$

10-172.   Atmospheric pressure P (in lbs. per square inch) under typical conditions can be approximately calculated by using the formula below, where h represents the number of feet above sea level.

$$P = 14.7e^{-0.00003h}$$

      a.   What is pressure at sea level?

      b.   Use the formula to calculate the atmospheric pressure in the mile-high city of Denver, Colorado.

      c.   The lowest point in Death Valley is 285 feet below sea level. What is the atmospheric pressure in Death Valley?

10-173.   Omar was 8 years old when he received $25,000 dollars from his grandmother's will. His father invested it for him in a fund that earned 6% annual interest compounded quarterly. He was hoping to see the investment double by the time Omar was ready for college. Another fund offered the same interest rate but the interest would compound continuously. This second fund was a little riskier, however.

   a.   Write an equation to represent each situation.

   b.   Which method of compounding the interest will double his money faster?

   c.   Is the difference in doubling time worth the extra risk?

10-174.   After graphing $y = 12x^3 + 55x^2 - 27x - 10$ on a graphing calculator, you can easily see that one x-intercept is $(-5, 0)$. Use this information to find all of the x-intercepts.

10-175.   Use the pattern for $(a + b)^3$ to expand $(2x - 3)^3$.

10-176.   This problem is a checkpoint for rewriting expressions with and solving equations with logarithms. It will be referred to as Checkpoint 10.

   In parts (a) through (b), rewrite each expression as a single logarithm. In parts (c) through (f), solve each equation.

   a. $\log_2(30x) - \log_2(6)$ b. $2\log_3(x) + \log_3(5)$

   c. $\log_7(3x - 2) = 2$ d. $\log(2x + 1) = -1$

   e. $\log_5(3y) + \log_5(9) = \log_5(405)$ f. $\log(x) + \log(x + 21) = 2$

   Check your answers by referring to the Checkpoint 10 materials located at the back of your book.

   If you needed help solving these problems correctly, then you need more practice. Review the Checkpoint 10 materials and try the practice problems. Also, consider getting help outside of class time. From this point on, you will be expected to do problems like these quickly and easily.

10-177. The sum of the digits of a two-digit number is 11, and when the digits are reversed the difference between the new number and the original is 27.

      a.   If you use t to represent the tens digit, and u to represent the units digit, how can you represent one of the numbers?

      b.   How can you represent the number with its digits reversed, still using t and $u?$

      c.   Use the information from the problem and parts (a) and (b) to write two equations that can be used to solve this problem.

      d.   What are the two numbers?

Chapter 10 Closure   What have I learned?

Reflection and Synthesis

The activities below offer you a chance to reflect
about what you have learned during this chapter. As
you work, look for concepts that you feel very
comfortable with, ideas that you would like to learn
more about, and topics you need more help with.
Look for connections between ideas as well as
connections with material you learned previously.

①   TEAM BRAINSTORM

What have you studied in this chapter? What ideas were important in what you
learned? With your team, brainstorm a list. Be as detailed as you can. To help
get you started, a list of Learning Log entries and Math Notes boxes are below.

What topics, ideas, and words that you learned *before* this chapter are connected
to the new ideas in this chapter? Again, be as detailed as you can.

Next consider the Standards for Mathematical Practice that follow "③
PORTFOLIO". What Mathematical Practices did you use in this chapter?
When did you use them? Give specific examples.

How long can you make your list? Challenge yourselves. Be prepared to share
your team's ideas with the class.

Learning Log Entries
- Lesson 10.1.2 – Arithmetic Series
- Lesson 10.2.1 – Geometric Series
- Lesson 10.2.2 – Infinite Geometric Series
- Lesson 10.3.1 – Pascal's Triangle

Math Notes
- Lesson 10.1.1 – Permutations and Combinations
- Lesson 10.1.2 – Series
- Lesson 10.1.3 – Arithmetic Series
- Lesson 10.1.4 – Summation Notation
- Lesson 10.2.2 – Geometric Series
- Lesson 10.3.1 – Binomial Theorem
- Lesson 10.3.2 – Compound Interest

②   MAKING CONNECTIONS

Below is a list of the vocabulary used in this chapter. Make sure that you are familiar with all of these words and know what they mean. Refer to the glossary or index for any words that you do not yet understand.

argument	arithmetic	Binomial Theorem
e	geometric	index
infinite	natural logarithm	Pascal's Triangle
series	sequence	summation notation
sigma		

Make a concept map showing all of the connections you can find among the key words and ideas listed above. To show a connection between two words, draw a line between them and explain the connection. A word can be connected to any other word as long as you can justify the connection. For each key word or idea, provide an example or sketch that shows the idea.

While you are making your map, your team may think of related words or ideas that are not listed here. Be sure to include these ideas on your concept map.

③   PORTFOLIO: EVIDENCE OF MATHEMATICAL PROFICIENCY

This section gives you an opportunity to show growth in your understanding of key mathematical ideas over time as you complete this course.

In this portfolio entry you are going to showcase your current understanding of series. You are also going to showcase your ability to write a meaningful portfolio entry.

Make a list of the big ideas of this chapter. What have you studied in this chapter? What ideas were important in what you learned? Try to keep your list short: limit yourself to the no more than five of the biggest ideas.

a.   Write your own description of each big idea.

b.   For each big idea, provide one or two representative example problems. Solve each problem completely, using multiple representations, if applicable. Include a thorough explanation and justification.

Next, consider the Standards for Mathematical Practice that follow. What Mathematical Practices did you use in this chapter? When did you use them? Give specific examples.

BECOMING MATHEMATICALLY PROFICIENT
The Common Core State Standards For Mathematical Practice

This book focuses on helping you use some very specific Mathematical Practices. The Mathematical Practices describe ways in which mathematically proficient students engage with mathematics everyday.

Make sense of problems and persevere in solving them:

Making sense of problems and persevering in solving them means that you can solve problems that are full of different kinds of mathematics. These types of problems are not routine, simple, or typical. Instead, they combine lots of math ideas and everyday situations. You have to stick with challenging problems, try different strategies, use multiple representations, and use a different method to check your results.

Reason abstractly and quantitatively:

Throughout this course, everyday situations are used to introduce you to new math ideas. Seeing mathematical ideas within a context helps you make sense of the ideas. Once you learn about a math idea in a practical way, you can "**reason abstractly**" by thinking about the concept more generally, representing it with symbols, and manipulating the symbols. **Reasoning quantitatively** is using numbers and symbols to represent an everyday situation, taking into account the units involved, and considering the meaning of the quantities as you compute them.

Construct viable arguments and critique the reasoning of others:

To **construct a viable argument** is to present your solution steps in a logical sequence and to justify your steps with conclusions, relying on number sense, facts and definitions, and previously established results. You communicate clearly, consider the real-life context, and provide clarification when others ask. In this course, you regularly share information, opinions, and expertise with your study team. You **critique the reasoning of others** when you analyze the approach of others, build on each other's ideas, compare the effectiveness of two strategies, and decide what makes sense and under what conditions.

Model with mathematics:

When you **model with mathematics**, you take a complex situation and use mathematics to represent it, often by making assumptions and approximations to simplify the situation. Modeling allows you to analyze and describe the situation and to make predictions. For example, you model when you use multiple representations, including equations, tables, graphs, or diagrams to describe a situation. In situations involving the variability of data, you model when you describe the data with equations. Although a model may not be perfect, it can still be very useful for describing data and making predictions. When you interpret the results, you may need to go back and improve your model by revising your assumptions and approximations.

Core Connections Algebra 2

Use appropriate tools strategically:

To **use appropriate tools strategically** means that you analyze the task and decide which tools may help you model the situation or find a solution. Some of the tools available to you include diagrams, graph paper, calculators, computer software, databases, and websites. You understand the limitations of various tools. A result can be check or estimated by strategically choosing a different tool.

Attend to precision:

To **attend to precision** means that when solving problems, you need to pay close attention to the details. For example, you need to be aware of the units, or how many digits your answer requires, or how to choose a scale and label your graph. You may need to convert the units to be consistent. At times, you need to go back and check whether a numerical solution makes sense in the context of the problem.

You need to **attend to precision** when you communicate your ideas to others. Using the appropriate vocabulary and mathematical language can help make your ideas and reasoning more understandable to others.

Look for and make use of structure:

To **looking for and making use of structure** is a guiding principal of this course. When you are involved in analyzing the structure and in the actual development of mathematical concepts, you gain a deeper, more conceptual understanding than when you are simply told what the structure is and how to do problems. You often use this practice to bring closure to an investigation.

There are many concepts that you learn by looking at the underlying structure of a mathematical idea and thinking about how it connects to other ideas you have already learned. For example, you understand the underlying structure of an equation such as $y = a(x - h)^2 + b$ which allows you to graph it without a table.

Look for and express regularity in repeated reasoning:

To **look for and express regularity in repeated reasoning** means that when you are investigating a new mathematical concept, you notice if calculations are repeated in a pattern. Then you look for a way to generalize the method for use in other situations, or you look for shortcuts. For example, the pattern of growth you notice in a geometric sequence results in being able to write a general exponential equation that highlights the growth and starting point.

WHAT HAVE I LEARNED?

Most of the problems in this section represent typical problems found in this chapter. They serve as a gauge for you. You can use them to determine which types of problems you can do well and which types of problems require further study and practice. Even if your teacher does not assign this section, it is a good idea to try these problems and find out for yourself what you know and what you still need to work on.

Solve each problem as completely as you can. The table at the end of the closure section has answers to these problems. It also tells you where you can find additional help and practice with problems like these.

CL 10-178. Find the sum of each series.

  a. $11 + 12 + 13 + ... + 40$

  b. $90 + 84 + 78 + ... + 24$

CL 10-179. For the series $3 + 3.3 + 3.6 + 3.9 + 4.2 + ... + 63$:

  a.   How many terms are there?

  b.   What is the sum of the series?

CL 10-180. From the ground, a rubber ball is thrown 20 feet into the air. If its rebound ratio is $\frac{7}{10}$, how far will it have traveled during the first five bounces?

CL 10-181. Write each series using summation ($\sum$) notation.

  a. $3 + 6 + 9 + 12 + ... + 30$

  b. $-7 + -4 + -1 + 2 + 5 + 8 + 11$

CL 10-182. Consider the series $\sum\limits_{n=0}^{\infty} 4\left(-\frac{2}{3}\right)^n$.

  a.   Is it arithmetic or geometric? Explain.

  b.   Does it have a finite sum? Explain.

  c.   If it has a sum, find it.

CL 10-183. Nitrous oxide, or NO_x, is a pollutant created by diesel engines that occurs when nitrogen and oxygen from the atmosphere are combined by the heat of the burning fuel. The EPA and many states limit the amount of NO_x a vehicle is permitted to produce. Assume that diesel cars and trucks on the road produce NO_x according to a normal distribution with a mean of 0.12 g/mile and a standard deviation of 0.04 g/mile. Imagine your state is lowering its limits of NO_x allowed over a 10-year time period.

    a.   If the 2015 limit for NO_x is 0.100 g/mile, what proportion of diesel engines running today meet that standard?

    b.   If the 2020 limit for NO_x is 0.065 g/mile, what proportion of diesel engines running today meet that standard?

    c.   Now think of things the other way. If the 2025 limit for NO_x is 0.030 g/mile, what proportion of diesel engines running today *would not* meet that standard?

CL 10-184. NBP Model 760 photocopiers print a mean of 76 pages per minute (ppm) with a standard deviation of 11 ppm. NBP Model S22 can scan 50 ppm with a standard deviation of 5 ppm. A software upgrade was tested on both models. After the upgrade, a prototype photocopier makes 90 copies per minute, while a prototype scanner makes 57 scans. Use percentiles to determine on which machine the upgrade had a bigger impact on performance.

CL 10-185. Part one of the final exam for Algebra 2 contains 10 questions and you get to choose any eight to answer.

    a.   How many different ways could you choose the eight problems?

    b.   If everyone must answer the first two questions, how many ways could you choose the remaining problems?

CL 10-186. Use the pattern for $(a+b)^4$ to expand $(2m + \frac{1}{m})^4$.

CL 10-187. What term of $(a-b)^8$ contains a^5? What is the whole term?

CL 10-188. Solve each of the following equations, accurate to the nearest 0.001.

    a. $1.8^x = 10$ b. $\log_2 x = 6$

CL 10-189. Find an equation of the parabola that passes through (2, 11), (−1, −4), and (0, −5).

CL 10-190. Sketch a graph of each of the following functions.

    a. $f(x) = \frac{2}{x-1} + 3$ b. $g(x) = -0.5(x+2)^3 - 3$

    c. $h(x) = |x+5| - 4$ d. $k(x) = 2\sqrt{x+1} + 3$

CL 10-191. Find the equation of the exponential function (with an asymptote of $y = 0$) that passes through the points (−3, 375) and (2, 0.12).

CL 10-192. Check your answers using the table at the end of this section. Which problems do you feel confident about? Which problems were hard? Have you worked on problems like these in math classes you have taken before? Use the table to make a list of topics you need help on and a list of topics you need to practice more.

Answers and Support for Closure Activity #4
What Have I Learned?

Note: MN = Math Note, LL = Learning Log

Problem	Solutions		Need Help?	More Practice
CL 10-178.	a. 765	b. 684	Section 10.1 MN: 10.1.2 and 10.1.3 LL: 10.1.2	Problems 10-17, 10-34, 10-35, 10-49, 10-63, and 10-89
CL 10-179.	a. 201	b. 6633	Lesson 10.1.1 MN: 10.1.2 and 10.1.3 LL: 10.1.2	Problems 10-17, 10-34, 10-35, 10-49, 10-62, and 10-89
CL 10-180.	110.924 feet		Section 10.2 MN: 10.2.2 LL: 10.2.1	Problems 10-87, 10-96, 10-105, 10-126, 10-147, and 10-156

Problem	Solutions	Need Help?	More Practice
CL 10-181.	a. $\displaystyle\sum_{n=1}^{10}(3n)$ b. $\displaystyle\sum_{n=1}^{7}(3n-10)$	Lesson 10.1.4 MN: 10.1.4	Problems 10-62 and 10-87 part (c)
CL 10-182.	a. Geometric, $r = -\frac{2}{3}$ b. Yes, $|r| < 1$ c. $\frac{12}{5}$	Section 10.1 and 10.2 MN: 10.1.4 and 10.2.2 LL: 10.1.2, 10.2.1, and 10.2.2	Problems 10-89, 10-90, 10-117, 10-126, and 10-148
CL 10-183.	a. normcdf(−10^99, 0.1, 0.12, 0.04) = 0.309 About thirty one percent would meet the standard. b. normcdf(−10^99, 0.065, 0.12, 0.04) = 0.0846 Only about eight percent would meet the standard. c. normcdf(0.03, 10^99, 0.12, 0.04) = 0.988 About ninety nine percent would not meet the standard.	Lesson 9.3.2 MN: 9.3.2 LL: 9.3.2	Problems 9-88, 9-105, 10-12, 10-41, 10-67, and 10-152
CL 10-184.	Photocopier: (normalcdf (−10^99, 90, 76, 11) = 89.8 percentile Scanner: normalcdf(−10^99, 90, 76, 11) = 91.9 percentile The scanner had better performance in relation to its population.	Lesson 9.3.2 MN: 9.3.2 LL: 9.3.2	Problems 9-88, 9-105, 10-12, 10-41, 10-67, and 10-152
CL 10-185.	a. $_{10}C_8 = 45$ b. $_8C_6 = 28$	MN: 10.1.1	Problems 10-20, 10-21, 10-36, 10-37, 10-52, 10-66, 10-91, 10-118, and 10-127

Problem	Solutions	Need Help?	More Practice
CL 10-186.	$16m^4 + 32m^2 + 24 + \frac{8}{m^2} + \frac{1}{m^4}$	Lesson 10.3.1 MN: 10.3.1 LL: 10.3.1	Problems 10-145, 10-146, 10-157, and 10-175
CL 10-187.	$-56a^5b^3$	Lesson 10.3.1 MN: 10.3.1 LL: 10.3.1	Problems 10-146 and 10-155
CL 10-188.	a. $x \approx 3.917$ b. $x = 64$	Lessons 6.2.1 and 6.2.2 Checkpoint 10	Problems CL 6-151, 7-94, 7-149, 10-23, 10-56, 10-95, 10-103, and 10-176
CL 10-189.	$y = 3x^2 + 2x - 5$	Lesson 6.1.5 LL: 6.1.5	Problems CL 6-150, 7-7, 10-154, and 10-163
CL 10-190.	a. b. c. d.	Lesson 2.2.1 MN: 2.2.3 Parent Graph Toolkit	Problems CL 2-171, and 7-58, 8-107, and 10-11
CL 10-191.	$y = 3 \cdot (\frac{1}{5})^x$	Lesson B.2.1, B.2.2, and 6.2.3	Problems CL B-110 and CL 7-175

Chapter 11 Simulating Sampling Variability

In this chapter, you will use computer simulations to model complex probabilities—probabilities that are often too difficult to compute mathematically. Then you will simulate sample-to-sample variability. Your knowledge of sample-to-sample variability will help you place a margin of error on your predictions about certain characteristics of populations and will help you make statistical decisions.

Guiding Question

Mathematically proficient students model with mathematics.

As you work through this chapter, ask yourself:

How can I model this situation with a simulation in order to understand it better and to solve the problem?

Chapter Outline

Section 11.1 You will perform simulations to determine complex probabilities. Then you will use simulations to determine sample-to-sample variability. You will use the variability to put a margin of error on characteristics you predict about a population.

Section 11.2 You will use what you know about sample-to-sample variability and margin of error to conduct a statistical hypothesis test. You will observe the effect of sample size on sample-to-sample variability. Then you will use a hypothesis test to determine whether two results in an experiment are truly different. Finally, you will learn how statistics are used in quality control and process control in manufacturing.

Section 11.3 You will evaluate decisions and strategies based on area or models of probability. You will use probability to solve problems whose solutions are counterintuitive.

11.1.1 How can I estimate complex probabilities?

Simulations of Probability

If you toss a coin ten times, what is the probability of having a run of three or more "heads" in a row?

If an airline "overbooks" a certain flight, what is the chance more passengers show up than the airplane has seats for?

When 67 people get cancer in the 250 homes in a small town, could that be chance alone, or is polluted well water a more likely explanation of the cluster of cancer cases?

When the mathematics becomes too complex to figure out the theoretical probability of certain events, statisticians often use **simulations** instead. Simulations can also be used to check statistical computations, or they can be used in place of a study that is too expensive, time-consuming, or unethical. A simulation is a model—often computer-based—that uses the probabilities of a real-life situation.

All simulations require random numbers. Random numbers have no pattern; they cannot be predicted in any way. Knowing one random number in no way allows you to predict the next random number.

Complex simulations, such as those that model the weather, traffic patterns, cancer radiation therapy, or stock market swings, require tens of billions of random numbers and a large computer that runs for hours or even days. However, many simpler simulations can be done with graphing calculators.

As you work with your team today, consider the following questions:

How can we set up a simulation for this situation?

How many trials are sufficient?

How can we compute the theoretical probability?

11-1.   A GIRL OR ALL BOYS?

Mr. and Mrs. Sittman want to have children and would love to have a girl, but they don't want to have more than four children. They want to figure out the chances of having a girl if they have children until they have a girl, or until they have four children, whichever comes first. Since a coin has a 50% chance of landing on "heads," a coin can be used to model the real-life probability that a girl is born.

   a.   Talk with your team about how you can use flipping a coin to determine the probability of a couple having a daughter if they try until the first girl or the fourth child is born, whichever comes first.

   b.   Once your class has planned the simulation and found a method for tallying results, run the simulation and tally the results until your team has modeled 25 possible families (25 trials).

   c.   Combine your results with those of rest of the class. According to your class's simulation, what is the couple's probability of having a girl in this situation?

11-2.   In the simulation for problem 11-1, do you think that more trials would lead to a better estimate of the probability? Tossing coins can become tedious, but we can use a calculator or computer to complete many more trials.

   a.   Your teacher will show you how to use your calculator to randomly generate a family of four children. You can use "0" to represent a boy, and "1" to represent a girl. Since they will stop having children after their first girl, you can ignore all the digits in the family after the first girl. For example, "0101" would represent a family with one boy and one girl, and you would mark "Girl in Family" on the tally sheet.

   b.   Be prepared to share your team results with the rest of the class. Use the class results to estimate the probability of a couple having a girl if they try until they have a girl, or until they have four children, whichever comes first. Do you think this result is a better estimate of the theoretical probability than the result in problem 11-1? Why or why not?

11-3.   For the situation you simulated in problems 11-1 and 11-2, the theoretical probability is not too complicated to work out. Work with your team to calculate the theoretical probability for the problem posed by Mr. and Mrs. Sittman in problem 11-1.

11-4.   According to a mathematical principal known as the **Law of Large Numbers**, the more times you run your simulation, the closer your result will come to the theoretical value. Was this what happened when you compared results from problem 11-1 with problem 11-2? Were you close to the expected theoretical value from problem 11-3?

METHODS AND MEANINGS

MATH NOTES

Area Models for Probability

One way to represent the probabilities that two independent events occur is with an area model. In this type of model, the situation is represented by a square with area of 1. The areas of the parts are the probabilities of the different events that occur.

For example, Mrs. Pimentel goes to a lot of charity events where she needs to dress up. The probabilities she will wear either her red dress or her black dress, with a certain piece of jewelry, are represented by the table at right.

		dress	
		red	black
		0.40	0.60
jewelry	pearls 0.70	0.28	0.42
	diamond 0.20	0.08	0.12
	pendant 0.10	0.04	0.06

Notice that the length and width of the area model table are both 1 (0.40 + 0.60 = 1 and 0.70 + 0.20 + 0.10 = 1). The area of the model is 1. The area of any one of the parts is its length × width. For example, the area of the black-dress-with-diamonds rectangle is $0.60 \cdot 0.20 = 0.12$. The probability that Mrs. Pimentel will wear the black dress and the diamonds is 12%.

A conditional probability means that we know that some event has occurred with certainty, and therefore we look only at that portion of the table. For example, what is the conditional probability Mrs. Pimentel will wear diamonds given that she is wearing the red dress? Since we know with certainty that she is wearing the red dress, we will consider only the red-dress column and ignore the black dress column completely. The conditional probability is calculated using P(diamonds with red dress)/P(red dress). The conditional probability she wears diamonds given that she wears a red dress is $\frac{0.08}{0.28+0.08+0.04} = 0.20$.

11-5.　Consider each of the survey questions below. Decide whether any bias may be influencing the survey results.

　　a.　Jolly Juice has twice the Vitamin E of other brands. Which brand of juice is the healthiest?

　　b.　Do you think that people who hurt defenseless animals should be punished?

　　c.　Do you agree that Hal Poppington is the best man to be elected Mayor?

　　d.　What is your favorite kind of juice?

11-6.　In problem 9-8 Katelyn recorded the number of cups of coffee sold at her coffee shop each hour during a 48-hour time period.

Katelyn then sorted the data and made the following histogram:

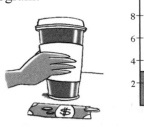

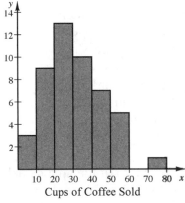

Cups of Coffee Sold

Cups of Coffee Sold		
1	22	37
5	22	38
7	23	38
12	24	40
12	25	41
12	26	41
12	26	42
12	29	47
14	29	47
16	30	49
17	30	51
19	31	52
20	32	55
21	33	55
21	35	59
22	36	76
checksum 1444		

　　a.　Katelyn decides to model her sales with a normal distribution, but Duncan thinks that this is not a good idea. What advice would you give Katelyn about using a normal model?

　　b.　Katelyn needs to sell more than 15 cups per hour to make a profit. What percentile is 15 cups per hour? Explain the percentile to Katelyn in terms of profits.

　　c.　Duncan thinks Katelyn should expand her business. He estimates that if they hire another server and add more tables and equipment, they will need to sell 48 cups per hour to make a profit. What percentile does 48 cups sold represent? Use the percentile to explain to Duncan whether or not expansion is a good idea.

11-7.   Coach Kenadt has 12 players on his basketball team and needs to select one player to be the team representative to the athletic student council. He wants the selection to be fair, meaning each player has an equal chance of being selected. Rummaging through his gym bag, he finds a single six-sided die and a nickel. How could he use the nickel and die to select the team representative fairly?

11-8.   Eeeeew! Hannah's volleyball teammates left their egg salad sandwiches sitting in their lockers over the weekend. When they got back on Monday, the sandwiches were moldy. *"Perfect!"* said Hannah. *"I can use these sandwiches for my biology project. I'll study how quickly mold grows."*

Using a transparent grid, Hannah estimated that about 12% of the surface of one sandwich had mold on it. She threw the sandwich out. For the rest of the week, Hannah came back when she had time. Each time she measured somebody else's sandwich and threw it out. She collected the following data:

Day 1 (Monday)	Day 2 (Tuesday)	Day 2 (Tuesday)	Day 4 (Thursday)	Day 4 (Thursday)	Day 4 (Thursday)	Day 5 (Friday)
12%	15%	13%	26%	27%	24%	38%

a.   Create a scatterplot and sketch it. Is a linear model reasonable?

b.   Based on the story, what kind of equation do you think will best fit the situation?

c.   Fit an exponential model to the data and write the equation. What percentage of a sandwich did Hannah predict was covered on Wednesday? Consider the precision of Hannah's measurements when deciding how many decimal places to use in your answer.

11-9.   Consider the function $f(x) = e^x$.

a.   What is its inverse function, $f^{-1}(x)$?

b.   Investigate $f(x)$ and $f^{-1}(x)$.

c.   For what integer values of n is the graph of $f^{-1}(x)$ between the graphs of $y = \log_n x$ and $y = \log_{n+1} x$?

d.   For what values of x is the graph of $f^{-1}(x)$ above each of the graphs in your answer to part (c)? For what x-values is it below?

11-10.   Natural logs and exponential functions with base *e* are often used in formulas. But many problems can be solved equally well using either a base-10 logarithm or a base-*e* logarithm. Solve each of the following problems, first using the LOG key (base 10) and then using the LN key (base *e*) on your calculator.

      a. $10{,}000(1.08)^x = 20{,}000$

      b. $30{,}000(0.8)^x = 15{,}000$

      c.   Interpret the answer for part (a) if the equation represents an amount of money invested at 8% annual interest.

      d.   Interpret the answer for part (b) if the equation represents the price paid for a car that depreciates at 20% per year.

11-11.   Find the sum of the integers $-10 + -9 + -8 + ... + 40$.

11-12.   Compute each complex product.

      a. $(1+i)^2$ b. $(1+i)^3$

11-13.   75% of the homes in a small town in England have large backyards, and 80% have garages. Assume that having a garage is independent of whether you have a large backyard.

      a.   What is the probability a home has neither a garage nor a large backyard? Decide what the two variables in this situation are and make an area model to help answer the question. (See the Math Notes box in this lesson.)

      b.   Given that a house has a garage, what is the conditional probability it has a large backyard?

11.1.2 How many in a streak?

More Simulations of Probability

The serious study of probability started when two mathematicians, Blaise Pascal and Pierre de Fermat, became interested in determining probabilities for casino games, particularly dice games. Roulette is one of the more straightforward casino games to analyze, and it provides a good opportunity for examining streaks.

In American roulette the bettor places a bet, then the croupier (game manager) spins the wheel and drops the ball. Everyone waits for the ball to land in one of 38 slots. The 38 slots on the wheel are numbered 00, 0, 1, 2, 3, ..., 36. Eighteen of the slots are colored red and eighteen are black; 0 and 00 are green.

Before the ball is dropped, players make bets by placing their chips on the roulette layout (the region that has the numbers and their colors printed on it). One of the most popular bets is that the ball will drop into a red or a black slot on the wheel.

11-14.   Players who watch play, and then make a bet are called "lurkers." A commonly held belief among "lurkers" is that once they see the ball land on red three times in a row, they should join the game and bet a lot on the black (or vice versa). What do you think? Discuss this with your team. Be prepared so share your ideas with the rest of the class.

11-15.   The new owner of the One-Eyed Jack Casino wanted to test the two roulette wheels that were included in the purchase. There were rumors that some of the games were rigged under the old ownership. He decided to watch each of the wheels for 200 spins and record whether red or black came up. He chose to ignore the green slots; if green came up, he just spun again.

Problem continues on next page →

11-15.   *Problem continued from previous page.*

Roulette Wheel I: RBRRRRBBRBRBRBRRRRBBRBRBBBBBBBBBRBRBRBBBR
BBBRRBBRBRBBBBBRBBRBBRRBRBRBRRRRRBBRBRB
RBRRRBRRRRBBRRRRBRRRRBRRRRBBBRBRBBRRRBRR
RBRRBBRBBBRBBBBBRBBBRRBBBRBBRRRRRRRBRRRB
RRRBRRBRRRBRRBBBBRBBBBRRRBRRRRRRRBBRBRRRBB

Roulette Wheel II: RBRBRRRBRRRRBBRBRRRBRRBBBRBBRBRBRBRRRRBB
RRBBRRBBBRBBBRRBBBRRBBBBRBBBBRRRBRBRBBBB
RBRRBBBRBBRBRRRBBRBBBBRBBBBRRBRBBRBBBRRRB
RBBBRBBBRRRBBBRRRBBBBRBRBBBBBRBRRBBRRRRBRB
RBRRBRBBRRBRRRBRRRRBBBBRBRBBBBRRBBRBBBRBBR

Discussion Points

How many streaks are likely in 200 spins?

How long will streaks be?

How can we set up a computer simulation for a roulette wheel?

What do the results of the simulation tell us about the casino owner's results?

Your Task: Run a simulation of 200 spins of a roulette wheel. Use the results of your simulation to justify whether either wheel is rigged. If a wheel were rigged, would that be advantageous to the One-Eyed Jack Casino? Write up a brief report explaining your results and what they imply about his roulette wheels.

Further Guidance

11-16.   You will investigate how many streaks of red and black numbers occur randomly when the game is played 200 times.

a.   Use the results to make a conjecture: which roulette wheel, if either, is rigged in some way? Explain why you think so.

b.   Work with a partner to set up and run a simulation of 200 spins of a roulette wheel. Record the color of each spin — red or black — in order.

c.   How many streaks of five or more reds or five or more blacks did you get? Compare with your team and other classmates.

d.   Which wheel might have been rigged?

e.   Would it be to the advantage of the owner of the One-Eyed Jack Casino to leave it that way?

f.   Write up your results in a report to the casino owner.

————————   *Further Guidance*   ————————
section ends here.

11-17.   Katelyn is going to be babysitting her nephew a lot this summer. She has the great idea that one way to entertain him is to walk to McBurger's for a Kids' Meal for lunch. The Kids' Meal comes packed randomly with one of six equally-likely action figures. Katelyn is worried that her nephew will be disappointed unless he gets all six figures. She wants to know how many meals she can expect to buy before he will get all six figures.

a.   Model the action figures with the digits 1 through 6. Simulate a large number of meals (such as 200) and put the results into a list. How many meals did you have to buy in order to get all six action figures?

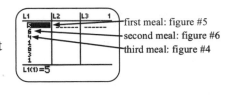

b.   Run your simulation ten more times, each time generating a new list of about 200 meals. Keep track of how many Kid's Meals it takes to get all six action figures. Calculate your **wait time**, or the average number of meals it took to get all six figures.

c.   Combine your results with those of your team. On average, how many Kid's Meals do you think you need to buy in order to get all six action figures?

d.   Estimate a range for the number of meals you might need to buy. What is the most you need to buy? The least? Do you think it possible that you may have to buy 50 meals to get all six action figures? 100 meals?

11-18.   Myriah hates doing the dishes, but her parents insist that she must help out and take a turn sometimes. Since Myriah wants to leave whether or not she will have to do the dishes to chance, her mom proposes that they roll two dice. If the sum of the dice is 6 or less, Myriah will do the dishes. If the sum is 7 or more, one of her parents will do the dishes.

How many days each week can Myriah expect to have to do the dishes? Create a simulation of rolling the two dice (generate two random integers between 1 and 6) and record the sum. Run the simulation 30 times to determine how often Myriah can expect to do the dishes.

11-19.   Calculate the theoretical probability that Myriah will have to wash the dishes.

11-20. The term "curving" is often misused as it applies to test scores. Many believe it refers to adding points or otherwise adjusting test scores such that the highest paper is 100% or the average score is raised to some passing level. To curve is actually to model test scores with the normal distribution (normal "curve") and then use percentiles to assign letter grades.

a. A "curve" sometimes used is shown below:

Grade	D	C	B	A
Number of Standard Deviations Above or Below Mean	−2	−1	+1	+2
Minimum Percentile	2nd	16th	84th	98th

Using this curve, what percentage of students would earn each letter grade?

b. The following statistics are from problem 9-98, the test scores on Mrs. Abraha's Chapter 11 test in Geometry. The mean was 76.5, and the standard deviation was 17.4.

If Mrs. Abraha used the curve in part (a), the minimum score for a B would be one standard deviation above the mean, or 92.9. What would be the minimum test scores for the other letter grades on Mrs. Abraha's test?

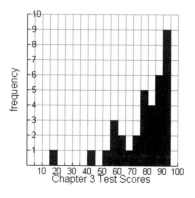

c. Shown at right is a histogram of the scores from Mrs. Abraha's Chapter 11 test in Geometry. Is using the curve from part (a) reasonable to assign letter grades? What advice would you give students who want the test "curved"?

11-21. Using the given population and assuming your math class is a sample from that population, come up with a research question that could be asked to determine parameters from the given population. Write each survey question and what you are hoping to show from each question. Examples are given for each population.

a. Population: Students at my school

Example:

I would ask my math class this survey question: *If the school library were open at 7:15 a.m., would you use it at least once per week?*

The research question I am trying to answer is: *How many students at our school would take advantage of extended library hours?*

Problem continues on next page →

Core Connections Algebra 2

11-21.   *Problem continued from previous page.*

    b.   Population: All high school math students in the U.S.

Example:

I would ask my math class this survey question:

The main reason I'm taking this class is:
1) It is a graduation requirement.   *2) It is a college prerequisite.*
3) My parents are making me.   *4) I'm interested in math.*
5) For some other reason.

The research question I am trying to answer is: *Why do high school students take math?*

    c.   Population: U.S. teenagers

Example:

I would ask my math class this survey question: *How far is it from where you live to school or work?*

The research question I am trying to answer is: *What is the average commute distance to school or work for teenagers?*

11-22.   Solve each system of equations below.

    a. $x - 2y = 7$
          $2x + y = 3$

    b. $\dfrac{x+4y}{3} - \dfrac{6y-x}{4} = -3$
          $\dfrac{x}{10} + 5y = 2$

11-23.   Find the infinite sum (if possible).

    a. $6 + 3 + \frac{3}{2} + \ldots$

    b. $\displaystyle\sum_{k=1}^{\infty} \left(\frac{1}{3}\right)^k$

11-24.   Eddie told Allison, *"I'll bet if I flip three coins, I can get exactly two heads."*
Allison replied, *"I'll bet I can get exactly two heads if I flip four coins!"*
Eddie scoffed, *"Well, so what? That's easier."*
Allison argued, *"No, it's not. It's harder."*

Who is correct? Show all of your work and be prepared to defend your conclusion.

11-25.   Given $\ln 2 \approx 0.69315$ and $\ln 3 \approx 1.0986$, why is $\ln 2 < 1$ and $\ln 3 > 1$? For what value of x does $\ln x = 1$?

11-26.   Use the values for $\ln 2$ and $\ln 3$ given in problem 11-25 to evaluate each of the following expressions. Do not use a calculator.

a. $\ln 6$ b. $\ln 12$ c. $\ln 16$ d. $\ln \frac{1}{3}$

11.1.3 How much do samples vary?

Simulating Sampling Variability

In Chapter 9 you developed the idea that if a sample is selected randomly, taking care to avoid bias, we can be confident that the sample represents the whole population. Making inferences from samples about whole populations is at the heart of statistics.

Your friend Ramien says that you have to have the latest, hottest πPhone—everybody else already has it! What proportion of young people have the πPhone? We cannot possibly ask everybody in the United States who is between the ages of 12 and 20, but we can take a random sample of this population and calculate the proportion that have the phone.

If in a random sample of 1000 members of our population, 250 have the πPhone, it still does not mean that exactly $\frac{1}{4}$ of all people between the ages of 12 and 20 in the U.S. have the πPhone. The proportion of young people with the phone will naturally vary from sample to sample—some samples of young people will have more phones, some will have less.

If we knew how much the proportion naturally varied from sample-to-sample, we could establish a range of estimates for the proportion of phones in the teen population. This **margin of error** is frequently reported in statistical studies. You might read in a newspaper that the percentage of teens with πPhones is 23% with a margin of error of 3%. This means that statisticians can be reasonably certain, based on their small sample, that between 20% and 26% of all teens own the πPhone.

As you work with your team on today's investigation, keep the following discussion questions in mind:

Why do we give a margin of error?

How certain are statisticians when they give a margin of error?

How do statisticians decide on a margin of error?

11-27.   WERE THERE ENOUGH BLUE ONES?

Abigail is eagerly looking forward to Friday,
when each student in her fifth grade class has
been promised a bag of candy-coated chocolates
as a reward for figuring out the percentages of the
different colors. Abigail loves the blue ones.

What proportion of candy-coated chocolates are blue? We
cannot just open one bag and count, because the number of blue
candies will vary naturally from bag to bag.

Since we cannot count every candy in the world, we can take a
sample. We are assuming a bag of candy-coated chocolates makes a reasonable
sample that represents the whole population. We will investigate how much the
proportion of blue candies naturally varies from bag to bag.

a.   Get a sample from your teacher. Calculate the proportion of blue candies
in your sample. Write your answer as a decimal and share it with the
class.

b.   Use your calculator to make a histogram of all the proportions of blue
candies your classmates found in each of their samples. A histogram that
shows the results of taking many samples is called a **sampling
distribution**. Sketch the histogram.

c.   What is the mean proportion for the whole class? This gives an estimate
of the proportion of blue candies in the population.

d.   We are interested in typical results, not the extreme ones. We will call the
middle 90% typical. Between what upper and lower bounds are the
middle 90% of the blue proportions? That is, 90% of the time, we expect
the proportion of blue candies in the sample to be between _____ and _____.

e.   Tell Abigail your prediction of the proportion of blue candies in the whole
population and give the **margin of error**. The margin of error is half the
spread between the upper and lower bounds.

11-28. **HOW MANY GAMES IN A WORLD SERIES?**

In baseball's World Series, the first team to win four games wins the championship. The series might last four, five, six, or seven games. A fan who buys tickets would like to know how many games, on average, he can expect a championship series to last. Assume the two teams are equally matched, and set aside such potentially confounding factors as the advantage of playing at home. We want to know the expected value for the number of games that will be played in the World Series.

   a. Simulate a World Series on your calculator or computer. Let a "**1**" represent Team 1 winning a game, and a "**2**" represent Team 2 winning. You will simulate seven "games," but as soon as one team wins four games the World Series is over and you have to ignore any results that follow that. See below for an example.

Record how many games it took to win the series. In the example at right, it took 5 games.

first two games won by Team 1
third game won by Team 2
Team 1 wins Series

ignore

Repeat the simulation at least 25 times.
Each time, record the number of games it took to win the World Series. You do not care *which team* won, you only care *how long* the series took.

   b. Based on your simulation, what is the average number of games a World Series lasts?

11-29. Sports announcers frequently get excited when basketball players make several free throw shots in a row. They say things like "He's on a hot streak tonight!" or "He's really in the zone—what an amazing performance!" Are these "hot" streaks really special, or are they just a natural run to be expected by probability? Assume a basketball player has a 50% free throw average, and a typical game has 20 free throw attempts. Use your calculator to set up a simulation for 20 free throws.

   a. Run the simulation 25 times, and each time record the length of the longest streak.

   b. How long would a streak have to be before you considered it unusual?

11-30. A music company wants to know the music preference of people in Cleveland. Their surveyor asks people who are walking out of a business office building, "What is your favorite type of music?" What kind of problems may arise that will not produce accurate results? (List as many problems as you can.)

11-31. Solve the following systems of equations and describe the shapes of the intersections.

a. $z^2 = x^2 + y^2$ b. $z^2 = x^2 + y^2$
   $z = x + 2$ $z = 7$

11-32. For the sequence $0.52, 0.55, 0.58, ..., 2.02$:

a. How many terms are there?

b. What is the sum of the associated series?

11-33. What do you notice about the two problems below when you simplify them?

a. $\frac{x^{1/2}}{x^{-3/2}}$ b. $\sqrt{x} \div (\frac{1}{\sqrt{x}})^3$

11-34. Given the points A $(3, 2)$ and B $(-21, 0)$, determine each of the following.

a. The slope of the line $\overrightarrow{AB}$.   b. The length of $\overline{AB}$.

c. The midpoint of $\overline{AB}$.   d. An equation of $\overrightarrow{AB}$.

11-35.   Solve each ratio problem below for x.

      a.   Forty-two percent of x is 112.

      b.   Forty-two is x percent of 112.

      c.   Twenty-seven is x percent of 100.

      d.   Twenty-seven percent of 500 is x.

11-36.   In the casino game of roulette, some players think that when the ball lands on red several times in a row that it will be more likely to land on black on the next spin. You can calculate probabilities to demonstrate that this is not the case. In other words, the outcome of one spin of a roulette wheel does not have any effect on the outcome of the next one.

      a.   Make an area model for two spins of the wheel. Remember that there are 18 red numbers, 18 black numbers, and two greens.

      b.   What is the probability that the ball will land on red twice in a row?

      c.   Based on your diagram, what is the probability that the ball will land on red on the second spin?

      d.   Calculate the conditional probability that the first spin was red given that the second spin is red.

      e.   How do your answers to parts (c) and (d) compare to the simple probability of the ball landing on red for any single spin? If they are all the same, you have demonstrated that the probability of the ball landing on red is independent of where it landed before.

11.2.1 Can I make a decision based on my sample?

±10%

· ·

Statistical Test Using Sampling Variability

In Lesson 11.1.3 you used a sample to determine what the population value is within a margin of error, and simulation to predict the sample-to-sample variability. In future courses, you will use mathematical theory (based on the normal distribution) to predict the population and margin of error from a sample.

Today, you will take what you know about sample-to-sample variability and margin of error and conduct a **hypothesis test**. A claim will be made about the population, and we will use a sample to test whether there is convincing evidence for the claim.

Then you will consider how a difference in sample size can affect how much the means of the samples may vary.

As you work, think about the following questions:

How large should the sample be?

How could the size of the sample affect our conclusions?

Do we have convincing evidence?

11-37. The principal of Algieres High School cancelled the Winter Formal dance because he believed that students preferred an all-school trip to an amusement park during spring break. However, he told the student council that if they could convince him that more than 50% of the school preferred the Winter Formal, he would reinstate it.

The student council decided that they should select a random sample of students to respond to a survey, but they disagreed about how large the sample should be. Some thought they should ask at least 100 students, but others thought that 25 would be enough. For convenience, they decided to randomly survey 25 students. It turned out that 60% preferred to keep the dance.

Unfortunately, the principal was not convinced. He said that because of natural sample-to-sample variability, the true proportion of dance supporters might not be more than 50%.

Problem continues on next page →

11-37.   *Problem continued from previous page.*

    a.   To investigate the sample-to-sample variability of a survey that concludes 60% of students support the dance, work with a partner to set up a calculator or computer simulation. You could generate a sample of 25 random numbers between 1 and 100. Numbers from 1 to 60 can represent a student who supports the dance, while the numbers from 61 to 100 represent students who do not support the dance.

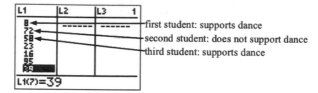

        Because of natural sample-to-sample variability, the proportion of students who support the dance in your random sample is probably not exactly 0.60. What proportion of students in your sample supported the dance?

    b.   Each team member should repeat the simulation with 5 more trials and record the proportion of dance supporters each time.

    c.   If you were to combine your proportions with those of your classmates, what do you suppose the mean of all the samples would be close to? Why?

    d.   For the whole class, what are the lower and upper 5% bounds of your sample-to-sample variability?

    e.   Predict the proportion of all the students at Algieres High that support the dance and give the margin of error.

11-38.   In the previous problem, a claim was made about the student population: more than 50% support the dance. To test that claim (to find evidence to support the claim), a sample was taken from the student population, and the sample-to-sample variability was considered. This procedure is called a **hypothesis test**.

Based on your results for problem 11-37, does the principal have convincing evidence that more than 50% of all the students support the dance?

11-39.   When the student council at Algieres High presented their results, the principal was not convinced that at least 50% supported the dance. However, the council is still determined to persuade him otherwise, so they have called an emergency meeting. They have agreed that they should survey a larger sample of 100 students.

a. Why would the student council want to survey more students?

b. Do you think the margin of error for a sample of 100 students will be larger or smaller than for the samples of 25? Discuss this with your team.

c. With a partner, set up and run another simulation for 100 students. Assume that the student council finds the same 60% support for the dance in this larger sample. Record the results for 5 trials.

d. Share your results from part (c) with the rest of the class and use the data to compute the lower and upper 5% bounds for the class data. Report the margin of error.

e. Do you think this new evidence will convince the principal? Explain how you will make the case for or against the student council.

11-40.   LEARNING LOG

Create a Learning Log entry titled "Sample-to-Sample Variability" and label it with today's date. Discuss the pros and cons of larger or smaller samples. Explain why the margin of error might lead the principal in problem 11-37 to reject the first study even though he was convinced it was not biased and it reported that more than 50% of the students said they supported the dance.

METHODS AND MEANINGS

Sample-to-Sample Variability

MATH NOTES

We take samples to learn about a population when it is too time-consuming, expensive, or impractical to study the whole. Even if we are very careful to avoid bias so that our sample represents the whole population, statistics (measurements) vary naturally from sample to sample. To make an inference about the population, we need to quantify this **sample-to-sample variability**. With this knowledge, we can state a margin of error for our prediction of the true parameters of the whole population.

In Lesson 11.1.3, Abigail wanted an estimate of the proportion of blue candy-coated chocolates in the population of all candies. One sample (one bag) was not very much information due to natural sample-to-sample variability. Since taking many samples is often not practical, computer simulations, like the one conducted in this lesson, are one way to estimate the sample-to-sample variability. In future courses, you will learn theoretical ways to predict sample-to-sample variability based on the normal distribution.

Review & Preview

11-41.   It's bad enough when Myriah has to do the dishes. But Myriah really hates doing the dishes several days in a row! Myriah and her mom have agreed to roll two dice. When the sum of the dice is 6 or less, Myriah has to do the dishes. If the sum is 7 or more, one of her parents does the dishes. Myriah wants to know how many times in the next two months she will end up doing the dishes 3 or more days in a row.

   a.   Run a simulation of rolling the two dice and record the sum of each roll to simulate the 60 days (2 months).

   b.   How often can Myriah expect to have to do the dishes 3 or more days in a row during two months?

Core Connections Algebra 2

11-42.   The Bright Idea Lighting Company wants to determine what proportion of LED flashlights that come off of its assembly line are defective. It takes many samples of 100 flashlights over the week and determines the proportion that are defective in each sample. The results of their tests as shown below:

Proportion of defective flashlights in 100 samples.				
0.09	0.05	0.05	0.05	0.09
0.07	0.06	0.10	0.07	0.09
0.08	0.09	0.05	0.05	0.08
0.07	0.07	0.08	0.08	0.09
0.10	0.08	0.11	0.08	0.09
0.09	0.13	0.08	0.09	0.09
0.07	0.06	0.06	0.08	0.08
0.06	0.10	0.11	0.09	0.09
0.05	0.07	0.05	0.09	0.10
0.04	0.07	0.09	0.08	0.06
0.08	0.09	0.06	0.06	0.07
0.08	0.08	0.08	0.09	0.09
0.10	0.07	0.09	0.08	0.12
0.12	0.09	0.06	0.05	0.02
0.11	0.05	0.05	0.05	0.06
0.08	0.10	0.08	0.10	0.06
0.06	0.07	0.08	0.11	0.09
0.09	0.08	0.07	0.07	0.05
0.10	0.07	0.11	0.06	0.06
0.10	0.08	0.10	0.10	0.07

checksum 7.83

a.   What is the mean proportion of defective flashlights (as a percent)?

b.   What are the upper and lower 5% bounds of the sample-to-sample variability?

c.   Predict the proportion of defective flashlights (in percent) in the whole population and give the margin of error.

11-43.   Avra, Evan, and Tam were working on a survey. They each polled 25 people over the weekend if the subject of a large new mural downtown should be wildlife, sports, or black history. Avra forgot about her homework until the last minute, so she quickly surveyed her family and any relatives she could reach on the phone.  Evan talked to some of the people in the stands at his baseball game Saturday, and Tam questioned people leaving a local church. Each got very different results. Explain why.

11-44.   For the sequence: $7, -2, -11, -20, \ldots$

      a.   Find $t(40)$, the 40th term.

      b.   Find $S(40)$, the sum of the first 40 terms.

11-45.   If $p = \ln 2$ and $q = \ln 3$, solve for x in terms of p and/or q.

      a. $e^x = 2^{10}$ b. $4e^x = 27$

11-46.   Solve the system at right. $\frac{z+y}{4} + \frac{z-y}{2} = 1$

                                                      $\frac{3z-y}{4} + \frac{4z+2y}{11} = 3$

11-47.   Harold sorted his jellybeans into two jars. He likes the purple ones best and the black ones next best, so these are both in one jar. His next favorites are yellow, orange, and white, and these are in another jar. He gave all the rest to his little sister. Harold allows himself to eat only one jellybean from *each* jar per day. He wears a blindfold when he selects his jellybeans so he cannot choose his favorites first.

Make an area model that represents the probabilities. What is the probability that Harold gets one black jellybean and one orange jellybean if the first jar has 60% black and 40% purple jellybeans, and the second jar has 30% yellow, 50% orange, and 20% white jellybeans?

11-48.   Where do the graphs of $x^2 - y = 4$ and $y = 2x - 1$ intersect?

11-49.   Logarithms are used to measure the "loudness" of sound. Decibels (dB) are logarithmic units used to describe a ratio of two levels of intensity or pressure. The difference between two levels of sound pressure (P_1 and P_2) is defined as $10 \log(\frac{P_1}{P_2}) \text{dB}$. Usually, when decibels are used to describe just one sound, it is assumed that that sound is being compared to a reference level of 20 micropascals.

      a.   How many decibels correspond to doubling the pressure of a sound?

      b.   What is the sound pressure of a noise described as 60 dB?

      c.   What does 0 decibels mean?

      d.   How many times more pressure is in a sound of 40 dB than of 20 dB?

11.2.2 Did my experiment show results?

···

Variability in Experimental Results

Today you will use what you know about sample-to-sample variability to determine whether two results in an experiment are truly different.

11-50.   ENDANGERED FROGS

The female red-eyed poison-dart frog visits numerous bromeliads ("air plants") where pools of water have collected in the leaves. In each pool, she lays a single egg that grows into a tadpole. The tadpoles feed on mosquito larvae in the pools, but local health officials have been killing the mosquito larvae. Environmentalists are concerned because they are unsure whether the tadpoles will adapt to eat some other food source.

Luis led a team of environmental scientists to the Costa Rican rain forest. They tagged 100 female tadpoles and determined the number that grew to adulthood. Mosquito larvae were placed in 50 bromeliads, and the other 50 bromeliads were treated so that mosquitoes could not live there.

36 of the 50 tadpoles (72%) with mosquitoes survived, while 29 of the 50 (58%) non-mosquito tadpoles survived. The difference in the proportion that survived is $0.72 - 0.58 = 0.14$. Investigate whether a difference in the proportion of tadpoles that survived of 0.14 can be explained by natural sample-to-sample variability, or if there is a true difference between the two groups.

First, explore the sample-to-sample variability using a computer simulation.

a.   72% of the mosquito-fed tadpoles survived. For the simulation, the numbers 1 to 72 can represent the mosquito-fed tadpoles that survived. The numbers 73 to 100 will represent a tadpole that died. Simulate one sample of 50 mosquito-fed tadpoles. What proportion of your sample survived?

b.   58% of the non-mosquito tadpoles survived. Simulate one sample of 50 non-mosquito tadpoles. What proportion of your sample survived?

c.   What is the *difference* between these two proportions (mosquito-fed proportion that survived minus non-mosquito proportion survived)?

Problem continues on next page. →

11-50.   *Problem continued from previous page.*

   d.   The difference of proportions in your random sample that survived is
         likely to be higher or lower than 0.14, or even negative, because of natural
         sample-to-sample variability. What does a positive difference mean?
         What would a negative difference mean?

   e.   If we take repeated random samples by repeating the simulation, we can
         estimate the sample-to-sample variability, and then the margin of error.
         Below are the results of 100 trials. The table shows the differences in the
         proportion that survived (mosquito-fed proportion that survived minus
         non-mosquito proportion survived).

Proportion survived minus proportion did not survive.				
Simulation mean = 0.14				
0.10	0.33	0.13	0.13	0.10
0.05	0.10	0.02	−0.05	0.14
0.21	0.12	0.22	0.22	0.17
0.13	0.24	−0.07	0.23	0.14
0.16	0.30	0.12	0.21	0.11
0.17	0.19	0.14	0.13	0.09
0.05	0.10	0.23	0.29	0.30
0.26	0.08	0.07	0.30	0.05
0.12	−0.04	0.16	0.03	0.13
0.26	0.16	0.08	0.14	0.07
0.27	0.19	−0.01	0.19	0.16
0.06	0.17	0.18	0.06	0.13
0.15	0.11	0.07	0.05	0.15
0.18	0.24	−0.02	0.10	0.16
0.19	0.18	0.36	0.20	0.06
0.22	0.17	0.16	0.26	−0.04
0.13	0.05	0.05	0.15	0.19
0.13	0.18	0.10	0.13	0.10
0.16	0.21	0.17	0.09	0.03
0.13	0.13	0.12	0.15	0.23

checksum 14.1

         Find an upper and lower bound on the middle 90% of the proportions and
         the margin of error.

   f.   You have found the sample-to-sample variability. You are ready to make
         a prediction for the entire population. Report your prediction for the
         difference between the proportion of mosquito-fed tadpoles that survived
         and the proportion of non-mosquito tadpoles that survived.

   g.   What does a difference of zero mean in the context of this problem?

   h.   Are you convinced (do you have evidence) there is a true difference in the
         tadpoles that ate mosquitoes and those that did not? Explain why or
         why not.

Core Connections Algebra 2

11-51.   LEARNING LOG

Create a Learning Log explaining the steps you would take
to determine whether two results in an experiment are truly
different. You can use Endangered Frogs as an example or
create an example of your own. Title this entry "Comparing
Experimental Results" and label it with today's date.

MATH NOTES

Margin of Error

Using a statistic from a representative random sample to make an
inference about a population parameter is an important application of
statistics, but because of natural sample-to-sample variability you
cannot say for certain what the true value for the population is based on
a statistic. But you can have confidence that the true value lies within
an interval called the **margin of error**.

To compute a margin of error, a computer simulation can be used to estimate
sample-to-sample variability. Then the middle 90% (or 95% or 99%) of the data
are used as the upper and lower bounds of our estimate. By sorting the simulated
samples from lowest to highest and determining where the lowest 5% and upper
5% of the data begin, we can find the margin of error. The margin of error is half
this range.

For example, data from 100 simulated samples from a population in which 48%
support the president might look like this:

43% 44% 44% 45% 45% 45%…(88 more samples)…50% 51% 51% 52% 52% 54%

The lowest five samples (lowest 5% of 100 samples) are at 45% support and the
upper five samples are at 51% support. So the range is 6%, and we would report
that 48% of the voters support the president with a margin of error of ± 3%.

11-52.   A survey of 80 seniors at Algieres High School found that 65% had been accepted to a four-year university. A computer simulation was conducted and the proportions sorted to determine the sample-to-sample variability:

Proportion of students attending four-year universities (sorted). Simulation mean 0.65.				
0.51	0.60	0.63	0.66	0.69
0.52	0.61	0.63	0.66	0.70
0.54	0.61	0.63	0.66	0.70
0.54	0.61	0.63	0.67	0.71
0.56	0.61	0.63	0.67	0.71
0.56	0.61	0.64	0.67	0.71
0.56	0.62	0.64	0.67	0.71
0.57	0.62	0.64	0.67	0.71
0.57	0.62	0.64	0.67	0.71
0.58	0.62	0.65	0.67	0.72
0.58	0.62	0.65	0.67	0.73
0.59	0.62	0.65	0.67	0.73
0.59	0.62	0.65	0.68	0.73
0.59	0.62	0.65	0.68	0.73
0.59	0.62	0.65	0.68	0.74
0.59	0.62	0.65	0.68	0.74
0.59	0.63	0.65	0.68	0.75
0.59	0.63	0.65	0.68	0.76
0.60	0.63	0.65	0.69	0.76
0.60	0.63	0.66	0.69	0.77

checksum 64.64

a.   Use the technique of problem 11-27 to find the upper and lower 5% bounds of the sample-to-sample variability.

b.   Predict the proportion of the seniors at Algieres High that have been accepted to four-year universities and give the margin of error.

11-53.   A consumer magazine randomly selects 250 of its readers and asks whether their luggage was lost on their last airplane flight. Seven out of the 250 lost their luggage. The consumer magazine conducted a simulation to determine the sample-to-sample variability and concluded that about 3% ± 1.7% of all passengers lose their luggage. Make a conjecture about what the number of passengers who lose their luggage might be if the magazine had surveyed 1000 readers instead.

Core Connections Algebra 2

11-54.   Daylight Saving Time was adopted in the U.S. in 1918. During the oil crisis of the 1970s, the Department of Transportation found that daylight saving time decreased national energy usage by about 1 percent compared with standard time. Since then, energy use in the U.S. has changed and daylight saving time has been extended. In 2007 a group of researchers found that daylight saving time decreased national energy usage by 0.2% with a margin or error of 1.5%. If a 1% decrease in energy use will save the state of Indiana $9 million, what conclusion(s) can you draw from the 2007 study in relation to the state of Indiana?

11-55.   A team of 8 students has finished an investigation on the many uses of parabolas. They must select a single group member to present their findings to the class. They have only a single coin to make chance selections, but they can flip it as many times as necessary to select a student fairly.

   a.   Using a single coin, find a fair way to select the presenter.

   b.   What is the smallest number of coin tosses needed to select a presenter fairly? Describe the method.

   c.   Two of the group members realize they won't be in class the day of the presentation because they are playing in a baseball tournament. Can a presenter still be chosen fairly with a single coin? Explain why or why not?

11-56.   Change each equation to graphing form. Sketch the graph and label each vertex and axis of symmetry.

   a. $y = 2x^2 + 7x - 7$ b. $y = 3x^2 - x - 8$

11-57.   Sketch the graph of $g(x) = (x-2)^2 - 1$.

   a.   On the same set of axes (in a different color) sketch the graph of $|g(x)|$, which is $|g(x)| = |(x-2)^2 - 1|$.

   b.   On a new set of axes, sketch the graph of $g(|x|)$, which is $g(|x|) = (|x| - 2)^2 - 1$.

   c.   Describe how each of the graphs in parts (a) and (b) are related to the original graph of $g(x)$.

11-58. In the summer of 1994, a couple was going through their attic and found a $1000 bond issued by the State of Nevada in 1865. It read, "Pay to the Bearer" (whoever has possession). States issue bonds when they need to borrow money. In 1865, Nevada was a new state and in great need of cash, so it issued this bond at an interest rate of 24% compounded annually.

   a. Do you think it would have been possible to cash in this bond?

   b. If $1000 were invested in 1865 at an interest rate of 24% compounded annually, how much would the investment be worth in 1994?

   c. What is the place value of the first digit in the answer to part (b)?

   d. Would the amount be significantly different if was compounded continuously instead?

11-59. Rewrite each equation as an equivalent equation using $\log_{10}$. You do not need to find a numerical answer. These are sometimes known as **change of base** problems.

   a. $\log_2(3) = x$　　b. $\log_5(8) = x$　　c. $\log_7(12) = x$　　d. $\log_a(b) = x$

11-60. In a certain town, 45% of the population has dimples and 70% has a widow's peak (a hairline above the forehead that makes a "V" shape). Assuming that these physical traits are independently distributed, what is the probability that a randomly selected person has both dimples and a widow's peak? What is the probability that he or she will have neither? Use a generic area model or a tree diagram to represent this situation.

11.2.3   Should I reject for poor quality?

Quality Control

When companies accept items for shipment or distribution, they often do not test every single item for quality. In many processes, testing every item would be far too time-consuming and expensive. For example, when testing 2-liter soda bottles for bursting strength, sometimes testing destroys the item. If companies tested every item, there would be nothing left to ship. Instead, quality control testing is done on a small sample of items. If the sample does not meet quality standards, the entire batch is thrown out or recycled.

11-61.   Your task is to assure quality control for the P.C.I. (Probability Cubes Incorporated) dice company. The quality of their product is critical for the success of P.C.I. We plan to take 10 dice out of each case and test to see whether they fall within company specifications. If the dice fail to fall within the acceptable range, the entire case will be thrown out.

First we need to determine the acceptable range for well-functioning dice. We will use a simulation.

a.   Work with a partner to set up a simulation for rolling ten dice. Record the mean of the ten dice.

b.   Have each person in your team run five simulations of the rolling of a perfectly manufactured set of ten dice and record the mean for each simulated sample.

c.   Combine your results with those of your classmates. Make a histogram of the sampling distribution. What is the mean of the sampling distribution?

d.   Find the upper 5% and lower 5% bounds for the class as you did in previous lessons.

11-62.   Consider the bounds you found in problem 11-61 to be the upper and lower bounds of a normal manufacturing process of ten dice. A set of ten dice that does not fall within this range will be considered defective and the entire case will be thrown out.

Problem continues on next page →

11-62.   *Problem continued from previous page.*

a.   Your teacher will have one or more samples of ten
     dice from P.C.I., each from a different case that was
     "manufactured" early this morning. Roll the sample
     of ten dice once and calculate the mean roll. Did
     your batch fall within the quality control bounds? If
     not, P.C.I. will need to discard the entire case they came from.

b.   Repeat part (a) for another sample of dice if you have one.
     Was this sample of dice within your quality control bounds?

11-63.   How many cases of dice were rejected by the quality control engineers in your
          class? What percent of the cases were rejected?

METHODS AND MEANINGS

Statistical Hypothesis Tests

MATH NOTES

You have looked at two different types of **statistical hypothesis
tests**. In Lesson 11.2.1, you took a sample and compared the sample
statistic to a **claim** about the population. Specifically, you compared the
survey results of 60% to the principal's claim that the true value of the
population was 50% or less. By simulating the sample-to-sample
variability, you created a margin of error. If the claim was within the
margin of error, you concluded that the claim was plausible. If the claim
was not within the margin of error, you concluded that the claim was not
plausible.

In the experiment with frog tadpoles, you performed a different kind of statistical
test. You had two samples, and you calculated the *difference* between those two
samples. Then you looked at the sample-to-sample variability of the differences
between the two samples. A margin of error was created for the true difference
between the two populations. If a difference of zero was within that margin of
error, you concluded that it was plausible that there was no difference between
the two populations; you could *not* conclude that the two populations were in fact
different. On the other hand, if a difference of zero was not within the margin of
error, you could conclude that it was plausible that there was actually a true
difference between the two populations.

There are many other kinds of hypothesis tests you will learn about in future
Statistics courses.

11-64. A copy machine company advertises that its copiers will make at least 25,000 copies before requiring maintenance. A consumer research group tested the claim by collecting data from users of the particular copy machine in 30 different regions of the country. The means for each of the 30 regions are listed in the table below.

24928	24574	24652	24758	24691
24893	25024	24767	24791	24609
25249	24914	24895	24656	24883
24551	24928	25025	24798	25041
24782	25020	24618	24904	24764
24705	24889	24656	24600	24735

checksum 744300

Find the upper and lower 5% bounds of the sample-to-sample variability and predict the number of copies that can be made before a machine requires maintenance. Do you think the consumer research group will support the company's claim?

11-65.   Students in Miss Hampton's science class tested the
effectiveness of detergent in getting dishes clean. They started
by weighing each plate. Then they created a gooey paste of
hard-to-clean foods (spaghetti sauce, mustard,
mashed potatoes, peanut butter, and grape jelly)
and smeared 250 clean dinner plates with a
measured amount of the food paste. They weighed
each plate and randomly placed them into
commercial dishwashers. Half the dishwashers had
detergent in them, and half had only clean water. After
cleaning the dishes, they weighed each plate to determine the
portion of food paste that remained. 84% of the food was
removed from dishes cleaned with detergent, while only 72%
of the food was removed from dishes cleaned without
detergent. Does using detergent really help get dishes cleaner?

a.   What is the difference in the proportions (detergent minus plain water)?
Express your answer as a decimal.

b.   Mrs. Hampton's class ran a computer simulation and determined the
sample-to-sample variability of the *difference* between the proportion of
food removed by the detergent compared to plain water. They concluded
that the *difference* in the true proportion of food removed was
0.12 ± 0.085.

Is a difference of zero a plausible result considering their margin of error?
What does a difference of zero mean in the context of this problem?

c.   Are you convinced that there is a true difference between cleaning with
detergent and cleaning with plain water?

11-66.   As part of a lesson in survey design, Janette asks her study team of four students
the following question: *"Given the association between movie violence and
crime, what kind of movie would you rather watch: romantic comedy or
action?"* All four indicate they would rather watch a romantic comedy. She
states in her conclusion, *"It is obvious romantic comedies are the best."*

a.   If the population of movie goers is actually equally split between those
who prefer romantic comedies versus action movies, what is the chance of
finding a group of 4 who unanimously prefer one genre over the other? Is
it plausible?

b.   Write a few sentences commenting on the validity of Janette's methods
and her conclusion.

11-67.   The Algiers High School booster club is
          planning a fund-raiser to collect money for a
          new synthetic turf field and stadium lights.
          The football field is $100 \times 53\frac{1}{3}$ yards. They
          cover it completely with playing cards (
          2.5×3.5 inches) face down. All the cards
          are aligned in the same direction as the
          football field (long side of the card along the
          long side of the field). There will be exactly
          one joker card placed at random among the face-down cards on the field.

          Contestants pay five dollars for every card they wish to turn over. Whoever
          finds the joker wins one million dollars.

          a.   What is the probability that the first contestant finds the joker?

          b.   The playing cards used to cover the field cost $0.99 per pack (52 cards per
                pack). What is the largest amount of money the boosters could lose in this
                fundraiser?

          c.   What is the maximum amount of money the boosters could make?

          d.   What is a reasonable expected profit for the booster club? That is, if this
                fundraiser were done many, many times, what would be the average
                profit?

          e.   A state Mega Millions lottery advertises odds of 176 million to one. If the
                state lottery were played like the booster club fundraiser, how many
                football fields covered with non-joker playing cards would be needed?

11-68.   What is the solution for the system of equations at right?

$$\frac{7}{13}x + \frac{4}{15}y = 0$$
$$\frac{5}{8}x + \frac{12}{7}y = 0$$

11-69.   Let $p = 2 + 5i$ and $q = 3 - 4i$.
          Calculate the following values and simplify to $a + bi$ form.

          a. $p + q$ b. $p - q$ c. $p \cdot q$ d. $\frac{p}{q}$

11-70.   Solve and graph each inequality.

          a. $|7 - y| \le 3$ b. $3|2m + 1| - 1 > 8$

11-71. The graphs of $f(x) = 2x^2 + 5x - 3$ and $g(x) = x^2 + 4x + 3$ are shown at right. Use the graphs to solve:

a. $f(x) = g(x)$

b. $f(x) > g(x)$

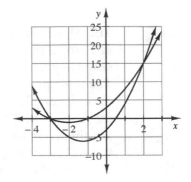

11.2.4 Is the process out of control?

±10%

Statistical Process Control

In Lesson 11.2.3 you checked the quality of an item after it was manufactured to verify that it was within the natural sample-to-sample manufacturing specifications. Today we will explore whether the manufacturing process remains constant over time.

Natural variation occurs in all manufacturing processes, no matter how precise, computerized, or state-of-the-art. For example, a manufacturer of ball bearings for precision aircraft parts needs to be sure the ball bearings are always the correct size. If they are slightly too large or too small, they may cause an airplane crash!

Each ball bearing is a slightly different size than the next one due to small variations in the metals being used, impurities in raw materials, wear of the machinery, temperature, and humidity, among other possibilities. Since variation is always present, engineers must control the manufacturing process so that the final product remains useful. The ball bearing cannot be manufactured to an exact size each and every time, but it can be manufactured to fall within a specification, say 50mm +/− 0.2mm.

Checking quality over a time period is called **statistical process control**. The process needs to remain stable over time so that the output or product of that process remains of high quality.

In Lesson 11.2.3 you verified the quality of an item (the set of dice) *after* it was manufactured. If the quality was poor, large quantities of the item had to be discarded or recycled at great expense. A fundamental tenet of manufacturing is that it is far less expensive to control the manufacturing *process*—to catch and fix problems early—than to wait to test the quality of the finished product when it can no longer be fixed.

11-72. *x*-BAR CONTROL CHART

The Brrrr! Ice Company must keep the size of the
ice cubes it makes within certain specifications for
the ice cubes to be useful for restaurants. Brrr! Ice
keeps track of the process of making ice cubes by
taking a sample of 10 ice cubes every hour and then
plotting the mean size over time. Some of their data
from yesterday is below.

Hour	1	2	3	4	5	6	7	8	9	10
mean cube size (mm)	273.1	262.7	264.1	206.9	295.4	238.6	197.8	277.2	284.5	256.6

Hour	11	12	13	14	15	16	17	18	19	20	
mean cube size (mm)	220.3	303.1	278.9	306.3	263.3	208.9	253.3	213.7	216.4	263.3	*checksum 5084.4*

a. Create a scatterplot with mean cube size as the
dependent variable and time as the independent
variable. Use the option on your calculator or
computer to connect the dots as shown in the
display at right.

b. The process data is useful only if we know what
size ice cubes are acceptable. These specifications
are called the upper control limit (UCL) and lower
control limit (LCL). The Brrrr! Ice Company will
tolerate ice cubes that are between 250mm +/–
100mm. Add the control limits to your scatterplot.
Your graph will look something like the one shown
at right.

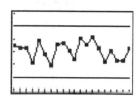

This kind of chart is called an ***x*-bar process control chart** because it plots
the mean ($\bar{x}$) data from the manufacturing process. Since all of the means
are within the process control limits, this manufacturing process is said to
be **in control**.

11-73.   AN OUT-OF-CONTROL PROCESS

The mean ice cube size for today's data at Brrr! Ice is below.

hour	1	2	3	4	5	6	7	8	9	10
mean cube size (mm)	242.5	277.1	250.0	234.2	229.7	243.6	282.8	303.0	247.7	217.0

hour	11	12	13	14	15	16	17	18	19	20	
mean cube size (mm)	278.6	244.2	195.4	224.3	382.1	242.4	226.5	284.4	239.1	288.2	*checksum 5132.8*

a.   Create an x-bar process control chart.

b.   At which hour did the process go **out of control**? Consider the context and make conjectures about what might have happened during the manufacturing process this hour to make the process go out of control.

11-74.   The mean ice cube size for yet another day at Brrr! Ice is below.

hour	1	2	3	4	5	6	7	8	9	10
mean cube size (mm)	275.4	213.8	182.6	250.1	228.7	275.3	220.1	166.0	258.5	240.9

hour	11	12	13	14	15	16	17	18	19	20	
mean cube size (mm)	255.3	309.1	270.0	255.7	306.8	338.2	336.6	311.3	332.5		*checksum 5026.9*

a.   Create an x-bar process control chart.

b.   What do you notice about the process control chart that might concern you as a quality control engineer at Brrr! Ice? Why would the engineers stop the process after the 19th hour?

c.   Even though a process is entirely within the process control limits, a process is considered out of control if nine consecutive points lie above or below the centerline of the process control limits. What size of ice cube is in the center between the UCL and the LCL?

d.   Add the centerline to your graph and determine whether this process is out of control.

e.   Make a conjecture in the context of the problem as to what in the manufacturing process may cause a "nine points loss of control."

11-75.   The principal at Algieres High School believes that over 20% of students are text-messaging at least once a week during class. He believes this is an impediment to effective learning. Students claim that the actual percentage is much lower and that stricter rules are not necessary. Mrs. Rahil secretly observed her homeroom class very carefully for a week; only 13% of students actually text-messaged during class. Assuming her homeroom is representative of the whole school, Mrs. Rahil's class did a computer simulation and determined a margin of error of 10%. Is it plausible that the principal is correct and 20% of the whole school is text-messaging?

11-76.   MINIATURE GOLF

Olivia loves playing putt-putt golf. In putt-putt golf you do not swing at a golf ball, but rather you only putt the golf ball (tap the ball with a club so that it rolls into a hole). Olivia experimented with her new club to determine whether or not she played better with it. Each time before she putted a golf ball, Olivia flipped a coin to determine whether she would use her new club or the old one. She experimented on 80 putts. With the new club, Olivia made 25% of the 40 putts, while with the old one, she made only 15% of the 40 putts. Using the steps below, help Olivia decide whether or not her new golf club is really better, or if this difference can be explained by sample-to-sample variability.

a.   What is the difference in the proportions (new club minus old club)? Express your answer as a decimal.

b.   Olivia needs a computer simulation to determine the sample-to-sample variability:

   i.   Out of the 80 putts, how many went into the hole?

   ii.   In our computer model, there are 80 putts. What will the numbers 1 to 16 represent? What will the numbers 17 to 80 represent?

   iii.   Conduct one simulation of 80 putts. What proportion of the putts in your simulation went into the hole? What proportion did not go into the hole? What is the *difference* in the proportion (proportion that went into the hole minus proportion that did not go in)?

Problem continues on next page →

11-76.   *Problem continued from previous page.*

Olivia ran the simulation 50 times and calculated the *difference* in the proportion of putts that went into the hole and those that did not go into the hole for each simulation. From her results, she predicted the true *difference* in proportion of all her putts was 0.10 ± 0.146.

    c.   What does a difference of zero mean in the context of this problem? Is a difference of zero a plausible result considering your margin of error?

    d.   Are you convinced that there is a true difference between the new club and the old club?

11-77.   Because of natural variability in manufacturing, a 12-ounce can of soda does not usually hold exactly 12 ounces of soda. A can is permitted to hold a little more or a little less. The specifications for the soda-filling machine are that it needs to fill each can with 12 ± 0.25 ounces of soda. If a can of soda is filled with 11.97 ounces of soda, is the filling machine operating within specifications?

11-78.   Every hour, Katie's Konfections weighs a sample of chocolates from their manufacturing process. For each of the process control charts below, describe whether the process is in control, and if not, what in the manufacturing process could have led to the out-of-control state.

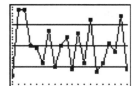 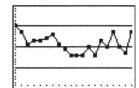 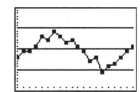

11-79.   Graph each equation below.

    a. $x^2 + (y-3)^2 = 9$ b. $(x-5)^2 + (y-1)^2 = 4$

11-80. Solve each equation below for x. Show all of your work. (Your answers will contain the variables a, b, and/or c.)

a. $cx - a = b$

b. $\frac{x}{a} - b = c$

c. $(x-a)(x-b) = 0$

d. $ax^2 - acx = 0$

e. $\frac{x}{a+b} = \frac{1}{c}$

f. $\frac{1}{x} + a = b$

11-81. Solve the equations below.

a. $\frac{3x}{x+2} + \frac{7}{x-2} = 3$

b. $\frac{x-7}{x-5} = \frac{6}{x}$

11-82. Solve the equations below.

a. $(x+2)^2 - (x-2)^2 = 8$

b. $(x+2)^2 + (x-2)^2 = (2x)^2$

11-83. Kendra has programmed her cell phone to randomly show one of six photos when she turns it on. Two of the photos are of her parents, one is of her niece, and three are of her boyfriend, Bruce. Today, she will need to turn her phone on twice: once before school and again after school.

a. Create an area model to represent this situation.

b. Given that the before-school photo was of her boyfriend, what is the conditional probability the after-school photo will also be of her boyfriend?

c. What is the probability that neither photo will be of her niece?

d. Given that neither photo was of her niece, what is the conditional probability that the before-school photo was of her boyfriend?

11.3.1 When is probability counterintuitive?

Analyzing Decisions and Strategies

In today's problems you will have the opportunity to see how probability can play an important role in decision-making. In *Midnight Mystery,* the results of your investigation will shed light on the accusation that one of the Measleys is guilty of the curling trophy prank, and in *Testing for AIDS,* your results can be used in an argument about mandatory testing. There are many other similar applications. As you work through this lesson, discuss the following questions:

How can we find the probability?

What model should we use?

How should we set up the model?

Which probabilities do we need to compute?

11-84.   SHIFTY SHAUNA

Shauna has a bad relationship with the truth—she doesn't usually tell it! In fact, whenever Shauna is asked a question, she rolls a die. If it comes up 6, she tells the truth. Otherwise, she lies.

a.   If Shauna flips a fair coin and you ask her how it came out, what is the probability that she says "heads" and is telling the truth? Use an area model to solve this problem and carefully record your work. Be ready to share your solution method with the class.

b.   Suppose Shauna flips a fair coin and you ask her whether it came up heads or tails. What is the probability that she says "heads"? (Hint: The answer is not $\frac{1}{12}$!)

11-85.   MIDNIGHT MYSTERY

Each year, the students at Haardvarks School randomly select a student to play a prank. Late last night, Groundskeeper Lily Smilch saw a student steal the school's National Curling Championship trophy from the trophy case. All Lily can tell the headmaster about the crime is that the student who stole the trophy looked like he or she had red hair.

Problem continues on next page →

Core Connections Algebra 2

11-85.   *Problem continued from previous page.*

Unfortunately, of the 100 students at Haardvarks, the only ones with red hair are your friend Don Measley and his siblings. Groundskeeper Smilch insists that one of the five Measleys committed the crime and should be punished. Don is incensed: *"We Measleys would never play such a stupid prank! Groundskeeper Smilch claims to have seen someone with red hair, but it was so dark at the time and Smilch's eyes are so bad, there is no way she could have identified the color of someone's hair!"*

The Headmaster isn't convinced, so he walks around with Lily at night and points to students one by one, asking her whether each one has red hair. Lily is right about the hair color 4 out of every 5 times.

This looks like bad news for Don, but Professor McMonacle agrees to take up his defense. *"I think,"* McMonacle says, *"that the thief probably wasn't one of the Measleys."*

Your Task: Develop the basis for McMonacle's argument as follows:

a.   Model the probabilities in this situation with an area model. The two chance events in your model should be "The thief is/is not a redhead" and "Lily is/is not correct about the thief's hair color."

b.   If you performed this experiment with 100 students, how many times would you expect Lily to say the student had red hair and be correct about it?

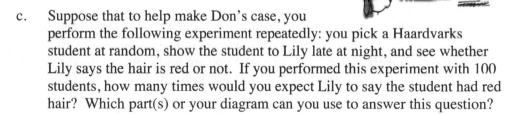

c.   Suppose that to help make Don's case, you perform the following experiment repeatedly: you pick a Haardvarks student at random, show the student to Lily late at night, and see whether Lily says the hair is red or not. If you performed this experiment with 100 students, how many times would you expect Lily to say the student had red hair? Which part(s) or your diagram can you use to answer this question?

d.   If you performed this experiment with 100 students, what percentage of the students Lily *said* had red hair would *actually* have red hair?

e.   How can you use these calculations to defend the Measleys? Is it likely that a Measley was the thief?

f.   Have you *proven* that none of the Measleys stole the Curling Trophy?

11-86.   TESTING FOR AIDS

An understanding of probability is valuable in relation to important policy issues that are often decided for political reasons. As the issues get more complicated, knowledge of probability and statistics could make a big difference in the decisions each of us will help to make. For example, with the growing number of AIDS cases, some people have called for mandatory testing of healthcare professionals (doctors, dentists) for the HIV virus, with public disclosure of the results. Others argue that mandatory testing jeopardizes the lives and livelihood of many people who do not have the disease and is therefore an unwarranted and unjust invasion of their privacy. Furthermore, they argue that if results are not ever made public for anybody, more people who are not required to test (like health technicians) will volunteer for testing, increasing the likelihood of identifying and helping people who do have the disease.

In order to explore these issues further we will consider a hypothetical situation. Suppose that the currently used test for HIV is 99% accurate, and suppose that in the population to be tested (in this case it is doctors, dentists, and other health practitioners) 100 out of 100,000 people actually are HIV positive. The question is: what is the probability that a health practitioner would be identified as having the AIDS virus who actually did not?

a.   Make a model for this situation.

b.   How does the number of people who are HIV positive compare with the number of people who will be told they are HIV positive but really are not?

c.   If a randomly tested health practitioner's test comes back positive, what is the probability that he is *not* actually HIV positive? (This is called a **false positive**.) In other words, if you are told that you are sick, what is the conditional probability that you are not sick?

d.   Write up your statistical conclusions about mandatory testing of health practitioners. How might your statistics change if the study was about subjects in the general population who volunteered for testing?

e.   Are the test results mathematically independent of the fact that the person tested does or does not have aids? How could you check this? Explain.

11-87.   A never-ending game?

Jack and Jill are playing a game in which Jack has 2 pennies and Jill has
4 pennies. A coin is tossed. If it lands on heads Jill has to give a penny to Jack.
If it lands on tails, Jack gives a penny to Jill. The game is won when one of
them has all of the pennies. They think that they can keep playing all day since
the coin has an equal chance of landing on heads or tails, so they will just keep
passing coins back and forth.

Simulate the coin tosses on your calculator and keep track of the pennies with
pencil and paper. Can they keep playing all day, or does one player have a
better chance of winning the game?

11-88.   Any system that is responsible for detecting relatively rare events is going to
have problems with false positives. In section 3 you saw this in problems
regarding testing for HIV and substance abuse. Consider other cases such as
burglar alarms, smoke detectors, red light cameras and drug testing for athletes.
All of these systems have proven accuracy and all have a persistent problem of
false positives (false alarms).

Consider a hypothetical situation. Suppose that rare event A occurs with a
frequency of 1/1000. Suppose that a detection system for event A responsible
for sounding an alarm is 96% accurate. The question is: if the alarm is
sounding, what is the probability that event A has not occurred (false alarm)?

a.   Make a model for this situation.

b.   If the alarm has been activated, what is the probability that it is false?

c.   Are the test results mathematically independent of whether event A occurs
      or not? How could you check this? Explain.

11-89.   Find the equation of the line passing through the point $(-2,5)$ that is
perpendicular to the line $y = -5x + 2$.

11-90.   Solve the system of equations at right.
$$x^2 + y^2 = 16$$
$$y = x^2 - 4$$

11-91. Multiply and simplify each expression.

    a. $(3 + 2i)(4 + i)$

    b. $(2 + 3i)(2 - 3i)$

    c. $(5 - 2i)(5 + 2i)$

    d. $(a + bi)(a - bi)$

11-92. Graph at least one full cycle of each graph.

    a. $y = 2 \sin x$

    b. $y = \cos (2x)$

    c. $y = -1 + 2 \cos(x)$

    d. $y = -1 + 2 \sin(x + \frac{\pi}{2})$

11-93. Each of the following sums is the beginning of an arithmetic series. Find the nth term of each series, for the specified value of n.

    a. $(-2) + (-5) + (-8) + ..., n = 12$

    b. $9 + 15 + 21 + ..., n = 20$

11-94. This problem is a checkpoint for solving rational equations. It will be referred to as Checkpoint 11.

Solve each of the following rational equations.

    a. $\frac{x}{3} = \frac{4}{x}$ b. $\frac{x}{x-1} = \frac{4}{x}$ c. $\frac{1}{x} + \frac{1}{3x} = 6$ d. $\frac{1}{x} + \frac{1}{x+1} = 3$

Check your answers by referring to the Checkpoint 11 materials located at the back of your book.

If you needed help solving these problems correctly, then you need more practice. Review the Checkpoint 11 materials and try the practice problems. Also, consider getting help outside of class time. From this point on, you will be expected to do problems like these quickly and easily.

11-95. Sketch a graph, $f(x)$, that has the number and types of roots described for each situation below.

    a.   5 real roots

    b.   3 real and 2 complex roots

    c.   4 complex roots

    d.   4 complex and 2 real roots

Chapter 11 Closure What have I learned?

Reflection and Synthesis

The activities below offer you a chance to reflect
about what you have learned during this chapter. As
you work, look for concepts that you feel very
comfortable with, ideas that you would like to learn
more about, and topics you need more help with.
Look for connections between ideas as well as
connections with material you learned previously.

①   TEAM BRAINSTORM

What have you studied in this chapter? What ideas were important in what you
learned? With your team, brainstorm a list. Be as detailed as you can. To help
get you started, a list of Learning Log entries and Math Notes boxes are below.

What topics, ideas, and words that you learned *before* this chapter are connected
to the new ideas in this chapter? Again, be as detailed as you can.

How long can you make your list? Challenge yourselves. Be prepared to share
your team's ideas with the class.

Learning Log Entries

- Lesson 11.2.1 – Sample-to-Sample Variability
- Lesson 11.2.2 – Comparing Experimental Results

Math Notes

- Lesson 11.1.1 – Area Models for Probabilities
- Lesson 11.2.1 – Sample-To-Sample Variability
- Lesson 11.2.2 – Margin of Error
- Lesson 11.2.3 – Statistical Hypothesis Tests

② MAKING CONNECTIONS

Below is a list of the vocabulary used in this chapter. Make sure that you are familiar with all of these words and know what they mean. Refer to the glossary or index for any words that you do not yet understand.

area model	claim	conditional probability
hypothesis test	in/out of control	Law of Large Numbers
margin of error	population	process control
quality control	random number	sample-to-sample variability
sampling distribution	simulation	streak
upper/lower bound	upper/lower control limit	x-bar chart

Make a concept map showing all of the connections you can find among the key words and ideas listed above. To show a connection between two words, draw a line between them and explain the connection. A word can be connected to any other word as long as you can justify the connection.

While you are making your map, your team may think of related words or ideas that are not listed here. Be sure to include these ideas on your concept map.

③ PORTFOLIO: EVIDENCE OF MATHEMATICAL PROFICIENCY

This section gives you an opportunity to show growth in your understanding of key mathematical ideas over time as you complete this course.

You now have enough mathematical knowledge to analyze the results of a survey. Obtain the questions you created and refined in Chapter 9 (problems 9-1, 9-6, 9-21, and 9-33) for your own survey. In your portfolio, explain why you chose the wording of your questions the way you did. Consider everything you know about biased questions. For what population are your survey results valid? How will you sample? Refine your questions again if you choose. Explain the difference between open and closed questions.

Then conduct your survey as instructed by your teacher. Analyze the results, and make a conclusion about the population you defined. Include a margin of error.

Activity continues on next page →

③   *Activity continued from previous page.*

Your teacher may assign the following portfolio entry:

AIDS IN SOUTH AFRICA

In this investigation, you will showcase your understanding of estimating sample-to-sample variability and conducting a hypothesis test.

A drug manufacturer claims that only 13% of the population of South Africa is living with HIV/AIDS. As a United Nations World Health Organization researcher, you collect evidence to test this claim. You use statistical techniques to sample 125 random residents of South Africa and find that 20 of them have HIV/AIDS.

a.   Simulate one sample of 125 residents by randomly selecting 125 integers between 1 and 100. Carefully explain what the random numbers represent and why you picked 125 of them. What proportion of the 125 people in your simulated sample is living with HIV/AIDS? How do you know?

b.   Obtain the results of 100 simulations from your teacher. Without actually making the computation, what do you suppose the mean of the 100 proportions would be close to? Why? What is the margin of error?

c.   Are you able to support the claim of the drug manufacturer?

d.   Is margin of error you obtained reasonable for this study? Why or why not?

e.   What could be done to make the margin of error smaller? Why does that make sense?

④   WHAT HAVE I LEARNED?

Most of the problems in this section represent typical problems found in this chapter. They serve as a gauge for you. You can use them to determine which types of problems you can do well and which types of problems require further study and practice. Even if your teacher does not assign this section, it is a good idea to try these problems and find out for yourself what you know and what you still need to work on.

Solve each problem as completely as you can. The table at the end of the closure section has answers to these problems. It also tells you where you can find additional help and practice with problems like these.

CL 11-96. If 75 percent of people do not believe in ghosts, design a simulation that would estimate the probability of randomly selecting a group of 5 non-believers:

a. Using two coins.   b. Using a calculator.

CL 11-97. Mr. Knolsen takes pride in his difficult chemistry tests, 60 multiple-choice questions with 4 possible answers for each question. He tells the students to study hard because the mean score is 15 correct, but just 20 correct is all you need to earn an A. Mr. Knolsen admits that only about 10% of the students earn an A on the test. Jeff is wondering the value of Mr. Knolsen's pep talk so he runs a simulation of 100 students taking Mr. Knolsen's exam who blindly guess the answers for each question.

Questions correct in a simulation of 100 tests (the data is sorted)				
8	11	14	16	18
8	11	14	16	19
8	11	14	16	19
9	12	14	16	19
9	12	14	16	19
10	12	14	16	19
10	12	14	16	19
10	12	15	16	19
10	13	15	16	19
10	13	15	17	19
11	13	15	17	20
11	13	15	17	20
11	13	15	17	20
11	13	16	17	20
11	13	16	18	20
11	13	16	18	21
11	13	16	18	22
11	13	16	18	22
11	13	16	18	22
11	14	16	18	24

checksum 1489

a. What is the mean number of questions answered correctly by the simulated students? As a percent?

b. What percentage of the simulated students earned an A?

c. Compare Jeff's simulated students to Mr. Knolsen's claims about his actual students.

d.   What advice would you give Jeff about preparing for Mr. Knolsen's famous chemistry tests?

Core Connections Algebra 2

CL 11-98.   A survey of 1024 people found 580 of them eat chicken soup when they have a cold or flu and concluded that a majority of the population believes that chicken soup helps relieve cold and flu symptoms. A computer simulation found the margin of error to be 3%. Does the conclusion seem reasonable? Why?

CL 11-99.   A company makes metal plates on which they put a special coating. Flaws appear in the finish of these metal plates and the company wants to establish a quality control system. A machine scans each plate after it is finished and reports the number of flaws. The data they collected for 50 samples are shown below.

7	10	9	3	13	7	5	8	8	10
13	9	21	10	6	8	3	12	7	11
5	10	6	13	3	2	7	4	11	8
1	7	5	2	0	11	3	4	3	1
4	14	7	12	6	1	10	6	2	12

checksum 361

Discuss the quality control bounds for this company with your team. Should you reject plates that have too few flaws? What upper and lower bounds make sense?

CL 11-100.   Students at Algieres High think they are safer drivers than average teenagers. In a random sample of 120 students at Algieres High, 18 students said that they got into a car accident when they were 16 years old.

a.   What percent of 16-year-olds in this sample got into a car accident?

b.   Set up a simulation of the sample-to-sample variability. Explain exactly what you would type into your calculator to do this simulation. After doing the simulation once, what would the numbers in your calculator screen represent?

c.   Chase ran the simulation 100 times and obtained the following proportions of 16-year-olds that got into a car accident.

Problem continues on next page →

CL 11-100. *Problem continued from previous page.*

Proportion of 16-year-old students in a car accident. Simulation mean = 0.15				
0.19	0.14	0.13	0.12	0.20
0.13	0.17	0.15	0.16	0.14
0.12	0.13	0.14	0.12	0.17
0.11	0.13	0.16	0.18	0.20
0.10	0.17	0.15	0.17	0.19
0.14	0.19	0.11	0.15	0.10
0.12	0.14	0.19	0.09	0.13
0.18	0.20	0.14	0.11	0.17
0.20	0.15	0.20	0.18	0.15
0.11	0.16	0.12	0.20	0.14
0.17	0.10	0.18	0.17	0.19
0.18	0.11	0.11	0.14	0.13
0.15	0.13	0.18	0.17	0.28
0.14	0.15	0.13	0.11	0.13
0.11	0.11	0.15	0.15	0.12
0.20	0.15	0.22	0.17	0.11
0.15	0.18	0.12	0.26	0.15
0.13	0.11	0.13	0.15	0.16
0.14	0.15	0.23	0.15	0.08
0.19	0.15	0.15	0.18	0.10

checksum 15.17

Consider the lower and upper 5% bounds to determine the margin of error for the proportion of students who got into an accident at Algieres High.

d. According to the U.S. Census Bureau, 21% of 16-year-olds nationwide get into a car accident. But in the sample at Algiers High, only 15% got into a car accident. Can students at Algieres make the claim that they are safer drivers?

CL 11-101. Jenn and Ryan needed to save money for their trip to the Galapagos Islands. They currently have $3000. They figure they will need $4000 for the trip.

a. They can put the $3000 into a CD account that earns interest compounded continuously. What annual interest rate will the account need so that they have $4000 in the account in ten years?

b. Instead, they can put the money in a savings account that earns 2.75% interest annually, compounded quarterly. In how many years will they have $4000?

CL 11-102.   Find the infinite sum (if possible).

a. $8 - 6 + \frac{9}{2} - \frac{27}{8} + -...$

b. $\sum_{k=0}^{\infty} \frac{1}{8}(2)^k$

CL 11-103.   For the sequence: $150, 100, 50, 0, ...$

a.   Find $t(10)$, the 10th term.

b.   Find $S(10)$, the sum of the first 10 terms.

CL 11-104.   For each equation, state the amplitude, period, vertical shift, and horizontal shift, and sketch two cycles of the graph.

a. $y = 3\cos(2x)$

b. $y = \cos 2(x + \frac{\pi}{4})$

CL 11-105.   Bias is present in the following observational studies.

a.   Explain why the question is biased:

A political pollster seeking information on public attitudes toward funding of pornographic art by the National Endowment for the Arts (NEA) asks an SRS of 2000 U.S. adults, "Instead of supporting government censorship of artistic expression, are you in favor of continuing federal funding for artists whose work may be controversial?" Eight-five percent of those surveyed answered "yes."

b.   Explain why the sample is biased:

A flour company in Minneapolis wants to know what percentage of local households bake at least twice a week. A company representative calls 500 households during the daytime and finds that 50% of them bake at least twice a week.

c.   What is a possible lurking variable?

Dentists would like to determine if eating an apple a day keeps cavities away. Fifty patients who say they routinely eat an apple a day, and 50 patients who say they eat less than one apple a week, will have their dental records checked. The dentists will compare the number of cavities in the two groups.

CL 11-106. Check your answers using the table at the end of this section. Which problems do you feel confident about? Which problems were hard? Have you worked on problems like these in math classes you have taken before? Use the table to make a list of topics you need help on and a list of topics you need to practice more.

Answers and Support for Closure Activity #4
What Have I Learned?

Note: MN = Math Note, LL = Learning Log

Problem	Solutions	Need Help?	More Practice
CL 11-96.	a. There are 4 equally likely outcomes when you toss two coins HH HT TH TT. Assign one of the outcomes to represent a ghost-believer. The other three outcomes represent the 75% chance of a non-believer being selected. Toss the coins in sets of 5 representing the selection of 5 people in a group. Divide the number of groups without a ghost believer by the total number of groups. b. Assign numbers 1 – 25 to represent selecting a believer and 26 – 100 to selecting a non-believer. Using randInt(1,100,5) generate sets of 5 numbers representing the selection of 5 people in a group. Divide the number of groups without a ghost believer by the total number of groups.	Lesson 11.1.1	Problems 11-7, 11-18, 11-28, 11-29, 11-41, and 11-55
CL 11-97	a. $1489/100 = 14.89$, $14.89/60 = 24.82\%$ b. $10/100 = 10\%$ c. They are nearly identical. d. If the real students are preparing for the exam, it doesn't help because students blindly guessing would perform just as well.	Lessons 11.1.3 and 11.2.1. MN: 11.2.1, 11.2.2, and 11.2.3 LN: 11.2.1	Problems 11-42, 11-52, 11-53, 11-54, 11-64, 11-65, 11-75, 11-76, and 11-77

Problem	Solutions	Need Help?	More Practice
CL 11-98.	Yes, 580/1024 = 0.566. Adding and subtracting the margin of error, we can be reasonably sure the population proportion is between 0.536 and 0.596, which is greater than 0.500 (a majority).	Lesson 11.2.1 MN: 11.2.1, 11.2.2, and 11.2.3 LL: 11.2.1	Problems 11-64, 11-65, 11-75, 11-76, and 11-77
CL 11-99.	Students should reject the upper 10% of the data. Flaws should be ≤ 12.	Lesson 11.2.1 MN: 11.2.1, 11.2.2, and 11.2.3 LL: 11.2.1	Problems 11-64, 11-65, 11-75, 11-76, and 11-77
CL 11-100.	a. 15% b. [MATH] PRB randInt(1,100,120) [STO▸] [2nd] [L1]. That stores 120 students in List1. The numbers 1 to 15 represent a student who had an accident when they were 16 years old, while the numbers 16 to 100 represent a student who did not have an accident. c. $15\% \pm 5\%$ d. Yes. 21% is outside of the interval of the margin of error. There is convincing evidence that the rate of accidents at Algieres is lower than the nationwide rate.	Lesson 11.2.1 MN: 11.2.1, 11.2.2, and 11.2.3 LL: 11.2.1	Problems 11-64, 11-65, 11-75, 11-76, and 11-77
CL 11-101.	a. $4000 = 3000 \cdot e^{r \cdot 10}$; $r = 2.87\%$. b. $4000 = 3000(1.006875)^q$ $q = 42.0$ quarters $= 10.5$ years	Lesson 10.3.2 MN: 10.3.2	Problems 10-170, 10-172, 10-173, 11-10, and 11-58
CL 11-102.	a. $\frac{32}{7}$ b. No sum, $r > 1$.	Lessons 10.1.4 and 10.2.2 MN: 10.1.2, 10.1.4, 10.2.1, and 10.2.2 LL: 10.2.1 and 10.2.2	Problems 11-11, 11-23, 11-32, 11-44, and 11-93

Problem	Solutions	Need Help?	More Practice
CL 11-103.	a. −300 b. −750	Lesson 10.1.3 MN: 10.1.3	Problems 11-11, 11-23, 11-32, 11-44, and 11-93
CL 11-104.	a. amplitude: 1 period: π vertical shift: 0 horizontal shift: 0 b. amplitude: 1 period: π vertical shift: 0 horizontal shift: $-\frac{\pi}{4}$ 	Lessons 7.2.1, 7.2.2, and 7.2.3 MN: 7.2.4 LL: 7.2.4	Problems CL 8-188, CL 8-189, 9-69, 9-82, 10-94, and 11-92
CL 11-105.	a. Before asking the question, the person conducting the survey is connecting funding decisions to censorship. b. People at home during the day are more likely to have time to bake than the genreral population. c. Possibly healthy habits. Healthy habits might increase the nunber of apples you eat and also decrease the number of cavities you have. The apples are not preventing the cavities, the healthy habits are.	Lessons 9.1.1, 9.1.2, and 9.1.3 LL: 9.1.3	Problems 9-50, 9-75, CL 9-112, 11-5, 11-21, 11-30, 11-43, and 11-66

Chapter 12   Analytic Trigonometry

In Chapter 7 you began your study of trigonometric functions when you learned about radians and how to transform the graphs of $y = \sin(x)$, $y = \cos(x)$, and $y = \tan(x)$. In this chapter, you will continue your study of trigonometry with the investigation of solutions to trigonometric equations. You will learn about three new trigonometric ratios (secant, cosecant, and cotangent) and their corresponding functions.

By the end of this chapter, you will be able to solve a wide variety of trigonometric equations. You will make statements, based on the unit circle and the graph, about how many solutions there are and why.

Guiding Question

Mathematically proficient students reason abstractly and quantitatively.

As you work through this chapter, ask yourself:

How can I rewrite this in another useful form?

Chapter Outline

Section 12.1 In this section, you will solve trigonometric equations. You will learn about inverse and reciprocal trigonometric functions. You will understand solutions to trigonometric equations in multiple representations: algebraically, from the graphs of the functions, and based on the unit circle. You will also learn how to determine the number of solutions for a trigonometric equation.

Section 12.2 Here, you will identify trigonometric identities (statements that are always true). These identities will allow you to rewrite trigonometric equations, which will enable you to solve a broader range of equations.

12.1.1 When is it true?

· ·

Analyzing Trigonometric Equations

Throughout your study of algebra, you have encountered algebraic statements that are always true, sometimes true, or never true. In Chapter 7, you learned about the trigonometric functions $y = \sin(x)$, $y = \cos(x)$, and $y = \tan(x)$. You learned how to represent these functions in a table, on a graph, and with a unit circle. In this chapter, you will expand your understanding of trigonometric functions and develop strategies to determine when trigonometric equations are true. All answers in this chapter should be given in radians unless otherwise stated in the problem.

12-1.   How can you tell which values of x make an algebraic statement true? For each of the following statements, work with your team to decide if it is always true, sometimes true, or never true. If it is always true, justify how you know; if it is sometimes true, give the exact values of x that make it true; and if it is never true, explain why it is never true.

a. $5(x-7) = 5x - 35$

b. $2x^2 = 50$

c. $4x - (3x+2) = x - 7$

d. $\frac{2}{3}(x-9) = \frac{3}{4}(2x+5)$

12-2.   WHEN IS IT TRUE?

Your teacher will assign your team one of the following equations. Your task is to decide if the equation is always true, sometimes true, or never true, and to justify your decision using as many representations as you can.

- If the equation is always true, explain how you know. Then look for ways you could change the equation so that it would never be true.

- If the equation is sometimes true, find the exact values of x that make it true. Then decide how you could change the equation so that it would never be true.

- If the equation is never true, explain how you know. Then decide how you could change the equation so that it would sometimes be true.

a. $\sin(x) = \frac{1}{2}$

b. $\cos(x) = 2$

c. $\sin(x) = \cos(\frac{\pi}{2} - x)$

d. $\sin(x) = \sin(\frac{\pi}{2} - x)$

e. $\tan(x) = 0$

f. $2\sin(x) = \sqrt{3}$

g. $\sin(x) = \frac{3}{2}$

h. $\cos(x) = \sin(\frac{\pi}{2} - x)$

12-3.   Organize your work from problem 12-2 into a poster that will serve as a visual aid for a presentation. Be sure to include all of your justifications and reasoning. Use colors, arrows, and other math tools to help make your thinking clear. When you have prepared your poster and presentation, go back to problem 12-2 and evaluate the equations your team did not work on.

12-4.   With your team, discuss the meaning of solutions. Record what you know about the solutions of an equation that are:

a.   Always true.   b.   Sometimes true.   c.   Never true.

12-5.   Decide if each of the following statements are always true, sometimes true, or never true. If a statement is always true, justify how you know; if it is sometimes true, give the exact values of x that make it true; and if it is never true, explain why it is never true.

a. $3x - 2 - 4(x + 1) = -x - 6$ b. $3x - 5 = 2(x + 1) + x$

c. $\sin(x) = \cos\left(\frac{\pi}{2} - x\right)$ d. $\tan(x) = 1$

12-6.   Factor each of the following expressions.

a. $x^2 - 4$ b. $y^2 - 81$

c. $1 - x^2$ d. $1 - \sin^2(x)$

12-7.   Solve for x in each of the following triangles. What methods can be used for finding unknown parts of triangles?

a.
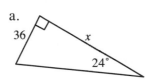

b.
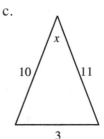

c.

12-8.   Show that $\cos(2x)$ never equals $2\cos(x)$.

12-9.   Given the function $f(x) = 2 + \sqrt{2x - 4}$, find:

   a.   The domain and range.

   b.   The inverse equation.

   c.   The domain and range of the inverse.

12-10.   Consider the function $f(x) = 3 \sin(x + \frac{\pi}{2}) - 4$.

   a.   How is its graph different from $f(x) = \sin(x)$?

   b.   Sketch the graph.

12-11.   Every hour, Miguel's Microchips measures the signal strength of a chip from their manufacturing process. For each of the process control charts below, say whether the process is in control, and if not, what in the manufacturing process could have led to the out-of-control state.

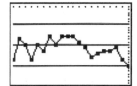   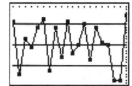   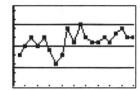

12-12.   If you remember what $n!$ means, you can do some messy calculations quickly or compute problems that are too large for your calculator's memory. For instance, if you wanted to calculate $\frac{9!}{6!}$, you could use the $n!$ button on your calculator and find that $9! = 362{,}880$ and $6! = 720$, so $\frac{9!}{6!} = \frac{362{,}880}{720} = 504$. You could also use a simplification technique. Since $9! = 9 \cdot 8 \cdot 7 \cdot 6 \cdot 5 \cdot 4 \cdot 3 \cdot 2 \cdot 1!$ and $6! = 6 \cdot 5 \cdot 4 \cdot 3 \cdot 2 \cdot 1$, you can rewrite $\frac{9!}{6!} = \frac{9 \cdot 8 \cdot 7 \cdot 6 \cdot 5 \cdot 4 \cdot 3 \cdot 2 \cdot 1}{6 \cdot 5 \cdot 4 \cdot 3 \cdot 2 \cdot 1} = 9 \cdot 8 \cdot 7 = 504$.

   Use this simplification technique to simplify each of the following problems before computing the result.

   a. $\frac{10!}{8!}$ b. $\frac{20!}{18!2!}$ c. $\frac{7!}{4!3!}$ d. $\frac{75!}{72!}$

12-13.   If the PEP squad has 12 members, in how many ways can five students:

   a.   Line up for a picture in the school newspaper?

   b.   Be chosen to visit the rival school before the big game?

12-14. List three possible values for h that will make the equation $\cos(x - h) = \sin(x)$ true.

12-15. If $\pi \le \theta \le \frac{3\pi}{2}$, what must be true about the sign of:

   a. $\sin(\theta)$ b. $\cos(\theta)$ c. $\tan(\theta)$ d. $\frac{1}{\cos(\theta)}$

12-16. Find all values of a for which the equation $ax^2 + 5x + 6 = 0$ has a solution that is a real number. Express a in terms of one or more inequalities.

12-17. Using a graph of $f(x) = \cos(x)$ for reference, graph $f(x) = |\cos(x)|$.

12-18. Factor and reduce the rational expression $\frac{5x+10}{x^2+6x+8}$. Justify each step.

12-19. Solve each equation.

   a. $\sqrt{x+7} + 5 = x$

   b. $\frac{a}{a^2-36} + \frac{2}{a-6} = \frac{1}{a+6}$

12-20. Change the angle measures below from radians to degrees or degrees to radians.

   a. $108°$ b. $320°$ c. $\frac{7\pi}{9}$

   d. $\frac{19\pi}{12}$ e. $\frac{17\pi}{2}$ f. $260°$

12-21. A jar contains five red, four white, and three blue balls. If three balls are randomly selected, find the probability of choosing:

   a. Two red and one white.   b. Three white.

   c. One of each color.   d. All the same color.

   e. One red and two white.   f. Two of one color and one of another.

12-22. Expand.

   a. $(a+b)^3$ b. $(2m+5)^3$

12.1.2 How many solutions are there?

Solutions to Trigonometric Equations

In Lesson 12.1.1, you recognized that an equation could be always true, sometimes true, or never true. In the next few lessons you will focus on trigonometric equations that are sometimes true as you learn how to solve them and how to determine the number of solutions they have.

12-23.   When is the equation $\cos(x) = \frac{1}{2}$ true?

     a.   What do the solutions to this equation represent?

     b.   Solve the equation graphically. How many solutions can you find on the graph?

     c.   Draw a unit circle showing the solutions to $\cos(x) = \frac{1}{2}$. How many solutions do you see?

12-24.   Just as taking the square root ($\sqrt{}$) can be used to undo a square when solving an equation algebraically, there is an undo (inverse) operation for cosine.

     a.   With your team, see if you can find the undo operation for cosine on your calculator. What does it look like? How can you be sure that it is undoing cosine?

     b.   Use the undo operation for cosine on your calculator to solve the equation $\cos(x) = \frac{1}{2}$. Show where the solution given by the calculator can be seen on the graph and on the unit circle.

12-25.   With your team, decide how many solutions there are to the equation $\cos(x) = \frac{1}{2}$. Justify your decision using as many representations as you can. How can you write all of them?

12-26.   How do all of the solutions to $\cos(x) = \frac{1}{2}$ relate to the one given by $\cos^{-1}(\frac{1}{2})$ on your calculator?

12-27. Find all of the solutions for each equation below. You may use your calculator, but you must represent your solutions graphically and on a unit circle. After you have found all of the solutions, identify which ones lie in the domain $0 \le x \le 2\pi$. Then work with your team to write a summary statement about your solutions.

a. $2\cos(x)+1=0$

b. $\tan(x)=1$

12-28. Jeremy used the $\sin^{-1}$ button on his calculator to solve a trigonometric equation and got the solution 37°. He knows that there must be more than one solution. What are the rest of the solutions to Jeremy's equation? Explain how you found them. Use a unit circle and a graph in your explanation.

12-29. For each of the following equations, find the solutions that lie in the domain $0 \le x \le 2\pi$.

a. $2\sin(x)-1=0$

b. $2\cos(x)=-\sqrt{3}$

c. $2\sin(x)=\sqrt{2}$

d. $\cos(x)=1$

12-30. Salina, Tamara, and Uma are working on their homework together. Salina tells her friends that she got $\theta = 52°$ for the inverse cosine problem she is working on and asks if they got the same answer. Tamara says she got $\theta = 128°$, and Uma volunteers her answer of $\theta = 308°$. Is it possible that these are all solutions to the same problem? Justify your answer.

12-31. Graph $f(x)=1+\tan(x-\frac{\pi}{4})$.

12-32. What is the inverse of $f(x)=-x+6$? Justify your answer.

12-33. Simplify, then add $\frac{x-2}{x+2}+\frac{2x-6}{x^2-x-6}$. Justify each step.

12-34. Josephina thinks that she has discovered a new pattern, shown at right.

$$\frac{x-1}{x-1} = 1$$

$$\frac{x^2-1}{x-1} = x+1$$

$$\frac{x^3-1}{x-1} = x^2 + x + 1$$

$$\frac{x^4-1}{x-1} = x^3 + x^2 + x + 1$$

    a.   Check her equations by multiplying. Does her pattern work?

    b.   Based on her pattern, what does $\frac{x^5-1}{x-1}$ equal? Is it true? Justify your answer.

    c.   Make a conjecture about how to represent the result for $\frac{x^n-1}{x-1}$. You will need "…" in the middle of your expression.

12-35. A number of states are considering legislation that calls for people to get mandatory drug testing in order to qualify for public assistance money. Some argue that mandatory testing of welfare recipients would jeopardize the livelihood of many people who do not have substance abuse problems and is therefore an unwarranted invasion of their privacy.

Consider a hypothetical situation. Suppose that the currently used test for illegal drugs is 99% accurate, and suppose that in the population to be tested (in this case it is the population of people on public assistance of a given state) 2,300 out of 100,000 people are substance abusers. The question is: what is the probability of a "false negative"? That is, the probability that the test identifies a person on public assistance as using drugs when they actually do not use drugs?

    a.   Make a model for this situation.

    b.   How does the proportion of people who are using drugs compare with the proportion of people who will be told they are using drugs but really are not?

    c.   If a randomly tested recipient's test comes back positive, what is the probability that he or she is *not* actually using drugs?

    d.   Write up your statistical conclusions.

    e.   Are the test results mathematically independent of using or not using drugs? How could you check this? Explain.

12-36.   If five cards are dealt from a shuffled deck of playing cards:

   a.   What is the probability of getting a five-card hand that is all red?

   b.   Express your solution to part (a) in the form: $\frac{_aC_b}{_dC_e}$.

   c.   What is the probability of getting a five-card hand that is all clubs?

   d.   Express your solution to part (c) in the form $\frac{_aC_b}{_dC_e}$.

   e.   What is the probability of getting 5 cards from any one suit?

12-37.   Three light bulbs are chosen at random from 15 bulbs, of which five are defective. What is the probability that:

   a.   None of the three are defective?

   b.   Exactly two are defective?

12.1.3 Is it a function?

True?
When?

Inverses of Trigonometric Functions

In Lesson 12.1.2, you learned how to use the inverse trigonometric functions to undo operations and solve trigonometric equations. You also learned that the keys for the inverse trigonometric functions on your calculator give you only one of the possible solutions to these equations. In this lesson, you will investigate the inverse trigonometric functions more thoroughly. You will determine whether the inverses are also functions.

12-38.   Obtain the Lesson 12.1.3 Resource Page from your teacher.

   a.   Make a careful graph of $y = \sin(x)$. Is it a function? What are its domain and range?

   b.   Graph the line $y = x$.

   c.   Reflect the graph of $y = \sin(x)$ across the line $y = x$ to make a graph of its inverse, $x = \sin(y)$. Is it a function? What are its domain and range?

   d: Discuss with your team the restriction you would need to make on the domain of $y = \sin(x)$ so that its inverse is a function.

12-39.   Now graph $y = \sin^{-1}(x)$ on your graphing calculator. How is the result different from the graph that you made? Does it make sense in terms of your answer to part (d) in the problem above? Highlight the portion of your graph that represents the inverse function and label it with its domain and range. Also highlight the portion of the unit circle (provided on the resource page) that shows the restriction on the domain of $y = \sin(x)$ required to make its inverse a function.

12-40.   Consider the equation $\sin(x) = -\frac{\sqrt{3}}{2}$.

   a.   How many solutions does the equation have?

   b.   Without using a calculator, find the solutions and show them on the unit circle.

   c.   Which solution do you predict your calculator will give? How do you know? Once you have made your prediction, use your calculator to solve $\sin(x) = -\frac{\sqrt{3}}{2}$. Were you correct? (Note that this solution can be written as $\sin^{-1}(-\frac{\sqrt{3}}{2})$.)

12-41. Obtain two more copies of the Lesson 12.1.3 Resource Page from your teacher. Sketch $y = \cos(x)$ and $y = \tan(x)$ on separate axes and label the domain and range of each.

    a. Reflect each graph across the line $y = x$ to generate graphs of the inverse relations.

    b. Find the domain and range of the relations $x = \cos(y)$ and $x = \tan(y)$.

    c. Use your graphing calculator to graph the functions $y = \cos^{-1}(x)$ and $y = \tan^{-1}(x)$. Highlight the portion of your graph that represents the inverse function. Find the domain and range for each function. Then highlight a portion of the unit circle (provided on the resource pages) that shows the domain restrictions required to make the inverses of $y = \cos(x)$ and $y = \tan(x)$ functions.

12-42. For each of the following problems, find all of the solutions without using a calculator. Draw a graph or unit circle to support your answers. Then predict the solution that your calculator will give and use your calculator to check your prediction.

    a. $2\cos(x) - 1 = 0$ b. $\tan(x) = \sqrt{3}$

    c. $2\sin(x) = \sqrt{3}$ d. $4\sin^2(x) - 3 = 0$

12-43. Solve each equation for $0° \le \theta \le 360°$, or if you prefer, $0 \le \theta \le 2\pi$. You may need your calculator, but remember that it only gives *one* answer.

    a. $\sin(\theta) = 0.5$ b. $\cos(\theta) = -0.5$

    c. $4\tan(\theta) - 4 = 0$ d. $3\sin^2(\theta) = 1$

12-44.   State the domain and range for each graph below. Then state whether or not it
          is a function.

a.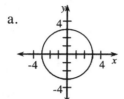

b.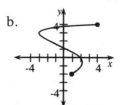

c.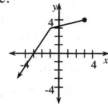

d.

12-45.   Solve each equation. Check for extraneous solutions.

a. $\sqrt{x+7} = x+1$

b. $\frac{2}{x+3} - \frac{1}{x} = \frac{-6}{x^2+3x}$

12-46.   Graph.

a. $(-2, 3, -2)$

b. $3x - 2y - 3z = -6$

12-47.   Solve each system.

a. $\frac{x}{2} + \frac{y}{4} = 4$

  $\frac{x}{4} - \frac{3y}{8} = -2$

b. $x + 2y + z = -1$

  $4x - y - z = -1$

  $-3y = 2z$

12-48.   Governments and security companies are coming to rely more heavily on facial
          recognition software to locate persons of interest.

          Consider a hypothetical situation. Suppose that facial recognition software can
          accurately identify a person 99.9% of the time, and suppose the suspect is among
          200,000 facial images available to a government agency. When the software
          makes a positive identification, what it the probability that it is not the suspect?

a.   Make a model for this situation.

b.   If a person has been identified as the suspect, what is the probability that
      he or she is *not* actually the suspect?

12-49.   A pizza parlor has 12 toppings other than cheese. How many different pizzas can be created with five *or fewer* toppings? List all subproblems and calculate the solution.

12-50.   Find $(2x^5 - 6x^4 - 2x^2 + 7x - 4) \div (x - 3)$.

12-51.   A glass factory makes a continuous ribbon of glass by pouring a continuous stream of hot liquid silicon on a lake of molten tin. The liquid silicon spreads out evenly on the tin and then cools into glass. It is a process that must continue uninterrupted 24 hours a day, so adjustments to equipment and materials are ongoing. Assume that inspectors work eight-hour shifts, watching the glass ribbon as it flows from the lake of tin, marking and counting the number of defects on the new glass. The number of defects identified by the inspectors for a 24-hour period is shown below:

Hour	1	2	3	4	5	6	7	8	9	10	11	12
Defects	43	40	42	40	38	39	36	38	44	41	45	42

Hour	13	14	15	16	17	18	19	20	21	22	23	24
Defects	40	37	39	39	43	40	42	42	38	41	38	37

a.   Create an *x*-bar process control chart with a UCL of 45 and an LCL of 35.

b.   What do you notice about the process control chart that might concern you as a quality control engineer?

12-52.   Hector missed the beginning of this lesson, and he is confused about domains for inverse functions. Explain why restrictions are needed. Describe specifically the restrictions that each trigonometric function (sine, cosine, and tangent) requires in order to find its inverse function.

12-53.   For each of the following problems, find all of the solutions without using a calculator. Use a graph or unit circle to support your answers. Then predict the solution that your calculator will give and use your calculator to check your prediction.

a. $4 \sin(x) + 2 = 0$ b. $2 \cos(x) = \sqrt{3}$

c. $\tan(x) + 1 = 0$ d. $4 \cos^2(x) - 4 = 0$

12-54.   Explain each transformation below in terms of the parent graph $f(\theta) = \tan\theta$.

   a. $f(\theta) = \tan\theta + 1$ b. $f(\theta) = \tan(\theta + \frac{\pi}{4})$

   c. $f(\theta) = -\tan(\theta)$ d. $f(\theta) = 4\tan\theta$

12-55.   Quickly sketch each of the following functions.

   a. $f(x) = (x-1)^2(x-3)^3(x-5)^2$

   b. $g(x) = -(x-1)^2(x-3)^3(x-5)^2$

   c.   Express $g(x)$ in terms of $f(x)$.

12-56.   Rewrite each sum below as a single expression.

   a. $\frac{1}{2} + \frac{1}{3}$ b. $\frac{3}{2x} + \frac{4}{x^2}$

   c. $\frac{x}{x+1} + \frac{3}{x-1}$ d. $\frac{\sin\theta}{\cos\theta} + \frac{1}{\sin\theta}$

12-57.   Rewrite $f(x) = 2x^2 - 4x + 1$ in graphing form. State its domain, range, vertex and line of symmetry. Include a labeled sketch as part of your solution.

12-58.   Solve the following equations. Round to three decimal places. Be sure to check your answers.

   a. $7 = 4.2^x$ b. $3x^5 = 126$ c. $14 = 2 \cdot 4^x - 10$

12-59.   Expand.

   a. $(a+b)^4$ b. $(3m-2)^4$

12-60.   Another pizza parlor is had a super special. The parlor had a rack of small pizzas, each with three or four different toppings. The price was really low because an employee forgot to indicate on the boxes what toppings were on each pizza. Eight toppings were available, and one pizza was made for each of the possible combinations of three or four toppings.

   a.   How many pizzas were on the rack?

   b.   What was the probability of getting a pizza that had mushrooms on it?

12.1.4 What is the reciprocal?

True?
When?

Reciprocal Trigonometric Functions

In this lesson, you will investigate the reciprocal trigonometric functions and their graphs.

12-61.   Your team will investigate the graph of the reciprocal of $y = \sin(x)$.
Obtain a Lesson 12.1.4A Resource Page from your teacher.

    a.   Using values on the x-axis as your inputs, complete the table on your resource page and make a careful graph of $y = \sin(x)$.

    b.   Now you will use the values in your table to help you make a graph of the reciprocal of $y = \sin(x)$, which can be written as $y = \frac{1}{\sin(x)}$. Label the third column in your table $\frac{1}{\sin(x)}$. To find the values that go in this column, calculate the reciprocal of each value for $\sin(x)$.

    c.   Where are the outputs for $\sin(0)$, $\sin(\frac{\pi}{2})$, and $\sin(\pi)$ located on the graph? What is true about the reciprocal function at these locations in your table? How would they appear on your graph?

    d.   Now, using a colored pencil, graph $y = \frac{1}{\sin(x)}$ carefully.

    e.   This ratio that is the reciprocal of sine is named **cosecant**. The cosecant function can be abbreviated by $f(x) = \csc(x)$. Label your graph with its name, "Cosecant."

12-62.   Is $y = \csc(x)$ a function?

    a.   What are its domain and range?

    b.   What are the intercepts?

    c.   Are there asymptotes? If so, what are their equations?

    d.   Describe the relationship between the sine and cosecant graphs.

12-63.   Use your graph to solve each of the following equations in the domain $0 \le x \le 2\pi$. What do you notice about each of the solutions?

    a. $\sin(x) = \frac{1}{2}$ b. $\csc(x) = 2$ c. $\sin(x) = 1$

    d. $\csc(x) = 1$ e. $\sin(x) = \frac{\sqrt{3}}{2}$ f. $\csc(x) = \frac{2}{\sqrt{3}}$

12-64.   Is there an inverse cosecant button on your calculator? How could you use your calculator to solve $\csc(x) = 3.5$?

12-65.   Obtain the Lesson 12.1.4C and Lesson 12.1.4D Resource Pages from your teacher. Use the same process as you did in problem 12-61 to create graphs of the reciprocal of the cosine function (named **secant** and abbreviated $f(x) = \sec(x)$) and the reciprocal of the tangent function (named **cotangent** and abbreviated $f(x) = \cot(x)$). What are the domains and ranges for these functions?

12-66.   For each of the following equations, work with your team to decide if it is always true, sometimes true, or never true. If it is always true, explain how you know; if it is sometimes true, give the exact values of x that make it true; and if it is never true, explain why it is never true. Hint: Use what you have learned above and the idea of rewriting to get started.

a. $\sin^2(x)\csc(x) = \frac{\sqrt{3}}{2}$

b. $\sec^2(x) = \frac{2}{\cos(x)}$

c. $\tan(x)\sec(x)\sin(x) = 0$

d. $\sec^2(x)\cos(x) = 0$

e. $\cos(x)\sec(x) = 1$

MATH NOTES

ETHODS AND MEANINGS

Inverses of Trigonometric Functions

To find the inverse function for a trigonometric function, the domain of the original function has to be restricted. For each function, the restriction is different.

For sine, restricting the domain to $-\frac{\pi}{2} \le x \le \frac{\pi}{2}$ leads to the inverse function, $y = \sin^{-1} x$ with domain $-1 \le x \le 1$ and range $-\frac{\pi}{2} \le y \le \frac{\pi}{2}$.

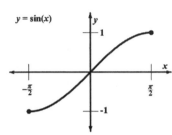
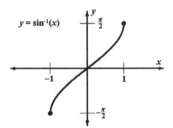

For cosine, restricting the domain to $0 \le x \le \pi$ gives a good piece of the graph close to the origin, and gives an inverse function $y = \cos^{-1} x$, with domain $-1 \le x \le 1$ and range $0 \le y \le \pi$.

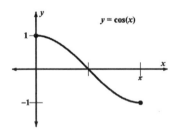
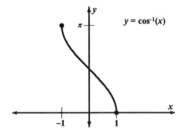

For tangent, the restriction is $-\frac{\pi}{2} < x < \frac{\pi}{2}$, so the domain for the inverse tangent $y = \tan^{-1} x$ is all real numbers and the range is $-\frac{\pi}{2} < y < \frac{\pi}{2}$.

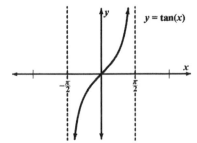
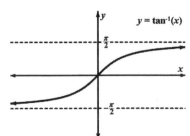

12-67. Using the triangle on the right, find:

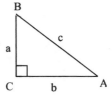

   a. $\sin A$ b. $\sec A$

   c. $\csc B$ d. $\tan B$

12-68. Solve each equation below for x if $-2\pi \le x \le 2\pi$.

   a. $4\sin^2(x) = 1$ b. $3\tan^2(x) = 1$

12-69. Solve $2\sin(x)\cos(x) - \sin(x) = 0$ in the domain $0 \le x \le 2\pi$. Give answers in degrees or radians.

12-70. Solve for x in the figure at right.

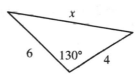

12-71. If the cost of a CD now averages $15.95 and in 4 years will be $21.95, what are the annual multiplier and the annual percent increase?

12-72. Multiply the expressions in parts (a) through (d).

   a. $(a+b)(a^2 - ab + b^2)$ b. $(x-2)(x^2 + 2x + 4)$

   c. $(y+5)(y^2 - 5y + 25)$ d. $(x-y)(x^2 + xy + y^2)$

   e. What did you notice about these products?

   f. Make up another multiplication problem that follows the same pattern.

12-73.   Parts (a) through (d) of problem 12-72 represent a general pattern known as the **sum and difference of cubes**. Use this pattern to factor each of the following polynomials.

   a. $x^3 + y^3$ b. $x^3 - 27$ c. $8x^3 - y^3$ d. $x^3 + 1$

   e.   Make up another problem involving the sum or difference of cubes and show how to factor it.

12-74.   Find the equation of a cubic function that has $y = x^3$ as its parent graph, a locator point at $(-6, -10)$, and passes through the origin.

12-75.   From the 13 spades in a deck of cards, four are selected. Find the probability that:

   a.   Exactly one card is a "face" card (Jack, Queen, or King).

   b.   The four cards can be rearranged to form a sequence $(A, 2, 3, 4; 2, 3, 4, 5; \ldots; J, Q, K, A)$.

12-76.   Using the triangle on the right, find:

   a. $\sec B$ b. $\tan A$

   c. $\cot A$ d. $\csc A$

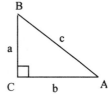

12-77.   Find all solutions to $2\sin(x)\cos(x) + \cos(x) = 0$. Give your answers in degrees or radians.

12-78.   If $f(x) = 2x^2 - 3$ and $g(x) = x + 1$, find $f(g(x))$.

12-79.   Use the sum or difference of cubes and what you already know about factoring to factor the following expressions as completely as possible.

    a. $x^5 + 8x^2y^3$ b. $8y^6 - 125x^3$

    c. $x^6 - y^6$ (Note: This is tricky. If you start it as the difference of two cubes, you will not be able to factor it completely. Think of it as the difference of two squares and then factor the factors as the sum and difference of two cubes.)

12-80.   Write an equation for the curve at right. Then sketch the graph of the inverse of this function and write its equation.

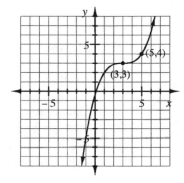

12-81.   An exponential function has an asymptote at $y = 5$ and passes through the points $(2, 5.64)$ and $(-1, 15)$. Find the equation of the function.

12-82.   What is the fifth term of each expansion?

    a. $(a + b)^9$ b. $(2x + y)^8$

12-83.   Write a quadratic equation with roots $x = 3 \pm 5i$.

12-84.   Sure Shot Jane can hit the bull's eye with a bow and arrow 90% of the time. If she shoots five arrows, what is the probability that three or more arrows hit the bull's eye?

12.2.1 How can I rewrite it?

Trigonometric Identities

To solve many trigonometric equations, it is first necessary to rewrite the equation in a simpler form. In this lesson, you will solve trigonometric equations graphically and will develop methods for rewriting those equations so that you can solve them algebraically.

12-85.   Consider the equation $2 \sin(x) \cos(x) = \frac{1}{2}$ for the domain $0 \le x \le 2\pi$.

    a.   Do you have tools to solve this equation algebraically?

    b.   Use your graphing calculator to graph $y = 2 \sin(x) \cos(x)$ and $y = \frac{1}{2}$ in the domain $0 \le x \le 2\pi$. Copy the graph onto your paper and use it to approximate the solutions to $2 \sin(x) \cos(x) = \frac{1}{2}$. How many solutions are there in this domain?

    c.   Crystal was working on this problem and noticed that the graph of $y = 2 \sin(x) \cos(x)$ looked just like the graph of a regular cyclic function. She thought it must be possible to write a different equivalent equation for this graph. Work with your team to write a cyclic equation for this graph. Is there more than one? If so, which is the simplest?

    d.   Using your equivalent equation from part (c), rewrite the equation $2 \sin(x) \cos(x) = \frac{1}{2}$ and solve it algebraically. How do your solutions compare to those you approximated from your graph?

    e.   Write an algebraic statement showing that these two expressions are equivalent. This is called the **Double Angle Identity** for sine.

12-86.   DISCOVERING IDENTITIES GRAPHICALLY

The graphs of some other trigonometric functions can be used to rewrite the functions and create new identities. Use a method similar to the method used in problem 12-85 to rewrite each of the following equations. Then use your result to write a new identity.

$y = \cos(-x)$ $y = \sin(-x)$

$y = \cos(\frac{\pi}{2} - x)$ $y = \sin(\frac{\pi}{2} - x)$

$y = \sin^2(x)$ $y = \cos^2(x)$

$y = \cos^2(x) - \sin^2(x)$ $y = \cos^2(x) + \sin^2(x)$

12-87.   Obtain the Lesson 12.2.1 Resource Page from your teacher. This resource page will be referred to as your Identity Toolkit. Record each identity you have discovered along with its justification.

12-88.   Use your new identities to help you rewrite and solve the following equations in the given domains.

   a. $2\cos(\frac{\pi}{2} - x) = 1$ for all x b. $\cos^2(x) - \sin^2(x) = \frac{\sqrt{3}}{2}$ for $0 \le x \le 2\pi$

12-89.   One of the identities in problem 12-86 you initially worked with in Chapter 7. Recall that $\cos^2(x) + \sin^2(x) = 1$ is called the **Pythagorean Identity**. It is one of the most useful identities you will learn.

   a.   Work with your team to explore the following question: Why is $\cos^2(x) + \sin^2(x) = 1$ called the Pythagorean Identity? Does it have anything to do with the Pythagorean Theorem? Be prepared to share your ideas with the class.

   b.   Two more very useful identities can come directly from the Pythagorean Identity. To discover the first related identity, divide both sides of the equation by $\cos^2(x)$. For the second related identity, divide both sides of the equation by $\sin^2(x)$. Add these two new identities to your Identity Toolkit (Lesson 12.2.1 Resource Page).

12-90.   Rewrite each of the following expressions in a simpler form.

a. $\cos^2(\theta - \pi) + \sin^2(\theta - \pi)$ b. $\cos^2(2w) - \sin^2(2w)$ c. $\frac{\sin\theta}{\cos\theta}$

12-91.   An isosceles triangle has sides with lengths 10, 10, and 5 cm. What are the measures of the angles in the triangle?

12-92.   Solve for x in *degrees*.

a. $2\sin(x) = 1$ b. $\cos^2(x) + 4\cos(x) + 4 = 0$

12-93.   Divide $(6x^3 - 5x^2 + 5x - 2)$ by $(2x - 1)$.

12-94.   Divide $(x^4 - 7x^2 + 3x + 18)$ by $(x + 2)$.

12-95.   Mr. Dobson is planning to give a quiz to his class tomorrow. Unfortunately for his students, Mr. Dobson is notorious for writing quizzes that seem to have no relevance to the subject. With this in mind, his students know that their efforts will be purely guesswork. If the quiz contains ten questions that the students will have to match with ten given answers, what is the probability that Rodney Random will get all ten questions matched correctly?

12-96.   Which is greater: $(5-2)!$ or $(5-3)!$? Justify your answer.

12-97.   If $f(x) = x^2 + 7x$, calculate the value of:

a. $f(2)$ b. $f(-3)$ c. $f(i)$

d. $f(-3.5 + 1.5i)$ e. x if $f(x) = 0$.

12-98.   Each labeled point on the graph below is either a maximum or a minimum.

   a.   Find the period and amplitude of the graph.

   b.   Find an equation for the graph.

   c.   Use one of the labeled points to check your equation.

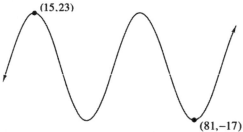

(15,23)

(81,–17)

12-99.   Rewrite the Pythagorean Identity as many ways as you can. One way to change the identity is to solve the equation for one trigonometric function. Another way is to use factoring. Try several different ways.

12-100.   If $\pi \le \theta \le \frac{3\pi}{2}$ and $\sin\theta = -\frac{3}{5}$, find $\cos\theta$. Use what you know about the Pythagorean Identity and the unit circle to get started.

12-101.   Rewrite each of the following expressions in terms of either $\sin(\theta)$ or $\cos(\theta)$.

   a. $\tan(\theta)$ b. $\csc(\theta)$ c. $\cot(\theta)$ d. $\sec(\theta)$

12-102.   Given the points $(2, 9)$ and $(4, 324)$:

   a.   Write the equation of a line that passes through them.

   b.   Write the equation of an exponential function with an asymptote at $y = 0$ that passes through them.

12-103.   Without graphing, determine where the graphs of $f(x) = 2x^2 - 3x + 1$ and $g(x) = 4x - 2$ intersect.

12-104.   Simplify each rational expression below.

   a. $\dfrac{\frac{x+1}{2x}}{\frac{x^2-1}{x}}$ b. $\dfrac{\frac{4}{x+3}}{\frac{1}{x}+3}$

12-105.   Find $m\angle C$ in each triangle below.

a.

b.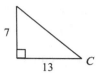

12-106.   For the function $f(x) = 5x^2 + 4x + 20$, find the roots and the vertex of the graph. Then rewrite the equation in graphing form.

12-107.   Hospital records show that 10% of all the cases of a certain disease are fatal. If five patients suffer from this disease, find the probability that:

a.   All will recover.   b.   At least three will die.

12.2.2 How can I prove it?

Proving Trigonometric Identities

In Lesson 12.2.1 you investigated trigonometric identities by graphing trigonometric functions and determining what other trigonometric functions were equivalent. Now you will learn how to use your algebra skills to prove trigonometric identities.

12-108.   Polly Parabola has a cousin named Thomas Trig. The Functions of America and Professional Parabola Productions companies have enjoyed such huge success that Thomas has decided to open a company called Identity Island. However, to do this, he needs some help and has sent your team the following memo.

> *Dear Study Team,*
>
> *My goal for Identity Island is to be able to offer a wide selection of trigonometric identities to interested customers. I found a list of identities on the Internet, but I know that lots of information on the Internet is false! I cannot afford to be embarrassed in front of my potential customers by offering identities that are not true.*
>
> *I need your help. I need a solid algebraic proof on file for each identity that we offer. Please submit a report by the end of the day that demonstrates each of the identities algebraically.*
>
> *I have the utmost faith in your team's abilities. Thank you for your time!*
>
> *Sincerely,*
>
> *Thomas Trig*

Your Task: Work with your team to demonstrate algebraically if each of the identities below is always true, never true, or sometimes true. To prove some of the identities, you will need to refer to the identities that you developed in Lesson 12.2.1.

a. $\cot(x) + \tan(x) = \sec(x)\csc(x)$

b. $(1 - \sin x)(1 + \sin x) = \frac{1}{1 + \tan^2(x)}$

c. $\frac{1}{\sec^2(x)} + \frac{1}{\csc^2(x)} = 1$

d. $\sec^2(x) - \csc^2(x) = \tan^2(x) - \cot^2(x)$

e. $\frac{\sec(x)}{\tan(x) + \cot(x)} = \sin(x)$

f. $\sin^2(x)\cot^2(x) + \cos^2(x)\tan^2(x) = 1$

g. $\frac{\csc^2(x) - 1}{\csc^2(x)} = \cos^2(x)$

h. $\frac{\sin x}{\cos x} + \frac{\cos x}{\sin x} = 2$

12-109.   A 125-foot redwood tree is leaning 20° off vertical. How long will its shadow be when the angle the sunlight makes with the ground is 68°?

12-110.   Divide each of the following polynomials, $P(x)$, by $D(x)$ to find the quotient $Q(x)$ and then rewrite the polynomial in the form $P(x) = D(x) \cdot Q(x) + R$, where R is the remainder.

   a. $P(x) = 2x^4 - x^2 + 3x + 5$ b. $P(x) = x^5 - 2x^3 + 1$

          $D(x) = x - 1$ $D(x) = x - 3$

12-111.   Without using a calculator, solve each equation below in the domain $0 \le x \le 2\pi$.

   a. $\sin(x) = -1$ b. $2\cos(x) - 1 = 0$

   c. $\tan(x) = 1$ d. $2\sin(x) = 4\sin(x) + 1$

12-112.   Solve for x.

   a.   b.

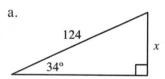   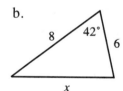

12-113.   Andrea has just purchased a five-digit combination lock that allows her to set up her own combination. She can use the numbers 0 through 9 for her combination, and she must use five digits.

   a.   How many five-digit combinations can she make so that no digit is repeated?

   b.   How many five-digit combinations are possible if she *can* repeat the digits, but cannot use the same digit twice in a row?

12-114.   Use the Pythagorean Identity to find the missing coordinate of this point on the unit circle: $(?, \frac{4}{5})$.

12-115.　Change the equation $x^2 + 8x + y^2 - 12y = 12$ to graphing form and sketch a graph.

12-116.　At the Bright Idea Lighting Company 10 flashlights are sampled each hour to determine whether the manufacturing process is in control. The UCL is 0.10 defective, and the LCL is 0.05 defective.

　　a.　Create a process control chart for the following hours.

Hour	1	2	3	4	5	6	7	8	9	10	11	12	13
proportion defective	0.06	0.08	0.09	0.06	0.05	0.08	0.08	0.07	0.11	0.10	0.05	0.07	0.04

hour	14	15	16	17	18	19	20	21	22	23	24	25	
proportion defective	0.08	0.08	0.09	0.08	0.09	0.09	0.08	0.09	0.10	0.06	0.05	0.05	checksum 1.88

　　b.　As a quality control engineer for Bright Light, what do you report about the process control?

12-117.　Simplify each expression.

　　a.　$\dfrac{2x^2 - 5x - 3}{3x^2 - 11x + 6}$
　　　　　　　　　　　　　　　b.　$\dfrac{x^3 - 8}{4x^3 - 3x^2 - 10x}$

12-118.　Prove that each of the following equations is an identity. In other words, prove that they are each true for all values for which the functions are defined.

　　a.　$(\sin\theta + \cos\theta)^2 = 1 + 2\sin\theta\cos\theta$

　　b.　$\tan\theta + \cot\theta = \sec\theta\csc\theta$

　　c.　$(\tan\theta\cos\theta)(\sin^2\theta + \frac{1}{\sec^2\theta}) = \sin\theta$

12-119.　Solve $\frac{2+\sin^2\theta}{3} = \frac{3}{4}$ in the domain $0 \le \theta \le 2\pi$. Show your solutions on a unit circle.

12-120.　If the side lengths of $\triangle ABC$ are $a = 9$, $b = 10$, and $c = 5$, calculate the measure of the largest angle.

12-121. Write an equation for the curve shown at right. Is it a function? Justify your answer.

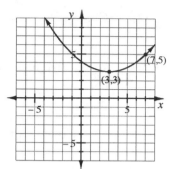

12-122. Solve for x, correct to three decimal places.

a $27 = 6^x$

b. $27 = \frac{1}{6^x}$

c. $27 = \frac{1}{(\frac{1}{6})^x}$

d. Show that $\frac{1}{(\frac{1}{6})^x} = 6^x$.

12-123. Solve each system of equations. Explain the graphical implications of your answer.

a. $3x - 2y = -10$
    $4x + y = 49$

b. $7x - 2y = 11$
    $14x - 4y = 3$

12-124. Here is another way to think about the question: *"What is 0! ?"*

a. How many ways are there to choose all five items from a group of five items? What happens when you substitute into the factorial formula to compute $_5C_5$? Since you know (logically) what the result has to be, use this to explain what 0! must be equal to.

b. On the other hand, how many ways are there to choose *nothing* from a group of five items? And what happens when you try to use the factorial formula to compute $_5C_0$?

12-125. The area of $\triangle ABC$ is 24 square inches. If $\overline{AB} \perp \overline{BC}$ and $BC = 8$ inches, find AC.

12-126. Find a polynomial function of degree three with roots $x = 3, 1 \pm i$. Express your answer in standard form.

12.2.3 What about sums and differences?

Angle Sum and Difference Identities

In this lesson you will use your knowledge of relationships in the unit circle to develop four new identities called the Angle Sum and Difference Identities.

12-127.   Danny and Damian were working on finding identities. They thought it would be useful to look at the sums and differences of angles. They started with a unit circle and created the angles α and β as shown at right. They recognized that they had formed a triangle, $\triangle POQ$.

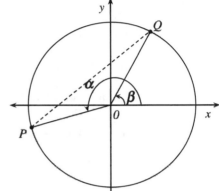

   a.   Write the measure of the obtuse angle in $\triangle POQ$ in terms of α and β.

   b.   Danny and Damian each realized that they could calculate the length of side PQ of their triangle, but they wanted to use two different methods. What are the two methods they could have been thinking of?

   c.   Danny wanted to use the idea of distance between points P and Q to calculate the length. In order to do that, he needed to label the coordinates of points P and Q. Based on angles α and β, represent the coordinates of each point using trigonometric functions.

   d.   Use your answer from part (c) to write an expression for the distance between points P and Q.

   e.   Damian realized that since this is a unit circle, the lengths of OP and OQ are both one unit, so he wanted to use the Law of Cosines. Use the Law of Cosines to write an expression for the length of side PQ.

   f.   Since the expressions you wrote for parts (c) and (d) both represent the length of PQ, what equation can you write? Simplify your equation to write a formula for $\cos(\alpha - \beta)$. This is called the **Angle Difference Identity** for cosine. Add this to your Identity Toolkit (Lesson 12.2.1 Resource Page).

12-128.   Danny and Damian were so pleased with this result that they wanted to keep going. They wanted to know how they could rewrite $\cos(\alpha + \beta)$. As they were thinking about this, Damian had a realization. *"I know how we could figure it out!"* he exclaimed. *"We could use the identity we already found to rewrite it as $\cos(\alpha - (-\beta))$, since that's the same thing as $\cos(\alpha + \beta)$."* Work with your team to use this idea to find the **Angle Sum Identity** for cosine.

12-129.   *"So now we have the sum and difference formulas for cosine, but what about for sine?"* Damian asked. Danny pondered this for a while and then remembered an identity he thought they could use to figure these out. *"Don't we have an identity that relates sine to cosine?"* he asked.

   a.   Which identity is Danny thinking of?

   b.   Danny and Damian realized that they could use this to rewrite $\sin(\alpha + \beta)$. Work with your team to rewrite $\sin(\alpha + \beta)$ and find the **Angle Sum Identity** for sine.

   c.   Now work with your team to develop the **Angle Difference Identity** for the sine. Be prepared to share your strategies with the class.

METHODS AND MEANINGS

MATH NOTES

Trigonometric Identities

Identities are equations that are true for all values for which the functions are defined.

$$\cos(-x) = \cos(x) \qquad \sin(-x) = -\sin(x)$$

Reciprocal Trigonometric Functions:

$$\csc(x) = \tfrac{1}{\sin(x)} \qquad \sec(x) = \tfrac{1}{\cos(x)} \qquad \cot(x) = \tfrac{1}{\tan(x)}$$

Pythagorean Identities:

$$\sin^2(x) + \cos^2(x) = 1 \qquad \tan^2(x) + 1 = \sec^2 x \qquad 1 + \cot^2(x) = \csc^2(x)$$

Cofunction Identities:

$$\sin(x) = \cos\left(\tfrac{\pi}{2} - x\right) \qquad \cos(x) = \sin\left(\tfrac{\pi}{2} - x\right) \qquad \sec(x) = \csc\left(\tfrac{\pi}{2} - x\right)$$

$$\csc(x) = \sec\left(\tfrac{\pi}{2} - x\right) \qquad \tan(x) = \cot\left(\tfrac{\pi}{2} - x\right) \qquad \cot(x) = \tan\left(\tfrac{\pi}{2} - x\right)$$

Angle Sum and Difference Identities:

$$\sin(x + y) = \sin(x)\cos(y) + \cos(x)\sin(y)$$

$$\sin(x - y) = \sin(x)\cos(y) - \cos(x)\sin(y)$$

$$\cos(x + y) = \cos(x)\cos(y) - \sin(x)\sin(y)$$

$$\cos(x - y) = \cos(x)\cos(y) + \sin(x)\sin(y)$$

Double Angle Identities:

$$\sin(2x) = 2\sin(x)\cos(x)$$

$$\cos(2x) = \cos^2(x) - \sin^2(x)$$

12-130. Write $\frac{\pi}{12}$ as the difference of two special angles. Then use the appropriate angle difference formula to find the exact sine and cosine of $\frac{\pi}{12}$.

12-131. Write each angle as the sum or difference of two special angles and then find the exact sine or cosine.

   a. $\sin\frac{7\pi}{12}$

   b. $\cos\frac{11\pi}{12}$

12-132. Show how to derive the double angle formulas for $\sin(2x)$ and $\cos(2x)$ by substituting x for both α and β in the formulas for $\sin(\alpha + \beta)$ and $\cos(\alpha + \beta)$, then simplifying.

12-133. Consider the function $f(x) = \cos(x + \frac{\pi}{2})$.

    a.   Make a complete graph of $f(x)$.

    b.   Write a simpler trig function that is represented by the same graph.

    c.   Now use the angle sum identity to expand and simplify $\cos(x + \frac{\pi}{2})$.

    d.   Does your work in part (c) agree with your graphical results from parts (a) and (b)? Explain.

12-134. Express $\frac{\cos x}{1-\tan x} - \frac{\sin x}{\cot x - 1}$ in terms of $\sin x$ and $\cos x$ and then simplify.

12-135. Latisha had graphed the polynomial $y = x^3 - 5x^2 + 8x - 6$ during class and remembered that it had one real root at $x = 3$. Explain how you could use division to find the other roots, and then find them.

12-136. Without using a calculator, solve these two problems from a college entrance exam.

    a.   If $x^{-4/3} + 1 = 17$, find $x^{-1/3}$.

    b.   If $\log(A) = a$, find $\log(\frac{A}{100})$.

12-137. In a certain family, the probability of any one child having dark hair is $\frac{3}{4}$. If the family has three children, what is the probability that exactly one has dark hair?

Chapter 12 Closure What have I learned?

Reflection and Synthesis

The activities below offer you a chance to reflect about what you have learned during this chapter. As you work, look for concepts that you feel very comfortable with, ideas that you would like to learn more about, and topics you need more help with. Look for connections between ideas as well as connections with material you learned previously.

①   TEAM BRAINSTORM

What have you studied in this chapter? What ideas were important in what you learned? With your team, brainstorm a list. Be as detailed as you can. To help get you started, a list of Math Notes boxes are below. (There were no Learning Log entries in this chapter.)

What topics, ideas, and words that you learned *before* this chapter are connected to the new ideas in this chapter? Again, be as detailed as you can.

How long can you make your list? Challenge yourselves. Be prepared to share your team's ideas with the class.

Math Notes

- Lesson 12.1.4 – Inverses of Trigonometric Functions
- Lesson 12.2.3 – Trigonometric Identities

②   MAKING CONNECTIONS

Below is a list of the vocabulary used in this chapter. Make sure that you are familiar with all of these words and know what they mean. Refer to the glossary or index for any words that you do not yet understand.

$\cos^{-1}$	cosecant	cotangent
identity	inverse	reciprocal
secant	$\sin^{-1}$	solution
$\tan^{-1}$		

Make a concept map showing all of the connections you can find among the key words and ideas listed above. To show a connection between two words, draw a line between them and explain the connection. A word can be connected to any other word as long as you can justify the connection. For each key word or idea, provide an example or sketch that shows the idea.

While you are making your map, your team may think of related words or ideas that are not listed here. Be sure to include these ideas on your concept map.

③   PORTFOLIO: EVIDENCE OF MATHEMATICAL PROFICIENCY

This section gives you an opportunity to show growth in your understanding of key mathematical ideas over time as you complete this course.

In this portfolio entry you are going to showcase your current understanding of Analytic Trigonometry. You are also going to showcase your ability to write a meaningful portfolio entry.

Make a list of the big ideas of this chapter. What have you studied in this chapter? What ideas were important in what you learned? Try to keep your list short: limit yourself to the no more than five of the biggest ideas.

a.   Write your own description of each big idea.

b.   For each big idea, provide one or two representative example problems. Solve each problem completely, using multiple representations, if applicable. Include a thorough explanation and justification.

④   WHAT HAVE I LEARNED?

Most of the problems in this section represent typical problems found in this chapter. They serve as a gauge for you. You can use them to determine which types of problems you can do well and which types of problems require further study and practice. Even if your teacher does not assign this section, it is a good idea to try these problems and find out for yourself what you know and what you still need to work on.

Solve each problem as completely as you can. The table at the end of the closure section has answers to these problems. It also tells you where you can find additional help and practice with problems like these.

CL 12-138.   Decide if each of the following statements is sometimes true, always true, or never true. If it is sometimes true, give the values for x that make it true; if it is always true or never true, explain how you know.

     a. $\cos(x) = \frac{3}{4}$ b. $2\tan(x) = 0$

     c. $\sin(x) = \frac{5}{2}$ d. $\sin(x) = \cos\left(\frac{\pi}{2} - x\right)$

CL 12-139.   Solve each of the following equations in the domain $0 \le x < 2\pi$.

     a. $2\cos(x) = 1$ b. $4\tan(x) + 4 = 0$

     c. $2\sin^2(x) - \sin(x) - 1 = 0$ d. $\csc(x) = -2$

CL 12-140.   An angle θ on the unit circle has a cosine of $\frac{1}{3}$. Find the exact coordinates of point Q by using the Pythagorean Identity.

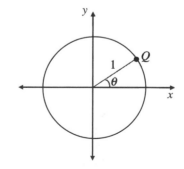

CL 12-141. Solve each of the following equations in the domain $0 \le x \le 2\pi$.

    a. $\cot (x) = 1.2$ b. $\cos (x) = -1$

    c. $\frac{1}{4}\csc (x) = \sin (x)$ d. $\cos (2x) = \frac{1}{2}$

CL 12-142. Using radian measure, represent all possible solutions to each equation.

    a. $\tan(x) = \sqrt{3}$ b. $\cos(x) = -\frac{\sqrt{2}}{2}$

    c. $\sin(x) = \frac{\sqrt{3}}{2}$ d. $\cot(x) = -1$

CL 12-143. Graph each of the following functions.

    a. $y = 3\sin 2(x - \frac{\pi}{4}) + 1$ b. $f(x) = -2\cos(x + \frac{\pi}{12}) - 1$

CL 12-144. Find the roots of the function $f(x) = x^4 + x^3 + 2x - 4$.

CL 12-145. Find the vertex of the parabola given by each quadratic equation below.

    a. $f(x) = x^2 + 8x + 12$ b. $g(x) = x^2 - 2x + 3$

CL 12-146. Write a possible equation for the graph at right.

CL 12-147. Solve each of the following equations.

    a. $5^x = 72$ b. $2^{3x} = 7$ c. $3^{(2x+4)} = 17$

CL 12-148. Check your answers using the table at the end of this section. Which problems do you feel confident about? Which problems were hard? Have you worked on problems like these in math classes you have taken before? Use the table to make a list of topics you need help on and a list of topics you need to practice more.

Answers and Support for Closure Activity #4
What Have I Learned?

Note: MN = Math Note, LL = Learning Log

Problem	Solutions	Need Help?	More Practice
CL 12-138.	a. True when $x \approx 0.72 + 2\pi n$ radians or when $x \approx 5.56 + 2\pi n$ radians. b. True for $x = \pi n$ radians. c. Never true. The range of sine is $-1 \le y \le 1$. d. Always true.	Lesson 12.1.1	Problems 12-2, 12-5, 12-14, 12-23, and 12-66
CL 12-139.	a. $\frac{\pi}{3}, \frac{5\pi}{3}$ b. $\frac{3\pi}{4}, \frac{7\pi}{4}$ c. $\frac{7\pi}{6}, \frac{11\pi}{6}, \frac{\pi}{2}$ d. $\frac{7\pi}{6}, \frac{11\pi}{6}$	Lessons 12.1.2, 12.1.4, and 12.2.1 MN: 12.1.4	Problems 12-29, 12-43, 12-53, 12-63, 12-68, 12-69, 12-77, 12-111, and 12-119
CL 12-140.	$\left(\frac{1}{3}, \frac{\sqrt{8}}{3} \right)$	Lesson 7.1.4 and problem 12-94	Problems 7-53, 7-64, 7-89, 12-90 part (a), 12-100, and 12-114
CL 12-141.	a. $x \approx 0.69$ radians or $x \approx 3.84$ radians b. $x = \pi$ c. $x = \frac{\pi}{6}, \frac{5\pi}{6}, \frac{7\pi}{6}, \frac{11\pi}{6}$ d. $x = \frac{\pi}{6}, \frac{5\pi}{6}, \frac{7\pi}{6}, \frac{11\pi}{6}$	Lessons 12.1.2 and 12.1.4 MN: 12.1.4 and 12.2.3	Problems 12-63, 12-64, 12-68, 12-69, 12-77, 12-111, and 12-119
CL 12-142.	a. $\frac{\pi}{3} + \pi n$ b. $\frac{3\pi}{4} + 2\pi n, \frac{5\pi}{4} + 2\pi n$ c. $\frac{\pi}{3} + 2\pi n, \frac{2\pi}{3} + 2\pi n$ d. $-\frac{\pi}{4} + \pi n$ or $\frac{3\pi}{4} + \pi n$	Lesson 12.1.2 MN: 12.1.4	Problems 12-27, 12-40, 12-42, 12-53, 12-63, 12-68, and 12-77

Problem	Solutions	Need Help?	More Practice
CL 12-143.	a. [graph] b. [graph]	Chapter 7 MN: 7.2.4 LL: 7.2.4	Problems 12-10, 12-31, 12-54, 12-98, and 12-133
CL 12-144.	$x = 1, -2, \pm\sqrt{2}i$	Lesson 8.3.2 MN: 8.3.2	Problems 12-83, 12-106, 12-126, and 12-135
CL 12-145.	a. $(-4, -4)$ b. $(1, 2)$	Lesson 2.1.4 MN: 2.1.3 and 2.1.4 LL: 2.1.5 and 2.2.2	Problems 11-56, 12-57, and 12-106
CL 12-146.	$y = -x^2(x-2)^2(x+2)^2$	Section 8.1 and Lesson 8.3.3	Problems 10-38, 10-39, 10-57, 10-151, 12-126, and 12-135
CL 12-147.	a. $x \approx 2.657$ b. $x \approx 0.936$ c. $x \approx -0.711$	Lesson 6.2.1	Problems 10-56, 10-162, CL 10-188, 12-58, and 12-122

SEQUENCES

Appendix A

Sequences

Appendix A provides you an opportunity to review and strengthen your algebra skills while you learn about arithmetic and geometric sequences.

Early in this chapter, you will use familiar strategies such as looking for patterns and making tables to write algebraic equations describing sequences of numbers.

Later in this chapter, you will develop shortcuts for writing equations for certain kinds of sequences.

Guiding Question

Mathematically proficient students look for and express regularity in repeated reasoning.

Think about this question throughout the chapter:

When patterns are repeated, can I find shortcuts that lead to equations?

Chapter Outline

Section A.1 This section begins with lessons that ask you to describe the growth of a rabbit population and the decreasing rebound height of a bouncing ball. You will use tables, graphs, and equations to represent the growth.

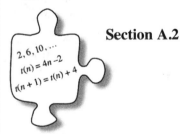

Section A.2 You will do an investigation where you categorize several sequences. You will also learn some of the specialized vocabulary used when discussing sequences. You will create multiple representations of arithmetic sequences, including equations for sequences that depend on previous terms.

Section A.3 In this section you will compare the growth of various sequences and recognize growth by multiplication and growth by addition. Then you will create multiple representations of geometric sequences and compare sequences to functions.

A.1.1 How does the pattern grow?

Representing Exponential Growth

So far in this course, you have been investigating the family of linear functions using multiple representations (especially $x \rightarrow y$ tables, graphs, and equations). In this chapter, you will learn about a new family of functions and the type of growth it models.

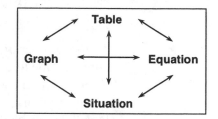

A-1.   MULTIPLYING LIKE BUNNIES

In the book *Of Mice and Men* by John Steinbeck, two good friends named Lenny and George dream of raising rabbits and living off the land. What if their dream came true?

Suppose Lenny and George started with two rabbits and that in each following month those rabbits have two babies. Also suppose that every month thereafter, each pair of rabbits has two babies.

Your Task: With your team, determine how many rabbits Lenny and George would have after one year (12 months). Represent this situation with a written description of the growth pattern, a diagram, and a table. What patterns can you find and how do they compare to other patterns that you have investigated previously?

Discussion Points

What strategies could help us keep track of the total number of rabbits?

What patterns can we see in the growth of the rabbit population?

How can we predict the total number of rabbits after many months have passed?

A-2.   How can you determine the number of rabbits that will exist at the end of one year? Consider this as you answer the questions below.

    a.   Draw a diagram to represent how the total number of rabbits is growing each month. How many rabbits will Lenny and George have after three months?

    b.   As the number of rabbits becomes larger, a diagram becomes too cumbersome to be useful. A table might work better. Organize your information in a table showing the total number of rabbits for the first several months (at least 6 months). What patterns can you find in your table? Describe the pattern of growth in words.

    c.   If you have not done so already, use your pattern to determine the number of rabbits that Lenny and George would have after one year (12 months) has passed.

    d.   How does the growth in the table that you created compare to the growth patterns that you have investigated previously? How is it similar and how is it different?

———— *Further Guidance section ends here.* ————

A-3.   Lenny and George want to raise as many rabbits as possible, so they have a few options to consider. They could start with a larger number of rabbits, or they could raise a breed of rabbits that reproduces faster. How do you think that each of these options would change the pattern of growth you observed in the previous problem? Which situation might yield the largest rabbit population after one year?

    a.   To help answer these questions, model each case below with a table for the first five months.

       Case 2: Start with 10 rabbits; each pair has 2 babies per month.

       Case 3: Start with 2 rabbits; each pair has 4 babies per month.

       Case 4: Start with 2 rabbits; each pair has 6 babies per month.

    b.   Which case would appear to give Lenny and George the most rabbits after one year? How many rabbits would they have in that case?

A-4.   A NEW FAMILY

Look back at the tables you created in problems A-1 and A-3.

a.   What pattern do they all have in common? Functions that have this pattern are called **exponential functions**.

b.   Obtain the Lesson A.1.1 Resource Page from your teacher. Graph the data for Case 2. Give a complete description of the graph.

A-5.   LEARNING LOG

To represent the growth in number of rabbits in problems A-1 and A-3, you discovered a new function family that is not linear. Functions in this new family are called exponential functions. Throughout this chapter and later in Appendix B, you will learn more about this special family of functions.

Write a Learning Log entry to record what you have learned so far about exponential functions. For example, what do their graphs look like? What patterns do you observe in their tables? Title this entry "Exponential Functions" and include today's date.

─────────── Review & Preview ───────────

A-6.   What if the data for Lenny and George (from problem A-1) matched the data in each table below? Assuming that the growth of the rabbits continues as it did in problem A-1, complete each of the following tables. Show your thinking or give a brief explanation of how you found the missing entries.

a.

Months	Rabbits
0	4
1	12
2	36
3	
4	

b.

Months	Rabbits
0	6
1	
2	24
3	
4	96

A-7.   Solve the following systems of equations algebraically. Then graph each system to confirm your solution.

a. $x + y = 3$
      $x = 3y - 5$

b. $x - y = -5$
      $y = -2x - 4$

A-8.   For the function $f(x) = \frac{6}{2x-3}$, find the value of each expression below.

a. $f(1)$ b. $f(0)$ c. $f(-3)$ d. $f(1.5)$

e. What value of x would make $f(x) = 4$?

A-9.   Benjamin is taking Algebra 1 and is stuck on the problem shown below.
Examine his work so far and help him by showing and explaining the remaining
steps.

Original problem: Simplify $(3a^{-2}b)^3$.

He knows that $(3a^{-2}b)^3 = (3a^{-2}b)(3a^{-2}b)(3a^{-2}b)$. Now what?

A-10.   Simplify each expression below. Assume that the denominator in part (b) is not
equal to zero.

a. $(x^3)(x^{-2})$ b. $\frac{y^5}{y^{-2}}$ c. 4^{-1} d. $(4x^2)^3$

A-11.   The equation of a line describes the relationship between the x- and
y-coordinates of the points on the line.

a. Plot the points $(3, -1)$, $(3, 2)$, and $(3, 4)$ and draw the line that passes
through them. State the coordinates of two more points on the line. Then
answer this question: What will be true of the coordinates of any other
point on this line? Now write an equation that says exactly the same thing.
(Do not worry if it is very simple! If it accurately describes all the points
on this line, it is correct.)

b. Plot the points $(5, -1)$, $(1, -1)$, and $(-3, -1)$. What is the equation of the
line that goes through these points?

c. Choose any three points on the y-axis. What must be the equation of the
line that goes through those points?

A-12.   Jill is studying a strange bacterium. When she first looks at the bacteria, there
are 1000 cells in her sample. The next day, there are 2000 cells. Intrigued, she
comes back the next day to find that there are 4000 cells!

a. Should the graph of this situation be linear or curved?

b. Create a table and graph for this situation. The inputs are the days that
have passed after she first began to study the sample, and the outputs are
the number of cells of bacteria.

Core Connections Algebra 2

A-13.   Write each expression below in a simpler form.

a. $\dfrac{5^{723}}{5^{721}}$

b. $\dfrac{3^{300}}{3^{249}}$

c. $\left(\dfrac{3 \cdot 4^3}{3^{-2} \cdot 4^{-7}}\right)^0$

d. $\left(\dfrac{4 \times 10^3}{10^{-2}}\right)^2$

A-14.   Jackie and Alexa were working on homework together when Jackie said, *"I got x = 5 as the solution, but it looks like you got something different. Which solution is right?"*

$(x+4)^2 - 2x - 5 = (x-1)^2$

$x^2 + 16 - 2x - 5 = x^2 + 1$

$16 - 2x - 5 = 1$

$11 - 2x = 1$

$-2x = -10$

$x = 5$

"I think you made a mistake," said Alexa. Did Jackie make a mistake? Help Jackie figure out whether she made a mistake and, if she did, explain her mistake and show her how to solve the equation correctly. Jackie's work is shown above right.

A-15.   Solve each of the following equations.

a. $\dfrac{m}{6} = \dfrac{15}{18}$

b. $\dfrac{\pi}{7} = \dfrac{a}{4}$

A-16.   Write the equation of each line described below.

a.   A line with slope –2 and *y*-intercept 7.

b.   A line with slope $-\dfrac{3}{2}$ and *x*-intercept $(4, 0)$.

A-17.   The dartboard shown at right is in the shape of an equilateral triangle. It has a smaller equilateral triangle in the center, which was made by joining the midpoints of the three edges. If a dart hits the board at random, what is the probability that:

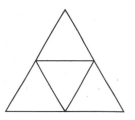

a.   The dart hits the center triangle?

b.   The dart misses the center triangle but hits the board?

A.1.2 How high will it bounce?

Rebound Ratios

Many games depend on how a ball bounces. For example, if different basketballs rebounded differently, one basketball would bounce differently off of a backboard than another would, and this could cause basketball players to miss their shots. For this reason, manufacturers have to make balls' bounciness conform to specific standards. In this lesson, you will investigate the relationship between the height from which you drop a ball and the height to which it rebounds.

A-18.   Listed below are "bounciness" standards for different kinds of balls.

- Tennis balls: Must rebound approximately 111 cm when dropped from 200 cm.

- Soccer balls: Must rebound approximately 120 cm when dropped from 200 cm onto a steel plate.

- Basketballs: Must rebound approximately 53.5 inches when dropped from 72 inches onto a wooden floor.

- Squash balls: Must rebound approximately 29.5 inches when dropped from 100 inches onto a steel plate at 70° F.

Discuss with your team how you can measure a ball's bounciness. Which ball listed above is the bounciest? Justify your answer.

A-19.   THE BOUNCING BALL

How can you determine if a ball meets expected standards?

Your Task: With your team, find the rebound ratio for a ball. Your teacher will provide you with a ball and a measuring device. You will be using the same ball again later, so make sure you can identify which ball your team is using. Before you start your experiment, discuss the following questions with your team.

Discussion Points

What do we need to measure?

How should we organize our data?

How can we be confident that our data is accurate?

You should choose one person in your team to be the recorder, one to be the ball dropper, and two to be the spotters. When you are confident that you have a good plan, ask your teacher to come to your team and approve it.

A-20.   MODELING YOUR DATA

Work with your team to model the data you collected in problem A-19 by considering parts (a) through (c) below.

a.   In problem A-19, does the height from which the ball is dropped depend on the rebound height, or is it the other way around? With your team, decide which is the independent variable and which is the dependent variable.

b.   Graph your results on a full sheet of graph paper. Draw a line that best fits your data. Should this line go through the origin? Why or why not? Justify your answer in terms of what the origin represents in this problem situation.

c.   Find an equation for your line.

A-21.   What is the rebound ratio for your team's ball? How is the rebound ratio reflected in the graph of your line of best fit? Where is it reflected in the equation for your data? Where is it reflected in your table?

Save your data and your graph in a safe place. You will need them for the next lesson.

METHODS AND MEANINGS

Continuous and Discrete Graphs

When the points on a graph are connected, and it *makes sense* to connect them, the graph is said to be **continuous**. If the graph is not continuous, and is just a sequence of separate points, the graph is called **discrete**.

For example, the graph on the left represents the cost of buying x shirts and is discrete because you can only buy whole numbers of shirts. The graph on the right represents the cost of buying x gallons of gasoline and is continuous because you can buy any (non-negative) amount of gasoline.

Discrete Graph

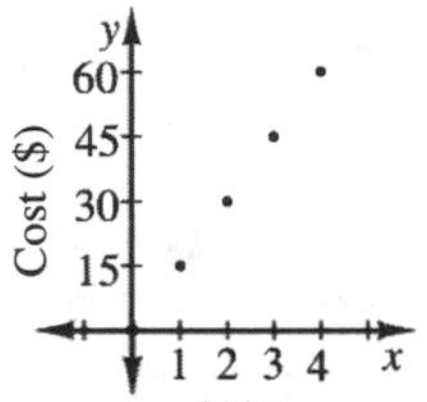

Continuous Graph

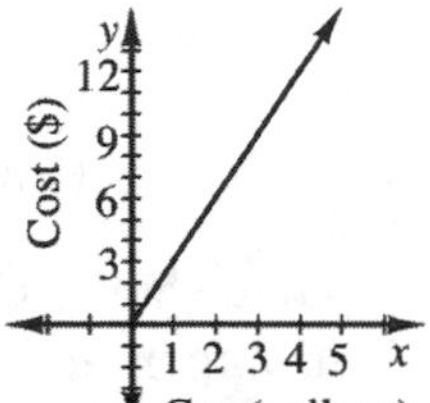

Review & Preview

A-22.   Solve each system of equations below.

   a. $y = 3x + 1$
          $x + 2y = -5$

   b. $2x + 3y = 9$
          $x - 2y = 1$

A-23.   Solve each equation for the indicated variable.

   a. $t = an + b$ (for b)

   b. $\frac{y}{3} - a = b$ (for y)

   c. $m = \frac{y}{x}$ (for y)

   d. $m = \frac{y}{x}$ (for x)

A-24.   Simplify each expression below.

   a. $\frac{6x^2 y^3}{3xy}$

   b. $(-mn)^3$

   c. $(mn)^{-3}$

   d. $\frac{3.2 \times 10^{-2}}{8 \times 10^3}$

A-25.   Determine the domain and range of each of the following graphs.

a.
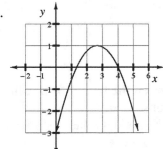

b.
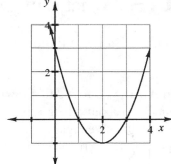

c.
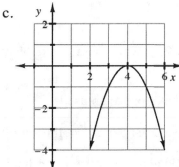

d.
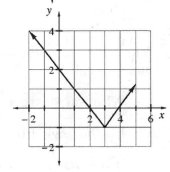

A-26.   The graph at right compares the age and the number of pets for a certain population.

Describe the association for this population.

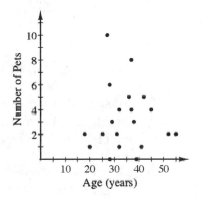

A-27.   At his aunt's wedding, Nicolas collected data about an ice sculpture that was slowly melting. A graph of his data is shown at right.

   a.   Calculate the equation of a line of best fit.

   b.   Based on your equation, how tall was the ice sculpture one hour before Nicolas started measuring?

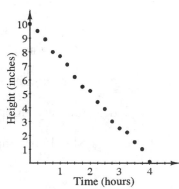

A.1.3 What is the pattern?

The Bouncing Ball and Exponential Decay

In Lesson A.1.2, you found that the relationship between the height from which a ball is dropped and its rebound height is determined by a constant multiplier. In this lesson, you will continue this investigation by exploring the mathematical relationship between how many times a ball has bounced and the height of each bounce.

A-28. Consider the work you did in Lesson A.1.2, in which you found the rebound ratio for a ball.

    a. What was the rebound ratio for the ball your team used?

    b. Did the height from which you dropped the ball affect this ratio?

    c. If you were to use the same ball again and drop it from *any* height, could you predict its rebound height? Explain how you would do this.

A-29. **A MODEL FOR MANY BOUNCES**

Imagine that you drop the same ball that you used in problem A-19 from a height of 200 cm, but this time you let it bounce repeatedly.

    a. As a team, discuss this situation. Then sketch a picture showing what this situation would look like. Your sketch should show a minimum of 6 bounces after you release the ball.

    b. Predict your ball's rebound height after each successive bounce if its starting height is 200 cm. Create a table with these predicted heights.

    c. What are the independent and dependent variables in this situation?

    d. Graph your predicted rebound heights.

    e. Should the points on your graph be connected? How can you tell?

A-30.   TESTING THE MANY-BOUNCE MODEL

Now you will test the accuracy of the
predictions you made in problem A-29.

Your Task: Test your predictions by collecting
experimental data. Use the same Team Roles
as you used in problem A-19. Drop your ball,
starting from an initial height of 200 cm, and
record your data in a table. Then compare your
experimental data to your predictions using your table and your graph. How do
they compare? What might cause your experimental data to be different from
your predictions? Do you think that your table and graph model the situation
appropriately? Why or why not?

These suggestions will help you gather accurate data:

- Have a spotter catch the ball just as it reaches the top of its first rebound
  and have the spotter "freeze" the ball in place.

- Record the first rebound height and then drop the ball again from that
  new height.

- Catch and "freeze" it again at the second rebound height.

- Repeat this process until you have collected at least 6 data points (or until
  the height of the bounce is so small that it is not reasonable to continue).

A-31.   Compare your graph for the height of successive bounces in problem A-29 to
the graph for drop height versus bounce height that you investigated in Lesson
A.1.2.

a.   Can you use the same kind of equation to model the two situations? That
is, what family of functions do you think would make the best fit for each
data set? Discuss this with your team and be ready to report and justify
your choice.

b.   Describe how the pattern of growth for successive bounces is the same as
or different from other models that you have looked at previously.

A-32.   If you continued to let your ball bounce uninterrupted, how high would the ball
be after 12 bounces? Would the ball ever stop bouncing? Explain your answer
in terms of both your experimental data and your equation.

A-33.   Notice that your investigations of rebound patterns in Lessons A.1.2 and A.1.3 involved both a linear and an exponential model. Look back over your work and discuss with your team why each model was appropriate for its specific purpose. Be prepared to share your ideas with the class.

A-34.   DeShawna and her team gathered data for their ball and recorded it in the table shown at right.

Drop Height	Rebound Height
150 cm	124 cm
70 cm	59 cm
120 cm	100 cm
100 cm	83 cm
110 cm	92 cm
40 cm	33 cm

a.   What is the rebound ratio for their ball?

b.   Predict how high DeShawna's ball will rebound if it is dropped from 275 cm. Look at the precision of DeShawna's measurements in the table. Round your calculation to a reasonable number of decimal places.

c.   Suppose the ball is dropped and you notice that its rebound height is 60 cm. From what height was the ball dropped? Use appropriate precision for your answer.

d.   Suppose the ball is dropped from a window 200 meters up the Empire State Building. What would you predict the rebound height to be after the first bounce?

e.   How high would the ball in part (d) rebound after the second bounce? After the third bounce?

A-35.   Look back at the data given in problem A-18 that describes the rebound ratio for an official tennis ball. Suppose you drop such a tennis ball from an initial height of 10 feet.

a.   How high would it rebound after the first bounce?

b.   How high would it rebound after the second bounce?

c.   How high would it rebound after the fifth bounce?

A-36.   Solve the following systems of equations algebraically and then confirm your solutions by graphing.

a. $y = 3x - 2$
       $4x + 2y = 6$

b. $x = y - 4$
       $2x - y = -5$

A-37.   Lona received a stamp collectio[n]
The collection is in a leather b[ook]
120 stamps. Lona joined a sta[mp]
12 new stamps each month.
maximum of 500 stamps.

a.   Complete the table a[t]

b.   How many stamps
one year from nov[w]

c.   Write an equatio[n]
represent the to[tal]
has in her coll[ection]
be represente[d]

d.   Solve your equation fro[m]
able to fill her book exactly wiu[n]
know? When will the book be filled?

A.2.1   How can I [...]
Generating and Investigatin[g]

In the bouncing ball act[...]
A.1.3, you used multi[...]
an equation, and a g[...]
involving a boun[...]
learn about a n[...]
also called a [...]

A-41

A-38.   Use slope to determine whether the points $A(3,5)$, $B(-2,6)$, and $C(-5,7)$ are on
the same line. Justify your conclusion algebraically.

A-39.   Serena wanted to examine the graphs of the equations below on her graphing
calculator. Rewrite each of the equations in y= form (when the equation is
solved for y) so that she can enter them into the calculator.

a. $5-(y-2)=3x$ b. $5(x+y)=-2$

A-40.   The graph at right shows a comparison of the
length of several gold chain necklaces (including
the clasp) to the total mass.

a.   Write an equation for the line of best fit.

b.   Based on your equation, what would you
expect to be the mass of a 26-inch chain?

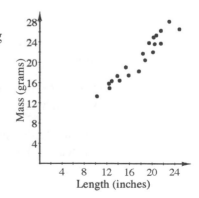

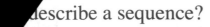 describe a sequence?

$2, 6, 10, \ldots$
$t(n) = 4n - 2$
$t(n+1) = t(n) + 4$

Sequences

vity from Lessons A.1.2 and
ple representations (an $x \to y$ table,
raph) to represent a discrete situation
ing ball (a situation). Today you will
w way to represent a discrete pattern,
equence.

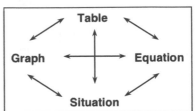

Samantha was thinking about George and Lenny and their rabbits. When she listed the number of rabbits George and Lenny could have each month, she ended up with the ordered list below, called a **sequence**.

$$2, 6, 18, 54, \ldots$$

She realized that she could represent this situation using a sequence-generating machine that would generate the number of rabbits each month by doing something to the previous month's number of rabbits. She tested her generator by putting in a **first term** of 2 and she recorded each output before putting it into the next machine. Below is the diagram she used to explain her idea to her teammates.

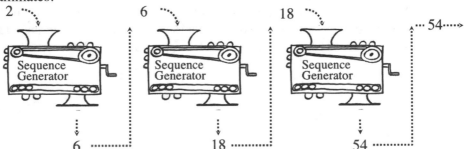

a. What does Samantha's **sequence generator** seem to be doing to each input?

b. What are the next two terms of Samantha's sequence? Show how you got your answer.

c. Samantha decided to use the same sequence generator, but this time she started with a first term of 5. What are the next four terms in this new sequence?

A-42.   SEQUENCE FAMILIES

Samantha and her teacher have been busy creating new sequence generators and the sequences they produce. Below are the sequences Samantha and her teacher created.

a. $-4, -1, 2, 5, \ldots$ b. $1.5, 3, 6, 12, \ldots$

c. $0, 1, 4, 9, \ldots$ d. $2, 3.5, 5, 6.5, \ldots$

e. $1, 1, 2, 3, 5, 8, \ldots$ f. $9, 7, 5, 3, \ldots$

g. $48, 24, 12, \ldots$ h. $27, 9, 3, 1, \ldots$

i. $8, 2, 0, 2, 8, 18, \ldots$ j. $\frac{5}{4}, \frac{5}{2}, 5, 10, \ldots$

Your teacher will give your team a set of Lesson A.2.1A Resource Pages with the above sequences on strips so that everyone in your team can see and work with them in the middle of your workspace.

Your Task: Working together, organize the sequences into families of similar sequences. Your team will need to decide how many families to make, what common features make the sequences a family, and what characteristics make each family different from the others. Read and carry out the directions that follow. As you work, use the following questions to help guide your team's discussion.

Discussion Points

How can we describe the pattern?

How does it grow?

What do the patterns have in common?

(1)   As a team, initially sort the sequence strips into groups based on your first glance at the sequences. Remember that you can sort the sequences into more than two families. You will have a chance to revise your groups of sequences throughout this activity, so just sort them in a way that makes sense to start out with. Which seem to behave similarly? Record your groupings and what they have in common before proceeding.

(2)   If one exists, find a sequence generator (growth pattern) for each sequence and write it on the strip. You can express the sequence generator either in symbols or in words. Also record the next three terms in each sequence on the strips. Do your sequence families still make sense? If so, what new information do you have about your sequence families? If not, reorganize the strips and explain how you decided to group them.

Problem continues on next page. →

A-42.   *Problem continued from previous page.*

    (3)   Get a set of Lesson A.2.1B Resource Pages for your team. Then record each sequence in a table. Your table should compare the **term number**, n, to the value of each **term**, $t(n)$. This means that your sequence itself is a list of *outputs* of the relationship and the *inputs* are a list of integers! The first term in a sequence is always $n = 1$. Attach each table to the sequence strip it represents. Do your sequence families still make sense? Record any new information or reorganize your sequence families if necessary.

    (4)   Now graph each sequence on a Lesson A.2.1C Resource Page. Include as many terms as will fit on the existing set of axes. Be sure to decide whether your graphs should be discrete or continuous. Use color to show the growth between the points on each graph. Attach each graph to the sequence strip it represents. Do your sequence families still make sense? Record any new information and reorganize your sequence families if necessary.

A-43.   Choose one of the families of sequences you created in problem A-42. With your team, write clear summary statements about this family of sequences. Refer to the Discussion Points in problem A-42 to help you write summary statements. Be sure to use multiple representations to justify each statement. Be prepared to share your summary statements with the class.

A-44.   Some types of sequences have special names.

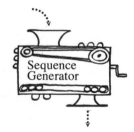

    a.   When the sequence generator *adds* a constant to each previous term, it is called an **arithmetic sequence**. Which of your sequences from problem A-42 fall into this family? Should you include the sequence labeled (f) in this family? Why or why not?

    b.   When the sequence generator *multiplies* a constant times each previous term, it is called a **geometric sequence**. Which of the sequences from problem A-42 are geometric? Should sequence (h) be in this group? Why or why not?

A-45.   Find the slope of the line you would get if you graphed each sequence listed below and connected the points.

a. $5, 8, 11, 14, \ldots$ b. $3, 9, 15, \ldots$

c. $26, 21, 16, \ldots$ d. $7, 8.5, 10, \ldots$

A-46.   For the line passing through the points $(-2, 1)$ and $(2, -11)$,

a.   Calculate the slope of the line.

b.   Find an equation of the line.

A-47.   Allie is making 8 dozen chocolate chip muffins for the Food Fair at school. The recipe she is using makes 3 dozen muffins. If the original recipe calls for 16 ounces of chocolate chips, how many ounces of chocolate chips does she need for her new amount? (Allie buys her chocolate chips in bulk and can measure them to the nearest ounce.)

A-48.   The area of a square is 225 square centimeters.

a.   Make a diagram and determine the length of each side.

b.   Use the Pythagorean theorem to find the length of its diagonal.

A-49.   Refer to sequences (c) and (i) in problem A-42.

a.   How are these two sequences similar?

b.   The numbers in the sequence in part (e) of problem A-42 are called **Fibonacci numbers**. They are named after an Italian mathematician who discovered the sequence while studying how fast rabbits could breed. What is different about this sequence than the other three you discovered?

A-50.   Chelsea dropped a bouncy ball off the roof while Nery recorded its rebound height. The table at right shows their data. Note that the 0 in the "Bounce" column represents the starting height.

Bounce	Rebound Height
0	800 cm
1	475 cm
2	290 cm
3	175 cm
4	100 cm
5	60 cm

   a.   To what family does the function belong? Explain how you know.

   b.   Show the data as a sequence. Is the sequence arithmetic, geometric, quadratic, or something else? Justify your answer.

A-51.   For the function $f(x) = \sqrt{3x-2}$, find the value of each expression below.

   a. $f(1)$ b. $f(9)$ c. $f(4)$ d. $f(0)$

   e.   What value of x makes $f(x) = 6$?

A-52.   Simplify each expression below.

   a. $y + 0.03y$ b. $z - 0.2z$ c. $x + 0.002x$

A-53.   A tank contains 8000 liters of water. Each day, half of the water in the tank is removed. How much water will be in the tank at the end of:

   a.   The 4th day?   b.   The 8th day?

A-54.   Solve each system.

   a. $y + 3x = -10$ b. $6x = 7 - 2y$
        $5x - y = 2$ $4x + y = 4$

A-55.   Draw a slope triangle and use it to find the equation of the line shown in the graph at right.

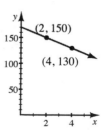

A-56.   Simplify each expression. In parts (e) through (f) write the final answer in scientific notation.

   a. $4^2 \cdot 4^5$ b. $(5^0)^3$ c. $x^{-5} \cdot x^3$

   d. $(x^{-1} \cdot y^2)^3$ e. $(8 \times 10^5) \cdot (1.6 \times 10^{-2})$ f. $\dfrac{4 \times 10^3}{5 \times 10^5}$

Core Connections Algebra 2

A.2.2 How do arithmetic sequences work?

....

Generalizing Arithmetic Sequences

In Lesson A.2.1, you learned how to identify arithmetic and geometric sequences. Today you will solve problems involving arithmetic sequences. Use the questions below to help your team stay focused and start mathematical conversations.

What type of sequence is this? How do we know?

How can we find the equation?

Is there another way to see it?

A-57.   LEARNING THE LANGUAGE OF SEQUENCES

Sequences have their own notation and vocabulary that help describe them, such as "term" and "term number." The questions below will help you learn more of this vocabulary and notation.

Consider the sequence $-9, -5, -1, 3, 7, \ldots$ as you complete parts (a) through (f).

a.   Is this sequence arithmetic, geometric, or neither? How can you tell?

b.   What is the first term of the sequence?

c.   When the sequence generator adds a number to each term, the value that is added is known as the **common difference**. It is the difference between each term and the term before it.

What is the sequence generator?

d.   Record the sequence in a table. Remember a sequence table compares the term number, n, to the value of each term, $t(n)$.

e.   What is $t(n)$ when $n = 0$?

f.   Graph the sequence. Should the graph be continuous or discrete? Why?

g.   Write an equation (beginning $t(n) = $) for the nth term of this sequence.

h.   What is the domain for the sequence equation that you have written?

i.   How is the common difference related to the graph and the equation? Why does this make sense?

A-58.   Consider the sequence $t(n) = -4, -1, 2, 5, \ldots$

        a.   If the first term is $t(1)$, what is $t(0)$ for this sequence? What is the common difference?

        b.   Write an equation for $t(n)$. Verify that your equation works for each of the first 4 terms of the sequence.

        c.   Is it possible for $t(n)$ to equal 42? Justify your answer.

        d.   For the function $f(x) = 3x - 7$, is it possible for $f(x)$ to equal 42? Explain.

        e.   Explain the difference between $t(n)$ and $f(x)$ that makes your answers to parts (b) and (c) different.

A-59.   Trixie wants to create an especially tricky arithmetic sequence. She wants the 5th term of the sequence to equal 11 and the 50th term to equal 371. That is, she wants $t(5) = 11$ and $t(50) = 371$. Is it possible to create an arithmetic sequence to fit her information? If it is possible, find the sequence generator, the initial value $t(0)$, and then find the equation for the arithmetic sequence. If it is not possible, explain why not.

A-60.   Seven years ago, Kodi found a box of old baseball cards in the garage. Since then, he has added a consistent number of cards to the collection each year. He had 52 cards in the collection after 3 years and now has 108 cards.

        a.   How many cards were in the original box? Is this $t(0)$ or $t(1)$? Write the first few terms of the sequence.

        b.   Kodi plans to keep the collection for a long time. How many cards will the collection contain 10 years from now?

        c.   Write an equation that determines the number of cards in the collection after n years. What does each number in your equation represent?

A-61.   Trixie now wants an arithmetic sequence with a sequence generator of -17 and a 16th term of 93. (In other words, $t(16) = 93$.) Is it possible to create an arithmetic sequence to fit her information? If it is possible, find the equation. If it is not possible, explain why not.

A-62. Your favorite radio station, WCPM, is having a contest. The DJ poses a question to the listeners. If the caller answers correctly, he or she wins the prize money. If the caller answers incorrectly, $20 is added to the prize money and the next caller is eligible to win. The current question is difficult, and no one has won for two days.

    a. Lucky you! Fourteen people already called in today with incorrect answers, so when you called (with the right answer, of course) you won $735! How much was the prize worth at the beginning of the day today?

    b. Suppose the contest always starts with $100. How many people would have to guess incorrectly for the winner to get $1360?

A-63. Trixie is at it again. This time she wants an arithmetic sequence that has a graph with a slope of 22. She also wants $t(8) = 164$ and the 13th term to have a value of 300. Is it possible to create an arithmetic sequence to fit her information? If it is possible, find the equation. If it is not possible, explain why not.

A-64. Find the equation for each arithmetic sequence represented by the tables below.

a.

n	$t(n)$
7	54
3	10
19	186
16	153
40	417

b.

n	$t(n)$
100	10
70	100

A-65. Trixie exclaimed, *"Hey! Arithmetic sequences are just another name for linear functions."* What do you think? Justify your idea based on multiple representations.

A-66.   Determine whether 447 is a term of each sequence below. If so, which term is it?

   a. $t(n) = 5n - 3$ b. $t(n) = 24 - 5n$

   c. $t(n) = -6 + 3(n-1)$ d. $t(n) = 14 - 3n$

   e. $t(n) = -8 - 7(n-1)$

A-67.   Choose one of the sequences in problem A-66 for which you determined that 447 is *not* a term. Write a clear explanation describing how you can be sure that 447 is not a term of the sequence.

A-68.   Find the sequence generator for each sequence listed below. Write an equation for the nth term in each sequence below, keeping in mind that the first term of each sequence is $t(1)$.

   a. $4, 7, 10, 13, \ldots$ b. $3, 8, 13, \ldots$

   c. $24, 19, 14, \ldots$ d. $7, 9.5, 12, \ldots$

A-69.   Great Amusements Park has been raising its ticket prices every year, as shown in the table at right.

   a.   Describe how the ticket prices are growing.

   b.   What will the price of admission be in year 6?

Year	Price
0	$50
1	$55
2	$60.50
3	$66.55

A-70.   Solve the system at right for m and b.

$$1239 = 94m + b$$
$$810 = 61m + b$$

A-71.   Write an equation or system of equations and then solve the problem below.

   The French club sold rose bouquets and chocolate hearts for Valentine's Day. The roses sold for $5 and the hearts sold for $3. The number of bouquets sold was 15 more than the number of hearts sold. If the club collected a total of $339, how many of each gift was sold.

Core Connections Algebra 2

A.2.3 How else can I write the equation?

Recursive Sequences

$$2, 6, 10, \ldots$$
$$t(n) = 4n - 2$$
$$t(n+1) = t(n) + 4$$

In this chapter you have been writing equations for arithmetic sequences so that you could find the value of any term in the sequence, such as the 100th term, directly. Today you will investigate recursive sequences. A term in a recursive sequence depends on the term(s) before it.

A-72.   Look at the following sequence:

$$-8, -2, 4, 10, \ldots$$

a.   What are two ways that you could find the 10th term of the sequence? What is the 10th term?

b.   If you have not done so already, write an equation that lets you find the value of any term $t(n)$. This kind of equation is called an **explicit equation**.

c.   The next term after $t(n)$ is called $t(n+1)$. Write an equation to find $t(n+1)$ if you know what $t(n)$ is. An equation that depends on knowing other terms is called a **recursive equation**.

A-73.   Alejandro used the recursive equation from part (c) of problem A-72 to write a sequence and came up with the following:

$$0, 6, 12, 18, 24$$

a.   Does Alejandro's sequence match the recursive equation from problem A-72?

b.   Why did Alejandro get a different sequence than the one from problem A-72? How can you mathematically write down the information he needs so that he can write the correct sequence?

A-74.   Avery and Collin were trying to challenge each other
         with equations for sequences. Avery wrote:

$$t(n+1) = t(n)^2 - 1$$
$$t(1) = 3$$

   a.   Help Collin write the first 4 terms of this
         sequence.

   b.   Is Avery's sequence arithmetic, geometric, or some other kind of
         sequence? How do you know?

   c.   Describe to Collin how he could find the 10th term of this sequence.
         You do not need to actually find the 10th term.

A-75.   Avery and Collin were still at it.

   a.   Collin wrote: $t(2) = 19$
                        $t(n+1) = t(n) - 2$

         Help Avery write an explicit equation. Is the sequence arithmetic,
         geometric, or neither?

   b.   Then Avery wrote $t(n) = 6n + 8$. Help Collin write a recursive equation.

A-76.   The Fibonacci sequence is a famous sequence
         that appears many times in mathematics. It
         can describe patterns found in nature, such as
         the number of petals on flowers, the
         arrangements of seeds in sunflowers, or scales
         on pinecones. It is named after Leonardo of
         Pisa, who was known as Fibonacci. He
         introduced the sequence to Western European
         mathematicians in 1202, though it had been
         described earlier by others including mathematicians in India.

   The equation that describes the Fibonacci sequence can $t(1) = 1$
   be written as: $t(2) = 1$

   a.   Write the first 10 terms of the Fibonacci sequence. $t(n+1) = t(n) + t(n-1)$

   b.   Is the Fibonacci sequence arithmetic, geometric, or neither?

   c.   Describe what you would need to do in order to find the 100th term of the
         Fibonacci sequence. Do not actually calculate the 100th term.

A-77. Avery and Collin were challenging each other with more equations for sequences. Avery was looking at an explicit equation that Collin wrote.

$$t(n) = 4.5n - 8$$

a. Write the first 4 terms for the sequence.

b. What would Avery do to write the 15th term of this sequence?

A-78. Write both an explicit equation and a recursive equation for the sequence: 5, 8, 11, 14, 17, ...

A-79. Draw a slope triangle and use it to find the equation of the line shown in the graph at right.

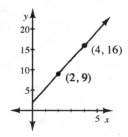

A-80. Find the following products.

a. $(4x+5)(4x-5)$

b. $(4x+5)^2$

A-81. Write an equation or system of equations to solve the problem below.

Apollo and Zeus are both on diets. Apollo currently weighs 105 kg and is gaining 2 kg per month. Zeus currently weighs 130 kg and is losing 3 kg per month. In how many months will they weigh the same?

A-82. Solve each system.

a. $6x - 2y = 10$
$3x - 2 = y$

b. $3x - 9y = 3$
$2x = 16 - y$

A-83. For each sequence defined recursively, write the first 5 terms and then define it explicitly.

a. $t(1) = 12$
$t(n+1) = t(n) - 5$

b. $a_1 = 32$
$a_{n+1} = \frac{1}{2} a_n$

A.3.1 What is the rate of change?

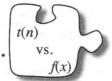

Patterns of Growth in Tables and Graphs

So far in this chapter you have looked at several types of sequences and compared linear and exponential growth patterns in situations, tables, and graphs. In this lesson you will compare patterns of growth rates to each other. This work will also help you write equations for exponential sequences in the next lesson.

A-84.   **PATTERNS OF GROWTH**

Sequence A	
n	$t(n)$
1	27
2	54
3	81
4	108

Sequence B	
n	$t(n)$
1	9
2	36
3	81
4	144

Sequence C	
n	$t(n)$
1	6
2	12
3	24
4	48

Your Task:

- Represent these three sequences on a graph (the Lesson A.3.1A Resource Page). Use a different color for each sequence. Although the graph should be discrete, connect the lines so you can see the trends easier.

- Consider the discussion points below for each sequence as you investigate the growth of these three sequences. You can discuss the sequences in any order.

- Be prepared to share your results with the class.

Discussion Points

How do the inputs, n, and the outputs of the sequence generator, $t(n)$, increase?

How does the sequence grow? Is the rate of change constant or changing? How? (You can make growth triangles to help answer this question.)

If we know a specific term, how would we find the next term? For example, if we knew the 10th term, could we find the 11th term?

Which family of functions best models each sequence?

A-85.   GROWTH RATES IN SEQUENCES

Consider how fast each of the sequences is growing
by looking at the tables and the graph. Do not make
any additional computations. Instead make
conjectures based on the tables and graphs.

a.   If *n* represents the number of years, and $t(n)$
      represents the amount of money in your
      savings account, which account would you want, Sequence A, B, or C?

b.   Would your answer change if you kept the account for many years?

c.   Obtain the Lesson A.3.1C Resource Page from your teacher. Extend the
      tables and the graph to $n = 7$. The table for Sequence B has been
      completed for you.

d.   Based on your new graph, do you want to change your answer to part (b)?
      Why or why not?

A-86.   WHICH GROWS THE MOST?

a.   Will an exponentially growing bank account eventually contain more
      money than a linearly growing bank account for the same amount of initial
      savings, no matter how fast (steep) the rate of growth of the linear account?
      Use the slope triangles on your graph from problem A-85 to help you
      explain.

b.   Sequence B shows quadratic growth. How does the growth of a quadratic
      sequence, like Sequence B, compare to exponential growth?

A-87.   Identify the following sequences as linear, exponential, or other. For the linear
         and exponential sequences, identify the rate of change and whether it is a
         constant that is added or multiplied.

a. $12, 144, 1728, \ldots$ b. $0, 5, 10, 15, 20, 25, \ldots$

c. $0, 4, 16, 36, 64, \ldots$ d. $1.5, 2.25, 3.375, 5.0625, \ldots$

A-88.   Solve the system of equations at right. $y = -x - 2$
                                                          $5x - 3y = 22$

A-89.   Write the first five terms of each sequence.

   a. $t(1) = -3$

   $t(n+1) = -2 \cdot t(n)$

   b. $t(1) = 8$

   $t(n+1) = t(n) - 5$

   c. $t(1) = 2$

   $t(n+1) = (t(n))^{-1}$

A-90.   The graph at right compares the gas mileage to the weight of numerous vehicles.

   Describe the association between these two quantities.

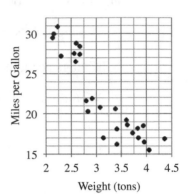

A-91.   **Multiple Choice:** Which line below is parallel to $y = -\frac{2}{3}x + 5$?

   a. $2x - 3y = 6$

   b. $2x + 3y = 6$

   c. $3x - 2y = 6$

   d. $3x + 2y = 6$

A-92.   Use the given information to find an equation of the line.

   a.   Slope 2 and passing through $(10, 17)$.

   b.   Passing through $(1, -4)$ and $(-2, 5)$.

   c.

x	–6	–3	0	3	6
y	–6	–4	–2	0	2

   d.

A.3.2 How can I use a multiplier?

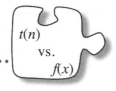

$t(n)$
vs.
$f(x)$

Using Multipliers to Solve Problems

In the past few lessons, you have investigated sequences that grow by adding (arithmetic) and sequences that grow by multiplying (geometric). In today's lesson, you will learn more about growth by multiplication as you use your understanding of geometric sequences and multipliers to solve problems. As you work, use the following questions to move your team's discussion forward:

What type of sequence is this? How do we know?

How can we describe the growth?

How can we be sure that our multiplier is correct?

A-93.   Thanks to the millions of teens around the world seeking to be just like their math teachers, industry analysts predict that sales of the new πPhone will skyrocket!

> ## πPHONES SWEEP THE NATION
> *Millions demand one!*
>
> (API) – Teenagers and Hollywood celebrities flocked to an exclusive shop in Beverly Hills, California yesterday, clamoring for the new πPhone. The store expects to start by selling 100 and expects to sell an average of 15% more each week after that.
>
> "I plan to stand in line all night!" said Nelly Hillman. "As soon as I own one, I'll be cooler than everyone else."
>
> Across the globe, millions of fans

a.   The article provides a model for how many πPhones the store expects to sell. They start by selling 100 πPhone pre-orders in week zero. Predict the number sold in the 4th week.

b.   If you were to write the number of πPhones the store received each week as a sequence, would your sequence be arithmetic, geometric, or something else? Justify your answer.

c.   The store needs to know how many phones to order for the last week of the year. If you knew the number of πPhones sold in week 51, how could you find the sales for week 52? Write a recursive equation to show the predicted sales of πPhones in the nth week.

d.   Write an explicit equation that starts with "$t(n) =$" to find the number of πPhones sold during the nth week without finding all of the weeks in between.

e.   How many πPhones will the store predict it sells in the 52nd week?

A-94. A new πRoid, a rival to the πPhone, is about to be introduced. It is cheaper than the πPhone, so more are expected to sell. The manufacturer plans to make and then sell 10,000 pre-orders in week zero and expects sales to increase by 7% each week.

    a. Write an explicit and a recursive equation for the number of πRoids sold during the nth week.

    b. What if the expected weekly sales increase were 17% instead of 7%? Now what would the new explicit equation be? How would it change the recursive equation?

A-95. Oh no! Thanks to the lower price, 10,000 πRoid were made and sold initially, but after that, weekly sales actually decreased by 3%.

Find an explicit and a recursive equation that models the product's actual weekly sales.

A-96. In a geometric sequence, the sequence generator is the number that one term is multiplied by to generate the next term. Another name for this number is the **multiplier** or the **common ratio**.

    a. Look back at your work for problems A-94, and A-95. What is the multiplier in each of these three situations?

    b. What is the multiplier for the sequence $8, 8, 8, 8, \ldots$?

    c. Explain what happens to the terms of the sequence when the multiplier is less than 1, but greater than zero. What happens when the multiplier is greater than 1? Add this description to your Learning Log. Title this entry "Multipliers" and add today's date.

A-97.   MULTIPLE REPRESENTATIONS ON THE GRAPHING CALCULATOR

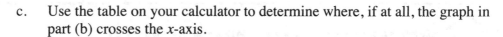

a.   According to the model in problem A-95, how many weeks will it take for the weekly sales to drop to only one πRoid per week? Make a conjecture.

b.   Before calculating the exact answer to the question in part (a), become comfortable with using your graphing calculator. On your calculator, make a graph for the sales of πPhones (problem A-93) for the first year. Sketch the graph on your paper. Make sure you show the scale of the axes on your sketch.

c.   Use the table on your calculator to determine where, if at all, the graph in part (b) crosses the x-axis.

d.   Enter the explicit equations for both problems A-93, $t(n) = 100 \cdot 1.15^n$, and problem A-94, $t(n) = 10\,000 \cdot 1.07^x$, in your calculator. Use your table to find the number of weeks it takes for sales in the first equation to exceed the sales in the second equation.

e.   Make a sketch of the graph of both equations in part (d). Be sure to show the point of intersection. Label the scale on both axes.

f.   Now use your calculator to answer the question in part (a). How close was your conjecture?

A-98.   Write an explicit and a recursive equation for each table below. Be sure to check that your equations work for all of the entries in the table.

a.

n	$t(n)$
0	1600
1	2000
2	2500
3	3125
4	3906.25

b.

n	$t(n)$
0	3906.25
1	3125
2	2500
3	2000
4	1600

c.

n	$t(n)$
0	50
1	72
2	103.68
3	149.2992

d.

n	$t(n)$
0	
1	50
2	
3	72
4	
5	103.68
6	
7	149.2992

Problem continues on next page.→

A-98.   *Problem continued from previous page.*

   e.   How are the tables in (a) and (b) related? How are the multipliers for (a)
        and (b) related? Why does this make sense?

   f.   What strategies did you use to find the equation for part (d)? How is the
        table in part (d) related to the one in part (c)?

   g.   In part (d), why is term 2 *not* 61?

MⒺTHODS AND MEANINGS

Types of Sequences

An **arithmetic sequence** is a sequence with an addition (or
subtraction) **sequence generator**. The number added to each
term to get the next term is called the **common difference**.

A **geometric sequence** is a sequence with a multiplication (or
division) generator. The number multiplied by each term to get the
next term is called the **common ratio** or the **multiplier**.

A multiplier can also be used to increase or decrease by a given
percentage. For example, the multiplier for an increase of 7% is
1.07. The multiplier for a decrease of 7% is 0.93.

A **recursive sequence** is a sequence in which each term depends
on the term(s) before it. The equation of a recursive sequence
requires at least one term to be specified. A recursive sequence
can be arithmetic, geometric, or neither.

For example, the sequence $-1, 2, 5, 26, 677, \ldots$ can be defined by the
recursive equation:
$$t(1) = -1, \quad t(n+1) = \left(t(n)\right)^2 + 1$$

An alternative notation for the equation of the sequence above is:
$$a_1 = -1, \quad a_{n+1} = (a_n)^2 + 1$$

A-99.   For each table below, find the missing entries and write an equation.

a.

Month (x)	0	1	2	3	4	5	6
Population (y)	2	8	32				

b.

Year (x)	0	1	2	3	4	5	6
Population (y)	5	6	7.2				

A-100.   Convert each percent increase or decrease into a multiplier.

a.   3% increase   b.   25% decrease

c.   13% decrease   d.   2.08% increase

A-101.   Mr. C is such a mean teacher! The next time Mathias gets in trouble, Mr. C has designed a special detention for him. Mathias will have to go out into the hall and stand exactly 100 meters away from the exit door and pause for a minute. Then he is allowed to walk exactly halfway to the door and pause for another minute. Then he can again walk exactly half the remaining distance to the door and pause again, and so on. Mr. C says that when Mathias reaches the door he can leave, *unless* he breaks the rules and goes more than halfway, even by a tiny amount. When can Mathias leave? Prove your answer using multiple representations.

A-102.   Simplify each expression.

a. $(2m^3)(4m^2)$ b. $\dfrac{6y^5}{3y^2}$

c. $\dfrac{-4y^2}{6y^7}$ d. $(-2x^2)^3$

A-103.   For this problem, refer to the sequences graphed below.

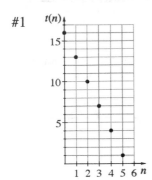 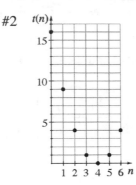 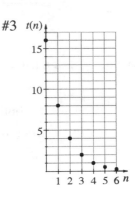

a.   Identify each sequence as arithmetic, geometric, or neither.

b.   If it is arithmetic or geometric, describe the sequence generator.

A-104.   Read the Math Notes box in this lesson for information about an alternative notation for sequences and write the first 5 terms of these sequences.

a. $a_n = 2n - 5$

b. $a_1 = 3$
     $a_{n+1} = -2 \cdot a_n$

A-105.   Solve each equation.

a. $(x+2)(x+3) = x^2 - 10$

b. $\frac{1}{2}x + \frac{1}{3}x - 7 = \frac{5}{6}x$

c. $|2x - 1| = 9$

d. $\frac{x+1}{3} = \frac{x}{2}$

A.3.3 Is it a function?

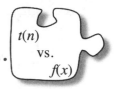

•••

Comparing Sequences to Functions

Throughout this chapter, you have been learning about sequences. In Chapter 1, you worked with various function families. But what is the difference between a sequence and a function? In this lesson, you will compare and contrast sequences with functions. By the end of the lesson, you will be able to answer these questions:

Is a sequence different from a function?

What is the difference between a sequence $t(n)$ and the function $f(x)$ with the same equation?

A-106.   Consider sequence $t(n)$ below.

$$-5, -1, 3, 7, \ldots$$

a.   Create multiple representations, including a table, a graph, and an equation (recursive or explicit), for the sequence $t(n)$.

b.   Is it possible for the equation representing $t(n)$ to equal 400? Justify your answer.

c.   Create the same multiple representations as you did in part (a) for the function $f(x) = 4x - 9$. How are $f(x)$ and $t(n)$ different? How can you see their differences in each of the representations?

d.   For the function $f(x) = 4x - 9$, is it possible for $f(x)$ to equal 400? Explain why or why not.

A-107.   Let us consider the difference between $t(n) = 2 \cdot 3^n$ and $f(x) = 2 \cdot 3^x$.

a.   Is $f(x) = 2 \cdot 3^x$ a function? Why or why not? Is $t(n) = 2 \cdot 3^n$ a function?

b.   Is it possible for $t(n)$ to equal 1400? If so, find the value of n that makes $t(n) = 1400$. If not, justify why not.

c.   Is it possible for $f(x)$ to equal 1400? Be prepared to share your justification with the class.

d.   How are the functions similar? How are they different?

A-108. **LEARNING LOG**

Is a sequence a function? Justify your answer completely. If so, what makes it different from the functions that are usually written in the form $f(x) =$ _____ ? If it is not a function, why not? Be prepared to share your ideas with the class. After a class discussion about these questions, answer the questions in your Learning Log. Title this entry "Sequences vs. Functions" and label it with today's date.

A-109. Janine was working on her homework but lost part of it. She knew that one output of $p(r) = 2 \cdot 5^r$ is 78,000, but she could not remember if $p(r)$ is a sequence or if it is a regular function. With your team, help her figure it out. Be sure to justify your decision.

A-110. **Additional Challenge:** Khalil is working with a geometric sequence. He knows that $t(0) = 3$ and that the sum of the first three terms ($t(0)$, $t(1)$, and $t(2)$) is 63. Help him figure out the sequence. Be prepared to share your strategies with the class.

A-111. **Additional Challenge:** Discuss with your team how you can use your graphing calculator to solve each of the following equations for x, accurate to the nearest 0.01.

a. $200(0.5)^x = 3.125$ b. $318 = 6 \cdot 3^x$

A-112. Is it possible for the sequence $t(n) = 5 \cdot 2^n$ to have a term with the value of 200? If so, which term is it? If not, justify why not.

A-113. Is it possible for the function $f(x) = 5 \cdot 2^x$ to have an output of 200? If so, what input gives this output? If not, justify why not.

A-114.   Consider the following sequences as you complete parts (a) through (c) below.

Sequence 1	Sequence 2	Sequence 3
2, 6, ...	24, 12, ...	1, 5, ...

a.   Assuming that the sequences above are arithmetic with $t(1)$ as the first term, find the next four terms for each sequence. For each sequence, write an explanation of what you did to get the next term and write an equation for $t(n)$.

b.   Would your terms be different if the sequences were geometric? Find the next four terms for each sequence if they are geometric. For each sequence, write an explanation of what you did to get the next term and write an equation for $t(n)$.

c.   Create a totally different type of sequence for each pair of values shown above, based on your own equation. Write your equation clearly (using words or algebra) so that someone else will be able to find the next three terms that you want.

A-115.   For the function $g(x) = x^3 + x^2 - 6x$, find the value of each expression below.

a. $g(1)$ b. $g(-1)$ c. $g(-2)$ d. $g(10)$

e.   Find at least one value of x for which $g(x) = 0$.

f.   If $f(x) = x^2 - x + 3$, find $g(x) - f(x)$.

A-116.   Write equations to solve each of the following problems.

a.   When the Gleo Retro (a trendy commuter car) is brand new, it costs \$23,500. Each year it loses 15% of its value. What will the car be worth when it is 15 years old?

b.   Each year the population of Algeland increases by 12%. The population is currently 14,365,112. What will the population be 20 years from now?

A-117.   An arithmetic sequence has $t(8) = 1056$ and $t(13) = 116$. Write an equation for the sequence. What is $t(5)$?

A-118.   Describe the domain of each function or sequence below.

a.   The function $f(x) = 3x - 5$.   b.   The sequence $t(n) = 3n - 5$.

c.   The function $f(x) = \frac{5}{x}$.   d.   The sequence $t(n) = \frac{5}{n}$.

Appendix A Closure What have I learned?

Reflection and Synthesis

The activities below offer you a chance to reflect about what you have learned during this chapter. As you work, look for concepts that you feel very comfortable with, ideas that you would like to learn more about, and topics you need more help with. Look for connections between ideas as well as connections with material you learned previously.

①   TEAM BRAINSTORM

What have you studied in this chapter? What ideas were important in what you learned? With your team, brainstorm a list. Be as detailed as you can. To help get you started, a list of Learning Log entries and Math Notes boxes are below.

What topics, ideas, and words that you learned *before* this chapter are connected to the new ideas in this chapter? Again, be as detailed as you can.

How long can you make your list? Challenge yourselves. Be prepared to share your team's ideas with the class.

Learning Log Entries
- Lesson A.1.1 – Exponential Functions
- Lesson A.3.2 – Multipliers
- Lesson A.3.3 – Sequence vs. Functions

Math Notes
- Lesson A.1.2 – Continuous and Discrete Graphs
- Lesson A.3.2 – Types of Sequences

MAKING CONNECTIONS

Below is a list of the vocabulary used in this chapter. Make sure that you are familiar with all of these words and know what they mean. Refer to the glossary or index for any words that you do not yet understand.

arithmetic sequence	common difference	common ratio
continuous	discrete	domain
exponential function	first term	geometric sequence
initial value	linear function	multiplier
recursive sequence	sequence	sequence generator
$t(0)$	term	term number
y-intercept		

Make a concept map showing all of the connections you can find among the key words and ideas listed above. To show a connection between two words, draw a line between them and explain the connection, as shown in the model below. A word can be connected to any other word as long as you can justify the connection. For each key word or idea, provide an example or sketch that shows the idea.

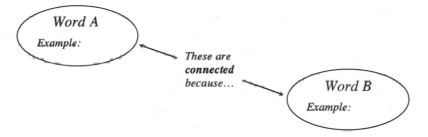

Your teacher may provide you with vocabulary cards to help you get started. If you use the cards to plan your concept map, be sure either to re-draw your concept map on your paper or to glue the vocabulary cards to a poster with all of the connections explained for others to see and understand.

While you are making your map, your team may think of related words or ideas that are not listed here. Be sure to include these ideas on your concept map.

PORTFOLIO: EVIDENCE OF MATHEMATICAL PROFICIENCY

Four members of a study team were analyzing the sequence 3, 7, 11, ... They found the equation for the sequence to be $t(n) = 4n - 1$, and they were trying to figure out if 200 could be a term of their sequence.

They made the following statements. Which students justified their statements? Are the justifications convincing? Explain why or why not.

Shinna: "I think it's not, because all the terms in the sequence are odd and 200 is an even number."

Aldo: "I think it is, because the equation $200 = 4n - 1$ has a solution."

James: "It can't be, because the solution to $200 = 4n - 1$ is $n = 50.25$, which is not a whole number. There can't be a 50.25ᵗʰ term!"

Leslie: "I think 199 and 203 are terms of the sequence, but not 200."

Now create your own sequence. Then figure out what the 110ᵗʰ term of your sequence would be and whether the number 419 is a term in your sequence. Use multiple representations to justify your answers thoroughly.

Alternatively your portfolio entry could showcase your early understanding of an exponential function by explaining everything you know about the function $f(x) = 2^x - 3$. Provide one or two representative example problems.

Obtain the Appendix A Closure Resource Page: Sequence vs. Function Graphic Organizer from your teacher. Use this page to compare and contrast sequences and functions in their multiple representations. How are they similar? How are they different?

④   WHAT HAVE I LEARNED?

Most of the problems in this section represent
typical problems found in this chapter. They
serve as a gauge for you. You can use them to
determine which types of problems you can
do well and which types of problems require
further study and practice. Even if your
teacher does not assign this section, it is a
good idea to try these problems and find out
for yourself what you know and what you need to work on.

Solve each problem as completely as you can. The table at the end of the
closure section has answers to these problems. It also tells you where you can
find additional help and practice with problems like these.

CL A-119.   Determine if the following sequences are arithmetic, geometric, or neither:

a. $-7, -3, 1, 5, 9, ...$ b. $-64, -16, -4, -1, ...$

c. $1, 0, 1, 4, 9, ...$ d. $0, 2, 4, ...$

CL A-120.   Find an equation to represent each table as a sequence.

a.

n	$t(n)$
1	4
2	1
3	-2
4	

b.

n	$t(n)$
1	6
2	7.2
3	8.64
4	

CL A-121.   Solve the following systems algebraically.

a. $x + 2y = 17$
      $x - y = 2$

b. $4x + 5y = 11$
      $2x + 6y = 16$

c. $4x - 3y = -10$
      $x = \frac{1}{4}y - 1$

d. $2x + y = -2x + 5$
      $3x + 2y = 2x + 3y$

CL A-122.   Solve each equation after first rewriting it in a simpler equivalent form.

  a. $3(2x-1)+12 = 4x-3$ b. $\frac{3x}{7}+\frac{2}{7}=2$

  c. $\frac{x-3}{x}=\frac{3}{5}$ d. $4x(x-2)=(2x+1)(2x-3)$

CL A-123.   Simplify each expression.

  a. $(-3x)^2$ b. $(3x)^{-2}$ c. $\frac{2(3x)^2}{3x^3}$ d. $\frac{2(3x)^2}{(3x)^{-2}}$

CL A-124.   Create multiple representations of each line described below.

  a. A line with slope 4 and y-intercept -6.

  b. A line with slope $\frac{3}{2}$ that passes through the point $(5,7)$.

CL A-125.   Create an explicit equation for each recursively-defined sequence below.

  a. $a_1 = 17,\ a_{n+1} = a_n - 7$

  b. $t(1) = 3,\ t(n+1) = 5 \cdot t(n)$

CL A-126.   Use a graph to describe the domain and range of each function or sequence below.

  a. The function $f(x) = (x-2)^2$.   b. The sequence $t(n) = 3n - 5$.

CL A-127.   When a family with two adults and three children bought tickets for an amusement park, they paid a total of $56.50. The next family in line, with four children and one adult, paid $49.50. Find the adult and child ticket prices by writing and solving a system of equations.

CL A-128.   Check your answers using the table at the end of this section. Which problems do you feel confident about? Which problems were hard? Have you worked on problems like these in previous math classes? Use the table to make a list of topics you need to learn more about, and a list of topics you just need to practice more.

Answers and Support for Closure Activity #4
What Have I Learned?

Note: MN = Math Note, LL = Learning Log

Problem	Solutions	Need Help?	More Practice
CL A-119.	a. arithmetic b. geometric c. neither d. arithmetic	Section A.2 MN: A.3.2	Problems A-42, A-44, A-50, A-87, and A-114
CL A-120.	a. $t(n) = -3n + 7$ b. $t(n) = 5(1.2)^n$ or $t(n) = 6(1.2)^{n-1}$	Lessons A.2.2 and A.3.2	Problems A-37, A-64, A-68, A-83, A-87, and A-99
CL A-121.	a. $(7, 5)$ b. $(-1, 3)$ c. $(-\frac{1}{4}, 3)$ d. $(1, 1)$	Explanations and practice of topics from previous courses are available in the *Core Connections Algebra Parent Guide with Extra Practice,* available free at www.cpm.org.	Problems A-7, A-22, A-36, A-54, A-70, and A-88
CL A-122.	a. -6 b. 4 c. 7.5 d. $\frac{3}{4}$	Topic from previous course	Problems 1-40, 1-52, A-15, A-87, and A-105
CL A-123.	a. $9x^2$ b. $\frac{1}{9x^2}$ c. $\frac{6}{x}$ d. $162x^4$	Topic from previous course	Problems A-9, A-10, A-13, A-24, A-56, and A-102

Problem	Solutions	Need Help?	More Practice

CL A-124. a. $y = 4x - 6$

x	y
-3	-18
-2	-14
-1	-10
0	-6
1	-2
2	2
3	6

b. $y = \frac{3}{2}x - \frac{1}{2}$

x	y
-3	-5
-2	-3.5
-1	-2
0	-0.5
1	1
2	2.5
3	4

(CL A-124 Need Help?) Topic from previous course

(CL A-124 More Practice) Problems A-11, A-16, A-37, A-46, and A-92

CL A-125. a. $t(n) = 24 - 7n$

b. $t(n) = \frac{3}{5}(5)^n$

Need Help? Lesson A.2.3

MN: A.3.2

More Practice Problems A-72, A-78, A-83, A-89, and A-104

CL A-126. a. Domain: all real numbers
Range: $y \geq 0$

b. Domain: all positive integers;
Range: all real numbers of the form $3n - 5$

Need Help? Lesson A.3.3

LL: A.3.3

More Practice Problems A-25 and A-118

CL A-127. $2a + 3c = 56.5$, $a + 4c = 49.5$

adults cost $15.50, children cost $8.50

Need Help? Topic from previous course

More Practice Problems A-71 and A-81

Appendix B
Exponential Functions

Appendix B provides an opportunity for you to learn more about the family of exponential functions. As you do this you will build more advanced algebra skills, such as solving for an indicated variable, simplifying or rewriting exponential expressions, working with fractional exponents, and finding the exponential function that passes exactly through any pair of given points.

You will also learn about several important applications of exponential functions.

Guiding Question

Mathematically proficient students make sense of problems and persevere in solving them.

As you work through this chapter, ask yourself:

Am I making connections between the multiple representations and making sense of the situations?

Chapter Outline

Section B.1

In Section B.1, you will investigate a family of exponential functions. You will recognize exponential growth when given situations, tables, graphs, or equations, and you will make connections between these representations. You will also extend your knowledge of exponents and their properties as you solve exponential equations. You will be introduced to step functions. At the end of the section, you will apply exponential functions to real-life situations involving growth and decay.

Section B.2

In Section B.2, you will find exponential equations that fit given data. In doing so, you will learn about fractional exponents.

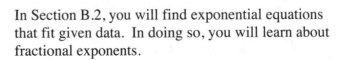

B.1.1 What do exponential graphs look like?

Investigating $y = b^x$

In this lesson you will investigate the characteristics of the family of functions $y = b^x$. As a team, you will generate data for various functions in this family, form questions about your data, and answer each of these questions using multiple representations. Your team will show what you have learned on a stand-alone poster.

B-1.   BEGINNING TO INVESTIGATE EXPONENTIALS

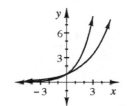

In Appendix A, you graphed several exponential functions. Some graphs, like those that modeled the rabbit populations in problem A-4, were *increasing* exponential functions and looked similar to the two exponential functions graphed at right.

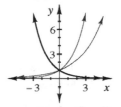

Other graphs, such as the rebound-height graphs from the bouncing ball activity (problem A-20), represented *decreasing* exponential functions and looked similar to the third curve, shown in bold at right.

You already know that equations of the form $y = mx + b$ represent the family of lines, and you know what effect changing the parameters m and b have on the graph. Today you will begin to learn more about the exponential function family. In their simplest form, the equations of exponential functions look like $y = b^x$.

By experimenting with different values of b, find three equations in $y = b^x$ form that have graphs appearing to match the two graphs shown above. Confirm your results using your graphing calculator and be ready to share your results with the class.

B-2.   INVESTIGATING $y = b^x$, Part One

What types of graphs exist for equations of the form $y = b^x$?

Your Task: With your team, try different values of b to try to find as many different looking graphs as possible. (Stick to small values of b, for example, less than 10. Keep the window on your calculator set from -10 to 10 in both the x and y direction.)

Decide as a team what different values of b to try so that you find as many different looking graphs as possible. Be sure to keep track of what you have tried with a sketch of the resulting graph so that you may refer to it later. Use the questions listed below to help get you started.

Discussion Points

What special values of b should we consider?

Are there any other values of b we should try?

How many different types of graphs can we find?

How do we know we have found all possible graphs?

B-3.   The graph of the function $y = \left(\frac{1}{2}\right)^x$ is shown at right.

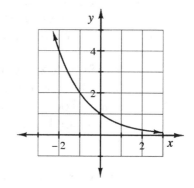

a.   Describe what happens to y as x gets bigger and bigger. For example, what is y when $x = 20$? $x = 100$? $x = 1000$? $x = $ (a much larger number)?

b.   Does the graph of $y = \left(\frac{1}{2}\right)^x$ have an x-intercept? Explain how you know.

c.   When x is very large, the graph of $y = \left(\frac{1}{2}\right)^x$ approaches the x-axis. That is, as x gets larger and larger (farther to the right along the curve), the closer the curve gets to the x-axis. In this situation, the x-axis is called an asymptote of $y = \left(\frac{1}{2}\right)^x$. You can remind yourself about asymptotes by rereading the Math Notes box in Lesson 1.2.2.

Does $y = \left(\frac{1}{2}\right)^x$ have a vertical asymptote? In other words, is there a vertical line that the graph above approaches? Why or why not?

B-4.   INVESTIGATING $y = b^x$, Part Two

Now that you, with your class, have found all of the possible graphs for $y = b^x$, your teacher will assign your team one or two of the types of graphs to investigate further. Completely describe the graphs. Use the Discussion Point questions below to guide your investigation of this graph. Look for ways to justify your summary statements using more than one representation (equation, table, graph).

As a team, organize your graphs and summary statements into a stand-alone poster that clearly communicates what you learned about your set of graphs. Be sure to include all of your observations along with examples to demonstrate them. Anyone should be able to answer the questions below after examining your poster. Use colors, arrows, labels, and other tools to help explain your ideas.

Discussion Points

How can we describe the shape of the graph?

What happens when x gets larger? What happens when x gets smaller?

How does changing the value of b change the graph?
Which aspects of the graph do not change?

Are there any special points? Can they be explained with the equation?

Does the graph have any symmetry? If so, where?

B-5.   Exponential functions have some interesting characteristics. Consider functions of the form $y = b^x$ as you discuss the questions below.

a.   Exponential functions such as $y = b^x$ are defined only for $b > 0$. Why do you think this is? That is, why would you not want to use negative values of b?

b.   Can you consider $y = 1^x$ or $y = 0^x$ to be exponential functions? Why or why not? How are they different from other exponential function?

B-6.   LEARNING LOG

Look over your work from this lesson. What questions did you ask yourself as you were making observations and statements? How does changing the value of b affect a graph? What questions do you still have after this investigation? Write a Learning Log entry describing what mathematical ideas you developed during this lesson. Title this entry "Investigating $y = b^x$" and label it with today's date.

B-7.   A grocery store is offering a sale on bread and soup. Khalil buys four cans of soup and three loaves of bread for $11.67. Ronda buys eight cans of soup and one loaf of bread for $12.89.

a.   Write equations for both Khalil's and Ronda's purchases.

b.   Solve the system to find the price of one can of soup and the price of one loaf of bread.

B-8.   If two expressions are equivalent, they can form an equation that is considered to be *always true*. For example, since $3(x-5)$ is equivalent to $3x-15$, then the equation $3(x-5) = 3x-15$ is always true, that is, true for any value of x.

If two expressions are equal only for certain values of the variable, they can form an equation that is considered to be *sometimes true*. For example, $x+2$ is equal to $3x-8$ only when $x = 5$, so the equation $x+2 = 3x-8$ is said to be sometimes true.

If two expressions are not equal for any value of the variable, they can form an equation that is considered to be *never true*. For example, $x-5$ is not equal to $x+1$ for *any* value of x, so the equation $x-5 = x+1$ is said to be never true.

Is the equation $(x+3)^2 = x^2 + 9$ always, sometimes or never true? Justify your reasoning completely.

B-9.   Consider the sequence that begins $40, 20, 10, 5, \ldots$

a.   Based on the information given, can this sequence be arithmetic? Can it be geometric? Why?

b.   Assume this is a geometric sequence. On graph paper, plot the sequence on a graph up to $n = 6$.

c.   Will the values of the sequence ever become zero or negative? Explain.

B-10.   If a ball is dropped from 160 cm and rebounds to 120 cm on the first bounce, how high will the ball be:

a.   On the 2nd bounce?

b.   On the 5th bounce?

c.   On the nth bounce?

B-11.   Simplify or multiply each of the following expressions as appropriate.

    a. $(3x^2yz^4)^2$

    b. $\left(\frac{r^2s}{rs^3t}\right)^3$

    c. $(3m+7)(2m-1)$

    d. $(x-3)^2$

B-12.   Write and solve an equation for the problem below.

If 150 empty water bottles weigh 4.5 pounds, what would you expect 90 empty water bottles to weigh?

B-13.   Sketch the shape of the graph of the function $y = b^x$ given each of the following values of b.

    a. b is a number larger than 1.

    b. b is a number between 0 and 1.

    c. b is equal to 1.

B-14.   For parts (a) and (b), find a recursive equation in a_n form for each sequence. (For a reminder about a_n form see the Math Notes box in Lesson A.3.2.) For parts (c) and (d) find an explicit equation for each sequence.

    a. $108, 120, 132, \ldots$

    b. $\frac{2}{5}, \frac{4}{5}, \frac{8}{5}, \ldots$

    c. $3741, 3702, 3663, \ldots$

    d. $117, 23.4, 4.68, \ldots$

B-15.   Write the multiplier for each increase or decrease described below.

    a.   A 25% increase

    b.   A decrease of 18%

    c.   An increase of 39%

    d.   A decrease of 94%

B-16.   Eeeeew! Hannah's volleyball team left their egg salad
         sandwiches sitting in their lockers over the weekend. When
         they got back on Monday they were moldy. "Perfect!" said
         Hannah. "I can use these sandwiches for my biology project.
         I'll study how quickly mold grows."

         Using a transparent grid, Hannah estimated that about 12% of the surface of
         one sandwich had mold on it. She threw the sandwich out. For the rest of the
         week, Hannah came back when she had time. Each time she measured
         somebody else's sandwich and threw it out. She collected the following data:

Day 1 (Monday)	Day 2 (Tuesday)	Day 2 (Tuesday)	Day 4 (Thursday)	Day 4 (Thursday)	Day 4 (Thursday)	Day 5 (Friday)
12%	15%	13%	26%	27%	24%	38%

         a.   Create a scatterplot and sketch it. Is a linear model reasonable?

         b.   Based on the story, what kind of equation do you think will best fit the
               situation?

B-17.   In 1999, Charlie received the family heirloom marble collection consisting of
         1239 marbles. Charlie's great-grandfather had started the original marble
         collection in 1905. Each year, Charlie's great-grandfather had added the same
         number of marbles to his collection. When he passed them on to his son, he
         insisted that each future generation add the same number of marbles per year to
         the collection. When Charlie's father received the collection in 1966, there
         were 810 marbles.

         a.   By the time Charlie inherited the collection, how many years had it been in
               existence?

         b.   How many marbles are added to the collection each year?

         c.   Use the information you found in part (b) to figure out how many marbles
               were in the original collection when Charlie's great-grandfather started it.

         d.   Generalize this situation by writing a function describing the growth of the
               marble collection for each year (n) since Charlie's great-grandfather started
               it.

         e.   How old will the marble collection be when Charlie
               (or one of his children) has more than 2000
               marbles? In what year will this occur?

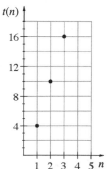

B-18.   Write an explicit equation for the sequence based on the
         graph at right.

B.1.2 What is the connection?

Multiple Representations of Exponential Functions

In Lesson 1.2.3 you looked at multiple representations (such as a table, graph, equation, or situation) of linear functions. In this chapter you will use multiple representations to learn more about the multiplier and starting point of exponential functions.

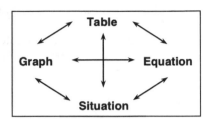

B-19.   Let's look at some of the connections between the multiple representations of an exponential function.

Bounce Number	Height (cm)
0	
1	
2	84.5
3	67.6
4	54.1

a.   Arnold dropped a ball during the bouncing ball activity and recorded its height in a table. Part of his table is shown at right. What was the rebound ratio of his ball? At what height did he drop the ball? Write an equation that represents his data. Explain your equation.

b.   A major technology company, ExpoGrow, is growing incredibly fast. The latest prospectus (a report on the company) said that so far, the number of employees, y, could be found with the equation $y = 3(4)^x$, where x represents the number of years since the company was founded. How many people founded the company? How can the growth of this company be described?

c.   A computer virus is affecting the technology center in such a way that each day, a certain portion of virus-free computers is infected. The number of virus-free computers is recorded in the table at right. How many computers are in the technology center? What portion of virus-free computers is infected each day? How many computers will remain virus-free at the end of the third day? Justify your answer.

Day	Uninfected Computers
0	27
1	18
2	12

d.   As part of a major scandal, it was discovered that several statements in the prospectus for ExpoGrow in part (b) were false. If the company actually had five founders and doubles in size each year, what equation should it have printed in its report?

B-20. Most of the exponential equations you have used in this chapter have been in the form $y = ab^x$.

    a.   What does a represent in this equation? What does b represent?

    b.   How can you identify a by looking at a table? How can you find it in a situation? Give an example for each representation.

    c.   How can you determine b in each representation? Use arrows or colors to add your ideas about b to the examples you created in part (b).

B-21. MULTIPLE-REPRESENTATIONS WEB

What connections are you sure you can use in an exponential functions web? For example, if you have an exponential equation, such as $y = 20(3)^x$, can you complete a table? If so, draw an arrow from the equation and point at the table, as shown at right.

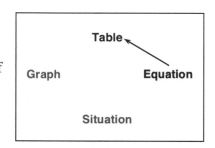

Copy the web, without any arrows, into your Learning Log. Discuss with your team the connections you have used so far in this chapter. Draw arrows to show which representations you can connect already. Which connections have you not used yet but you are confident that you could? Which connections do you still need to explore?

Can you think of examples from earlier in this lesson, or in Appendix A, to support your conclusions? Write down the problem numbers next to your arrows.

Title this entry "Multiple Representations Web for Exponential Functions" and label it with today's date. Be ready to share your findings with the rest of the class.

B-22. EQUATION → GRAPH

How can you sketch the graph of an exponential function directly from its equation without making a table first? Discuss this with your team. Then make a reasonable sketch of the graph of $y = 7(2)^x$ on your paper.

B-23.   Each table below represents an exponential function of the form $y = ab^x$. Copy and complete each table on your paper and find the corresponding equation.

a.
x	y
0	1.8
1	5.76
2	18.432
3	
4	

b.
x	y
0	5
1	
2	245
3	
4	

B-24.   Brianna is working on her homework. Her assignment is to come up with four representations for an exponential function of her choosing. She decides it is easiest to start by writing an equation, so she chooses $y = 1200\left(\frac{1}{2}\right)^x$. Help Brianna create the other three components of the web.

B-25.   Sketch the graphs of $y = x^2$, $y = 2x^2$, and $y = \frac{1}{2}x^2$ on the same set of axes. Describe the similarities and differences among the graphs.

B-26.   Write an equation or system of equations to solve this problem.

Morgan started the year with $615 in the bank and is saving $25 per week. Kendall started with $975 and is spending $15 per week. When will they both have the same amount of money in the bank?

B-27.   Examine each sequence below. State whether it is arithmetic, geometric, or neither. For the sequences that are arithmetic, find the formula for $t(n)$. For the sequences that are geometric, find the sequence generator for $t(n)$.

a. $1, 4, 7, 10, 13, \ldots$

b. $0, 5, 12, 21, 32, \ldots$

c. $2, 4, 8, 16, 32, \ldots$

d. $5, 12, 19, 26, \ldots$

e. $x, x+1, x+2, x+3, \ldots$

f. $3, 12, 48, 192, \ldots$

B-28.   Write an explicit equation for the sequence based on the graph at right.

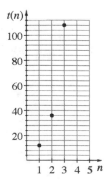

B.1.3   How does it grow?

••

More Applications of Exponential Growth

You may have heard the expression, "Money does not grow on trees." However, money does, in a sense, grow in a savings account. In today's lesson you will apply your understanding of exponential functions to solve problems involving money and interest. As you work, use the questions below to help focus your team's discussions.

How does it start?

How does it grow? What is the multiplier?

How is the rate written as a percent? As a decimal?

B-29.   SAVING FOR COLLEGE

Suppose you have $1000 to invest and know of two investment options. You can invest in bonds (which pay 8% *simple* interest) or put your money in a credit union account (which pays 8% *compound* interest). Will the option you choose make a difference in the amount of money you earn? Examine these two situations below.

Bonds with Simple Interest:

a.   If you invest in bonds, your $1000 would grow as shown in the table at right. How does money grow with simple interest?

b.   By what percent would your balance have increased by the 4th year? Show how you know.

VALUE OF BONDS

Number of Years	Amount of Money (in dollars)
0	1000.00 (initial value)
1	1080.00
2	1160.00
3	1240.00
4	

Accounts with Compound Interest:

c.   Instead, if you invest your $1000 in the credit union at 8% compound interest that is compounded once a year, its value would grow as shown in the table at right. Why is there $1166.40 in your account in the second year? Explain how the compound interest is calculated. How is it growing?

VALUE OF CREDIT UNION ACCOUNT

Number of Years	Amount of Money (in dollars)
0	1000.00 (initial value)
1	1080.00
2	1166.40
3	1259.71
4	

Problem continue on next page →

Core Connections Algebra 2

B-29.   *Problem continued from previous page.*

    d.   What will be the balance of the credit union account at the 4th year? By what percent would this account balance increase at four years? Show how you know.

    e.   Which type of account – a bond with simple interest or a credit union account with compound interest – grows most quickly?

B-30.   Assume that the interest is added at the beginning of a new year. Make one graph that shows how each type of investment (simple and compound) starts with $1000 and grows over 8 years. Discuss these questions in your team as you graph:

Discussion Points

Can we make the graph clearer with color?

What happens to the money in between the years?

How can we represent the "between" amount on a graph?

B-31.   In previous courses you may have used **models** as an estimate of real behavior. Creating a best-fit line for scattered data is one example of a model. Models give you a mathematical way to describe the data and to make predictions.

The simple and compound interest situations in problem B-30 were both step functions. Writing equations for step functions can be very complicated. However, you can model the step functions with other equations with which you are already familiar.

    a.   Think about the growth and the starting point for the simple and compound interest situations from this lesson. Model each of the two step functions with an equation. Let y represent the money in the account after x years.

    b.   Check that your equation represents the tables in problem B-29. If your models do not match the tables, correct your equation.

    c.   Use your model to predict how much your original $1000 investment would be worth at the end of 20 years in the credit union.

    d.   Why are the equations considered models, instead of representations of the real behavior? Is there an advantage to using the model to make predictions?

B-32. In this course, use continuous functions to model situations, unless indicated otherwise.

A third option for investing money is a money market account, which offers 8% annual interest *compounded quarterly* (four times per year). This means that the 8% is divided into four parts over the year, so the bank pays 2% every three months.

    a.   Model the value (every three months) of the $1000 investment in this money market account with an equation.
Let y represent the money in the account after x quarters.

    b.   Use the model to find the value of your $1000 investment at four years. How does this compare with your other investment options from problem B-29?

B-33. If you invested $1000 in the credit union from problem B-29 (interest compounded yearly at 8%), how much would you have at 20 years? If you wanted to earn this same amount of money with bonds with simple interest, what interest rate would the bonds need to earn? Show how you know.

METHODS AND MEANINGS

Compounding Interest

A bank can pay **simple interest**, in which case the amount in the bank grows linearly. For example, 3% simple interest compounded annually on an initial investment of $2500 would grow in a sequence with a common difference: $0.03(2500) = \$75$. The equation and table follow:

$$t(n) = 2500 + 75n$$

Number of Years, n	0	1	2	3	...	10
Amount in Bank, $t(n)$	2500.00	2575.00	2650.00	2725.00		3250.00

If the bank **compounds interest**, the relationship is exponential. For example, 3% annual interest, *compounded annually*, would have a multiplier of 1.03 every year. The equation and table using the example above are:

$$t(n) = 2500 \cdot 1.03^n$$

Number of Years, n	0	1	2	3	...	10
Amount in Bank, $t(n)$	2500	2575.00	2652.25	2731.82		3359.79

If the bank *compounds monthly*, the 3% annual interest becomes $\frac{3\%/\text{year}}{12 \text{ months/year}} = 0.25\%$ per month, and the multiplier becomes 1.0025. The equation and table for the first ten years follows:

$$t(m) = 2500 \cdot 1.0025^m$$

Number of Months, m	0	12	24	36	...	120
Amount in Bank, $t(m)$	2500	2576.00	2654.39	2735.13		3373.38

B-34. Your banker shows you the graph at right to explain what you can earn if you invest with him. Does this graph represent simple or compound interest? How can you tell? Write an equation to represent how much money you would have as time passes. Make sure you write a "let" statement.

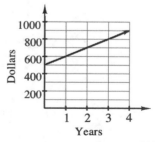

B-35.   Each table below represents an exponential function in $y = ab^x$ form. Copy and complete each table on your paper and find a corresponding equation.

a.

x	y
-1	3
0	
1	75
2	
3	

b.

x	y
0	
1	
2	96.64
3	77.312
4	

B-36.   Tickets for a concert have been in incredibly high demand, and as the date for the concert draws closer, the price of tickets increases exponentially. The cost of a pair of concert tickets was $150 yesterday, and today it is $162. As you complete parts (a) through (c) below, assume that each day's percent increase from the day before is the same.

    a.   What is the daily percent rate of increase? What is the multiplier?

    b.   What will be the cost of a pair of concert tickets one week from now?

    c.   What was the cost of a pair of tickets two weeks ago?

B-37.   Dusty won $125,000 on the *Who Wants to Be a Zillionaire?* game show. He decides to place the money into an account that earns 6.25% interest compounded annually and plans not to use any of it until he retires.

    a.   Write an expression that represents how much money Dusty will have in t years.

    b.   How much money will be in the account when he retires in 23 years?

B-38.   Solve the following systems of equations.

    a. $3x - 2y = 14$

         $-2x + 2y = -10$

    b. $y = 5x + 3$

         $-2x - 4y = 10$

    c.   Which system above is most efficiently solved by using the Substitution Method? Explain.

    d.   Which system above is most efficiently solved by using the Elimination Method? Explain.

B-39.   If you flip a fair coin, what is the probability that it comes up "heads"? "Tails"?

B.1.4 What if it does not grow?

Exponential Decay

To learn more about how exponents affect growth, today you will study new situations in which the exponential function "decays" or decreases. This will lead to studying negative exponents.

B-40.   THE PENNY LAB

What about situations that do not grow? In this activity, you will explore a situation that behaves exponentially, but whose results get smaller. This is an example of **exponential decay**.

Your Task: Follow the directions below to model exponential decay using pennies.

Trial #0:   Start with 100 pennies.

Trial #1:   Dump the pennies out on your team's workspace. Remove any pennies that have "tails" side up. Record the number of pennies that *remain* in a table where the input is the trial number and the output is the number of "heads."

Trial #2:   Gather the "heads-up" pennies, shake them up, and dump them on your workspace again. Remove any pennies that have the "tails" side up and count the number of pennies that remain.

Trial #x: Continue this process until the last penny is removed. Be sure to record all of your results in your table and then answer the questions below.

a.   Is it possible that a team conducting this experiment might never remove their last penny? Explain.

b.   Would the results of this experiment have been significantly different if you had removed the "heads" pennies each time?

c.   If you had started with 200 pennies, how would this have affected the results?

B-41.   Decide what your dependent and independent variables are for "The Penny Lab" data, clearly label them, and graph your data on your own graph paper. Then graph your data carefully on a team Lesson B.1.4 Resource Page transparency obtained from your teacher.

a.   Stack your team's transparency with those from other teams on an overhead projector or document camera so that the axes are aligned. Then examine and describe the resulting scatterplot. Where does the graph cross the y-axis? Does the graph have any asymptotes? Should the graph be continuous or discrete?

b.   Is this situation increasing or decreasing? What does this mean about the multiplier? Using what you know about the probability of flipping a fair coin, what would you expect or estimate the multiplier to be?

c.   Write an equation for an exponential function that models the data. Make sure you also write a "let" statement for your variables.

d.   What output does your function give for $x = 0$? What could this mean in relation to the situation?

e.   Could there be an output value for $x = -1$? If so, what might it mean?

f.   In the context of this situation, what should the domain of the model that you wrote in part (c) be? With the appropriate domain, what would a graph of your model look like?

g.   What family of functions that you saw in previous chapters has graphs like the one you made in this problem? What are the first few values of this function? What is the equation?

B-42.   HALF-LIFE

Carbon-14 dating is used to approximate the age of ancient discoveries and to learn more about things like dinosaur fossils. Scientists have studied the rate of decay of carbon-14 and have learned that no matter how much of this element they start with, only half of it will remain after about 5730 years (which is called its **half-life**).

All living things on this planet contain the same proportion of this carbon-14 relative to overall carbon in their bodies. Knowing how much carbon-14 to expect, scientists can then measure how much carbon-14 is left in ancient items to figure out how much time has passed since the object was living.

Problem continues on next page →

B-42.   *Problem continued from previous page.*

    a.   If a living object is supposed to contain 100 grams of carbon-14, how much would be expected to remain after one half-life (5730 years)? After two half-lives (11,460 years)?

    b.   Draw a graph showing the expected amount, y, of carbon-14 (in grams) remaining after x half-lives.

    c.   Write an equation for a function that represents the amount of carbon-14 that will remain after x half-lives. Write a "let" statement.

    d.   What output does your function give for $x = 0$? Does this make sense? Justify why or why not.

    e.   What output would the function give for $x = -1$?

B-43.   In addition to helping you learn about exponential decay, half-life can also provide insight into some special exponent properties.

    a.   For example, in part (d) of problem B-42, you determined that $100\left(\frac{1}{2}\right)^0 = 100$. So what must $\left(\frac{1}{2}\right)^0$ equal? What do you think 3^0 or $(-5)^0$ equals? How do your graphs from Lesson B.1.1 help you predict this? Use your calculator to check your predictions. Then write a conjecture about the value of x^0 (when $x \neq 0$).

    b.   What if $x = -1$? According to your graph, how much carbon-14 should there be when $x = -1$? Use this information to make sense of the value of $\left(\frac{1}{2}\right)^{-1}$. Confirm your conclusion with your calculator.

    c.   Now find the value of your equation when $x = -2$. Use this information to make sense of the value of $\left(\frac{1}{2}\right)^{-2}$. Then, as a team, write a conjecture about the value of x^{-2} when $x \neq 0$. Test your conjecture by predicting the value of 3^{-2} and $\left(\frac{2}{3}\right)^{-2}$. Be sure to test your predictions with your calculator.

B-44.   Use a graphing calculator to compare the graphs of $y = \left(\frac{1}{2}\right)^x$ and $y = 2^{-x}$.

a.   What do you notice? How does a negative exponent affect the base number?

b.   Use this idea to rewrite each of the following expressions in a different form. If you and your team members disagree, check your results with the calculator.

   i. $\left(\frac{1}{5}\right)^{-1}$ *ii.* 100^{-1} *iii.* $\left(\frac{5}{8}\right)^{-1}$ *iv.* $\left(\frac{1}{3}\right)^{-2}$

   v. $\left(\frac{2}{3}\right)^{-3}$ *vi.* 6^{-3} *vii.* $\left(\frac{3}{2}\right)^{-1}$ *viii.* 2^{-5}

MATH NOTES

METHODS AND MEANINGS

Basic Laws of Exponents

In the expression x^3, x is the **base** and 3 is the **exponent**.

$$x^3 = x \cdot x \cdot x$$

The patterns that you have been using during this section of the book are called the **laws of exponents**. Here are the basic rules with examples:

Law	Examples	
$x^m x^n = x^{m+n}$ for all x	$x^3 x^4 = x^{3+4} = x^7$	$2^5 \cdot 2^{-1} = 2^4$
$\frac{x^m}{x^n} = x^{m-n}$ for $x \neq 0$	$x^{10} \div x^4 = x^{10-4} = x^6$	$\frac{5^4}{5^7} = 5^{-3}$
$(x^m)^n = x^{mn}$ for all x	$(x^4)^3 = x^{4\cdot3} = x^{12}$	$(10^5)^6 = 10^{30}$
$x^0 = 1$ for $x \neq 0$	$\frac{y^2}{y^2} = y^0 = 1$	$9^0 = 1$
$x^{-1} = \frac{1}{x}$ for $x \neq 0$	$\frac{1}{x^2} = \left(\frac{1}{x}\right)^2 = (x^{-1})^2 = x^{-2}$	$3^{-1} = \frac{1}{3}$

B-45.   The leadership class at Mt. Heron High School is organizing a shoe drive. A local business has agreed to donate boxes to collect the shoes in. If each box can hold 20 pairs of shoes, draw a step graph relating the number of shoes collected to the number of boxes needed for up to 200 pair of shoes.

B-46.   Assume that a DVD loses 60% of its value every year it is in a video store. Suppose the initial value of the DVD was $80.

   a.   What multiplier would you use to calculate the video's new values?

   b.   What is the value of the DVD after one year? After four years?

   c.   Write a continuous function, $V(t)$, to model the value of a DVD after t years.

   d.   When does the video have no value?

   e.   Sketch a graph of this function. Be sure to scale and label the axes.

B-47.   For each problem, write one or two equations to represent the situation and then solve. Be sure to define your variable(s) and clearly answer the question.

   a.   The Lees have three children. The oldest is twice as old as the youngest. The middle child is five years older than the youngest. If the sum of the ages is 57, how old is each child?

   b.   In Katy's garden there are 105 ladybugs. They are increasing at two ladybugs per month. There are currently 175 aphids and the number of aphids is decreasing at three aphids per month. When will the number of ladybugs and aphids in Katy's garden be the same?

B-48.   Multiply and simplify each expression below.

   a. $(x-3)^2$ b. $(2m+1)^2$

   c. $x(x-3)(x+1)$ d. $(2y-1)(y^2+7)$

B-49.   Consider the sequence $2, 8, 3y+5, \ldots$

   a.   Find the value of y if the sequence is arithmetic.

   b.   Find the value of y if the sequence is geometric.

B-50.   After paying $20,000 for a car, you read that this model has decreased in value 15% per year over the last several years. If this trend continues, how much will the car be worth 5 years from now?

B-51.   Jerry says, "I've got my money in a great account that compounds interest monthly. The equation $y = 388(1.008)^m$ represents how much money I have at the end of any month." What is Jerry's monthly interest rate? What is his annual interest rate? Write an equation to represent your total money if you invest $500 in an account with the same rate of return. Let m represent the number of months the money has been invested.

B-52.   Solve each equation below for x. Check your solution.

    a. $3x - 7(4 + 2x) = -x + 2$ b. $-5x + 2 - x + 1 = 0$

B-53.   Solve each system of equations below.

    a. $2x + y = -7y$ b. $3x = -5y$

          $y = x + 10$ $6x - 7y = 17$

B-54.   Find the equation of the line with x-intercept $(-4, 0)$ and y-intercept $(0, 9)$.

B-55.   For each problem, write one or two equations to represent the situation and then solve. Be sure to define your variable(s) and clearly answer the question.

    a.   At the farmer's market Laura bought three pounds of heirloom tomatoes. If the tomatoes are priced at $8 for five pounds, what did Laura pay for her tomatoes?

    b.   Adult tickets for the school play cost $5 and student tickets cost $3. Thirty more student tickets were sold than adult tickets. If $1770 was collected, how many of each type of ticket were sold?

B-56.   Determine which of the following equations are true for all values (always true). For those that are not, decide whether they are true for certain values (sometimes true) or not true for any values (never true). Justify your decisions clearly.

    a. $(x - 5)^2 = x^2 + 25$ b. $(2x - 1)(x + 4) = 2x^2 + 7x - 4$

    c. $\frac{2x^2y^3}{y^2} = 2x^2y$ d. $(3x - 2)(2x + 1) = 6x^2 - x - 5$

B.1.5 What are the connections?

Graph → Equation

In Lesson B.1.2, you started a Multiple Representations Web for exponential functions. Today your team will develop methods for finding an equation from a graph. As you find ways to write equations based on a graph, you will build deeper understanding of exponential functions.

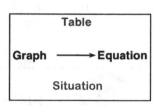

What information do we have?

Can we use other representations to help us think about our equation?

How can we be sure that our equation works?

B-57.   GRAPH → EQUATION

Use the clues provided in each graph below to find a possible corresponding equation in $y = ab^x$ form. Assume that if the graph has an asymptote, it is located on the x-axis.

a.

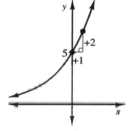

b.

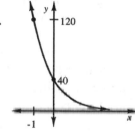

c.

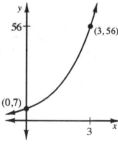

d.

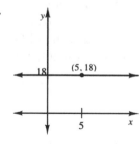

e.

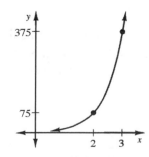

f.

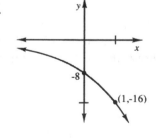

B-58.   LEARNING LOG

Create a Learning Log entry in which you describe
methods for creating an exponential equation given a
graph. Be sure to include examples to illustrate your
reasoning. Title this entry "Graph → Equation for
Exponential Functions" and label it with today's date.

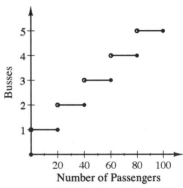

METHODS AND MEANINGS

MATH NOTES

Step Functions

A **step function** is a special kind of piecewise function (a function
composed of parts of two or more functions). A step function has a graph
that is a series of line segments that often looks like a set of steps. Step
functions are used to model real-world situations where there are abrupt
changes in the output of the function.

The endpoints of the segments on step
functions are either open circles
(indicating this point is not part of the
segment) or filled-in circles (indicating
this point is part of the segment).

The graph at right models a situation in
which a tour bus company has busses
that can each hold up to 20 passengers
with 5 available busses.

B-59.   The drama club found that the best price for renting a fog machine was $38 for
every three days, plus a one-time $60 delivery fee. Make a step graph that
shows the cost of renting the fog machine for up to three weeks.

B-60.   Use the clues in the graph at right to find a
         possible corresponding equation in $y = ab^x$ form.
         Assume the graph has an asymptote at the x-axis.

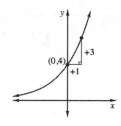

(0,4)

+3

+1

B-61.   Kristin's grandparents started a savings account for her when she was born.
         They invested $500 in an account that pays 8% interest compounded annually.

    a.   Write an equation to model the amount of money in the account on
          Kristin's x^{th} birthday.

    b.   How much money is in the account on Kristin's 16th birthday?

    c.   What are the domain and range of the equation that you wrote in part (a)?

B-62.   Graph $y = x^2 + 3$ and $y = (x + 3)^2$. What are the similarities and differences
         between the graphs? How do these graphs compare to the graph of $y = x^2$?

B-63.   Simplify.

    a. $\sqrt[3]{-1000}$ b. $\sqrt[3]{\frac{1}{8}}$ c. $\sqrt[3]{-125}$ d. $\sqrt[4]{81}$

B-64.   Solve each equation for the variable. Check your solutions, if possible.

    a. $8a + a - 3 = 6a - 2a - 3$ b. $8(3m - 2) - 7m = 0$

    c. $\frac{x}{2} + 1 = 6$ d. $|x - 3| + 5 = 11$

B.1.6 What is the connection?

Completing the Multiple Representations Web

Review the Multiple Representations Web for exponential functions that you created in Lesson B.1.2. Are there any connections you have made since Lesson B.1.2 that you need to add to your web? What connections between representations do you still need to explore?

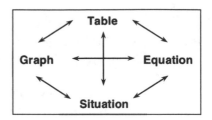

In today's lesson, design your own teamwork based on the connections that are incomplete in your web. Begin your teamwork today by planning which of the problems appear to your team to be the most challenging. The goal is for your team to complete the web by the end of this lesson.

B-65. WRITING A SITUATION

Each representation below represents a different set of data. For each part, brainstorm a situation that could fit the data. Provide enough information in your "problem" description so that someone else could generate the graph, table, or equation for the data. Be creative! Your team's situation may be selected for a future assessment!

a.

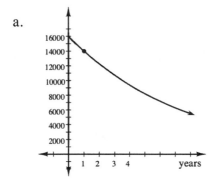

b. $B(t) = 180(1.22)^t$

c.

Year	Amount
1980	226 million
1981	
1982	
.	
.	
.	
1990	
___	1,000,000,000

x 1.02

x 1.02

B-66.   SITUATION → GRAPH

A virus has invaded Leticia's favorite mountain fishing lake. Currently there are an estimated 1800 trout in the lake, and the Fish and Game Department has determined that the rate of fish deaths will be one-third of the population per week if left untreated.

   a.   Sketch a graph showing how many fish are left in Leticia's favorite lake over several weeks.

   b.   Theoretically, will the trout ever completely disappear from the lake? Use the graph to justify your answer.

B-67.   GRAPH → EQUATION

Suppose the annual fees for attending a public university were $7000 in 2010 and the annual cost increase is shown in the graph at right. Note that x represents the number of years after 2010.

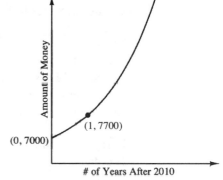

   a.   Write an equation to describe this situation.

   b.   Use this model to predict the cost of attending a public university in the first year you would be eligible to enroll.

   c.   What was the cost in 2000, assuming rate of increase was the same during the time period from 2000 to 2010?

   d.   Are you confident with your prediction in part (c)? Explain.

   e.   In 2012 the annual cost was actually $8244. How accurate was the model? What actually happened?

B-68.   EQUATION → GRAPH

For each equation below, make a reasonable sketch of the graph without making a table first. Discuss your strategy with your team before you begin.

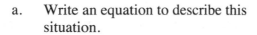

   a. $y = 5(3)^x$ b. $y = 10\left(\frac{1}{2}\right)^x$ c. $y = \frac{1}{10}(5)^x$

B-69.   SITUATION → ?

Use each of the situations below to complete missing pieces of the web or to practice moving from a situation directly to a specific representation. For each part, decide which representation you will generate from the situation description based on where your team needs to work.

a.   A 100-gram sample of a radioactive isotope decays at a rate of 6% every week. How big will the sample be one year from now?

b.   The math club is fast becoming one of the most popular clubs on campus because of the fabulous activities it sponsors annually for Pi Day on March 14. Each year, the club's enrollment increases by 30%. If the club has 45 members this year, how many members should it expect to have 5 years from now?

c.   Barbara made a bad investment. Rather than earning interest, her money is decreasing in value by 11% each week! After just one week, she is down to just $142.40. How much money did she start with? If she does not withdraw her money, how long will it be before she has less than half of what she originally invested?

d.   Larry loves music. He bought $285 worth of MP3 files on his credit card, and now he cannot afford to pay off his debt. If the credit-card company charges him 18% annual interest compounded monthly, how does Larry's debt grow as time passes? How much would he owe at the end of the year if he had a "no payments for 12 months" feature for his credit card?

B-70.   LEARNING LOG

Consider all of the things you have learned so far in this chapter. If you were creating a presentation for families for Open House Night and wanted to teach them the main ideas about exponential functions, what would they be? Write a Learning Log entry describing the main ideas and why they are important. Title this entry "Important Ideas about Exponential Functions" and include today's date.

B-71.　The U.S. Census Bureau takes a census every 10 years. The population in 2000 was estimated at 281.4 million people. A model created at the time predicted that the population grew at about 2% per year.

　　　a.　If the Census Bureau had conducted a count in 2005, how many people would it have expected to count?

　　　b.　How many people would the Census Bureau have expected to count in the 2010 census?

　　　c.　The actual 2010 census put the population at 309 million people. What is the residual? What does it mean?

B-72.　Find values of a and b that make each system of equations true (i.e., solve each system). Be sure to show your work or explain your thinking clearly.

　　　a.　　$6 = a \cdot b^0$
　　　　　　$24 = a \cdot b^2$

　　　b.　　$32 = a \cdot b^2$
　　　　　　$128 = a \cdot b^3$

B-73.　Jack and Jill were working on simplifying the expression at right, but they were having some trouble. Then Jill had an idea. $\dfrac{3x^2 y^{-3}}{x^{-1} y^2}$

　　　"Can't we separate the parts?" she said. "That way, it might be easier to tell what we can simplify." She rewrote the expression as shown at right. $3 \cdot x^2 \cdot \dfrac{1}{x^{-1}} \cdot y^{-3} \cdot \dfrac{1}{y^2}$

　　　"Okay," said Jack. "Now we can rewrite each of the parts with negative exponents and simplify."

　　　a.　Help Jack and Jill finish simplifying their expression.

　　　b.　Use their idea to rewrite and simplify $\dfrac{m^2 p q^{-1}}{4 m^{-2} p q^3}$.

B-74.   A particular sequence can be represented by $t(n) = 2(3)^n$.

    a.   What are $t(0)$, $t(1)$, $t(2)$, and $t(3)$?

    b.   Graph this sequence. What is the domain?

    c.   On the same set of axes, graph the function $f(x) = 2(3)^x$.

    d.   How are the two graphs similar? How are they different?

B-75.   Solve the system of equations at right algebraically.

$$2x - 3y = 12$$
$$y + x = -9$$

B-76.   The cows at the Evaleen Dairy produce enough milk to fill a 4800-gallon tanker truck each day. The milk is then hauled to a processing plant where it is put into smaller storage containers and then used to fill gallon jugs that are delivered to local stores. The storage containers each hold 600 gallons of milk. Make a graph that shows the amount of milk in the tanker truck as each storage tank is filled.

B.2.1 How can I find the equation?

Curve Fitting and Fractional Exponents

In the next few lessons, you will use your knowledge of linear equations to help develop algebraic strategies for finding exponential functions. You will also learn more about working with roots and exponents.

B-77.   Find the equation of the line in $y = mx + b$ form with slope 3 that passes through the point $(5, 19)$. Take careful note of how you find m and b.

B-78.   Can you use an idea similar to the one you used in problem B-77 to find an exponential equation in $y = ab^x$ form?

   a.   While trying to find the equation for the graph in part (c) of problem B-57 (shown again at right), Errol stated, *"I think 'a' must be 7 because the y-intercept is at (0, 7)."* Do you agree? Justify your answer.

   b.   *"But we still don't know what 'b' is,"* Errol noticed. His teammate, Sandy, had an idea. *"I think that $56 = 7(b)^3$."* How did she get this equation? Is it valid? Explain.

   c.   If you have not done so already, solve $56 = 7(b)^3$ for b. Explain how you solved this equation.

   d.   Use a and b to write the equation for this graph. Does it agree with the equation you found in part (c) of problem B-57?

B-79.   Use Errol's and Sandy's method from problem B-78 to find the equation of an exponential function with an asymptote at $y = 0$ that passes through the points $(0, 5)$ and $(3, 320)$.

B-80.   NEW NOTATION FOR ROOTS

a.   Addison's teacher challenged his team to find a
     way to write $\sqrt[3]{17}$ with exponents. Addison
     started by writing this equation: $17^x = \sqrt[3]{17}$.
     Her team needed to find what x was equal to.
     Do you have any guesses about what the
     exponent might be? Discuss this with your team.

b.   Addison said, *"But we also know that $(\sqrt[3]{17})^3 = 17$, and we want to write
     $\sqrt[3]{17}$ with an exponent instead, like 17^x. So why don't we combine this
     information and write $(17^x)^3 = 17$?"* Addison asked.

     Addison continued, *"Oh, so $(17^x)^3 = 17^{3x}$?"* Is she correct? Is it true that
     $(17^x)^3 = 17^{3x}$? Be ready to share your reasoning with the class.

c.   Addison wrote: $17^{3x} = 17^1$. Complete Addison's work to find
     the value of x in this equation. What does this tell you about
     another way to write $\sqrt[3]{17}$? Check your result by finding
     decimal approximations with your calculator.

d.   Use similar logic to find exponential expressions for $\sqrt{5}$ and $\sqrt[5]{11}$. Show
     your reasoning. Then use your graphing calculator to find their decimal
     equivalents, rounded to the nearest 0.001.

B-81.   REWRITING EXPRESSIONS

The property $(k^m)^n = k^{mn}$ can help you rewrite expressions with roots and
fractional exponents, as it helped you in part (d) of problem B-80.

For example, since $16^{3/2} = (16^3)^{1/2}$, $16^{3/2}$ can be rewritten as $\sqrt{16^3}$. However,
since $16^{3/2} = (16^{1/2})^3$, $16^{3/2}$ can also be rewritten as $(\sqrt{16})^3$ or 4^3.

With your team, find ways to rewrite the expressions below *two different ways*.
Be ready to justify your answers.

a. $10^{2/3}$ b. $(\sqrt[3]{9})^4$ c. $\sqrt[5]{x^3}$

d. $(\sqrt{2})^5$ e. $5^{7/2}$ f. $y^{3/3}$

B-82. Fractional exponents can give surprising results when used with negative bases. Answer the following questions using what you now know rewriting fractional exponents and your mental math skills. Avoid using your calculator.

a. Show or explain why $(-27)^{1/2}$ has no real solution but $(-27)^{1/3} = -3$.

b. Given that $(-27)^{1/3} = -3$, is $(-27)^{2/3}$ positive or negative, or does it have no real solution? What about $(-27)^{1/4}$? And $(-27)^{1/5}$? Justify your answers.

c. Mischa was working with her team on the idea of negative bases, but she got confused. Consider her thinking below.

    i. *"Wait,"* she said. *"Isn't it true that $(-100)^{1/2}$ has no real solution?"* What does Mischa mean? Is she right?

    ii. *"But,"* she continued, *"I can figure out that $(-100)^{2/4} = 10$."* Check her calculation. Is she correct?

    iii. *"That doesn't make any sense, since $\frac{2}{4}$ can be reduced to $\frac{1}{2}$!"* What do you think?

B-83. Recall that when you investigated $y = b^x$ in problem B-2, the graphing calculator produced graphs like the one at right for negative values of b when you used the "zoom decimal" option. Use what you have learned about the meaning of fractional exponents to explain why $y = (-2)^x$ is impossible to graph accurately.

B-84. LEARNING LOG

You have now worked with exponents that have been zero, exponents that have been negative numbers, and exponents that have been fractions. In your Learning Log, explain everything you know about these kinds of exponents. Show equivalent ways to write expressions with zero, negative, and fractional exponents. What does each kind of exponent mean? Explain using both words and examples. Title this entry "Zero, Negative, and Fractional Exponents" and label it with today's date.

B-85.   Find a possible exponential function in $y = a \cdot b^x$ form that represents each situation described below.

    a.   Has an initial value of 2 and passes through the point $(3, 128)$.

    b.   Passes through the points $(0, 4)$ and $(2, 1)$.

B-86.   Solve the following systems of equations. In other words, find values of a and b that make each system true. Be sure to show your work or explain your thinking clearly.

    a. $3 = a \cdot b^0$
           $75 = a \cdot b^2$

    b. $18 = a \cdot b^2$
           $54 = a \cdot b^3$

B-87.   Evaluate each expression below.

    a. $\sqrt[3]{-64}$
    b. $\sqrt[5]{32}$
    c. $\sqrt[3]{-8}$
    d. $\sqrt[4]{10000}$

B-88.   Rewrite $16^{3/4}$ in as many different ways as you can.

B-89.   Find the equation of the line passing through the points $(7, 16)$ and $(2, -4)$. Then state the slope and x- and y-intercepts. Explain how you found them.

B.2.2 How can I find the equation?

More Curve Fitting

In this lesson, you will continue your work from Lesson B.2.1 as you develop a new method to find linear and exponential equations given two points.

B-90. Mitchell was working on his algebra homework, when suddenly he had an idea about finding linear equations. He was trying to find the equation of the line that passes through the points $(5, 15)$ and $(3, 7)$. *"Look!"* he exclaimed. *"We know that the line can be written in the form $y = mx + b$, and we also know that the points (5, 15) and (3, 7) have to make the equation true. So we can substitute in these two points to create a system of equations. When we solve that, we'll know the values of m and b, and we'll have our equation!"*

   a. What is Mitchell talking about? Use his method to find the equation of the line through the points $(5, 15)$ and $(3, 7)$.

   b. Will Mitchell's method work to find the equation of a line through any two points? Justify your answer.

B-91. Use Mitchell's method from problem B-90 to find the equation of the line that passes through the points $(2, 3)$ and $(5, -6)$.

B-92. Can Mitchell's method from problem B-90 be used to find the *exponential* function that passes through the points $(2, 16)$ and $(6, 256)$? Consider this as you answer the questions below.

   a. What is the general form for an exponential function that has an asymptote at $y = 0$?

   b. Use the two points that you know to create a system of equations.

   c. Solve both equations for a. Then set the equations equal to each other to solve your system of equations for b. Next, find a, and write the equation that goes through the two points.

B-93.　Find an exponential function that passes through each pair of points.

　　a.　$(-1, -2)$ and $(3, -162)$　　　　　　b.　$(2, 1.75)$ and $(-2, 28)$

ＭETHODS AND ＭEANINGS

Negative and Fractional Exponents

MATH NOTES

For all x not equal to zero:

$$x^0 = 1 \qquad \text{Examples: } 2^0 = 1, \ (-3)^0 = 1, \ \left(\tfrac{1}{4}\right)^0 = 1$$

For positive values of x:

$$x^{-n} = \frac{1}{x^n} \qquad \text{Examples: } x^{-3} = \frac{1}{x^3}, \ y^{-4} = \frac{1}{y^4}, \ 4^{-2} = \frac{1}{4^2} = \frac{1}{16}$$

$$\frac{1}{x^{-n}} = x^n \qquad \text{Examples: } \frac{1}{x^{-5}} = x^5, \ \frac{1}{x^{-2}} = x^2, \ \frac{1}{3^{-2}} = 3^2 = 9$$

$$x^{a/b} = (x^a)^{1/b} = \sqrt[b]{x^a} \ \text{ or } \ x^{a/b} = (x^{1/b})^a = (\sqrt[b]{x})^a$$

$$\text{Examples:} \qquad 5^{1/2} = \sqrt{5}, \quad 3^{2/3} = \sqrt[3]{3^2} = \sqrt[3]{9},$$

$$16^{3/4} = (16^{1/4})^3 = (\sqrt[4]{16})^3 = 2^3 = 8$$

B-94.　Find an exponential function that passes through each pair of points.

　　a.　$(1, 7.5)$ and $(3, 16.875)$　　　　　　b.　$(-1, 1.25)$ and $(3, 0.032)$

B-95.　Consider the pattern at right.

　　a.　Continue the pattern to find $\frac{1}{2^{-1}}$, $\frac{1}{2^{-2}}$, $\frac{1}{2^{-3}}$, and $\frac{1}{2^{-4}}$.

　　b.　What is the value of $\frac{1}{2^{-n}}$?

　　c.　Write a conjecture about how to rewrite $\frac{1}{a^{-n}}$ without a negative exponent.

$$\frac{1}{2^3} = \frac{1}{8}$$
$$\frac{1}{2^2} = \frac{1}{4}$$
$$\frac{1}{2^1} = \frac{1}{2}$$
$$\frac{1}{2^0} = 1$$

B-96.   Find the domain and range for each of the relations graphed below.

a.

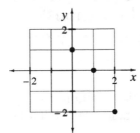

b.

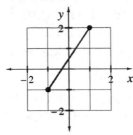

c.

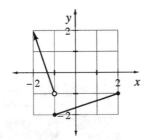

d.

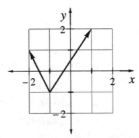

B-97.   If $f(x) = 3(2)^x$, find the value of the expressions in parts (a) through (c) below. Then complete parts (d) through (f).

a. $f(-1)$ b. $f(0)$ c. $f(1)$

d.   What value of x gives $f(x) = 12$?

e.   Where does the graph of this function cross the x-axis? The y-axis?

f.   If $g(x) = \frac{1}{3x}$, find $f(x) \cdot g(x)$.

B-98.   Show two steps to simplify each of the following expressions, and then calculate the value of each expression.

a. $64^{2/3}$ b. $25^{5/2}$ c. $81^{7/4}$

B-99.   What is the multiplier for the sequence shown in the graph at right?

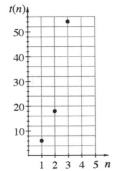

B.2.3   How can I use exponential functions?

Solving a System of Exponential Functions Graphically

In this lesson, you will apply your skills with exponential functions to a system of equations as you explore the value of cars in an investigation called "Fast Cars."

B-100.   FAST CARS

The moment you drive a new car off the dealer's lot, the car is worth less than what you paid for it. This phenomenon is called *depreciation*, which means you will sell the car for less than the price that you paid for it. Some cars depreciate more than others (that is, they depreciate at different rates), but most cars depreciate over time. On the other hand, some older cars actually increase in value. This is called *appreciation*. Let's suppose that in 2012, Jeralyn had a choice between buying a 2010 Fonda Concord EX for $27,000, which depreciates at 6% per year; a 2010 Padillac Escalate for $39,000, which depreciates at 22.5% per year; or a 1967 Fyord Rustang for $15,000 that is appreciating at 10% per year.

Your Task: Investigate the value of each of the three cars over time.

- Generate multiple representations of the value of each car over time.

- For each of the new cars, determine how much value they lost (in dollars) from the time they were new in 2010 until 2012.

- Decide which car Jeralyn should buy and defend your choice in as many ways as you can.

Discussion Points

What is the multiplier?

How can we represent this situation in a table? A graph? An equation?

What should we consider when deciding which car to buy?

Further Guidance

B-101.   Investigate the changing values of each of the cars by addressing the questions below.

   a.   What is the multiplier for the Concord? For the Escalate? For the Rustang?

   b.   Make a table like the one below and calculate the value for each car for each year shown.

Year	Concord	Escalate	Rustang
0	$27,000	$39,000	$15,000
1	$25,380	$30,225	
2			
3			
4			
5			
...			
10			
...			
n			

   c.   On your own graph paper, graph the data for all three cars on the same set of axes. Are the graphs linear? How are they similar? How are they different? You may want to use a different color for each car.

   d.   Write a function to represent the value of each car.

   e.   What were the values of the Concord and the Escalate when they were new? How much value (in dollars) did each car lose from 2010 to 2012?

   f.   Using the graph, which of the three cars is worth the most after one year? After 3 years? After 10 years? In how many years will the values of the Concord and Escalate be the same?

   g.   Pick one of the three cars and explain why Jeralyn should buy it. Has this problem changed your view of buying cars?

———————   *Further Guidance*   ———————
section ends here.

B-102.   As you saw in "The Penny Lab," half-life applies to situations other than radioactive decay. In fact, the idea can be applied to anything that is depreciating or decaying exponentially.

   a.   Using the values in problem B-100, Fast Cars, estimate the half-life of the value of the Concord and the Escalate.

   b.   According to the mathematical model, when will each car have no value?

B-103.   In 2009, a brand new SUV cost $35,000 to drive off the lot. In 2012 that same SUV was valued at $22,500. Write an exponential equation to represent this information. Then find the rate of depreciation for the SUV.

$\textbf{M}$ETHODS AND $\textbf{M}$EANINGS

Equations for Sequences

Arithmetic Sequences

The equation for an arithmetic sequence is: $t(n) = mn + b$ or $a_n = mn + a_0$ where n is the term number, m is the sequence generator (the common difference), and b or a_0 is the zeroth term. Compare these equations to a continuous linear function $f(x) = mx + b$ where m is the growth (slope) and b is the starting value (y-intercept).

For example, the arithmetic sequence 4, 7, 10, 13, ... could be represented by $t(n) = 3n + 1$ or by $a_n = 3n + 1$. (Note that "4" is the first term of this sequence, so "1" is the zeroth term.)

Another way to write the equation of an arithmetic sequence is by using the first term in the equation, as in $a_n = m(n-1) + a_1$, where a_1 is the first term. The sequence in the example could be represented by $a_n = 3(n-1) + 4$.

You could even write an equation using any other term in the sequence. The equation using the fourth term in the example would be $a_n = 3(n-4) + 13$.

Geometric Sequences

The equation for a geometric sequence is: $t(n) = ab^n$ or $a_n = a_0 \cdot b^n$ where n is the term number, b is the sequence generator (the multiplier or common ratio), and a or a_0 is the zeroth term. Compare these equations to a continuous exponential function $f(x) = ab^x$, where b is the growth (multiplier) and a is the starting value (y-intercept).

For example, the geometric sequence 6, 18, 54, ... could be represented by $t(n) = 2 \cdot 3^n$ or by $a_n = 2 \cdot 3^n$.

You can write a first term form of the equation for a geometric sequence as well: $a_n = a_1 \cdot b^{n-1}$. For the example, first term form would be $a_n = 6 \cdot 3^{n-1}$.

B-104. Find the equation of an exponential function that passes through the points $(2, 48)$ and $(5, 750)$.

B-105. After noon, the number of people in Mal-Wart grows steadily until 6:00 p.m. If the equation $y = 228 + 58x$ represents the number of people in the store x hours after noon:

a. How many people were in the store at noon?

b. At what rate is the number of shoppers growing?

c. When were there 402 shoppers in the store?

B-106. Wade and Dwayne were working together writing an equation for the sequence 12, 36, 108, 324, ... Wade wrote $t(n) = 4 \cdot 3^n$, and Dwayne wrote $t(n) = 12 \cdot 3^{n-1}$.

a. Make a table for the first four terms of each of their sequences. What do you notice?

b. How do you think Dwayne explained his method of writing the equation to Wade?

c. For the sequence 10.3, 11.5, 12.7, ..., Wade wrote $t(n) = 9.1 + 1.2n$ while Dwayne wrote $t(n) = 10.3 + 1.2(n-1)$. Make a table for the first four terms of each of their sequences. Are both forms of the equation correct?

d. Dwayne calls his equations the **"first term" form**. Why do you think he calls them "first term" form? Why does Dwayne subtract one in both situations?

B-107. Write an explicit equation for the sequence graphed at right.

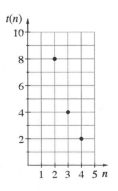

B-108.   Write an explicit equation for the sequence
         graphed at right.

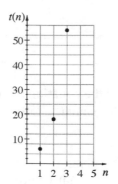

B-109.   Solve each system of equations.

    a. $y = 3x + 11$
          $x + y = 3$

    b. $y = 2x + 3$
          $x - y = -4$

    c. $x + 2y = 16$
          $x + y = 2$

    d. $2x + 3y = 10$
          $3x - 4y = -2$

Appendix B Closure   What have I learned?

Reflection and Synthesis

The activities below offer you a chance to reflect about what you have learned during this chapter. As you work, look for concepts that you feel very comfortable with, ideas that you would like to learn more about, and topics you need more help with. Look for connections between ideas as well as connections with material you learned previously.

①   TEAM BRAINSTORM

What have you studied in this chapter? What ideas were important in what you learned? With your team, brainstorm a list. Be as detailed as you can. To help get you started, a list of Learning Log entries and Math Notes boxes are below.

What topics, ideas, and words that you learned *before* this chapter are connected to the new ideas in this chapter? Again, be as detailed as you can.

How long can you make your list? Challenge yourselves. Be prepared to share your team's ideas with the class.

Learning Log Entries

- Lesson B.1.1 – Investigating $y = b^x$
- Lesson B.1.2 – Multiple Representations Web for Exponential Functions
- Lesson B.1.5 – Graph $\rightarrow$ Equation for Exponential Functions
- Lesson B.1.6 – Important Ideas about Exponential Functions
- Lesson B.2.1 – Zero, Negative, and Fractional Exponents

Math Notes

- Lesson B.1.3 – Compounding Interest
- Lesson B.1.4 – Basic Laws of Exponents
- Lesson B.1.5 – Step Functions
- Lesson B.2.2 – Negative and Fractional Exponents
- Lesson B.2.3 – Equations for Sequences

② **MAKING CONNECTIONS**

Below is a list of the vocabulary used in this chapter. Make sure that you are familiar with all of these words and know what they mean. Refer to the glossary or index for any words that you do not yet understand.

appreciation	asymptote	compound interest
depreciation	exponential function	fractional exponents
half-life	initial value	model
multiplier	parameter	roots
simple interest	step function	

Make a concept map showing all of the connections you can find among the key words and ideas listed above. To show a connection between two words, draw a line between them and explain the connection. A word can be connected to any other word as long as you can justify the connection.

While you are making your map, your team may think of related words or ideas that are not listed above. Be sure to include these ideas on your concept map.

③ **PORTFOLIO: EVIDENCE OF MATHEMATICAL PROFICIENCY**

If you took a photograph of your poster from Lesson B.1.1, include it in your portfolio. Your photo provides evidence of your growing understanding of exponential functions.

Showcase your early understanding of *x*-intercepts by answering the following questions:

How many different kinds of graphs can you create that have:

a. No x-intercepts?

b. One x-intercept?

c. Two x-intercepts?

d. Three or more x-intercepts?

For each type of graph, show a sketch, label the key points, and give its equation. Make sure that each graph you give as an example represents a different family, and describe the family in words or with a general equation. Show how to calculate the *x*-intercepts of each of your sample graphs.

Your teacher may give you the Appendix B Closure Resource Page: "Multiple Representations of Exponential Functions Graphic Organizer." Complete it to showcase your current understanding of the multiple representations of an exponential function.

④ WHAT HAVE I LEARNED?

Most of the problems in this section represent typical problems found in this chapter. They serve as a gauge for you. You can use them to determine which types of problems you can do well and which types of problems require further study and practice. Even if your teacher does not assign this section, it is a good idea to try these problems and find out for yourself what you know and what you still need to work on.

Solve each problem as completely as you can. The table at the end of the closure section has answers to these problems. It also tells you where you can find additional help and practice with problems like these.

CL B-110.   Find an exponential function in $y = ab^x$ form that satisfies each of the following sets of conditions.

a.   Has a y-intercept of $(0, 2)$ and a multiplier of 0.8.

b.   Passes through the points $(0, 3.5)$ and $(2, 31.5)$.

CL B-111.   Sam wants to create an arithmetic sequence and a geometric sequence, both of which have $t(1) = 8$ and $t(7) = 512$. Is this possible? If it is, help Sam create his sequences. If not, justify why not.

CL B-112.   Write each expression below as an equivalent expression without negative exponents.

a. 3^{-2} b. m^{-4} c. $(\frac{1}{2})^{-3}$ d. $(\frac{3}{5x})^{-1}$

CL B-113.   Write each expression below in radical form and compute the value without using a calculator.

a. $8^{1/3}$ b. $16^{3/4}$ c. $125^{4/3}$

CL B-114.   Best Price Parking charges $2 for the first hour of parking and $0.50 for each additional hour. Create a step function graph that represents this information.

CL B-115.   A share of ABC stock was worth $60 in 2005 and only worth $45 in 2010.

   a.   Find the multiplier and the percent decrease.

   b.   Write an exponential function that models the value of the stock starting from 2005.

   c.   Assuming that the decline in value continues at the same rate, use your answer to (b) to predict the value in 2020.

CL B-116.   Write an equation or system of equations to solve this problem.

   An adult ticket to the amusement park costs $24.95 and a child's ticket costs $15.95. A group of 10 people paid $186.50 to enter the park. How many were adults?

CL B-117.   Solve each system of equations.

   a. $2x - y = 9$
        $y = x - 7$

   b. $-4x + y = 5$
        $2x = -y - 13$

CL B-118.   Write a recursive equation for the sequence graphed at right.

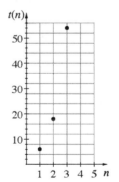

CL B-119.   Write an equation for the line that passes through the points $(-5, 4)$ and $(3, -2)$.

CL B-120.   Check your answers using the table at the end of this section. Which problems do you feel confident about? Which problems were hard? Have you worked on problems like these in previous math classes? Use the table to make a list of topics you need help on, and a list of topics you need to practice more.

Answers and Support for Closure Activity #4:
What Have I Learned?

Note: MN = Math Note, LL = Learning Log

Problem	Solutions	Need Help?	More Practice
CL B-110.	a. $y = 2(0.8)^x$ b. $y = 3.5(3)^x$	Lessons B.2.1 and B.2.2	Problems B-23, B-35, B-60, B-85, B-94, and B-104
CL B-111.	Arithmetic: $t(n) = 84n - 76$ Geometric: $t(n) = 4(2)^n$	Section A.2 MN: A.3.2 and B.2.3	Problems CL A-120, B-14, B-27, and B-106
CL B-112.	a. $\frac{1}{9}$ b. $\frac{1}{m^4}$ c. 8 d. $\frac{5x}{3}$	MN: B.1.4 and B.2.2	Problem CL A-123, B-11, B-75, and B-97
CL B-113.	a. $\sqrt[3]{8} = 2$ b. $(\sqrt[4]{16})^3 = 8$ c. $(\sqrt[3]{125})^4 = 625$	Lesson B.2.1 MN: B.2.2 LL: B.2.1	Problems B-87, B-88, and B-98
CL B-114.		MN: B.1.5	Problems B-45 and B-59
CL B-115.	a. annual multiplier ≈ 0.944 $\approx 5.6\%$ decrease b. $f(x) = 60(0.944)^x$ c. $f(15) = 25.28$	Section B.1 LL: B.1.6	Problem B-15, B-36, B-46, B-71, and B-103

Problem	Solutions	Need Help?	More Practice
CL B-116.	If $a = \#$ of adults, $c = \#$ of children $a + c = 10$ $24.95a + 15.95c = 186.50$ $a = 3$ adults	Explanations and practice of topics from previous courses are available in the *Core Connections Algebra Parent Guide with Extra Practice,* available free at www.cpm.org.	Problems B-7 and B-26
CL B-117.	a. $(2, -5)$ b. $(-3, -7)$	Topic from previous course	Problems CL A-121, B-38, B-53, B-75, and B-109
CL B-118.	$a_1 = 2,\ a_{n+1} = 3 \cdot a_n$	Topic from previous course	Problems B-99 and B-108
CL B-119.	$y = -\frac{3}{4}x + \frac{1}{4}$	Topic from previous course	Problems CL A-124 and B-89

Appendix C   Comparing Single-Variable Data

In this appendix you will learn how to compare data that only has one variable. You will start by modeling a golf game and comparing your results with other teams. You will review the ways to graphically represent data, and decide whether to use scatterplots or two histograms to compare two variables. You will use statistics to compare two sets of data: center, shape, spread and outliers. Finally, you will learn a new way to describe the variability (the spread) in data called the standard deviation.

Guiding Question

Mathematically proficient students make sense of problems and persevere in solving them.

As you work through this chapter, ask yourself:

Am I taking advantage of everything I know to really engage with the mathematics and understand the problems I am solving?

Chapter Outline

Section C.1   You will review the differences between graphical representations of single-variable data. Then you will compare the center, shape, spread, and outliers of two distributions. Finally you will develop a new way to describe the spread called standard deviation.

C.1.1 How do I represent consistency?

Investigating Data Representations

The field of Statistics is the application of probability theory to make sense of large quantities of data. The study of Statistics allows people to make decisions and predictions from the natural variability in data.

A **statistic** (with a lower-case "s") is a numerical fact or calculation that is formed from a large quantity of data. A "mean" or a "correlation coefficient," for example, is a statistic.

In this section you will continue your study of Statistics from previous courses by modeling a golf tournament.

C-1.   FORTY HOLES OF GOLF

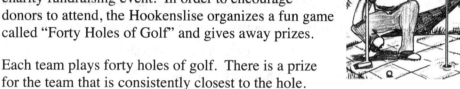

The Hookenslise Corporation is having its annual charity fundraising event. In order to encourage donors to attend, the Hookenslise organizes a fun game called "Forty Holes of Golf" and gives away prizes.

Each team plays forty holes of golf. There is a prize for the team that is consistently closest to the hole.
Your teacher has set up a "hole." Your team will "swing" forty pennies toward the "hole." You will then represent your data on a graph and with numerical statistics. Analyzing the statistics will help you decide which team was the most consistently close to the hole.

Your Task:

- Your teacher will give you ten pennies. Have one team member stand 200 cm from the "hole." That team member will toss all ten pennies. No "do-overs" and no practice shots are allowed. Then record the distance from the center of each penny to the "hole" (to the nearest centimeter), even if the penny rolled far away.

- Repeat with different team members until 40 pennies have been tossed. Do not take turns tossing pennies – each team member should toss all their pennies, one at a time. Then the next team member can take their turn.

- When directed by the teacher, return to your table or desks. Decide how you want to represent your data on your poster: dot plot, boxplot, circle graph ("pie chart"), scatterplot, histogram, or bar graph. Create a poster. Leave room for the task below.

Problem continues on next page →

C-1. *Problem continued from previous page.*

- Decide the five most important facts you wish to report about your team's golf shots and add them to your poster.

- Record your team's data in a safe place. You will need it for Lesson C.1.2.

- Your teacher will direct you on how to compare your team's results with the other teams. Which team was most consistently close to the hole?

C-2. LEARNING LOG

You had your choice of six graphical representations of data: dot plot, boxplot, circle graph ("pie chart"), scatterplot, histogram, or bar graph. Discuss with your team how to choose among them. Give examples. Consider the following discussion points.

Discussion Points

What is the difference between single-variable data and two-variable data?

What is the difference between numerical and categorical data?

Do a lot of data values repeat?

What are the advantages?

Record your conclusions in your Learning Log. Be sure to include examples. Title this entry "Representing Data Graphically" and include today's date.

Ⓜ️ETHODS AND MEANINGS

Interquartile Range and Boxplots

Quartiles are points that divide a data set into four equal parts (and thus, the use of the prefix "quar" as in "quarter"). One of these points is the **median**. The **first quartile (Q1)** is the median of the lower half, and the **third quartile (Q3)** is the median of the upper half.

To find quartiles, the data set must be placed in order from smallest to largest. Note that if there are an odd number of data values, the median is not included in either half of the data set.

Suppose you have the data set: 22, 43, 14, 7, 2, 32, 9, 36, and 12.

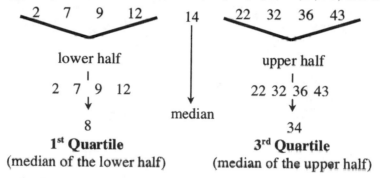

The **interquartile rage (IQR)** is the difference between the third and first quartiles. It is used to measure the spread (the variability) of the middle fifty percent of the data. The interquartile range is $34 - 8 = 26$.

A **boxplot** (also known as a box-and-whisker plot) displays a five-number summary of data: minimum, first quartile, median, third quartile, and maximum. The box contains "the middle half" of the data and visually displays how large the IQR is. The right segment represents the top 25% of the data and the left segment represents the bottom 25% of the data. A boxplot makes it easy to see where the data are spread out and where they are concentrated. The wider the box, the more the data are spread out.

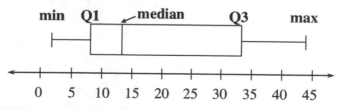

C-3.   A sample of 23 newborns at the Dallas University Health
        Center had the following lengths in centimeters. The
        measurements have been sorted from lowest to highest.

        46.4, 46.9, 47.7, 48.1, 48.5, 48.5, 48.8, 49.0, 49.3, 50.0, 50.1,
        50.4, 50.6, 51.1, 51.4, 51.8, 52.4, 52.5, 53.2, 53.8, 54.4, 55.1, 55.9

        Find the **five number summary** of the lengths of the newborns. A five number
        summary includes the minimum, first quartile, median, third quartile, and
        maximum. Do not use a calculator. If you need help, see the Math Notes box
        in this lesson.

C-4.   For each function, find the inverse function.

        a. $f(x) = \frac{x}{3} - 2$ b. $g(x) = \frac{1}{2}x + 5$

C-5.   Solve the equations and inequalities below, if possible.

        a. $\sqrt{x-1} + 13 = 13$ b. $6|x| > 18$ c. $|3x - 2| \le 2$

        d. $\frac{4}{5} - \frac{2x}{3} = \frac{3}{10}$ e. $(4x - 2)^2 \le 100$ f. $(x - 1)^3 = 8$

C-6.   Ten minutes after he left his home, Gerald was
        40 miles from his grandmother's house. Then,
        22 minutes after he left, he was 34 miles from her
        house. If he was traveling toward his
        grandmother's home at a constant rate and
        reached her house after 90 minutes, how far away
        from her house does he live?

C-7.   Write the inequality represented
        by the graph at right.

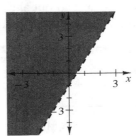

Core Connections Algebra 2

C-8.   Kiesha graphed $y = x(6 - x)$ in a standard calculator viewing window.

   a.   What is the best name for her graph?

   b.   Jamal has bet Kiesha that with his graphing calculator he can make the graph look like a horizontal line without changing, adding, or deleting functions. Kiesha doesn't think he can do this, but Jamal is sure he can. What strategy does Jamal have in mind?

C-9.   In the diagram at right, the point (x, y) is the same distance from $(-3, 4)$ as it is from $(2, -1)$. There are many possibilities for (x, y). Algebraically, what do they have in common?

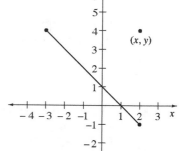

   a.   What is the distance from (x, y) to $(-3, 4)$?

   b.   What is the distance from (x, y) to $(2, -1)$?

   c.   Write the equation that states that the two expressions in (a) and (b) are equal and simplify.

   d.   What is the specific name of the geometric object represented by your equation from part (c)?

C-10.   Find the real solutions to the equations below using any method of your choice.

   a. $2x^2 = 2 - 3x$

   b. $(2x - 3)^2 + 4 = 0$

C-11.   The GPAs of a sample of 26 community college applicants were selected and listed in ascending order below. Do not use a calculator for this problem.

1.58	1.87	2.32	2.44	2.46	2.46	2.50	2.63	2.69
2.72	2.78	2.81	2.83	2.99	3.10	3.16	3.30	3.42
3.46	3.49	3.54	3.67	3.75	3.87	3.89	4.29	

   a.   Find the five-number summary of the GPAs of these applicants.

   b.   On grid paper, create a combination histogram and boxplot. Use an interval of 0.5 on the x-axis. (A combination histogram and boxplot starts with a histogram. Then place a boxplot on top of the histogram. Refer to the Math Notes box for this lesson, if needed. Use the same x-axis scale for both the histogram and the boxplot.)

Problem continues on next page →

C-11.   *Problem continued from previous page.*

     c.   Describe the center, shape, spread, and outliers. To review descriptions of "shape," see the Math Notes box in Lesson C.1.2. To describe "spread" use the IQR, reviewed in the Math Notes box in this lesson.

C-12.   Fully investigate the function $g(x) = \sqrt{x-3} + 1$.

C-13.   Find an equation that represents the number of tiles in the tile pattern at right.

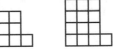

                                       Figure 0   Figure 1   Figure 2

C-14.   Write and solve an equation to solve the problem below. State your solution as a sentence.

Shu Min currently has 1980 digital songs, and downloads 30 more songs each month. Her older brother, Wei, currently has 2590 songs but he only downloads 20 more songs each month. The computer they share can only hold 5000 songs. After how many months will their computer be full?

C-15.   Solve the inequalities and equations below, if possible. Represent your solution on a number line.

    a. $|x| + 3 < 5$ b. $5(2x+1) \geq 30$ c. $\frac{1}{x} - \frac{5}{2} = \frac{3}{2}$

    d. $-5 - x > 3 - x$ e. $3\sqrt{4-x} + 1 = 13$ f. $|x+1| \leq 4$

C-16.   In one of the games at the County Fair, people pay to shoot a paint pistol at the target shown at right. The center has a radius of one inch. Each concentric circle has a radius one inch larger than the preceding circle. Assuming the paint pellet hits the target randomly, what is the probability that it hits:

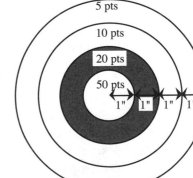

    a.   The 50-point ring?

    b.   The 20-point ring?

Core Connections Algebra 2

C-17.   Frank says that $\frac{a}{x+b} = \frac{a}{x} + \frac{a}{b}$, while Fred does not think that the two expressions are equivalent. Who is correct? Justify your answer.

C-18.   Where do the graphs below intersect?
You should be able to do these without a graphing calculator.

a. $2x + y = 10$
       $x + y = 25$

b. $2x + y = 10$
       $x^2 + y^2 = 25$

C-19.   Given the quadratic function $f(x) = -2(x-2)^2 + 6$:

a.   Without drawing a graph, tell the coordinates of the vertex and tell if the vertex represents the maximum or minimum value of the function.

b.   Use your graphing shortcuts to draw a graph and verify your answer to part (a).

C.1.2 How can I compare results?

Comparing Data

In Lesson C.1.1 you tried to decide which team was close to the hole most consistently. Comparing sets of data is an essential part of the study of Statistics. Data is often not meaningful unless it is compared to other data. What does your batting average or free throw average mean if you are the only person who has one? If there are no other SAT scores to compare to then what does your score matter?

C-20.   As the Managing Grower at All-Organic Orchards, you know the farmer's market will only accept fruit that is above average size for your orchard. However, they do not define how to calculate "average," with a mean or with a median. You want to sell as much fruit as possible for premium prices at the farmer's market.

a.   Your apple crop is represented by the histogram and boxplot at right. To get the maximum amount of fruit to the market, should you use the mean or the median for the "average"?

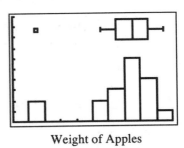

Weight of Apples

b.   Your lemon crop is represented by the histogram at right. Why do you suppose the right "whisker" is missing? Which average, mean or median, should you use?

c.   Why might the farmers at other orchards feel like you were being deceptive by reporting the mean for your fruit?

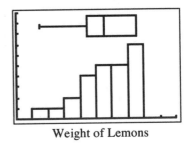

Weight of Lemons

d.   To best represent numerically the center, or the "typical" value, of a large quantity of data, when would you use the mean and when would you use the median?

C-21.   Home sales in Fancyville and Smallville are shown in the tables below.
Calculate the mean and median sales price in each town and compare
Fancyville to Smallville. In which town does the "typical" home cost less?

Fancyville Home Sales (in thousands of dollars)						
230	270	150	305	240	280	1100
340	160	320	440	2800	250	210

Smallville Home Sales (in thousands of dollars)						
255	289	275	247	299	281	272

C-22.   Cyrus had an idea, *"To compare sales in Fancyville to Smallville,
let's make a scatterplot with Fancyville on the x-axis and
Smallville on the y-axis. Then we can draw a line of best fit and
see if there is an association."* Ramien responded that it was a
great idea! What is wrong with Cyrus and Ramien's plan?

C-23.   CREATING HISTOGRAMS AND BOXPLOTS ON THE CALCULATOR

The difference between life and death is often just
minutes when it comes to stopping bleeding. Two
emergency procedures are being compared for their
speed in stopping bleeding at the scenes of accidents.
The time from when 911 was called to the time that
paramedics reported the bleeding stopped was
recorded for each procedure. The data is shown below (in minutes).

Procedure C-2: 7, 6, 7, 4, 24, 8, 10, 3, 3, 5, 4, 17, 6, 5, 19, 29, 5, 6, 10, 4
checksum 182

Procedure C-7: 11, 13, 8, 9, 12, 10, 10, 9, 12, 7, 10, 6, 14, 11, 11
checksum 153

Your teacher will show you how to make a combination histogram and
modified boxplot on your graphing calculator. (A **modified boxplot** displays
the outliers separately from the boxplot.) You will need to choose an
appropriate interval for each of the bins ("bars") on your histogram. This
interval is called the **bin width**. A very rough approximation of how wide the
bin width should be is to find the square root of the number of values in the
largest data set.

Obtain the Lesson C.1.2A Resource Page from your teacher. Make a sketch of
the combination histogram and boxplot for each emergency procedure.
Compare and contrast the two procedures. Which one would you recommend?
Why?

C-24.   CENTER, SHAPE, SPREAD, AND OUTLIERS

It takes several statistics to get a meaningful
description of single-variable data like the
sales prices of houses in Fancyville and
Smallville – comparing the medians alone
does not tell a useful story about the
difference in prices. Statisticians like to
report the **center**, **shape**, **spread**, and **outliers**
of single-variable data.

Your teacher will give you the data from a previous "Forty Holes of Golf"
fundraiser on the Lesson C.1.2B Resource Page. Compare the center, shape,
spread, and outliers of your team's performance to the data on the resource page.

C-25.   LEARNING LOG

To compare two collections of single-variable data,
statisticians often compare the center, shape, spread, and
outliers. Discuss with your team how to describe the four
statistics. Give examples. Consider the following Discussion Points:

Discussion Points

When do we use a histogram and when do we use a scatterplot?

How does the shape determine which statistics we will use?

Is there another statistic we can use instead?

What is spread? What is an outlier?

Record your descriptions of center, shape, spread, and outliers in your Learning
Log. Be sure to include examples. Title this entry "Describing Single-Variable
Data" and include today's date.

METHODS AND MEANINGS

Describing Shape (of a Data Distribution)

MATH NOTES

Statisticians use the words below to describe the shape of a data distribution.

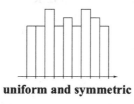

uniform and symmetric

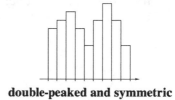

double-peaked and symmetric

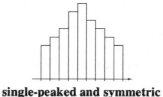

single-peaked and symmetric

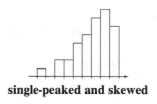

single-peaked and skewed

Outliers are any data values that are far away from the bulk of the data distribution. In the example at right, data values in the right-most bin are outliers. Outliers are marked on a modified boxplot with a dot.

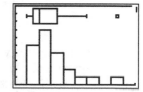

C-26. The auto repair shop is concerned about the reliability of its lathe, which is lathe is a rotating piece of equipment used in restoring parts. The shop's owner measured the rotations per minute at various times over the course of a month. These are his measurements:

250, 251, 253, 253, 253, 254, 257, 257, 259, 259, 261, 263, 265, 270, 291 rpm

a. On grid paper, draw a combination histogram and boxplot. Do not use a calculator.

b. Describe center, shape, spread, and outliers, similar to the way you did in problem C-11.

c. When reporting the center of this data, or the "typical RPM," which would be more appropriate, the mean or the median? Why?

Appendix C: Comparing Single-Variable Data   765

C-27.   Find an equation for each sequence.

a.
n	t(n)
1	7
2	4
3	1

b.
Year	Cost
2	$2000
3	$6000
4	$1800

C-28.   Given the quadratic function $f(x) = x^2 - 3$, find the new expression for each part below and describe the transformation.

a. $f(x) - 2$ b. $-2 \cdot f(x)$

c. $f(x - 2)$ d. $f(-2x)$

C-29.   For the quadratic function $f(x) = 2(x+1)^2 - 5$:

a.   Identify the vertex and tell if it is a maximum or minimum point on the graph.

b.   What is the value of the function at that minimum or maximum point?

C-30.   Aura currently pays $800 each month to rent her apartment. Due to inflation, however, her rent is increasing by $50 each year. Meanwhile, her monthly take-home pay is $1500 and she predicts that her monthly pay will only increase by $15 each year. Assuming that her rent and take-home pay will continue to grow linearly, will her rent ever equal her take-home pay? If so, when? And how much will rent be that year?

C-31.   Rewrite each of the expressions below with no parentheses and no fractions. Negative exponents are acceptable in your answer.

a. $(5a^{-2}b^3)^8 \cdot (5ab^{-2})^{-6}$ b. $\dfrac{15x^{-5}y^2}{(3x^2)^2 \cdot y^{-3}}$

C-32.   On Friday, Randy Random went to DJ's to get a cone.

a.   If he made a random selection, what is the probability that he got *all* three scoops the same?

b.   What is the probability that he got all three different?

Core Connections Algebra 2

C-33.   Find the distance between each pair of points.

     a.   (2, 3) and (4, 7)   b.   (2, 3) and (x, y)

C-34.   The function $f(x) = 200(0.7)^x + 72$ could represent the temperature over time of a hot cup of tea placed on the kitchen counter. Give a reasonable explanation of each numerical value.

C-35.   The Dallas University Health Center is running a clinical trial comparing two medicines to treat fibromyalgia. They need to compare the ages of the two groups receiving the medicines. The ages follow:

Group 7A: 72, 71, 59, 62, 48, 70, 57, 48, 68, 68, 57, 49, 53, 72, 60
checksum 914

Group 7B: 64, 29, 75, 55, 85, 51, 74, 34, 80, 28, 49, 79, 68, 45, 94, 32
checksum 942

     a.   Use your calculator to make a sketch of the combination histogram and boxplot for each treatment group. Sketch the graphs. Compare and contrast the distributions of ages between the two groups, using the center, shape, spread, and outliers of the two groups.

     b.   When reporting the typical age in each group, which is a more appropriate measure of center, the mean or the median? Explain.

C-36.   For the function $f(x) = 7x - 2$:

     a.   Find the inverse function.

     b.   Show that your inverse function is correct. Choose an input number for the function and calculate the output. Use this output as the input for the inverse function. Is your final output the same as your original input?

C-37.   Solve the following inequalities for x. Graph your solutions on a number line.

     a. $3x - 5 \leq 7 + 2x$ b. $|x| - 3 < 7$

     c. $5(2 - x) + 6 > 16$ d. $|x + 2| > 3$

C-38.   Complete the square to convert $y = 2x^2 + 4x + 6$ into graphing form.

C-39.   Solve each of the following equations or systems.

  a. $x^2 - 1 = 15$

  b. $y = 3x - 2$
        $y = 4x + 3$

  c. $x^2 - 2x - 8 = 0$

  d. $2x^2 = -x + 7$

C-40.   Graph and shade the solution for the system of inequalities below.

$$y \leq 4 + \tfrac{3}{4}x$$
$$y > -\tfrac{1}{2}x + 1$$

C-41.   Your teacher has decided that one person in your class will get an extra 50 points of credit. The lucky person has been narrowed down, so now it is between you and Newton. The teacher says, *"I'm thinking of a number between 0 and 10. Whoever can choose the number closest to it gets the 50 points."* Quickly, Newton yells out, *"Three!"* What number would you choose? Justify and explain your answer.

C-42.   Use your solving skills to complete parts (a) and (b) below.

  a.   Solve $\frac{x+3}{x-1} - \frac{x}{x+1} = \frac{8}{x^2-1}$ for x.

  b.   In part (a), the result of solving the equation is $x = 1$, but what happens when you substitute 1 for x? What does this mean in relation to the solutions for this equation?

C-43.   Use your knowledge of graphing short cuts to determine the number of points of intersections of this system. You do not need to solve it.

$$y = (x+2)^2 - 1$$
$$y = \tfrac{1}{2}x + 2$$

C.1.3 How can I measure variability?

Standard Deviation

Today you will use an example from the study of biology to reveal the importance of describing the spread (variability) of data and not just a measure of the center.

C-44.   A biologist is trying to determine which type of sugar is more successful in growing a particular eukaryotic cell. She measured the diameter of the cell and collected the data below (in micrometers, μm).

Sugar W: 10, 32, 32, 34, 34, 36, 37, 39, 39, 40, 41, 43, 43, 44, 45, 46, 46, 49, 70 *checksum 760*

Sugar P: 10, 10, 15, 20, 25, 28, 30, 32, 35, 40, 45, 48, 50, 52, 55, 60, 65, 70, 70 *checksum 760*

a.   Make a combination histogram and boxplot for each type of sugar. (Use an interval of 10 to 80 with a bin width of 10.)

b.   Find the mean and median of both collections of data.

c.   The two sets of data are obviously not the same. Which statistic(s) differentiate between these two data sets? You do not need to calculate the statistic. If the biologist wants to consistently grow large cells, which sugar should she use?

C-45.   MEASURING SPREAD

a.   One way to measure the spread of data is to calculate the **range** (maximum minus minimum). What range of cell sizes did each type of sugar grow in problem C-44? Why is the range often not a useful measure of spread?

b.   Another method for measuring the spread is the average distance to the mean, called the **mean absolute deviation**. Find the distance each value is from the mean (remember to use absolute value because distances are positive!), and find the mean distance. Compare the mean absolute deviation of Sugar W to Sugar P.

Problem continued from previous page. →

C-45.   *Problem continued from previous page.*

      c.   A mean absolute deviation should not be calculated if the data has outliers or is not symmetric. Why?

      d.   When the data is not symmetric or has outliers, the interquartile range (IQR) can be used to measure spread. Find and compare the IQR of the two sugars. If you need a reminder, reread the Math Notes box at the end of Lesson C.1.1.

C-46.   STANDARD DEVIATION

In addition to the methods in the previous problem, standard deviation is yet another measure of how much variability there is in a data set. **Standard deviation** is the average of all the distances to the mean. Instead of taking the absolute value to force the distances to the mean to be positive, statisticians square the distances to make them positive. After finding the average, then the square root of the average is taken so that the units come out right.

Without using your graphing calculator, find the standard deviation of each sugar in problem C-44. Compare the variability (the spread) of the two sugars using the standard deviation.

C-47.   Find the standard deviation for your team's tosses from the "Forty Holes of Golf" event from problem C-1 in Lesson C.1.1. Compare your result with the other teams in your class. Now which team was most consistently close to the hole?

C-48.   The standard deviation was probably not an appropriate way to report the spread of your team's golfing data. Why not? What would have been better?

C-49.   Your teacher will demonstrate how to find the standard deviation using your graphing calculator. Verify the standard deviations of the two sugars that you calculated in problem C-46 using your graphing calculator.

C-50.   LEARNING LOG

In your Learning Log, describe how to compute the
standard deviation of a set of data. Make up five pieces of
data and include an example. When is it best not to use the
standard deviation as a measure of spread? Title this entry "Standard
Deviation" and include today's date.

METHODS AND **M**EANINGS

Describing Spread (of a Data Distribution)

A distribution of data can be summarized by describing its center,
shape, spread, and outliers. You have learned three ways to
describe the spread.

Interquartile Range (IQR)
The variability, or spread, in the distribution can be numerically
summarized with the interquartile range (IQR). The IQR is found by
subtracting the first quartile from the third quartile. The IQR is the range
of the middle half of the data. IQR can represent the spread of any data
distribution, even if the distribution is not symmetric or has outliers.

Standard Deviation
Either the interquartile range or standard deviation can be used to represent
the spread if the data is symmetric and has no outliers. The standard
deviation is the square root of the average of the distances to the mean,
after the distances have been made positive by squaring.

For example, for the data 10 12 14 16 18 kilograms:

- The mean is 14 kg.
- The distances of each data value to the mean are $-4, -2, 0, 2, 4$ kg.
- The distances squared are $16, 4, 0, 4, 16$ kg^2.
- The mean distance-squared is 8 kg^2.
- The square root is 2.83. Thus the standard deviation is 2.83 kg.

Range
The range (maximum minus minimum) is usually not a very good way to
describe the spread because it considers only the extreme values in the
data, rather than how the bulk of the data is spread.

C-51.   An environmental engineering group has collected core samples from the earth to determine if they are contaminated. The samples were weighed, as follows:

15 40 69 65 10   60 34 20 43 40   10 25 44
65 32 45 30 36   45 50 35 39 50   46 55 31   *checksum 1034*

Determine if the mean and standard deviation is an appropriate way to summarize this data. If so, find the mean and standard deviation with your calculator. If not, use the median and IQR. Consider the precision of the measurement of weight when deciding how many decimal places to use in your answer.

C-52.   A farmer wonders if his crops grow better in sun or in shade. He measures the amount of fruit gathered from a sample of 50 trees growing in full sun and from a sample of 50 trees growing in mostly shade. The five-number summaries, (minimum, Q1, median, Q3, maximum), follow:

Amount of fruit gathered from sunny trees: $(10.8, 13.3, 22.1, 58.1, 100)$ bushels

Amount of fruit gathered from shady trees: $(10.9, 18.5, 29.3, 61.5, 127)$ bushels

a.   On the same set of axes on grid paper, create a boxplot for each type of tree. Compare the center, shape, spread, and outliers of amount of fruit from sunny trees to the amount from shady trees.

b.   The farmer wants to summarize the amount of fruit from each type of orchard with a mean and standard deviation. Is that appropriate? Explain.

C-53.   Based on the graph, give a possible equation for the parabola.

a.

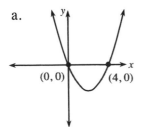

b.

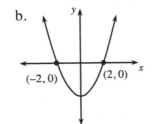

c.

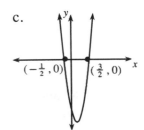

C-54.   Find all of the points at which the parabolas below intersect. Write your
         solution(s) in (x, y) form.

$$y = x^2 + 5x - 4$$
$$y = x^2 + x - 12$$

C-55.   Solve the equations and inequalities below. Check your solutions, if possible.

   a. $|5x + 8| \geq -4$ b. $x^2 + x - 20 < 0$

   c. $2x^2 - 6x = -5$ d. $\frac{5}{9} - \frac{x}{3} = \frac{4}{9}$

C-56.   Match the histogram to its corresponding boxplot.

   a.   b.   c. 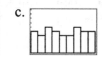 d.   e.

   i. 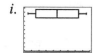 ii.   iii.   iv.   v.

C-57.   You roll three different-colored dice and use the numbers on the dice to
         determine the lengths of the sides of a triangle. For example, 3-3-5 would be an
         isosceles triangle with base 5. What is the probability of building a right
         triangle?

C-58.   Find the value of x in each triangle.

   a. 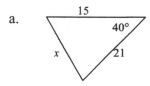   b.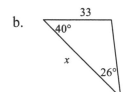

C-59.   Graph the piecewise function $f(x) = \begin{cases} 2^x & \text{if } x \geq 0 \\ |x| & \text{if } x < 0 \end{cases}$.

Appendix C Closure What have I learned?

Reflection and Synthesis

The activities below offer you a chance to reflect about what you have learned in this appendix. As you work, look for concepts that you feel very comfortable with, ideas that you would like to learn more about, and topics you need more help with. Look for connections between ideas as well as connections with material you learned previously.

①   TEAM BRAINSTORM

What have you studied in this appendix? What ideas were important in what you learned? With your team, brainstorm a list. Be as detailed as you can. To help get you started, a list of Learning Log entries and Math Notes boxes are below.

What topics, ideas, and words that you learned *before* this appendix are connected to the new ideas in this chapter? Again, be as detailed as you can.

How long can you make your list? Challenge yourselves. Be prepared to share your team's ideas with the class.

Learning Log Entries

- Lesson C.1.1 – Representing Data Graphically
- Lesson C.1.2 – Describing Single-Variable Data
- Lesson C.1.3 – Standard Deviation

Math Notes

- Lesson C.1.1 – Interquartile Range and Boxplots
- Lesson C.1.2 – Describing Shape (of a Data Distribution)
- Lesson C.1.3 – Describing Spread (of a Data Distribution)

②   MAKING CONNECTIONS

Below is a list of the vocabulary used in this appendix. Make sure that you are familiar with all of these words and know what they mean. Refer to the glossary or index for any words that you do not yet understand.

5-number summary	bar graph	boxplot
center	circle ("pie") graph	dot plot
histogram	IQR	mean
mean absolute deviation	median	outlier
quartile	range	scatterplot
shape	spread	standard deviation
statistic		

Make a concept map showing all of the connections you can find among the key words and ideas listed above. To show a connection between two words, draw a line between them and explain the connection. A word can be connected to any other word as long as you can justify the connection.

While you are making your map, your team may think of related words or ideas that are not listed here. Be sure to include these ideas on your concept map.

③   PORTFOLIO: EVIDENCE OF MATHEMATICAL PROFICIENCY

Your teacher will explain how to obtain two sets of data. Showcase your skills for comparing data by making combination histograms and boxplots and comparing the center, shape, spread, and outliers. Explain how you chose between using the median and IQR, and using the mean and standard deviation.

④ WHATHAVE I LEARNED?

Most of the problems in this section
represent typical problems found in
this appendix. They serve as a gauge
for you. You can use them to
determine which types of problems
you can do well and which types of
problems require further study and
practice. Even if your teacher does
not assign this section, it is a good
idea to try these problems and find out
for yourself what you know and what you still need to work on.

Solve each problem as completely as you can. The table at the end of the
closure section has answers to these problems. It also tells you where you
can find additional help and practice with problems like these.

CL C-60. Jet Set claims that they are more "on time"
than National Airways because National
was delayed over an hour a couple times.
Arin did not believe Jet Set was more "on
time" so he looked up the data for both
airlines during the last two weeks. Below
is the data he found for departure delays.
Negative numbers indicate that a flight departed
earlier than scheduled.

National Airways:
69, 22, –3, –7, 2, 25, 7, 0, –3, 14, –4, 0, –1, –9, –2, 4, 12, 25, 65, –10
checksum 206

Jet Set:
6, –5, 33, 4, 37, 10, 23, 5, 21, 31, 2, –5, 35, 42, 19 –8, 25, 15
checksum 290

a.   Compare the center, shape, spread, and outliers of the data sets. Use
the values you calculate to make an argument as to which airline is on
time more often. Use a bin width of 10 minutes on your histograms.

b.   Arin wants to summarize his findings with just two numbers: the center
and spread. Can he use mean and standard deviation, or should he use
median and IQR? Justify your choice, then summarize the data for
Arin.

CL C-61.   Given the system of equations: $y = (x+2)^2$
$$y = -2x - 4$$

a.   How many points of intersection should there be?

b.   Use your algebra skills to verify the answer to (a) and find the exact coordinates of the point(s) of intersection.

CL C-62.   For the parabola $y = 2x^2 - 12x + 6$:

a.   Is the vertex is a maximum or minimum? Explain your reasoning.

b.   Determine the coordinates of the vertex.

c.   Make a sketch of the graph without using a calculator.

CL C-63.   Without graphing, determine all of the points of intersections of these two equations.
$$y = -5x - 7$$
$$y = x^2 - 3x - 10$$

CL C-64.   Check your answers using the table at the end of the closure section. Which problems do you feel confident about? Which problems were hard? Use the table to make a list of topics you need help on and a list of topics you need to practice more.

Answers and Support for Closure Activity #4
What Have I Learned?

Note: MN = Math Note, LL = Learning Log

Problem	Solution	Need Help?	More Practice
CL C-60.	a. Median delay for Jet Set is about 16 minutes longer than for National. National's delays were skewed with a peak at about –5 minutes, meaning they had a lot of flights that left early or had only a little delay, while Jet Set's delays were uniformly distributed. Jet Set had more variability in delays than National did; the IQR for Jet Set's delays was 6 minutes wider than for National's IQR. National did have two extreme outliers. Even though National had two very large delays in the last couple weeks, their overall performance makes them more "on time" than Jet Set. Jet's Set's claims are misleading because they focused only on the outliers rather than on overall performance.	Lesson C.1.2 MN: C.1.2 and C.1.3 LL: C.1.2	Problems C-26, C-35, C-44, C-51, and C-52
	b. Although the distribution for National is symmetric with no outliers, National is skewed with outliers. Since he wants to compare data, he needs to use the same statistics for both airlines. Arin must use median and IQR. Median delay for National is 1 minute with an IQR of 21 minutes, while Jet Set has median delay if 17 minutes with an IQR of 27 minutes.		
CL C-61.	a. 2	Chapter 4	Problem C-43
	b. (–2,0), (–4,4)		

Problem	Solution	Need Help?	More Practice
CL C-62.	a. Parabola opens up so the vertex is a minimum. b. (3, 12) c. See graph at right. 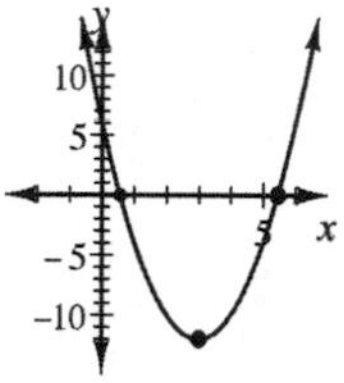	Chapter 2	Problems C-19, C-29, and C-53
CL C-63.	$(-3, 8)$ and $(1, -12)$	Chapter 4	Problem C-54

Core Connections Algebra 2
Checkpoint Materials

Note to Students (and their Teachers)

Students master different skills at different speeds. No two students learn exactly the same way at the same time. At some point you will be expected to perform certain skills accurately. Most of the Checkpoint problems incorporate skills that you should have developed in previous courses. If you have not mastered these skills yet it does not mean that you will not be successful in this class. However, you may need to do some work outside of class to get caught up on them.

Starting in Chapter 2 and finishing in Chapter 12, there are 18 problems designed as Checkpoint problems. Each one is marked with an icon like the one above. After you do each of the Checkpoint problems, check your answers by referring to this section. If your answers are incorrect, you may need some extra practice to develop that skill. The practice sets are keyed to each of the Checkpoint problems in the textbook. Each has the topic clearly labeled, followed by the answers to the corresponding Checkpoint problem and then some completed examples. Next, the complete solution to the Checkpoint problem from the text is given, and there are more problems for you to practice with answers included.

Remember, looking is not the same as doing! You will never become good at any sport by just watching it, and in the same way, reading through the worked examples and understanding the steps is not the same as being able to do the problems yourself. How many of the extra practice problems do you need to try? That is really up to you. Remember that your goal is to be able to do similar problems on your own confidently and accurately. This is your responsibility. You should not expect your teacher to spend time in class going over the solutions to the Checkpoint problem sets. If you are not confident after reading the examples and trying the problems, you should get help outside of class time or talk to your teacher about working with a tutor.

Checkpoint Topics

Checkpoint 2A
Problem 2-53
Finding the Distance Between Two Points and the Equation of a Line

Answers to problem 2-53: a: $\sqrt{45} = 3\sqrt{5} \approx 6.71$; $y = \frac{1}{2}x + 5$, b: 5; $x = 3$,
c: $\sqrt{725} \approx 26.93$; $y = -\frac{5}{2}x + \frac{5}{2}$, d: 4; $y = -2$

The distance between two points is found by using the Pythagorean Theorem. The most commonly used equation of a line is $y = mx + b$ where m represents the slope of the line and b represents the y-intercept of the line. One strategy for both types of problems is to create a generic right triangle determined by the given points. The lengths of the legs of the triangle are used in the Pythagorean Theorem to find the distance. They are also used in the slope ratio to write an equation of the line. This strategy is not necessary for vertical or horizontal pairs of points, however.

Example: For the points $(-1, -2)$ and $(11, 2)$, find the distance between them and determine an equation of the line through them.

Solution: Using a generic right triangle, the legs of the triangle are 12 and 4. The distance between the points is the length of the hypotenuse.

$$d^2 = 12^2 + 4^2 = 160 \Rightarrow d = \sqrt{160} = 4\sqrt{10} \approx 12.65$$

The slope of the line, $m = \frac{\text{vertical change}}{\text{horizontal change}} = \frac{4}{12} = \frac{1}{3}$. Substituting this into the equation of a line, $y = mx + b$, gives $y = \frac{1}{3}x + b$. Next substitute any point that is on the line for x and y and solve for b. Using $(11, 2)$, $2 = \frac{1}{3} \cdot 11 + b$, $2 = \frac{11}{3} + b$, $b = -\frac{5}{3}$.

The equation is $y = \frac{1}{3}x - \frac{5}{3}$.

Some people prefer to use formulas that represent the generic right triangle.

slope $= \frac{y_2 - y_1}{x_2 - x_1} = \frac{2-(-2)}{11-(-1)} = \frac{4}{12} = \frac{1}{3}$

distance $= \sqrt{(x_2 - x_1)^2 + (y_2 - y_1)^2} = \sqrt{(11-(-1))^2 + (2-(-2))^2} = \sqrt{12^2 + 4^2} = \sqrt{160}$

Notice that $x_2 - x_1$ and $y_2 - y_1$ represent the lengths of the horizontal and vertical legs respectively.

Now we can go back and solve the original problems.

a. $d^2 = 6^2 + 3^2 \Rightarrow d^2 = 45 \Rightarrow d = \sqrt{45} = 3\sqrt{5} \approx 6.71$

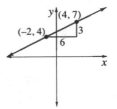

$m = \frac{3}{6} = \frac{1}{2} \Rightarrow y = \frac{1}{2}x + b$

Using the point $(4,7) \Rightarrow 7 = \frac{1}{2} \cdot 4 + b \Rightarrow b = 5$.
The equation is $y = \frac{1}{2}x + 5$.

b. Since this is a vertical line, the distance is simply the difference of the y values. $d = 4 - (-1) = 5$.

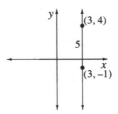

Vertical lines have an *undefined* slope and the equation of the line is of the form $x = k \Rightarrow x = 3$.

c. $d^2 = (-25)^2 + 10^2 \Rightarrow d^2 = 725 \Rightarrow d = \sqrt{725} \approx 26.93$

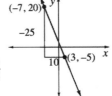

$m = \frac{-25}{10} = -\frac{5}{2} \Rightarrow y = -\frac{5}{2}x + b$

Using the point $(3,-5) \Rightarrow -5 = -\frac{5}{2} \cdot 3 + b \Rightarrow b = -5 + \frac{15}{2} = \frac{5}{2}$
The equation is $y = -\frac{5}{2}x + \frac{5}{2}$.

d. Since this is a horizontal line, the distance is simply the difference of the x-values. $d = 5 - 1 = 4$.

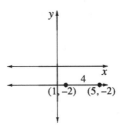

Horizontal lines have a slope of 0 and the equation of the line is of the form $y = k \Rightarrow y = -2$.

Here are some more to try. For each pair of points, compute the distance between them and then find an equation of the line through them.

1. $(2,3)$ and $(1,2)$ 2. $(-3,-5)$ and $(-1,0)$

3. $(4,2)$ and $(8,-1)$ 4. $(1,3)$ and $(5,7)$

5. $(0,4)$ and $(-1,-5)$ 6. $(-3,2)$ and $(2,-3)$

7. $(4,2)$ and $(-1,-2)$ 8. $(3,1)$ and $(-2,-4)$

9. $(4,1)$ and $(4,10)$ 10. $(10,2)$ and $(2,22)$

11. $(-10,3)$ and $(-2,-5)$ 12. $(-3,5)$ and $(12,5)$

13. $(-4,10)$ and $(-6,15)$ 14. $(-6,-3)$ and $(2,10)$

Answers:

1. $\sqrt{2} \approx 1.41;\ y = x + 1$ 2. $\sqrt{29} \approx 5.39;\ y = \frac{5}{2}x + \frac{5}{2}$

3. $5;\ y = -\frac{3}{4}x + 5$ 4. $\sqrt{32} = 4\sqrt{2} \approx 5.66;\ y = x + 2$

5. $\sqrt{82} \approx 9.06;\ y = 9x + 4$ 6. $\sqrt{50} = 5\sqrt{2} \approx 7.07;\ y = -x - 1$

7. $\sqrt{41} \approx 6.40;\ y = \frac{4}{5}x - \frac{6}{5}$ 8. $\sqrt{50} = 5\sqrt{2} \approx 7.07;\ y = x - 2$

9. $9;\ x = 4$ 10. $\sqrt{464} \approx 21.54;\ y = -\frac{5}{2}x + 27$

11. $\sqrt{128} = 8\sqrt{2} \approx 11.31;\ y = -x - 7$ 12. $15;\ y = 5$

13. $\sqrt{29} \approx 5.39;\ y = -\frac{5}{2}x$ 14. $\sqrt{233} \approx 15.26;\ y = \frac{13}{8}x + \frac{27}{4}$

Checkpoint 2B

Problem 2-152

Solving Linear Systems in Two Variables

Answers to problem 2-152: $(3, 2)$

You can solve systems of equations using a variety of methods. For linear systems, you can graph the equations, use the Substitution Method, or use the Elimination Method. Each method works best with certain forms of equations. Following are some examples. Although the method that is easiest for one person may not be easiest for another, the most common methods are shown below.

Example 1: Solve the system of equations $x = 4y - 7$ and $3x - 2y = 1$.

Solution: For this, we will use the Substitution Method. Since the first equation tells us that x is equal to $4y - 7$, we can substitute $4y - 7$ for x in the second equation. This allows us to solve for y, as shown at right.

$$3(4y - 7) - 2y = 1$$
$$12y - 21 - 2y = 1$$
$$10y - 21 = 1$$
$$10y = 22$$
$$y = \tfrac{22}{10} = 2.2$$

Then substitute $y = 2.2$ into either original equation and solve for x: Choosing the first equation, we get $x = 4(2.2) - 7 = 8.8 - 7 = 1.8$. To verify the solution completely check this answer in the second equation by substituting. $3(1.8) - 2(2.2) = 5.4 - 4.4 = 1$

Answer: The solution to the system is $x = 1.8$ and $y = 2.2$ or $(1.8, 2.2)$.

Example 2: Solve the system of equations $y = \tfrac{3}{4}x - 1$ and $y = -\tfrac{1}{3}x - 1$.

Solution: Generally graphing the equations is not the most efficient way to solve a system of linear equations. In this case, however, both equations are written in $y = $ form so we can see that they have the same y-intercept. Since lines can cross only at one point, no points or infinite points, and these lines have different slopes (they are not parallel or coincident), the y-intercept must be the only point of intersection and thus the solution to the system. We did not actually graph here, but we used the principles of graphs to solve the system. Substitution would work nicely as well.

Answer: $(0, -1)$

Example 3: Solve the system $x + 2y = 16$ and $x - y = 2$.

Solution: For this, we will use the Elimination Method. We can subtract the second equation from the first and then solve for y, as shown at right.

$$x + 2y = 16$$
$$-(x - y = 2)$$
$$\overline{0 + 3y = 14}$$
$$3y = 14$$
$$y = \tfrac{14}{3}$$

We then substitute $y = \tfrac{14}{3}$ into either original equation and solve for x. Choosing the second equation, we get $x - \tfrac{14}{3} = 2$, so $x = 2 + \tfrac{14}{3} = \tfrac{20}{3}$. Checking our solution can be done by substituting both values into the first equation.

Answer: The solution to the system is $(\tfrac{20}{3}, \tfrac{14}{3})$.

Example 4: Solve the system $x + 3y = 4$ and $3x - y = 2$.

Solution: For this, we will use the Elimination Method, only we will need to do some multiplication first. If we multiply the second equation by 3 and add the result to the first equation, we can eliminate y and solve for x, as shown at right.

$$x + 3y = 4$$
$$+\ 9x - 3y = 6$$
$$\overline{10x = 10}$$
$$x = 1$$

We can then find y by substituting $x = 1$ into either of the original equations. Choosing the second, we get $3(1) - y = 2$, which solves to yield $y = 1$. Again, checking the solution can be done by substituting both values into the first equation.

Answer: The solution to this system is $(1, 1)$.

Now we can return to the original problem.

Solve the following system of linear equations in two variables.

$$5x - 4y = 7$$
$$2y + 6x = 22$$

For this system, you can use either the Substitution or the Elimination Method, but each choice will require a little bit of work to get started.

Substitution Method:

Before we can substitute, we need to isolate one of the variables. In other words, we need to solve one of the equations for either x or for y. If we solve the second equation for y, it becomes $y = 11 - 3x$. Now we substitute $11 - 3x$ for y in the first equation and solve for x, as shown at right.

$$5x - 4(11 - 3x) = 7$$
$$5x - 44 + 12x = 7$$
$$17x - 44 = 7$$
$$17x = 51$$
$$x = 3$$

Then we can substitute the value for x into one of the original equations to find y. Thus we find that
$2y + 6(3) = 22 \Rightarrow 2y = 22 - 18 = 4 \Rightarrow y = \frac{4}{2} = 2$.

Elimination Method:

Before we can eliminate a variable, we need to rearrange the second equation so that the variables line up, as shown at right. Now we see that we can multiply the second equation by 2 and add the two equations to eliminate y and solve for x, as shown below right.

$$5x - 4y = 7$$
$$6x + 2y = 22$$

$$5x - 4y = 7$$
$$+ \ 12x + 4y = 44$$
$$\overline{17x = 51}$$
$$x = 3$$

We can then substitute $x = 3$ into the first equation to get $5(3) - 4y = 7$. Simplifying and solving, we get $-4y = -8$ and thus $y = 2$.

Answer: $(3, 2)$

Here are some more to try. Find the solution to these systems of linear equations. Use the method of your choice.

1. $y = 3x - 1$
   $2x - 3y = 10$

2. $x = -0.5y + 4$
   $8x + 3y = 31$

3. $2y = 4x + 10$
   $6x + 2y = 10$

4. $3x - 5y = -14$
   $x + 5y = 22$

5. $4x + 5y = 11$
   $2x + 6y = 16$

6. $x + 2y = 5$
   $x + y = 5$

7. $2x - 3 = y$
   $x - y = -4$

8. $y + 2 = x$
   $3x - 3y = x + 14$

9. $2x + y = 7$
   $x + 5y = 12$

10. $y = \frac{3}{5}x - 2$
    $y = \frac{x}{10} + 1$

11. $2x + y = -2x + 5$
    $3x + 2y = 2x + 3y$

12. $4x - 3y = -10$
    $x = \frac{1}{4}y - 1$

13. $4y = 2x$
    $2x + y = \frac{x}{2} + 1$

14. $3x - 2y = 8$
    $4y = 6x - 5$

15. $4y = 2x - 4$
    $3x + 5y = -3$

16. $\frac{x}{3} + \frac{4y}{3} = 300$
    $3x - 4y = 300$

Answers:

1. $(-1, -4)$

2. $(\frac{7}{2}, 1)$

3. $(0, 5)$

4. $(2, 4)$

5. $(-1, 3)$

6. $(5, 0)$

7. $(7, 11)$

8. $(-8, -10)$

9. $(\frac{23}{9}, \frac{17}{9})$

10. $(6, 1.6)$

11. $(1, 1)$

12. $(-\frac{1}{4}, 3)$

13. $(\frac{1}{2}, \frac{1}{4})$

14. no solution

15. $(\frac{4}{11}, -\frac{9}{11})$

16. $(300, 150)$

Checkpoint 3A

Problem 3-67

Expressions with Integral and Rational Exponents

Answers to problem 3-67:

a: $x^{1/5}$, b: x^{-3}, c: $\sqrt[3]{x^2}$, d: $x^{-1/2}$, e: $\frac{1}{xy^8}$, f: $\frac{1}{m^3}$, g: $xy^3\sqrt{x}$, h: $\frac{1}{81x^6y^{12}}$

The following properties are useful for rewriting expressions with integral (positive or negative whole numbers) or rational (fractional) exponents.

$x^0 = 1$ Examples: $2^0 = 1$, $(-3)^0 = 1$, $(\frac{1}{4})^0 = 1$ (Note that 0^0 is undefined.)

$x^{-n} = \frac{1}{x^n}$ Examples: $x^{-12} = \frac{1}{x^{12}}$, $y^{-4} = \frac{1}{y^4}$, $4^{-2} = \frac{1}{4^2} = \frac{1}{16}$

$\frac{1}{x^{-n}} = x^n$ Examples: $\frac{1}{x^{-5}} = x^5$, $\frac{1}{x^{-2}} = x^2$, $\frac{1}{3^{-2}} = 3^2 = 9$

$x^{a/b} = (x^a)^{1/b} = (\sqrt[b]{x})^a$ Examples: $5^{1/2} = \sqrt{5}$

        or   : $16^{3/4} = (\sqrt[4]{16})^3 = 2^3 = 8$

$x^{a/b} = (x^{1/b})^a = (\sqrt[b]{x})^a$ $4^{2/3} = \sqrt[3]{4^2} = \sqrt[3]{16} = 2\sqrt[3]{2}$

$x^a x^b = x^{(a+b)}$ Examples: $x^7 x^2 = x^9$, $y^{-4}y = y^{-3}$, $2^3 2^2 = 2^5 = 32$

$(x^a)^b = x^{ab}$ Examples: $(x^2)^3 = x^6$, $(a^6b^4)^{1/2} = a^3b^2$, $(3^3)^3 = 3^9 = 19683$

Now we can go back and solve the original problems.

a.   Using the fourth property above, $\sqrt[5]{x} = x^{1/5}$.

b.   Using the second property above, $\frac{1}{x^3} = x^{-3}$.

c.   Using the fourth property above, $x^{2/3} = \sqrt[3]{x^2}$.

d.   Using the second and fourth properties above, $\frac{1}{\sqrt{x}} = \frac{1}{x^{1/2}} = x^{-1/2}$.

e.   Using the second property above, $x^{-1}y^{-8} = \frac{1}{xy^8}$.

f.   Using the second and sixth properties above, $(m^2)^{-3/2} = m^{-3} = \frac{1}{m^3}$.

g.   Using the fourth, fifth, and sixth properties above, $(x^3y^6)^{1/2} = x^{3/2}y^3 = x^1x^{1/2}y^3 = xy^3\sqrt{x}$.

h.   Using the second and sixth properties above, $(9x^3y^6)^{-2} = 9^{-2}x^{-6}y^{-12} = \frac{1}{81x^6y^{12}}$.

                               Core Connections Algebra 2

Here are some exercises to try. For problems 1 through 12, rewrite each expression. For problems 13 through 24, simplify each expression. You should not need a calculator for any of these problems.

1. x^{-5}

2. m^0

3. 4^{-1}

4. $\sqrt[3]{y}$

5. $\frac{1}{c^4}$

6. $\frac{1}{b^{-2}}$

7. $12^{1/12}$

8. $z^{-3/4}$

9. $\frac{1}{(\sqrt[9]{7})^5}$

10. 0^0

11. $9^{1/2}$

12. $\sqrt[5]{a^3}$

13. $(f^3)\sqrt[3]{f^3}$

14. $(\frac{1}{27})^{-1/3}$

15. $(v^2 g^{3/4})^8$

16. $(\frac{1}{q^6})^7$

17. $d^{-9}d^{-4}$

18. $(3xw^4)^{-2}$

19. $(u^3 r^{-4})^{-2}$

20. $n^3(n^2)^5$

21. $4(\sqrt{4})^4$

22. $6(k^{1/2}t^5)^2$

23. $p^{15}p^{-15}$

24. $h^8 s^{12}(\sqrt[8]{h})(s^{1/4})$

Answers:

1. $\frac{1}{x^5}$

2. 1

3. $\frac{1}{4}$

4. $y^{1/3}$

5. c^{-4}

6. b^2

7. $\sqrt[12]{12}$

8. $\frac{1}{z^{3/4}}$

9. $7^{-1/6}$

10. undefined

11. 3

12. $a^{3/5}$

13. f^4

14. 3

15. $v^{16}g^6$

16. q^{-42}

17. $d^{-13} = \frac{1}{d^{13}}$

18. $\frac{1}{9x^2 w^{12}}$

19. $\frac{r^8}{u^6}$

20. n^{13}

21. 64

22. $6kt^{10}$

23. 1

24. hs^3

Checkpoint 3B
Problem 3-116
Using Function Notation and Identifying Domain and Range

Answers to problem 3-116: Domain: all x; Range: $y \geq 0$

    a. $g(-5) = 8$ b. $g(a+1) = 2a^2 + 16a + 32$

    c. $x = 1$ or $x = -7$ d. $x = -3$

An equation is called a function if there exists *no more than one* output for each input. If an equation has two or more outputs for a single input value, it is not a function. The set of possible inputs of a function is called the domain, while the set of all possible outputs of a function is called the range.

Functions are often given names, most commonly "f," "g," or "h." The notation $f(x)$ represents the output of a function, named f, when x is the input. It is pronounced "f of x." The notation $g(2)$, pronounced "g of 2," represents the output of function g when $x = 2$.

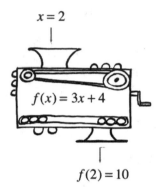

$x = 2$

$f(x) = 3x + 4$

$f(2) = 10$

Similarly, the function $y = 3x + 4$ and $f(x) = 3x + 4$ represent the *same function*. Notice that the notation is interchangeable, that is $y = f(x)$. In some textbooks, $3x + 4$ is called the **rule** of the function. The graph of $f(x) = 3x + 4$ is a line extending forever in both the x (horizontal) and the y (vertical) directions, so the domain and range of $f(x) = 3x + 4$ are all real numbers.

Examples 1 through 3:   **For each function below, give the domain and range. Then calculate $f(2)$ and solve $f(x) = 3$.**

Example 1: $f(x) = |x - 1| - 2$

Solution: We start by graphing the function, as shown at right. Since we can use any real number for x in this equation, the domain is all real numbers. The smallest possible result for y is -2, so the range is $y \geq -2$. By looking at the graph or substituting $x = 2$ into the equation, $f(2) = |2 - 1| - 2 = -1$. To solve $f(x) = 3$, find the points where the horizontal line $y = 3$ intersects the graph or solve the equation $3 = |x - 1| - 2$, which yields $x = -4$ or $x = 6$.

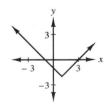

Example 2: $f(x)$ **is given by the graph below.**

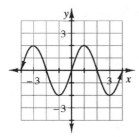

The arrows indicate that the graph continues indefinitely right and left and we see no disruption in the smooth function, so the domain is all real numbers. All of the y-values fall between -2 and 2, so the range is $-2 \le y \le 2$. We can see from the graph that when $x = 2$, the value of the function appears to be 0, or $f(2) \approx 0$. Since $-2 \le y \le 2$, the value of the function never gets as high as 3, so $f(x) = 3$ has no solution.

Example 3: $f(x) = \sqrt{x+3}$

Solution: Again, we start by making a graph of the function, which is shown at right. Since the square root of a negative number does not exist, we can only use x-values of -3 or larger. Thus, the domain is $x \ge -3$. We can see from the graph and the equation that the smallest possible y-value is zero, so the range is $y \ge 0$. Looking at the graph gives an approximate answer when $x = 2$ of $y \approx 2.25$. Or, by substituting $x = 2$ into the equation, we get $f(2) = \sqrt{2+3} = \sqrt{5}$. To solve $f(x) = 3$, find the point where $y = 3$ intersects the graph or solve $3 = \sqrt{x+3}$, which gives $x = 6$.

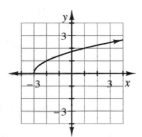

Now we can go back and solve the original problem.

The graph is a parabola opening upward with vertex $(-3, 0)$, as shown at right. Thus, the domain is all real numbers and the range is $y \ge 0$.

$$g(-5) = -2(-5+3) = 2(-2)^2 = 8$$

$$g(a+1) = 2(a+1+3)^2 = 2(a+4)^2$$
$$= 2(a^2 + 8a + 16) = 2a^2 + 16a + 32$$

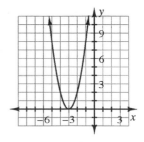

If $g(x) = 32$, then $32 = 2(x+3)^2$. Dividing both sides by 2, we get $16 = (x+3)^2$. Taking the square root of both sides gives $\pm 4 = x + 3$, which leads to the values $x = 1$ or -7.

If $g(x) = 0$, then $0 = 2(x+3)^2$. Diving both sides by two or applying the Zero Product Property gives $0 = (x+3)^2$ and then $0 = x + 3$. Thus $x = -3$.

Here are some more to try.

For each graph in problems 1 through 3, describe the domain and range.

1. 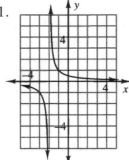 2. 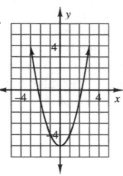 3.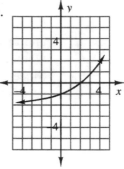

4. If $f(x) = 3 - x^2$, calculate $f(5)$ and $f(3a)$.

5. If $g(x) = 5 - 3x^2$, calculate $g(-2)$ and $g(a + 2)$.

6. If $f(x) = \frac{x+3}{2x-5}$, calculate $f(2)$ and $f(2.5)$.

7. If $f(x) = x^2 + 5x + 6$, solve $f(x) = 0$.

8. If $g(x) = 3(x - 5)^2$, solve $g(x) = 27$.

9. If $f(x) = (x + 2)^2$, solve $f(x) = 27$.

Answers:

1. Domain: $x \neq -2$, Range: $y \neq 0$

2. Domain: all real numbers, Range: $y \geq -5$

3. Domain: all real numbers, Range: $y > -2$

4. $f(5) = -22$, $f(3a) = 3 - 9a^2$

5. $g(-2) = -7$, $g(a + 2) = -3a^2 - 12a - 7$

6. $f(2) = -5$, not possible

7. $x = -2$ or $x = -3$

8. $x = 8$ or $x = 2$

9. $x = -2 \pm \sqrt{27}$

Checkpoint 4A
Problem 4-42
Writing Equations for Arithmetic and Geometric Sequences

Answers to problem 4-42: a: E $t(n) = -2 + 3n$; R $t(0) = -2$, $t(n+1) = t(n) + 3$,
b: E $t(n) = 6(\frac{1}{2})^n$; R $t(0) = 6$, $t(n+1) = \frac{1}{2}t(n)$, c: $t(n) = 10 - 7n$, d: $t(n) = 5(1.2)^n$,
e: $t(4) = 1620$

An ordered list of numbers such as: $4, 9, 16, 25, 36, \ldots$ creates a sequence. The numbers in the sequence are called terms. One way to identify and label terms is to use function notation. For example, if $t(n)$ is the name of the sequence above, the initial value is 4 and the second term after the initial value is 16. This is written $t(0) = 4$ and $t(2) = 16$. Some books use subscripts instead of function notation. In this case $t_0 = 4$ and $t_2 = 16$. The initial value is *not* part of the sequence. It is only a reference point and is useful in writing a rule for the sequence. When writing a sequence, start by writing the first term after the initial value, $t(1)$ or t_1.

Arithmetic sequences have a common difference between the terms. The rule for the values in an arithmetic sequences can be found by $t(n) = a + dn$ where a = the initial value, d = the common difference and n = the number of terms after the initial value.

Geometric sequences have a common ratio between the terms. The rule for the values in a geometric sequence may be found by $t(n) = ar^n$ where a = the initial value, r = the common ratio and n = the number of terms after the initial value.

Example 1: Find a rule for the sequence: $-2, 4, 10, 16, \ldots$

Solution: There is a common difference between the terms ($d = 6$) so it is an arithmetic sequence. Work backward to find the initial value: $a = -2 - 6 = -8$.
Now use the general rule: $t(n) = a + dn = -8 + 6n$.

Example 2: Find a rule for the sequence: $81, 27, 9, 3, \ldots$

Solution: There is a common ratio between the terms ($r = \frac{1}{3}$) so it is a geometric sequence. Work backward to find the initial value: $a = 81 \div \frac{1}{3} = 243$.
Now use the general rule: $t(n) = ar^n = 243(\frac{1}{3})^n$.

A rule such as $t(n) = 5 - 7n$ is called an explicit rule because any term can be found by substituting the appropriate value for n into the rule. To find the 10th term after the initial value, $t(10)$, substitute 10 for n. $t(10) = 5 - 7(10) = -65$.

A second way to find the terms in a sequence is by using a recursive formula. A recursive formula tells first term or the initial value and how to get from one term to the next.

Example 3: (using subscript notation)
Write the first five terms of the sequence determined by: $b_1 = 8$, $b_{n+1} = b_n \cdot \frac{1}{2}$

Solution: $b_1 = 8$ tells you the first term and $b_{n+1} = b_n \cdot \frac{1}{2}$ tells you to multiply by $\frac{1}{2}$ to get from one term to the next.

$b_1 = 8$ $\qquad\qquad\qquad\qquad$ $b_2 = b_1 \cdot \frac{1}{2} = 8 \cdot \frac{1}{2} = 4$ $\qquad\qquad$ $b_3 = b_2 \cdot \frac{1}{2} = 4 \cdot \frac{1}{2} = 2$

$b_4 = b_3 \cdot \frac{1}{2} = 2 \cdot \frac{1}{2} = 1$ $\qquad$ $b_5 = b_4 \cdot \frac{1}{2} = 1 \cdot \frac{1}{2} = \frac{1}{2}$

The sequence is: $8, 4, 2, 1, \frac{1}{2}, \ldots$

Now we can go back and solve the original problems.

a.   It is an arithmetic sequence $(d = 3)$. Working backward the initial value is $1 - 3 = -2$. Using the general formula the explicit rule: $t(n) = a + dn = -2 + 3d$. A possible recursive rule is $t(1) = 1$, $t(n+1) = t(n) + 3$.

b.   It is a geometric sequence $(r = \frac{1}{2})$. Working backward the initial value is $3 \div \frac{1}{2} = 6$. Using the general formula for the explicit rule: $t(n) = ar^n = 6(\frac{1}{2})^n$. A possible recursive rule is $t(0) = 6$, $t(n+1) = \frac{1}{2}t(n)$.

c. $t(2)$ is halfway between $t(1)$ and $t(3)$ so $t(2) = 10$. This means $d = -7$ and the initial value is 24. Using the general formula the explicit rule: $t(n) = a + dn = 24 - 7d$.

d.   The common ratio $r = \frac{8.64}{7.2} = 1.2$ so $t(1) = \frac{7.2}{1.2} = 6$, $t(0) = \frac{6}{1.2} = 5$. Using an initial value of 5 and a common ratio of 1.2 in the general formula for the explicit rule: $t(n) = ar^n = 5(1.2)^n$.

e.   The common difference is the difference in the values divided by the number of terms. $d = \frac{t(12) - t(7)}{12 - 7} = \frac{116 - 1056}{5} = -188$. Working backward three terms: $t(4) = 1056 - 3(-188) = 1620$.

Here are some more to try.

Write the first 6 terms of each sequence.

1. $t(n) = 5n + 2$

2. $t(n) = 6(-\frac{1}{2})^n$

3. $t(n) = -15 + \frac{1}{2}n$

4. $t_n = -3 \cdot 3^{n-1}$

5. $t(1) = 3, t(n+1) = t(n) - 5$

6. $t_1 = \frac{1}{3}, t_{n+1} = \frac{1}{3}t_n$

For each sequence, write an explicit and recursive rule.

7. $10, 50, 250, 1250, \ldots$

8. $4, 8, 12, 16, \ldots$

9. $-2, 5, 12, 19, \ldots$

10. $16, 4, 1, \frac{1}{4}, \ldots$

11. $-12, 6, -3, \frac{3}{2}, \ldots$

12. $\frac{5}{6}, \frac{2}{3}, \frac{1}{2}, \frac{1}{3}, \ldots$

For each sequence, write an explicit rule.

13. A geometric sequence

n	$t(n)$
0	
1	15
2	45
3	
4	

14. An arithmetic sequence

n	$t(n)$
0	27
1	15
2	
3	
4	

15. An arithmetic sequence

n	$t(n)$
1	
2	$3\frac{1}{3}$
3	
4	
5	$4\frac{1}{3}$

16. A geometric sequence

n	$t(n)$
1	
2	
3	-24
4	48
5	

Solve each problem.

17. An arithmetic sequence has $t(3) = 52$ and $t(10) = 108$.
Find a rule for $t(n)$ and find $t(100)$.

18. An arithmetic sequence has $t(1) = -17$, $t(2) = -14$ and $t(n) = 145$.
What is the value of n?

19. An arithmetic sequence has $t(61) = 810$ and $t(94) = 1239$.
Find a rule for $t(n)$.

20. A geometric sequence has $t(4) = 12$ and $t(7) = 324$.
Find the common ratio and a rule for $t(n)$.

Answers:

1. $7, 12, 17, 22, 27, 32$

2. $-3, \frac{3}{2}, -\frac{3}{4}, \frac{3}{8}, -\frac{3}{16}, \frac{3}{32}$

3. $-14\frac{1}{2}, -14, -13\frac{1}{2}, -13, -12\frac{1}{2}, -12$

4. $-3, -9, -27, -81, -243, -729$

5. $3, -2, -7, -12, -17, -22$

6. $\frac{1}{3}, \frac{1}{9}, \frac{1}{27}, \frac{1}{81}, \frac{1}{243}, \frac{1}{729}$

Rules for problems 7 through 20 may vary.

7. $t(n) = 2 \cdot 5^n$; $t(0) = 2, t(n+1) = 5t(n)$

8. $t(n) = 4n$; $t(0) = 0, t(n+1) = t(n) + 4$

9. $t(n) = -9 + 7n$; $t(0) = -9, t(n+1) = t(n) + 7$

10. $t(n) = 64(\frac{1}{4})^n$; $t(0) = 64, t(n+1) = \frac{1}{4}t(n)$

11. $t(n) = 24(-\frac{1}{2})^n$; $t(0) = 24, t(n+1) = -\frac{1}{2}t(n)$

12. $t(n) = 1 - \frac{1}{6}n$; $t(0) = 1, t(n+1) = t(n) - \frac{1}{6}$

13. $t(n) = 5 \cdot 3^n$

14. $t(n) = 27 - 12n$

15. $t(n) = 2\frac{2}{3} + \frac{1}{3}n$

16. $t(n) = 3(-2)^n$

17. $t(n) = 28 + 8n; t(100) = 828$

18. $n = 55$

19. $t(n) = 17 + 13n$

20. $t(n) = \frac{4}{27}(3)^n$

Checkpoint 4B

Problem 4-87

Solving for One Variable in an Equation with Two or More Variables

Answers to problem 4-87: a: $y = \frac{1}{3}x - 4$, b: $y = \frac{6}{5}x - \frac{1}{5}$, c: $y = (x+1)^2 + 4$, d: $y = x^2 + 4x$

When we want to solve for one variable in an equation with two or more variables it usually helps to start by simplifying, such as removing parentheses and fractions. Next isolate the desired variable in the same way as you solve an equation with only one variable. Here are two examples.

Example 1: Solve $\frac{x-3y}{4} + 2(x+1) = 7$ for y.

Solution: First multiply all terms by 4 to remove the fraction and then simplify, as shown at right. Then, to isolate y, we subtract $9x$ from both sides to get $-3y = -9x + 20$. Dividing both sides by -3 results in $y = 3x - \frac{20}{3}$.

$$(4)\frac{x-3y}{4} + 4(2)(x+1) = 4(7)$$
$$x - 3y + 8x + 8 = 28$$
$$9x - 3y = 20$$

Answer: $y = 3x - \frac{20}{3}$

Example 2: Solve $x + 2\sqrt{y+1} = 3x + 4$ for y.

Solution: First, we isolate the radical by subtracting x from both sides to get $2\sqrt{1+y} = 2x + 4$ and then dividing both sides by 2 to get $\sqrt{1+y} = x + 2$. Then, we remove the radical by squaring both sides, as shown at right. Lastly, we isolate y by subtracting 1 from both sides of the equation.

$$(\sqrt{y+1})^2 = (x+2)^2$$
$$y+1 = (x+2)(x+2)$$
$$y+1 = x^2 + 4x + 4$$

Answer: $y = x^2 + 4x + 3$

Now we can go back and solve the original problems.

a. $x - 3(y + 2) = 6$
$x - 3y - 6 = 6$
$x - 3y = 12$
$-3y = -x + 12$
$y = \frac{-x+12}{-3}$ or $y = \frac{1}{3}x - 4$

b. $\frac{6x-1}{y} - 3 = 2$
$\frac{6x-1}{y} = 5$
$(y)\frac{6x-1}{y} = 5(y)$
$6x - 1 = 5y$
$y = \frac{6x-1}{5}$ or $y = \frac{6}{5}x - \frac{1}{5}$

c. $\sqrt{y-4} = x + 1$
$(\sqrt{y-4})^2 = (x+1)^2$
$y - 4 = (x+1)^2$
$y = (x+1)^2 + 4$ or $x^2 + 2x + 5$

d. $\sqrt{y+4} = x + 2$
$(\sqrt{y+4})^2 = (x+2)^2$
$y + 4 = x^2 + 4x + 4$
$y = x^2 + 4x$

Here are some more to try. Solve each equation for y.

1. $2x - 5y = 7$

2. $2(x + y) + 1 = x - 4$

3. $4(x - y) + 12 = 2x - 4$

4. $x = \frac{1}{5}y - 2$

5. $x = y^2 + 1$

6. $\frac{5x+2}{y} - 1 = 5$

7. $\sqrt{y+3} = x - 2$

8. $(y+2)^2 = x^2 + 9$

9. $\frac{x+2}{4} + \frac{4-y}{2} = 3$

10. $\sqrt{2y+1} = x + 3$

11. $x = \frac{2}{4-y}$

12. $x = \frac{y+1}{y-1}$

Answers:

1. $y = \frac{2}{5}x - \frac{7}{5}$

2. $y = -\frac{1}{2}x - \frac{5}{2}$

3. $y = \frac{1}{2}x + 4$

4. $y = 5x + 10$

5. $y = \pm\sqrt{x-1}$

6. $y = \frac{5}{6}x + \frac{1}{3}$

7. $y = x^2 - 4x + 1$

8. $y = \pm\sqrt{x^2+9} - 2$

9. $y = \frac{1}{2}x - 1$

10. $y = \frac{1}{2}x^2 + 3x + 4$
or $y = \frac{1}{2}(x+4)(x+2)$

11. $y = \frac{4x-2}{x}$ or $y = 4 - \frac{2}{x}$

12. $y = \frac{x+1}{x-1}$

Checkpoint 5A

Problem 5-49

Multiplying Polynomials

Answers to problem 5-49:

a. $2x^3 + 2x^2 - 3x - 3$ b. $x^3 - x^2 + x + 3$

c. $2x^2 + 12x + 18$ d. $4x^3 - 8x^2 - 3x + 9$

The product of polynomials can be found by using the Distributive Property. Using generic rectangles or, in the case of multiplying two binomials, the FOIL Method can help you to keep track of the terms to be sure that you are multiplying correctly.

Example: Multiply $(3x - 2)(4x + 5)$.

Solution 1: When multiplying binomials, such as $(3x - 2)(4x + 5)$, you can use a generic rectangle. You consider the terms of your original binomials as the dimensions (length and width) of the rectangle. To find the area of each piece, you multiply the terms that represent the length and width of that piece. To get your final answer, you add the areas of each of the interior pieces and simplify by combining like terms. This process is shown in the diagram below.

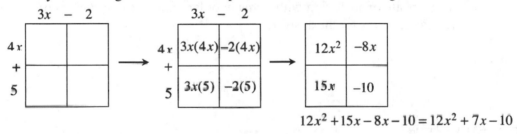

$$12x^2 + 15x - 8x - 10 = 12x^2 + 7x - 10$$

Solution 2: You might view multiplying binomials with generic rectangles as a form of double distribution. The $4x$ is distributed across the first row of the generic rectangle. Then the 5 is distributed across the second row of the generic rectangle. Some people write it this way:

$$(3x - 2)(4x + 5) = (3x - 2)4x + (3x - 2)5 = 12x^2 - 8x + 15x - 10 = 12x^2 + 7x - 10$$

Solution 3: Another approach to multiplying binomials is to the FOIL Method. This method uses the mnemonic "FOIL," which is an acronym for First, Outside, Inside, Last, to help you remember which terms to multiply.

F. Multiply the FIRST terms of each binomial. $(3x)(4x) = 12x^2$
O. Multiply the OUTSIDE terms. $(3x)(5) = 15x$
I. Multiply the INSIDE terms. $(-2)(4x) = -8x$
L. Multiply the LAST terms of each binomial   . $(-2)(5) = -10$

Finally combine like terms to get $12x^2 + 15x - 8x - 10 = 12x^2 + 7x - 10$.

Answer: $12x^2 + 7x - 10$

Now we can go back and solve the original problems.

a: $(x+1)(2x^2 - 3)$

Solution: We can use the FOIL Method here. Multiplying the *first* terms, we get $(x)(2x^2) = 2x^3$. Multiplying the *outside* terms, we get $(x)(-3) = -3x$. Multiplying the *inside* terms, we get $(1)(2x^2) = 2x^2$. Multiplying the *last* terms, we get $(1)(-3) = -3$. Adding these results, we get $2x^3 - 3x + 2x^2 - 3$. Generally, answers are expressed in with terms in order of decreasing powers of x, so we rearrange terms for the answer.

Answer: $2x^3 + 2x^2 - 3x - 3$

b: $(x+1)(x - 2x^2 + 3)$

Solution: This is a good problem for a generic rectangle, as shown at right. After calculating the area of each individual cell, we find our expression by adding them together to get $x^3 - 2x^2 + x^2 + 3x - 2x + 3$. Then we combine like terms to get a simplified answer.

	x^2	$-2x$	$+3$
x	x^3	$-2x^2$	$3x$
$+1$	x^2	$-2x$	3

Answer: $x^3 - x^2 + x + 3$

c: $2(x+3)^2$

Solution: Here we write out the factors and use the Distributive Property, as shown in the solution at right.

$$2(x+3)(x+3)$$
$$= (2x+6)(x+3)$$
$$= (2x+6)(x)+(2x+6)(3)$$
$$= 2x^2+6x+6x+18$$
$$= 2x^2+12x+18$$

Answer: $2x^2+12x+18$

d: $(x+1)(2x-3)^2$

Solution: Write out the factors. Multiply two of the factors together and then multiply that result by the third factor. This process is shown at right.

$$(x+1)(2x-3)(2x-3)$$
$$= (2x^2-x-3)(2x-3)$$
$$= 4x^3-6x^2-2x^2+3x-6x+9$$
$$= 4x^3-8x^2-3x+9$$

Answer: $4x^3-8x^2-3x+9$

Here are some more to try. Multiply and simplify.

1. $(2x+3)(x-7)$ 2. $(4x-2)(3x+5)$

3. $(x-2)(x^2+3x+5)$ 4. $(x+8)(x-12)$

5. $4(3x-5)^2$ 6. $(2x+y)(2x-y)$

7. $(2x+3)^2$ 8. $(5x-8)(2x+7)$

9. $(x+3)(x^2-4x+7)$ 10. $(x+7)(x-11)$

11. $-8x^2(5x^2+7)$ 12. $(2x+y)(x+1)^2$

Answers:

1. $2x^2-11x-21$ 2. $12x^2+14x-10$

3. x^3+x^2-x-10 4. $x^2-4x-96$

5. $36x^2-120x+100$ 6. $4x^2-y^2$

7. $4x^2+12x+9$ 8. $10x^2+19x-56$

9. $x^3-x^2-5x+21$ 10. $x^2-4x-77$

11. $-40x^4-56x^2$ 12. $2x^3+4x^2+2x+x^2y+2xy+y$

Checkpoint 5B
Problem 5-100
Factoring Quadratics

Answers to problem 5-100:

    a. $(2x+1)(2x-1)$ b. $(2x+1)^2$

    c. $(2y+1)(y+2)$ d. $(3m+1)(m-2)$

Factoring quadratics means changing the expression into a product of factors or to find the dimensions of the generic rectangle that represents the quadratic. You can use Diamond Problems with generic rectangles or just guess and check with FOIL Method or the Distributive Property to factor.

Here are some examples using Diamond Problems and generic rectangles:

Example 1: Factor $x^2 + 6x + 8$.

Solution: Multiply the x^2-term by the constant term and place the result in the top of the diamond. This will be the product of the two sides of the diamond. Then place the x-term at the bottom of the diamond. This will be the sum of the sides. Then find two terms that multiply to give the top term in the diamond and add to give the bottom term in the diamond, in this case $2x$ and $6x$. This tells us how the x-term is split in the generic rectangle. Once we have the area of the generic rectangle we can find the dimensions by looking for common factors among rows and columns. Study the example below.

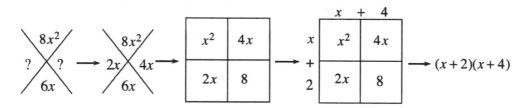

Example 2: Factor $5x^2 - 13x + 6$.

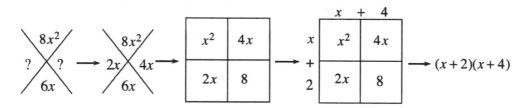

Now we can go back and solve the original problems.

a.

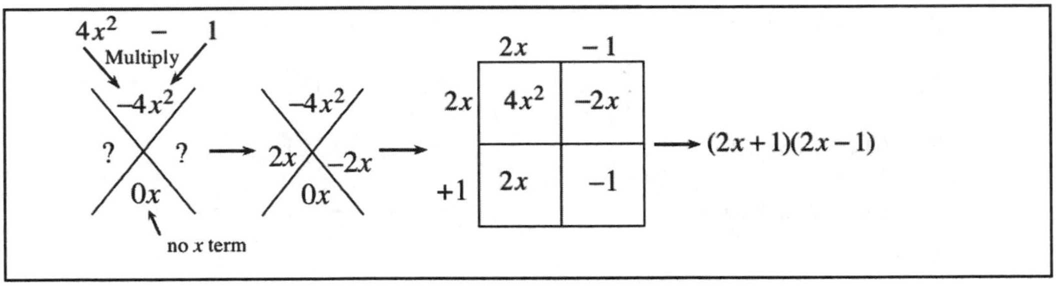
$4x^2 - 1$
Multiply
$-4x^2$
?
?
$0x$
no x term
$-4x^2$
$2x$
$-2x$
$0x$
$2x$
-1
$2x$
$4x^2$
$-2x$
$+1$
$2x$
-1
$(2x+1)(2x-1)$

b.

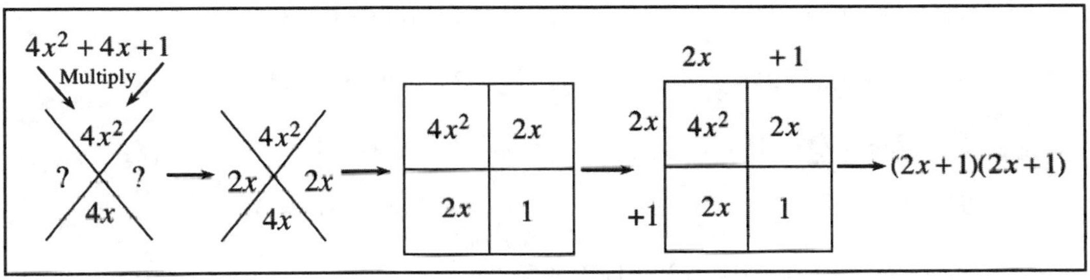
$4x^2 + 4x + 1$
Multiply
$4x^2$
?
?
$4x$
$4x^2$
$2x$
$2x$
$4x$
$4x^2$
$2x$
$2x$
1
$2x$
$+1$
$2x$
$4x^2$
$2x$
$+1$
$2x$
1
$(2x+1)(2x+1)$

c.

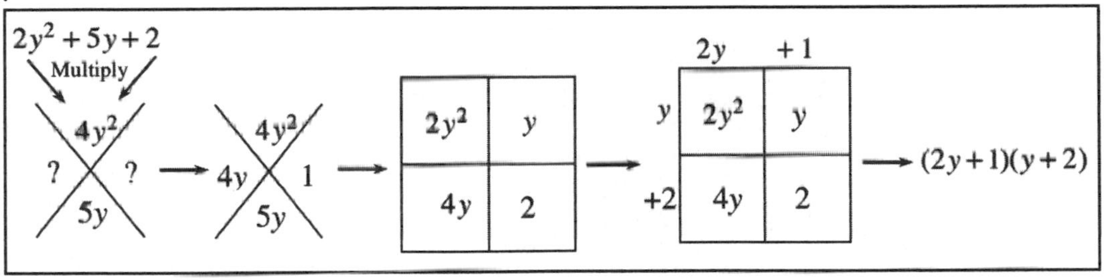
$2y^2 + 5y + 2$
Multiply
$4y^2$
?
?
$5y$
$4y^2$
$4y$
1
$5y$
$2y^2$
y
$4y$
2
$2y$
$+1$
y
$2y^2$
y
$+2$
$4y$
2
$(2y+1)(y+2)$

d.

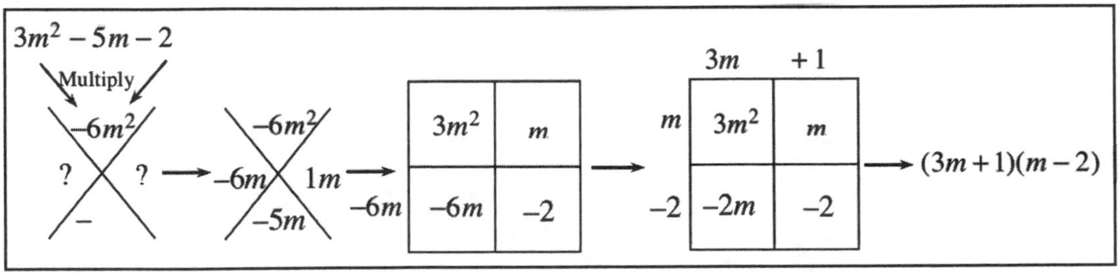
$3m^2 - 5m - 2$
Multiply
$-6m^2$
?
?
$-$
$-6m^2$
$-6m$
$1m$
$-5m$
$3m^2$
m
$-6m$
$-6m$
-2
$3m$
$+1$
m
$3m^2$
m
-2
$-2m$
-2
$(3m+1)(m-2)$

Here are some more to try. Factor each expression.

1. $2x^2 + 7x - 4$ 2. $7x^2 + 13x - 2$

3. $3x^2 + 11x + 10$ 4. $x^2 + 5x - 24$

5. $2x^2 + 5x - 7$ 6. $3x^2 - 13x + 4$

7. $64x^2 + 16x + 1$ 8. $5x^2 + 12x - 9$

9. $8x^2 + 24x + 10$ 10. $6x^3 + 31x^2 + 5x$

Answers:

1. $(x+4)(2x-1)$ 2. $(7x-1)(x+2)$

3. $(3x+5)(x+2)$ 4. $(x+8)(x-3)$

5. $(2x+7)(x-1)$ 6. $(3x-1)(x-4)$

7. $(8x+1)^2$ 8. $(5x-3)(x+3)$

9. $2(4x^2 + 12x + 5) = 2(2x+1)(2x+5)$

10. $x(6x^2 + 31x + 5) = x(6x+1)(x+5)$

Checkpoint 6A

Problem 6-73

Multiplying and Dividing Rational Expressions

Answers to problem 6-73: a: $\frac{x+3}{x+4}$, b: $\frac{1}{x(x+2)}$

Multiplication or division of rational expressions follows the same procedure used with numerical fractions. However, it is often necessary to factor the polynomials in order to simplify them. Factors that are the same in the numerator and denominator are equal to 1. For example: $\frac{x^2}{x^2}=1$, $\frac{(x+2)}{(x+2)}=1$ and $\frac{(3x-2)}{(3x-2)}=1$ but $\frac{5-x}{x-5}=\frac{-(x-5)}{x-5}=-1$.

When dividing rational expressions, change the problem to multiplication by inverting (flipping) the second expression (or any expression that follows a division sign) and completing the process as you do for multiplication.

In both cases, the simplification is only valid provided that the denominator is not equal to zero. See the examples below.

Example 1: Multiply $\frac{x^2+6x}{(x+6)^2}\cdot\frac{x^2+7x+6}{x^2-1}$ **and simplify the result.**

Solution:

After factoring, the expression becomes:

$$\frac{x(x+6)}{(x+6)(x+6)}\cdot\frac{(x+6)(x+1)}{(x+1)(x-1)}$$

After multiplying, reorder the factors:

$$\frac{(x+6)}{(x+6)}\cdot\frac{(x+6)}{(x+6)}\cdot\frac{x}{(x-1)}\cdot\frac{(x+1)}{(x+1)}$$

Since $\frac{(x+6)}{(x+6)}=1$ and $\frac{(x+1)}{(x+1)}=1$, simplify:

$$1\cdot1\cdot\frac{x}{x-1}\cdot1 \implies \frac{x}{x-1} \text{ for } x\neq-6,-1, \text{ or } 1.$$

Example 2: Divide $\frac{x^2-4x-5}{x^2-4x+4}\div\frac{x^2-2x-15}{x^2+4x-12}$ **and simplify the result.**

Solution:

First change to a multiplication expression by inverting (flipping) the second fraction:

$$\frac{x^2-4x-5}{x^2-4x+4}\cdot\frac{x^2+4x-12}{x^2-2x-15}$$

After factoring, the expression is:

$$\frac{(x-5)(x+1)}{(x-2)(x-2)}\cdot\frac{(x+6)(x-2)}{(x-5)(x+3)}$$

Reorder the factors (if you need to):

$$\frac{(x-5)}{(x-5)}\cdot\frac{(x-2)}{(x-2)}\cdot\frac{(x+1)}{(x-2)}\cdot\frac{(x+6)}{(x+3)}$$

Since $\frac{(x-5)}{(x-5)}=1$ and $\frac{(x-2)}{(x-2)}=1$, simplify:

$$\frac{(x+1)}{(x-2)}\cdot\frac{(x+6)}{(x+3)}$$

Thus, $\frac{x^2-4x-5}{x^2-4x+4}\div\frac{x^2-2x-15}{x^2+4x-12}=\frac{(x+1)}{(x-2)}\cdot\frac{(x+6)}{(x+3)}$ or $\frac{x^2+7x+6}{x^2+x-6}$ for $x\neq-3,\ 2,\text{ or } 5.$

Now we can go back and solve the original problems.

a. $\dfrac{x^2-16}{(x-4)^2} \cdot \dfrac{x^2-3x-18}{x^2-2x-24} \Rightarrow \dfrac{(x+4)(x-4)}{(x-4)(x-4)} \cdot \dfrac{(x-6)(x+3)}{(x-6)(x+4)} \Rightarrow \dfrac{(x+4)(x-4)(x-6)(x+3)}{(x+4)(x-4)(x-6)(x-4)} \Rightarrow \dfrac{x+3}{x-4}$

b. $\dfrac{x^2-1}{x^2-6x-7} \div \dfrac{x^3+x^2-2x}{x-7} \Rightarrow \dfrac{(x+1)(x-1)}{(x-7)(x+1)} \cdot \dfrac{(x-7)}{x(x+2)(x-1)} \Rightarrow \dfrac{(x+1)(x-1)(x-7)}{(x+1)(x-1)(x-7)x(x+2)} \Rightarrow \dfrac{1}{x(x+2)}$

Here are some more to try. Multiply or divide each pair of rational expressions. Simplify the result. Assume the denominator is not equal to zero.

1. $\dfrac{x^2+5x+6}{x^2-4x} \cdot \dfrac{4x}{x+2}$

2. $\dfrac{x^2-2x}{x^2-4x+4} \div \dfrac{4x^2}{x-2}$

3. $\dfrac{x^2-16}{(x-4)^2} \cdot \dfrac{x^2-3x-18}{x^2-2x-24}$

4. $\dfrac{x^2-x-6}{x^2+3x-10} \cdot \dfrac{x^2+2x-15}{x^2-6x+9}$

5. $\dfrac{x^2-x-6}{x^2-x-20} \cdot \dfrac{x^2+6x+8}{x^2-x-6}$

6. $\dfrac{x^2-x-30}{x^2+13x+40} \cdot \dfrac{x^2+11x+24}{x^2-9x+18}$

7. $\dfrac{15-5x}{x^2-x-6} \div \dfrac{5x}{x^2+6x+8}$

8. $\dfrac{17x+119}{x^2+5x-14} \div \dfrac{9x-1}{x^2-3x+2}$

9. $\dfrac{2x^2-5x-3}{3x^2-10x+3} \cdot \dfrac{9x^2-1}{4x^2+4x+1}$

10. $\dfrac{x^2-1}{x^2-6x-7} \div \dfrac{x^3+x^2-2x}{x-7}$

11. $\dfrac{3x-21}{x^2-49} \div \dfrac{3x}{x^2+7x}$

12. $\dfrac{x^2-y^2}{x+y} \cdot \dfrac{1}{x-y}$

13. $\dfrac{y^2-y}{w^2-y^2} \div \dfrac{y^2-2y+1}{1-y}$

14. $\dfrac{y^2-y-12}{y+2} \div \dfrac{y-4}{y^2-4y-12}$

15. $\dfrac{x^2+7x+10}{x+2} \div \dfrac{x^2+2x-15}{x+2}$

Answers:

1. $\dfrac{4(x+3)}{x-4}$

2. $\dfrac{1}{4x}$

3. $\dfrac{x+3}{x-4}$

4. $\dfrac{x+2}{x-2}$

5. $\dfrac{x+2}{x-5}$

6. $\dfrac{x+3}{x-3}$

7. $\dfrac{-x-4}{x}$

8. $\dfrac{17(x-1)}{9x-1}$

9. $\dfrac{3x+1}{2x+1}$

10. $\dfrac{1}{x(x+2)}$

11. 1

12. 1

13. $\dfrac{-y}{w^2-y^2}$

14. $(y+3)(y-6)$

15. $\dfrac{x+2}{x-3}$

Checkpoint 6B
Problem 6-145
Adding and Subtracting Rational Expressions

Answers to problem 6-145: a: $\frac{2(x+1)}{x+3}$, b: $\frac{3x^2-5x-3}{(2x+1)^2}$

Addition and subtraction of rational expressions uses the same process as simple numerical fractions. First, if necessary find a common denominator. Second, convert the original fractions to equivalent ones with the common denominator. Third, add or subtract the new numerators over the common denominator. Finally, factor the numerator and denominator and simplify, if possible. Note that these steps are only valid provided that the denominator is not zero.

Example 1: $\frac{3}{2(n+2)} + \frac{3}{n(n+2)}$

Solution:

The least common multiple of $2(n+2)$ and $n(n+2)$ is $2n(n+2)$.

$$\frac{3}{2(n+2)} + \frac{3}{n(n+2)}$$

To get a common denominator in the first fraction, multiply the fraction by $\frac{n}{n}$, a form of the number 1. Multiply the second fraction by $\frac{2}{2}$.

$$= \frac{3}{2(n+2)} \cdot \frac{n}{n} + \frac{3}{n(n+2)} \cdot \frac{2}{2}$$

Multiply the numerator and denominator of each term. It may be necessary to distribute the numerator.

$$= \frac{3n}{2n(n+2)} + \frac{6}{2n(n+2)}$$

Add, factor, and simplify the result. (Note: $n \neq 0 \ or \ -2$)

$$= \frac{3n+6}{2n(n+2)} \Rightarrow \frac{3(n+2)}{2n(n+2)} \Rightarrow \frac{3}{2n}$$

Example 2: $\frac{2-x}{x+4} + \frac{3x+6}{x+4}$

Solution:

$$\frac{2-x}{x+4} + \frac{3x+6}{x+4} \Rightarrow \frac{2-x+3x+6}{x+4} \Rightarrow \frac{2x+8}{x+4} \Rightarrow \frac{2(x+4)}{x+4} \Rightarrow 2$$

Example 3: $\frac{3}{x-1} - \frac{2}{x-2}$

Solution:

$$\frac{3}{x-1} - \frac{2}{x-2} \Rightarrow \frac{3}{x-1} \cdot \frac{x-2}{x-2} - \frac{2}{x-2} \cdot \frac{x-1}{x-1} \Rightarrow \frac{3x-6-2x+2}{(x-1)(x-2)} \Rightarrow \frac{x-4}{(x-1)(x-2)}$$

Now we can go back and solve the original problems.

a. $\frac{4}{x^2+5x+6}+\frac{2x}{x+2} \Rightarrow \frac{4}{(x+3)(x+2)}+\frac{2x}{(x+2)}\cdot\frac{(x+3)}{(x+3)} \Rightarrow \frac{2x^2+6x+4}{(x+2)(x+3)} \Rightarrow \frac{2(x+2)(x+1)}{(x+2)(x+3)} \Rightarrow \frac{2(x+1)}{(x+3)}$

b. $\frac{3x^2+x}{(2x+1)^2}-\frac{3}{(2x+1)} \Rightarrow \frac{3x^2+x}{(2x+1)^2}-\frac{3}{(2x+1)}\cdot\frac{(2x+1)}{(2x+1)} \Rightarrow \frac{3x^2+x-6x-3}{(2x+1)^2} \Rightarrow \frac{3x^2-5x-3}{(2x+1)^2}$

Here are a few more to try. Add or subtract each expression and simplify the result.
In each case assume the denominator does not equal zero.

1. $\frac{x}{(x+2)(x+3)}+\frac{2}{(x+2)(x+3)}$

2. $\frac{x}{x^2+6x+8}+\frac{4}{x^2+6x+8}$

3. $\frac{b^2}{b^2+2b-3}+\frac{-9}{b^2+2b-3}$

4. $\frac{2a}{a^2+2a+1}+\frac{2}{a^2+2a+1}$

5. $\frac{x+10}{x+2}+\frac{x-6}{x+2}$

6. $\frac{a+2b}{a+b}+\frac{2a+b}{a+b}$

7. $\frac{3x-4}{3x+3}-\frac{2x-5}{3x+3}$

8. $\frac{3x}{4x-12}-\frac{9}{4x-12}$

9. $\frac{6a}{5a^2+a}-\frac{a-1}{5a^2+a}$

10. $\frac{x^2+3x-5}{10}-\frac{x^2-2x+10}{10}$

11. $\frac{6}{x(x+3)}+\frac{2x}{x(x+3)}$

12. $\frac{5}{x-7}+\frac{3}{4(x-7)}$

13. $\frac{5x+6}{x^2}-\frac{5}{x}$

14. $\frac{2}{x+4}-\frac{x-4}{x^2-16}$

15. $\frac{10a}{a^2+6a}-\frac{3}{3a+18}$

16. $\frac{3x}{2x^2-8x}+\frac{2}{x-4}$

17. $\frac{5x+9}{x^2-2x-3}+\frac{6}{x^2-7x+12}$

18 $\frac{x+4}{x^2-3x-28}-\frac{x-5}{x^2+2x-35}$

19. $\frac{3x+1}{x^2-16}-\frac{3x+5}{x^2+8x+16}$

20. $\frac{7x-1}{x^2-2x-3}-\frac{6x}{x^2-x-2}$

Answers:

1. $\frac{1}{x+3}$ 2. $\frac{1}{x+2}$ 3. $\frac{b-3}{b-1}$ 4. $\frac{2}{a+1}$

5. 2 6. 3 7. $\frac{1}{3}$ 8. $\frac{3}{4}$

9. $\frac{1}{a}$ 10. $\frac{x-3}{2}$ 11. $\frac{2}{x}$ 12. $\frac{23}{4(x-7)}=\frac{23}{4x-28}$

13. $\frac{6}{x^2}$ 14. $\frac{1}{x+4}$ 15. $\frac{9}{a+6}$ 16. $\frac{7}{2(x-4)}=\frac{7}{2x-8}$

17. $\frac{5(x+2)}{(x-4)(x+1)}=\frac{5x+10}{x^2-3x-4}$ 18. $\frac{14}{(x-7)(x+7)}=\frac{14}{x^2-49}$

19. $\frac{4(5x+6)}{(x-4)(x+4)^2}$ 20. $\frac{x+2}{(x-3)(x-2)}=\frac{x+2}{x^2-5x+6}$

Checkpoint 7A

Problem 7-67

Finding the x- and y-Intercepts of a Quadratic Function

Answers to problem 7-67: y-intercept: $(0,-17)$, x-intercepts: $(-2+\sqrt{21},0)$ and $(-2-\sqrt{21},0)$

The y-intercepts of an equation are the points at which the graph crosses the y-axis. To find the y-intercept of an equation, substitute $x = 0$ into the equation and solve for y.

The x-intercepts of an equation are the points at which the graph crosses the x-axis. To find the x-intercepts of an equation, substitute $y = 0$ into the equation and solve for x. For a quadratic, you can do this by factoring and using the Zero Product Property or by using the Quadratic Formula, as well as other methods.

Example 1: Find the x-intercepts of the graph of the equation $y = x^2 + 4x - 12$.

Solution: If $y = 0$, then: $\qquad\qquad\qquad\qquad\qquad\qquad\qquad 0 = x^2 + 4x - 12$
$\qquad$ By factoring and using the Zero Product Property: $\qquad 0 = (x+6)(x-2)$
$\qquad\qquad\qquad\qquad\qquad\qquad\qquad\qquad\qquad\qquad\qquad x+6 = 0$ or $x-2 = 0$
$\qquad\qquad\qquad\qquad\qquad\qquad\qquad\qquad\qquad\qquad\qquad x = -6$ or $x = 2$

Answers: The x-intercepts are $(-6, 0)$ and $(2, 0)$.

Example 2: Find the x-intercepts of the graph of the equation $y = 2x^2 - 3x - 3$.

Solution: If $y = 0$, then: $\qquad\qquad\qquad\qquad\qquad\qquad\qquad 0 = 2x^2 - 3x - 3$

$\qquad$ Since we cannot factor the trinomial we use the Quadratic Formula to solve for x.

$\qquad$ If $ax^2 + bx + c = 0$ then: $\qquad\qquad\qquad x = \frac{-b \pm \sqrt{b^2 - 4ac}}{2a}$.

$\qquad$ Substitute $a = 2$, $b = -3$, $c = -3$. $\qquad x = \frac{-(-3) \pm \sqrt{(-3)^2 - 4(2)(-3)}}{2(2)}$

$\qquad$ Simplify. $\qquad\qquad\qquad\qquad\qquad\qquad x = \frac{3 \pm \sqrt{9+24}}{4} = \frac{3 \pm \sqrt{33}}{4}$

$\qquad$ Find $\sqrt{33}$ approximately: $\qquad\qquad \approx \frac{3 \pm 5.745}{4}$, so $\frac{3+5.745}{4}$ and $\frac{3-5.745}{4}$.

Answers: Simplify the fractions and the x-intercepts are approximately $(2.19, 0)$ and $(-0.69, 0)$. They can be expressed in exact form as $\left(\frac{3+\sqrt{33}}{4}, 0\right)$ and $\left(\frac{3-\sqrt{33}}{4}, 0\right)$.

Now we can find the x- and y-intercepts in the original problem.

Find the x- and y-intercepts of the graph of $y = x^2 + 4x - 17$.

Solution: To find the y-intercept, let $x = 0$ so $y = (0)^2 + 4(0) - 17 = -17$.
To find the x-intercept, let $y = 0$ so $0 = x^2 + 4x - 17$.
Since we cannot factor we use the Quadratic Formula with $a = 1$, $b = 4$ and $c = -17$.

$$x = \frac{-4 \pm \sqrt{4^2 - 4(1)(-17)}}{2(1)} = \frac{-4 \pm \sqrt{16+68}}{2} = \frac{-4 \pm \sqrt{84}}{2} = \frac{-4 \pm 2\sqrt{21}}{2} = -2 \pm \sqrt{21}$$

Answers: The y-intercept is $(0, -17)$. The x-intercepts are $(-2 \pm \sqrt{21}, 0)$, or approximately $(2.58, 0)$ and $(-6.58, 0)$.

Here are some more to try. Find the x- and y-intercepts for the graphs of each equation.

1. $y = x^2 + 2x - 15$

2. $y = 2x^2 + 7x + 3$

3. $y = 3x^2 - 5x + 2$

4. $y = 4x^2 - 8x$

5. $y = 2x^2 - 9x - 35$

6. $y = 2x^2 - 11x + 5$

7. $3x^2 + 2 + 7x = y$

8. $8x^2 + 10x + 3 = y$

9. $y + 2 = x^2 - 5x$

10. $(x - 3)(x + 4) - 7x = y$

11. $-4x^2 + 8x + 3 = y$

12. $0.009x^2 - 0.86x + 2 = y$

13. $y = 2x^3 - 50x$

14. $y = 3x^2 + 4x$

Answers:

1. $(3,0), (-5,0)$ and $(0,-15)$

2. $\left(-\frac{1}{2},0\right), (-3,0)$ and $(0,3)$

3. $\left(\frac{2}{3},0\right), (1,0)$ and $(0,2)$

4. $(0,0), (2,0)$ and $(0,0)$

5. $(7,0), \left(-\frac{5}{2},0\right)$, and $(0,-35)$

6. $(5,0), \left(\frac{1}{2},0\right)$, and $(0,5)$

7. $\left(-\frac{1}{3},0\right), (-2,0)$, and $(0,2)$

8. $\left(-\frac{3}{4},0\right), \left(-\frac{1}{2},0\right)$, and $(0,3)$

9. $\left(\frac{5 \pm \sqrt{33}}{2},0\right)$ or $(\approx 5.37,0), (\approx -0.37,0)$, and $(0,-2)$

10. $\left(\frac{-6 \pm \sqrt{84}}{2},0\right)$ or $(\approx 7.58,0), (\approx -1.58,0)$, and $(0,-12)$

11. $\left(\frac{-8 \pm \sqrt{112}}{-8},0\right)$ or $(\approx -0.32,0), (\approx 2.32,0)$, and $(0,3)$

12. $\left(\frac{0.86 \pm \sqrt{0.6676}}{0.018},0\right)$ or $(\approx 2.39,0), (\approx 93.17,0)$, and $(0,2)$

13. $(0,0), (5,0), (-5,0)$, and $(0,0)$

14. $(0,0), \left(-\frac{4}{3},0\right)$, and $(0,0)$

Checkpoint 7B
Problem 7-131
Completing the Square to Find the Vertex of a Parabola

Answers to problem 7-131: Graphing form: $y = 2(x-1)^2 + 3$, vertex $(1, 3)$
See graph in solution that follows examples.

If a quadratic function is in graphing form then the vertex can be found easily and a sketch of the graph can be made quickly. If the equation of the parabola is not in graphing form, the equation can be rewritten in graphing form by completing the square.

First, recall that $y = x^2$ is the parent equation for quadratic functions and the general equation can be written in graphing form as $y = a(x-h)^2 + k$ where (h, k) is the vertex, and relative to the parent graph the function has been:

- Vertically stretched, if the absolute value of a is greater than 1

- Vertically compressed, if the absolute value of a is less than 1

- Reflected across the x-axis, if a is less than 0.

Example 1: Complete the square to change $y = x^2 + 8x + 10$ into graphing form and name the vertex.

Solution: Use an area model to make $x^2 + 8x$ into a perfect square.
To do this, use half of the coefficient of the x-term on
each side of the area model, and complete the upper
right corner of the square, as shown at right.

4	$4x$	16
x	x^2	$4x$
	x	4

Your square shows that $(x+4)^2 = x^2 + 8x + 16$. Your original expression is $x^2 + 8x + 10$, which is 6 fewer than $(x+4)^2$. So you can write $y = x^2 + 8x + 10 = (x+4)^2 - 6$.

Because the function is now in graphing form, $y = a(x-h)^2 + k$, you know the vertex is (h, k), in this case $(-4, -6)$.

Example 2: Complete the square to change $y = x^2 + 5x + 7$ into graphing form and name the vertex.

Solution: We need to make $x^2 + 5x$ into a perfect square.
Again, we take half of the coefficient of x and fill in
the upper right of the area model, as shown below.

2.5	$2.5x$	6.25
x	x^2	$2.5x$
	x	2.5

The area model shows that $(x+2.5)^2 = x^2 + 5x + 6.25$. Your original expression, $y = x^2 + 5x + 7$, is 0.75 more than $(x+2.5)^2$.
So you can write: $y = x^2 + 5x + 7 = (x+2.5)^2 + 0.75$ and the vertex is $(-2.5, 0.75)$.

Example 3: Complete the square to change $y = 2x^2 - 6x + 2$ into graphing form and name the vertex.

Solution: This problem is different because the x^2 term has a coefficient. First factor the 2 out of the quadratic expression so that an x^2 term remains, as follows: $y = 2x^2 - 6x + 2 = 2(x^2 - 3x + 1)$. Then make $x^2 - 3x$ into a perfect square as before:

	$-1.5x$	2.25
-1.5		
x	x^2	$-1.5x$
	x	-1.5

Since $(x - 1.5)^2 = x^2 - 3x + 2.25$, the original expression $x^2 - 3x + 1$ is 1.25 less than $(x - 1.5)^2$. You can write:

$$y = 2x^2 - 6x + 2$$

$$y = 2(x^2 - 3x + 1)$$

$$y = 2\left((x - 1.5)^2 - 1.25\right)$$

which can be distributed to give

$$y = 2(x - 1.5)^2 - 2.5$$

The vertex is $(1.5, -2.5)$.

Now we can go back and solve the original problem.

Complete the square to change the equation $y = 2x^2 - 4x + 5$ to graphing form, identify the vertex of the parabola, and sketch its graph.

Solution: Factor out the coefficient of x^2, resulting in $y = 2\left(x^2 - 2x + \frac{5}{2}\right)$. Make a perfect square out of $x^2 - 2x$:

	$-1x$	1
-1		
x	x^2	$-1x$
	x	-1

Since $(x - 1)^2 = x^2 - 2x + 1$, the original expression $x^2 - 2x + \frac{5}{2}$ is $\frac{3}{2}$ more than $(x - 1)^2$. You can write:

$$y = 2x^2 - 4x + 5$$

$$y = 2(x^2 - 2x + \tfrac{5}{2})$$

$$y = 2\left((x - 1)^2 + \tfrac{3}{2}\right)$$

which can be distributed to give

$$y = 2(x - 1)^2 + 3$$

Because the function is now in graphing form, $y = a(x - h)^2 + k$, you know the vertex is $(h, k) = (1, 3)$.

To sketch the graph, we start by plotting the vertex, $(1, 3)$. From the standard form, $y = 2x^2 - 4x + 5$, we see that the y-intercept is $(0, 5)$, because when $x = 0, y = 5$. By symmetry, $(2, 5)$ must also be a point. Thus we get the graph at the right. If desired, additional points can be found by recognizing that the shape of this parabola is the shape of $y = x^2$ stretched by a factor of 2.

Answer: Graphing form: $y = 2(x - 1)^2 + 3$;
Vertex: $(1, 3)$;
See graph at right.

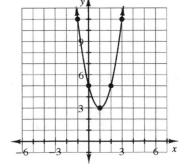

Here are some more to try. Write each equation in graphing form. If needed, complete the square to do so. Then state the vertex, y-intercept, and the stretch factor and sketch a graph.

1. $y = x^2 - 6x + 9$

2. $y = x^2 + 3$

3. $y = x^2 - 4x$

4. $y = x^2 + 2x - 3$

5. $y = x^2 + 5x + 1$

6. $y = x^2 - \frac{1}{3}x$

7. $y = 3x^2 - 6x + 1$

8. $y = 5x^2 + 20x - 16$

9. $y = -x^2 - 6x + 10$

Answers:

1. $y = (x - 3)^2$; $(3, 0)$; $(0, 9)$; $a = 1$

2. $y = (x - 0)^2 + 3$; $(0, 3)$; $(0, 3)$; $a = 1$

3. $y = (x - 2)^2 - 4$; $(2, -4)$; $(0, 0)$; $a = 1$

4. $y = (x + 1)^2 - 4$; $(-1, -4)$; $(0, -3)$ $a = 1$

5. $y = \left(x + \frac{5}{2}\right)^2 - 5\frac{1}{4}$; $\left(-\frac{5}{2}, -5\frac{1}{4}\right)$; $(0, 1)$; $a = 1$

6. $y = \left(x - \frac{1}{6}\right)^2 - \frac{1}{36}$; $\left(\frac{1}{6}, -\frac{1}{36}\right)$; $(0, 0)$; $a = 1$

7. $y = 3(x - 1)^2 - 2$; $(1, -2)$; $(0, 1)$; $a = 3$

8. $y = 5(x + 2)^2 - 36$; $(-2, -36)$; $(0, -16)$; $a = 5$

9. $y = -(x + 3)^2 + 19$ $(-3, 19)$; $(0, 10)$; $a = -1$

Checkpoint 8A
Problem 8-127
Solving and Graphing Inequalities

Answers to problem 8-127:

a.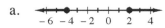

b.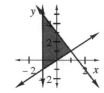

There are several methods for graphing different types of inequalities but there is one way that works for all types: Solve as you would an equation then use the solutions to break the graph into regions. If testing a point from a region makes the inequality "true," shade in that region as it is part of the solution. If a point from the region makes the inequality "false," then that region is not part of the solution.

Example 1: Graph $x^2 + 5x + 4 < 0$.

Solution: Change the inequality into an equation and solve.

$$x^2 + 5x + 4 = 0$$
$$(x+4)(x+1) = 0$$
$$x = -4 \text{ or } x = -1$$

Place the solutions on a number line to break the line into three regions. Use open circles since the original problem is a strict inequality. Test one point from each region in the original inequality. For example testing $x = -5$ we find:

$$(-5)^2 + 5(-5) + 4 < 0$$

$$4 < 0 \text{ False}$$

So that region is not shaded in. Continue in the same manner with one point from each of the other regions.

```
test        test        test
x = -5      x = -2       x = 0
  F           T            F
```

The solution may also be written $-4 < x < -1$.

Example 2: Graph the system $y \le x + 1$

$$y \ge x^2 - 4$$

Solution: Graph the line $y = x + 1$ and check the point $(0, 0)$. The point makes the first inequality "true" so the shading is in the $(0, 0)$ region or below the line.

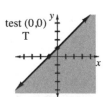

Next graph the parabola $y = x^2 - 4$ and again finding the point $(0, 0)$ to be "true" in the inequality, the shading is inside the parabola. The overlapping shaded region is the solution to the system.

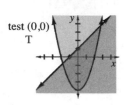

Core Connections Algebra 2

Now we can go back and solve the original problems.

a. $|x+1| \geq 3$

Solution: If $|x+1| = 3$ then $x+1 = \pm 3$ or $x = 2, -4$. Using solid dots to divide the number line into three regions and testing a point from each region gives the answer graph at right. This can also be written as: $x \leq -4$ or $x \geq 2$.

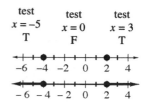

b. Graph: $y \leq -2x + 3 \quad y \geq x \quad x \geq -1$

Solution: Start by looking at the equation of the line that marks the edge of each inequality. The first has slope -2 and y-intercept $(0, 3)$. Checking $(0, 1)$ gives a true statement so we shade below the solid line. The second line has slope 1 and y-intercept $(0, 0)$. Again checking $(0, 1)$ gives a true statement, so we shade above the solid line. The third is a vertical line at $x = -1$. Checking a point tells us to shade the right side. The overlapping shading is a triangle with vertices $(-1, 5), (1, 1)$, and $(-1, -1)$. See the answer graph at right.

Here are a few more to try. In problems 1 through 6, graph each inequality. In problems 7 through 14 graph the solution region for each system of inequalities.

1. $|2x + 3| \leq 7$

2. $x^2 - 2x - 3 > 0$

3. $4 - x^2 \leq 0$

4. $|4r - 2| > 8$

5. $3m^2 \leq 9m$

6. $-|x + 3| < 10$

7. $y \leq -x + 2$
   $y \leq 3x - 6$

8. $y \geq \frac{2}{3}x + 4$
   $y \leq \frac{7}{12}x + 5$

9. $x < 3$
   $y \geq -2$

10. $y \leq 4x + 16$
    $y \geq -\frac{4}{3}x - 4$

11. $y \geq x^2 - 4$
    $y < -3x + 1$

12. $y < 2x + 5$
    $y \geq |x + 1|$

13. $y < x^2 - 2x - 3$
    $y \leq \frac{1}{2}x + 3$

14. $y \leq -\frac{1}{2}x + 2$
    $y \geq (x + 1)^2 - 3$

Answers:

1. −5   2

2. −1   3

3. −2   2

4. 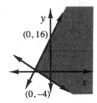 $-\frac{3}{2}$ $\frac{5}{2}$

5. 0   3

6. all numbers

7.

(0, 2)   (0, −6)

8. (0, 5)   (0, 4)

9. $x = 3$ $y = -2$

10. (0, 16)   (0, −4)

11. (−2, 0)   (0, 1)   (2, 0)

12. (0, 5)   (−1, 0)

13. (0, 3)   (0, −1)   (3, 0)

14. (0, 2) $\left(-1-\sqrt{3},0\right)$ $\left(\sqrt{3}-1,0\right)$

Checkpoint 8B
Problem 8-174
Solving Complicated Equations

Answers to problem 8-174: a: $x = 5$ or 1, b: $x = 4$ or 0, c: $x = 7$, d: $x = 1$

Often the best way to solve a complicated equation is to use a method such as the Looking Inside or Undoing Methods. Checking your answer(s) is important because sometimes solutions are accurately found but will not work in the original equation. These answers are called extraneous solutions.

Example 1: Solve $3(x+1)^3 - 1 = 80$

Solution: In this case we will undo everything.

		check
$3(x+1)^3 - 1 = 80$	original problem	
$3(x+1)^3 = 81$	add 1 to undo -1	$3(2+1)^3 = 81$
$(x+1)^3 = 27$	division undoes multiplication	$3(3)^3 = 81$
$x+1 = 3$	cube root undoes cubing	$3(27) = 81$
$x = 2$	subtract 1 to undo $+1$	$81 = 81$

Example 2: Solve $|2x+5| = x+4$

Solution: In this case we will use the Look Inside Method and the fact that absolute value of a quantity and its opposite are the same.

$2x+5 = x+4$ or $-(2x+5) = x+4$ checks

$x = -1$ $-2x-5 = x+4$ $|2(-1)+5| = -1+4$ $|2(-3)+5| = -3+4$

                $-3x = 9$ $|3| = |3|$ $|-1| = |1|$

                $x = -3$ $3 = 3$ True $1=1$ True

The solutions are $x = -1, x = -3$.

Now we can go back and solve the original problems.

a.
$$2|x-3|+7=11$$
$$2|x-3|=4$$
$$|x-3|=2$$
$$x-3=2 \text{ or } -(x-3)=2$$
$$x=5 \text{ or } x=1$$

checks

$$2|5-3|+7=11 \qquad 2|1-3|+7=11$$
$$2|2|+7=11 \qquad 2|-2|+7=11$$
$$4+7=11 \text{ True} \qquad 4+7=11 \text{ True}$$

The solutions are $x=5$, $x=1$.

b.
$$4(x-2)^2=16$$
$$(x-2)^2=4$$
$$x-2=\pm2$$
$$x=2\pm2=4 \text{ or } 0$$

checks

$$4(4-2)^2=16 \qquad 4(0-2)^2=16$$
$$4(2)^2=16 \qquad 4(-2)^2=16$$
$$4(4)=16 \text{ True} \qquad 4(4)=16 \text{ True}$$

The solutions are $x=4$, $x=0$.

c.
$$\sqrt{x+18}=x-2$$
$$(\sqrt{x+18})^2=(x-2)^2$$
$$x+18=x^2-4x+4$$
$$0=x^2-5x-14$$
$$0=(x-7)(x+2)$$
$$x=7 \text{ or } x=-2$$

checks

$$\sqrt{7+18}=7-2 \qquad \sqrt{-2+18}=-2-2$$
$$\sqrt{25}=5 \text{ True} \qquad \sqrt{16}=-4 \text{ False}$$

The only solution is $x=7$.

d.
$$|2x+5|=3x+4$$
$$2x+5=3x+4 \text{ or } -(2x+5)=3x+4$$
$$x=1 \qquad \text{or} \qquad x=-\tfrac{9}{5}$$

checks

$$|2(1)+5|=3(1)+4 \qquad |2(-\tfrac{9}{5})+5|=3(-\tfrac{9}{5})+4$$
$$|7|=7 \text{ True} \qquad \left|-\tfrac{18}{5}+\tfrac{25}{5}\right|=-\tfrac{27}{5}+\tfrac{20}{5}$$
$$\left|\tfrac{7}{5}\right|=-\tfrac{7}{5} \text{ False}$$

The only solution is $x=1$.

Here are some more to try. Solve each equation and check your solutions.

1. $|x+4|+3=17$

2. $|3w-6|-2=19$

3. $\sqrt{3w+4}-2=2$

4. $\sqrt{3x+13}=x+5$

5. $\sqrt[3]{x}-2=5$

6. $(x+1)^2+1=6$

7. $|2y-4|=12$

8. $|3m+5|=5m+2$

9. $\sqrt{y+7}+5=y$

10. $\sqrt{5-m}=m+1$

11. $\frac{2(x-1)^2}{3}-7=1$

12. $3(x-2)^3=81$

13. $|2m+5|=m+4$

14. $|2y+8|=3y+7$

15. $\sqrt{x+7}-x=1$

16. $\sqrt{y+2}=y$

17. $\sqrt[4]{x+1}+2=5$

18. $\frac{1}{2}(x+5)^3+1=10$

19. $\sqrt{x}+2=x$

20. $\sqrt{x}+2=\sqrt{x+6}$

Answers:

1. $x=-18,10$

2. $w=-5,9$

3. $w=4$

4. $x=-3,-4$

5. $x=343$

6. $x=-1\pm\sqrt{5}$

7. $y=-4,8$

8. $m=\frac{3}{2}$

9. $y=9$

10. $m=1$

11. $x=1\pm\sqrt{12}$

12. $x=5$

13. $m=-1,-3$

14. $y=1$

15. $x=2$

16. $y=2$

17. $x=80$

18. $x=-5+\sqrt[3]{18}$

19. $x=4$

20. $x=\frac{1}{4}$

Checkpoint 9A

Problem 9-41

Writing and Solving Exponential Equations

Answers to problem 9-41:

a.   The more rabbits you have, the more new ones you get, a linear model would grow by the same number each year. A sine function would be better if the population rises and falls, but more data would be needed to apply this model.

b. $R = 80,000(5.4772...)^t$ c. ≈ 394 million

d.   1859, it seems okay that they grew to 80,000 in 7 years, *if* they are growing exponentially.

e.   No, since it would predict a huge number of rabbits now. The population probably leveled off at some point or dropped drastically and rebuilt periodically.

Exponential functions are equations of the form $y = ab^x + c$ where a represents the initial value, b represents the multiplier, c represents the horizontal asymptote, and x often represents the time. Some problems simply involve substituting in the given information into the equation and then doing calculations. If you are trying to solve for the time (x), then you will usually need to use logarithms. If you need to find the multiplier (m), then you will need to find a root. Note that we often assume that $c = 0$, unless we are told otherwise.

Example 1: Lunch at our favorite fast food stands cost \$6.50. The price has steadily increased 4% per year for many years.

Question 1: What will lunch cost in 10 years?

Solution: In this case, we can use \$6.50 as the initial value and the multiplier is 1.04, so the equation for the situation is $y = 6.50(1.04)^x$. The time we are interested in here is 10 years. Substituting into the equation, $y = 6.50(1.04)^{10} = \$9.62$.

Question 2: What did it cost 10 years ago?

Solution: Using the same equation, only using -10 for the years, $y = 6.50(1.04)^{-10} = \$4.39$.

Question 3: How long before lunch costs \$10?

Solution: Again, we use the same equation, but this time we know the y-value, but not the value of x. To solve for x, we use logarithms, as shown in the work at right.

$$\$10 = 6.50(1.04)^x$$
$$1.04^x = \tfrac{10}{6.5}$$
$$\log 1.04^x = \log\left(\tfrac{10}{6.5}\right)$$
$$x \log 1.04 = \log\left(\tfrac{10}{6.5}\right)$$
$$x = \frac{\log\left(\tfrac{10}{6.5}\right)}{\log 1.04} \approx 11$$

Answer: About 11 years.

Example 2: **Tickets for a big concert first went on sale three weeks ago for $60. This week people are charging $100. Write an equation that represents the cost of the tickets w weeks from the time that they went on sale. Assume that they continue to increase in the same way.**

Solution: To find the multiplier, we can use what we are given. The initial value is $60, the time is 3 weeks, and the final value is $100. This gives $100 = 60k^3$. Solving for k gives $k = \sqrt[3]{\frac{100}{60}} \approx 1.186$.

Answer: The equation is approximately $y = 60(1.186)^w$.

Now we can go back and solve parts (b), (c), and (d) of the original problem.

When rabbits were first brought to Australia, they had no natural enemies. There were about 80,000 rabbits in 1866. Two years later, in 1868, the population had grown to over 2,400,000!

b. Write an exponential equation for the number of rabbits t years after 1866.

Solution: For 1866, 80000 would be the initial value, time would be 2 years, and the final amount would be 2400000, which gives the equation $2400000 = 80000m^2$. Solving for m, we get $30 = m^2$ so $m = \sqrt{30} \approx 5.477$. Thus the equation is approximately $R = 80,000(5.477)^t$.

c. How many rabbits do you predict would have been present in 1871?

Solution: The initial value is still 80,000, the multiplier ≈ 5.477, and now the time is 5 years. This gives $80,000(5.477)^5 \approx 394$ million.

d. According to your model, in what year was the first pair of rabbits introduced into Australia?

Solution: In this situation, we use 2 as the initial value, 80000 as the final value, and the multiplier is still 5.477 but now the time is not known. Using these values, we get $80000 = 2(5.477)^x$, which is solved at right. The answer 6.23 tells us that approximately 6.23 years had passed between the time of the first pair of rabbits, and the time when there were 80000. Thus, rabbits would have been introduced sometime in 1859.

$80000 = 2(5.477)^x$

$40000 = (5.477)^x$

$\log(5.477)^x = \log 40000$

$x \log(5.477) = \log 40000$

$x = \frac{\log(40000)}{\log(5.477)} \approx 6.23$

Here are some more to try:

1. A DVD loses 60% of its value every year it is in the store. The DVD costs $80 new. Write a function that represents its value in *t* years. What is it worth after 4 years?

2. Inflation is at a rate of 7% per year. Evan's favorite bread now costs $1.79. What did it cost 10 years ago? How long before the cost of the bread doubles?

3. A bond that appreciates 4% per year will be worth $146 in five years. Find the current value.

4. Sixty years ago, when Sam's grandfather was a kid, he could buy his friend dinner for $1.50. If that same dinner now costs $25.25 and inflation was consistent, write an equation that models the cost for the dinner at different times.

5. A two-bedroom house in Omaha is now worth $110,000. If it appreciates at a rate of 2.5% per year, how long will it take to be worth $200,000?

6. A car valued at $14,000 depreciates 18% per year. After how many years will the value have depreciated to $1000?

Answers:

1. $y = 80(0.4)^t$, $2.05

2. $0.91, 10.2 years

3. $120

4. $y = 1.50(1.048)^x$

5. 24.2 years

6. 13.3 years

Checkpoint 9B

Problem 9-111

Finding the Equation for the Inverse of a Function

Answers to problem 9-111:

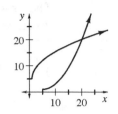

a. $f^{-1}(x) = \frac{1}{3}\left(\frac{x-5}{2}\right)^2 + 1 = \frac{1}{12}(x-5)^2 + 1$ for $x \ge 5$

b. See graph at right.

To find the equation for the inverse of a function, you can interchange the x and y variables and then solve for y. This also means that the coordinates of points that are on the graph of the function will be reversed on the graph of the inverse. Here are some examples:

Example 1: Write the equation for the inverse of $y = 2(x + 3)$.

Solution: We can interchange the x and the y to get the equation of the inverse. To get our final answer, we solve for y, as shown at right.

$$2(y + 3) = x$$
$$(y + 3) = \frac{x}{2}$$
$$y = \frac{x}{2} - 3$$

Answer: $y = \frac{x}{2} - 3$

Example 2: Write the equation for the inverse of $y = \frac{1}{2}(x + 4)^2 + 1$.

Solution: Again, we can interchange the x and the y to get the equation of the inverse and then solve for y to get our answer in $y =$ form, as shown at right.

$$x = \frac{1}{2}(y + 4)^2 + 1$$
$$\frac{1}{2}(y + 4)^2 = x - 1$$
$$(y + 4)^2 = 2x - 2$$
$$y + 4 = \pm\sqrt{2x - 2}$$
$$y = -4 \pm \sqrt{2x - 2}$$

Answer: $y = -4 \pm \sqrt{2x - 2}$. Note that because of the $\pm$, this inverse is not a function.

Example 3: Write the equation for the inverse of $y = -\frac{2}{3}x + 6$.

Solution: Interchanging the x and the y, we get $x = -\frac{2}{3}y + 6$. Solving for y gives
$y = -\frac{3}{2}(x - 6) = -\frac{3}{2}x + 9$.

Answer: $y = -\frac{3}{2}x + 9$

Example 4: Write the equation for the inverse of $y = \sqrt{x-2} + 3$.

Solution: Again, we exchange x and y and then solve for y, as shown at right.

$$x = \sqrt{y-2} + 3$$
$$\sqrt{y-2} = x-3$$
$$y - 2 = (x-3)^2$$
$$y = (x-3)^2 + 2$$

The original function is half of a sleeping parabola, so the inverse is only half of a parabola as well. Thus the domain of the inverse is restricted to $x \geq 3$.

Answer: $y = (x-3)^2 + 2$ in the domain $x \geq 3$.

Now we can go back and solve the original problem.

Find the equation for the inverse of the function $y = 2\sqrt{3(x-1)} + 5$. Then sketch the graph of both the original and the inverse.

Solution: Interchanging x and y we get $x = 2\sqrt{3(y-1)} + 5$. We then solve for y, as shown at right. This equation is simplified to get $y = \frac{(x-5)^2}{12} + 1$.

$$x = 2\sqrt{3(y-1)} + 5$$
$$2\sqrt{3(y-1)} = x - 5$$
$$\sqrt{3(y-1)} = \frac{x-5}{2}$$
$$3(y-1) = \left(\frac{x-5}{2}\right)^2$$
$$y - 1 = \frac{1}{3}\left(\frac{x-5}{2}\right)^2$$
$$y = \frac{1}{3}\left(\frac{x-5}{2}\right)^2 + 1$$

Note that the domain and range of the inverse are the interchanged domain and range of the original function. In other words, the original function has a domain of $x \geq 1$ and range of $y \geq 5$. The domain of the inverse, then, is $x \geq 5$ and the range is $y \geq 1$.

As you can see by the graph at right, the points on the inverse graph, have interchanged coordinates from the points on the graph of the original function. For example, two points on the original graph are $(1, 5)$ and $(4, 11)$. The corresponding points on the graph of the inverse are $(5, 1)$ and $(11, 4)$.

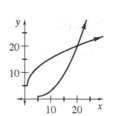

Answer: $y = \frac{(x-5)^2}{12} + 1$ in the domain $x \geq 5$.

Here are some more to try. Find an equation for the inverse of each function.

1. $y = 3x - 2$

2. $y = \frac{x+1}{4}$

3. $y = \frac{1}{3}x + 2$

4. $y = x^3 + 1$

5. $y = 1 + \sqrt{x+5}$

6. $y = 3(x+2)^2 - 7$

7. $y = 2\sqrt{x-1} + 3$

8. $y = \frac{1}{2+x}$

9. $y = \log_3(x+2)$

Answers:

1. $y = \frac{x+2}{3}$

2. $y = 4x - 1$

3. $y = 3x - 6$

4. $y = \sqrt[3]{x-1}$

5. $y = (x-1)^2 - 5$

6. $y = -2 \pm \sqrt{\frac{x+7}{3}}$

7. $y = \left(\frac{x-3}{2}\right)^2 + 1$

8. $y = \frac{1}{x} - 2$

9. $y = 3^x - 2$

Checkpoint 10

Problem 10-176

Rewriting Expressions with and Solving Equations with Logarithms

Answers to problem 10-176: a: $\log_2(5x)$, b: $\log_2(5x^2)$, c: 17, d: $-\frac{9}{20} = 0.45$, e: 15, f: 4

First a review of the properties based on the inverse relationship of exponentials and logarithms:

The following definitions and properties hold true for all positive $m \neq 1$.

Definition of logarithms: $\log_m(a) = n$ means $m^n = a$

Product Property: $\qquad\log_m(a \cdot b) = \log_m(a) + \log_m(b)$

Quotient Property: $\qquad\log_m(\frac{a}{b}) = \log_m(a) - \log_m(b)$

Power Property: $\qquad\log_m(a^n) = n \cdot \log_m(a)$

Inverse relationship: $\qquad\log_m(m)^n = n$ and $m^{\log_m(n)} = n$

Example 1: Write as a single logarithm: $3\log_5(x) + \log_5(x+1)$

Solution: $3\log_5(x) + \log_5(x+1) = \log_5(x^3) + \log_5(x+1)$ by the Power Property

$\qquad\qquad\qquad\qquad\quad = \log_5(x^3(x+1)) \qquad$ by the Product Property

$\qquad\qquad\qquad\qquad\quad = \log_5(x^4 + x^3) \qquad$ by simplifying

Example 2: Solve $\log_2(x) - \log_2(3) = 4$

Solution: $\log_2(x) - \log_2(3) = 4 \qquad$ problem

$\qquad\qquad\quad \log_2\left(\frac{x}{3}\right) = 4 \qquad$ by the Quotient Property

$\qquad\qquad\qquad\quad 2^4 = \frac{x}{3} \qquad$ by the definition of logarithms

$\qquad\qquad\qquad\quad 48 = x \qquad$ multiply both sides by 3

Now we can go back and solve the original problems.

a. $\log_2(30x) - \log_2(6)$

$\log_2(\frac{30x}{6}) = \log_2(5x)$

b. $2\log_3(x) + \log_3(5)$

$\log_3(x^2) + \log_3(5)$

$\log_3(x^2 \cdot 5) = \log_3(5x^2)$

c. $\log_7(3x - 2) = 2$

$7^2 = 3x - 2$

$49 = 3x - 2 \Rightarrow x = 17$

d. $\log(2x + 1) = -1$

$10^{-1} = 2x + 1$

$\frac{1}{10} = 2x + 1 \Rightarrow x = -\frac{9}{20} = 0.45$

e. $\log_5(3y) + \log_5(9) = \log_5(405)$

$\log_5(3y \cdot 9) = \log_5(405)$

$\log_5(27y) = \log_5(405)$

$27y = 405 \Rightarrow y = 15$

f. $\log(x) + \log(x + 21) = 2$

$\log(x^2 + 21x) = 2$

$x^2 + 21x = 10^2$

$x^2 + 21x - 100 = 0$

$(x + 25)(x - 4) = 0$

$x = -25, \ x = 4$

-25 is an extraneous solution so $x = 4$ only

Here are some more to try. In problems 1 through 8, write each expression as a single logarithm. In problems 9 through 26 solve each equation.

1. $\log_3(5) + \log_3(m)$

2. $\log_2(q) - \log_2(z)$

3. $\log_6(r) + 3\log_6(x)$

4. $\log(90) + \log(4) - \log(36)$

5. $\log_4(16x) - \log_4(x)$

6. $\log(\sqrt{x}) + \log(x^2)$

7. $\log_5(\sqrt{x}) + \log_5(\sqrt[3]{x})$

8. $\log_5(x - 1) + \log_5(x + 1)$

9. $\log_4(2x + 3) = \frac{1}{2}$

10. $\log_5(3x + 1) = 2$

11. $\log_9(9^2) = x$

12. $16^{\log_{16}(5)} = y$

13. $8^{\log_8(x)} = 3$

14. $\log_5(5^{0.3}) = y$

15. $\log_2(x) = 3\log_2(4) + \log_2(5)$

16. $\log_6(x) + \log_6(8) = \log_6(48)$

17. $\log_2(144) - \log_2(x) = \log_2(9)$

18. $\log_2(36) - \log_2(y) = \log_2(12)$

19. $\log_5(3x - 1) = -1$

20. $\log_2(x) - \log_2(3) = 4$

21. $\frac{1}{3}\log(3x + 1) = 2$

22. $\log_2(5) + \frac{1}{2}\log_2(x) = \log_2(15)$

23. $\frac{1}{2}\log(y) = 2\log(2) + \log(16)$

24. $\log_2(x^2 + 2x) = 3$

25. $2\log_4(x) - \log_4(3) = 2$

26. $\log_7(x + 1) + \log_7(x - 5) = 1$

Answers:

1. $\log_3(5m)$

2. $\log_2(\frac{q}{z})$

3. $\log_6(rx^3)$

4. $\log(10) = 1$

5. $\log_4(16) = 2$

6. $\log(x^{5/2})$

7. $\log_5(x^{5/6})$

8. $\log_5(x^2 - 1)$

9. $-\frac{1}{2}$

10. 8

11. 2

12. 5

13. 3

14. 0.3

15. 320

16. 6

17. 16

18. 3

19. $\frac{2}{5}$

20. 48

21. 333,333

22. 9

23. 4096

24. $-4, 2$

25. $\sqrt{48} = 4\sqrt{3}$

26. 6

Checkpoint 11

Problem 11-95

Solving Rational Equations

Answers to problem 11-95: a: $x = \pm 2\sqrt{3}$, b: $x = 2$, c: $x = \frac{2}{9}$, d: $x = \frac{-1 \pm \sqrt{13}}{6} \approx 0.434$ or -0.768

To solve rational equations (equations with fractions) it is usually best to first multiply everything by the common denominator to remove the fractions, a method known as **Fraction Busters**. After you have done this, you can solve the equation using your usual strategies. Following are a few examples.

Example 1: Solve $\frac{24}{x+1} = \frac{16}{1}$.

Solution: The common denominator in this case is $(x+1)$. Multiplying both sides of the equation by $(x+1)$ removes all fractions from the equation. You can then simplify and solve for x. This process is demonstrated at right.

$$(x+1)\left(\frac{24}{x+1}\right) = (x+1)\left(\frac{16}{1}\right)$$
$$24 = 16(x+1)$$
$$24 = 16x + 16$$
$$8 = 16x$$
$$x = \frac{1}{2}$$

Answer: $x = \frac{1}{2}$

Example 2: Solve $\frac{5}{2x} + \frac{1}{6} = 8$.

Solution: Again, we multiply both sides of the equation by the common denominator, which, in this case, is $6x$. We must be careful to remember to distribute so that we multiply each term on both sides of the equation by $6x$. Then we simplify and solve, as shown at right.

$$6x\left(\frac{5}{2x} + \frac{1}{6}\right) = 6x(8)$$
$$6x \cdot \frac{5}{2x} + 6x \cdot \frac{1}{6} = 48x$$
$$15 + x = 48x$$
$$15 = 47x$$
$$x = \frac{15}{47}$$

Answer: $x = \frac{15}{47}$

Now we can go back and solve the original problems.

a. $\frac{x}{3} = \frac{4}{x}$

$3x\left(\frac{x}{3}\right) = 3x\left(\frac{4}{x}\right)$

$x^2 = 12$

$x = \pm\sqrt{12} = \pm 2\sqrt{3}$

$x \approx \pm 3.46$

b. $\frac{x}{x-1} = \frac{4}{x}$

$x(x-1)\left(\frac{x}{x-1}\right) = x(x-1)\left(\frac{4}{x}\right)$

$x^2 = 4(x-1)$

$x^2 - 4x + 4 = 0$

$(x-2)(x-2) = 0$

$x = 2$

c. $\frac{1}{x} + \frac{1}{3x} = 6$

$3x\left(\frac{1}{x} + \frac{1}{3x}\right) = 3x(6)$

$3x\left(\frac{1}{x}\right) + 3x\left(\frac{1}{3x}\right) = 18x$

$3 + 1 = 18x$

$x = \frac{2}{9}$

d. $\frac{1}{x} + \frac{1}{x+1} = 3$

$x(x+1)\left(\frac{1}{x} + \frac{1}{x+1}\right) = x(x+1)(3)$

$x(x+1)\left(\frac{1}{x}\right) + x(x+1)\left(\frac{1}{x+1}\right) = x(x+1)(3)$

$x + 1 + x = 3x^2 + 3x$

$0 = 3x^2 + x - 1$

Using the Quadratic Formula,
$x \approx -0.434, -0.768$

Here are some more to try. Solve each of the following rational equations.

1. $\frac{3x}{5} = \frac{x-2}{4}$

2. $\frac{4x-1}{x} = 3x$

3. $\frac{2x}{5} - \frac{1}{3} = \frac{137}{3}$

4. $\frac{4x-1}{x+1} = x - 1$

5. $\frac{x}{3} = x + 4$

6. $\frac{x-1}{5} = \frac{3}{x+1}$

7. $\frac{x+6}{3} = x$

8. $\frac{2x+3}{6} + \frac{1}{2} = \frac{x}{2}$

9. $\frac{3}{x} + \frac{5}{x-7} = -2$

10. $\frac{2x+3}{4} - \frac{x-7}{6} = \frac{2x-3}{12}$

Answers:

1. $x = -\frac{10}{7}$

2. $x = \frac{1}{3}, 1$

3. $x = 115$

4. $x = 0, 4$

5. $x = -6$

6. $x = \pm 4$

7. $x = 3$

8. $x = 6$

9. $x = \frac{3 \pm \sqrt{51}}{2}$

10. $x = -13$

Glossary

3-dimensional coordinate system In three dimensions the z-axis is perpendicular to the x-y plane at $(0, 0)$. Points in 3-dimensions are represented with coordinates (x, y, z). The first octant where x,-y, and-z are positive is shown at right with the point $(2, 3, 1)$. (p. 257)

30°-60°-90 triangle A special right triangle with acute angle measures of 30° and 60°. The side lengths are always in the ratio of $1 : \sqrt{3} : 2$. (p. 320)

45°-45°-90 triangle A special right triangle with acute angle measures of 45°. The side lengths are always in the ratio of $1 : 1 : \sqrt{2}$. (p. 320)

absolute value The absolute value of a number is the distance of the number from zero. Since the absolute value represents a distance without regard to direction, it is always a positive real number. For example, $|-7| = 7$, and $|7| = 7$. The absolute value of a complex number is its distance from zero in the complex plane. For a complex number $a + bi$, $|a + bi| = \sqrt{a^2 + b^2}$. For example, $|3 - 2i| = \sqrt{3^2 + (-2)^2} = \sqrt{13}$. (p. 404)

algebraic strategies Using algebraic strategies means to write an algebraic representation of the problem and then to rewrite those expressions to get equivalent, but more useful results that lead to a solution for the problem or that reveal more information to help solve it.

amplitude The amplitude of a cyclic graph is one-half the distance between the highest and lowest points. In the graph at right, a is the amplitude. (p. 360)

angle An angle is formed by two rays joined at a common endpoint (the vertex). In geometric figures, angles are usually formed by two segments with a common endpoint.

angles of rotation. Angles with one vertex at the origin and formed by counter-clockwise rotation from the positive x-axis, are referred to as angles of rotation in standard position. For an angle θ, in standard position, the positive x-axis is the initial ray and the terminal ray may point in any direction. The measure of such an angle may have any real value. (p. 319)

Angle Sum and Difference Identities Trigonometric identities that involve angle sums or differences. They are: $\sin(x \pm y) = \sin(x)\cos(y) \pm \cos(x)\sin(y)$ and $\cos(x \pm y) = \cos(x)\cos(y) \mp \sin(x)\sin(y)$. (p. 649)

annual   Occurring once every year.

appreciation   An increase in value. (p. 742)

arccosine of x See *cosine inverse* ($\cos^{-1} x$).

arcsine of x See *sine inverse* ($\sin^{-1} x$).

arctangent of x See *tangent inverse* ($\tan^{-1} x$).

area   For a 2-dimensional region, the number of non-overlapping square units needed to cover the region.

area model   See *generic rectangle*. (p. 126)

argument   Used with sigma notation for sequences to describe the nth term. In the expression, $\sum_{k=1}^{10}(2k+1)$ the expression $2k+1$ is the argument. (p. 519)

arithmetic sequence   In an arithmetic sequence the difference between sequential terms is constant. Each term of an arithmetic sequence can be generated by adding the common difference to the previous term. For example in the sequence, $4, 7, 10, 13, \ldots$, the common difference is 3. (p. 692)

arithmetic series   An arithmetic series is the sum of the terms of an arithmetic sequence. Given the arithmetic sequence $3, 7, 11, \ldots, 43$, the corresponding arithmetic series is $3+7+11+\ldots+43$. (p. 510)

association   A relationship between two (or more) variables. An association between numerical variables can be displayed on a scatterplot, and described by its form, direction, strength, and outliers. Possible association between two categorical variables can be studied in a relative frequency table. Also see *scatterplot*.

asymptote   A line that a graph of a curve approaches as the x-values approach positive or negative infinity. An asymptote is often represented by a dashed line on a graph. For example, the graph at right has an asymptote at $y=-3$. (p. 37)

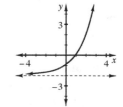

average   See *mean*.

average rate of change   The average rate of change of a function over an interval is the change in the value of the dependent quantity divided by the change in the independent quantity. It is the change in the y-value divided by the change in the x-value for two distinct points on the graph, which is the slope of the line through these two distinct points. (p. 137)

axes   In a coordinate plane, the two perpendicular number lines that intersect at the origin $(0, 0)$. The x-axis is horizontal and the y-axis is vertical. In 3-dimensions a third number line, the z-axis, is perpendicular to the x-y plane at the origin $(0, 0, 0)$. See *coordinate axes* and *3-dimensional coordinate system* for an illustration.

b   When the equation of a line is expressed in $y = mx + b$ form, the parameter b gives the y-intercept of the line. For example, the y-intercept of the line $y = -\frac{1}{3}x + 7$ is $(0, 7)$.

bar graph   A bar graph is a set of rectangular bars that have height proportional to the number of data elements in each category. Usually the bars are separated from each other. It is a way of displaying one-variable data that can be put into categories (like what color you prefer, your gender, or the state you were born in). Also see *histogram*.

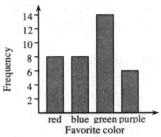

base   When working with an exponential expression in the form a^b, a is called the base. For example, 2 is the base in 2^5. (5 is the exponent, and 32 is the value.) Also see *exponent*.

best-fit line   See *line of best fit*.

bias   A systematic inaccuracy in data due to a process that favors certain outcomes. (p. 442)

biased wording   Words used in a survey question that intentionally or unintentionally influence results. (p. 443)

bin width   An interval, or the width of a bar, on a histogram. (p. 763)

binomial   An expression that is the sum or difference of exactly two terms, each of which is a monomial. For example, $-2x + 3y^2$ is a binomial. (p. 135)

The Binomial Theorem   The formula for the expansion of $(x + y)^n$ is called the Binomial Theorem. $(x + y)^n = {}_nC_n x^n + {}_nC_{n-1}x^{n-1}y + {}_nC_{n-2}x^{n-2}y^2 + ... + {}_nC_1 xy^{n-1} + {}_nC_0 y^n$
For example, $(x + y)^3 = {}_3C_3 x^3 + {}_3C_2 x^2 y + {}_3C_1 xy^2 + {}_3C_0 y^3 = 1x^3 + 3x^2 y + 3xy^2 + 1y^3$. (p. 544)

bound   The highest or lowest value that a statistical prediction is within. Also see *margin of error* and *boundary line*. (p. 589)

boundary line or curve   (1) A line or curve on a two-dimensional graph that divides the graph into two regions. A boundary line or curve is used when graphing inequalities with two variables. For example, the inequality $y < \frac{2}{3}x + 2$ is graphed at right. The dashed boundary line has equation $y = \frac{2}{3}x + 2$. A boundary line is also sometimes called a "dividing line." (2) A line drawn parallel to and above or below the least squares regression line at a distance equivalent to the largest residual. The line determines the upper or lower limit on the values that a prediction is likely to be. (p. 197)

boundary point   The endpoint of a ray or segment on a number line where an inequality is true. For strict inequalities (that is, inequalities involving < or >), the point is not part of the solution. We find boundary points by solving the equality associated with our inequality. For example, the solution to the equation $2x + 5 = 11$ is $x = 3$, so the inequality $2x + 5 \geq 11$ has a boundary point at 3. The solution to that inequality is illustrated on the number line at right. A boundary point is also sometimes called a "dividing point." (p. 186)

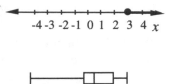

boxplot   A graphic way of displaying the five number summary of a distribution of data: minimum, first quartile, median, third quartile, and maximum. A **modified boxplot** displays outliers separately from the boxplot. Also see *five number summary*. (p. 757)

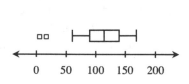

census   The process of measuring every member of the population. (p. 445)

center (of a data distribution)   A number that represents the middle of a data set, or that represents a "typical" value of the set. Two ways to measure the center of a data set are the mean and the median. When dealing with measures of center, it is often useful to consider the distribution of the data. For symmetric distributions with no outliers, the mean or median can represent the middle, or "typical" value, of the data well. However, in the presence of outliers or non-symmetrical data distributions, the median may be a better measure. Also see *mean* and *median*. (p. 764)

circle   In a plane, the set of all points equidistant from a single point. The general equation of a circle is $(x - h)^2 + (y - k)^2 = r^2$ where the point (h, k) is the center of the circle of radius r.

circle graph   A way of displaying data that can be put into categories (like what color you prefer, your gender, or the state you were born in). A circle graph shows the proportion each category is of the whole.

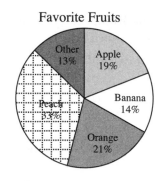

Favorite Fruits

circular functions   The periodic functions based on the unit circle, including $y = \sin x$, $y = \cos x$, and $y = \tan x$. See *sine function*, *cosine function*, and *tangent function*.

closed question   A question that limits respondents to some set number of responses from which to choose. (p. 444)

closed set   A set of numbers is said to be closed under an operation if the result of applying the operation to any two numbers in the set produces a number in the set. For example, the whole numbers are a closed set under addition, because if you add any two whole numbers the result is always a whole number. However, the whole numbers are not closed under division: if you divide any two whole numbers you do not always get a whole number. (p. 139)

closure properties   A closure properties states that a particular set of numbers is a closed set under a specific operation. For example, the closure property of rational numbers states that the product or sum of two rational numbers is a rational number. For example, $\frac{1}{2}$ and $\frac{3}{4}$ are both rational numbers; $\frac{1}{2} + \frac{3}{4}$ is $\frac{5}{4}$; and $\frac{5}{4}$ is a rational number. Also, 2.2 and 0.75 are both rational numbers; $2.2 \cdot 0.75$ is 1.65; and 1.65 is a rational number.

coefficient   When variable(s) are multiplied by a number, the number is called a coefficient of that term. The numbers that are multiplied by the variables in the terms of a polynomial are called the coefficients of the polynomial. For example, 3 is the coefficient of $3x^2$. (p. 135)

cofunction   A trigonometric function whose value for the complement of an angle is equal to the value of a given trigonometric function of the angle itself. For example, the cofunction of sine is cosine and the cofunction of tangent is cotangent. (p. 651)

cofunction identities   Trigonometric identities that relate sine and cosine, tangent and cotangent, and secant and cosecant. The value of a trigonometric function of an angle equals the value of the co-function of the complement of the angle. (p. 651)

coincide   Two graphs coincide if they have all their points in common. For example, the graphs of $y = 2x + 4$ and $3y = 6x + 12$ coincide; both graphs are lines with a slope of 2 and a y-intercept of 4. When the graphs of two equations coincide, those equations share all the same solutions and have an infinite number of intersection points.

combination   A combination is the number of ways we can select items from a larger set without regard to order. For instance, choosing a committee of 3 students from a group of 5 volunteers is a combination since the order in which committee members are selected does not matter. We write $_nC_r$ to represent the number of combinations of n things taken r at a time (or n choose r). For instance, the number of ways to select a committee of 3 students from a group of 5 is $_5C_3$. You can use Pascal's Triangle to find $_5C_3$ or use permutations and divided by the number of arrangements $\frac{_5P_3}{_3P_3} = \frac{5!}{3!2!}$. Formulas for combinations include: $_nC_r = \frac{_nP_r}{r!} = \frac{n!}{r!(n-r)!}$. (p. 503)

combination histogram and box plot   A way to visually represent a distribution of data. The box plot is drawn with the same x-axis as the histogram.

common difference   The difference between consecutive terms of an arithmetic sequence or the *generator* of the sequence. When the common difference is positive the sequence increases; when it is negative the sequence decreases. In the sequence $3, 7, 11, ..., 43$, the common difference is 4. (p. 692)

common factor   A common factor is a factor that is the same for two or more terms. For example, x^2 is a common factor of $3x^2$ and $-5x^2y$.

common logarithm   The logarithm with base 10. If no base is given, the logarithm is understood to be base 10. (p. 239)

common ratio   Common ratio is another name for the multiplier or *generator* of a geometric sequence. It is the number to multiply one term by to get the next one. In the sequence: $96, 48, 24, ...$ the common ratio is $\frac{1}{2}$. (p. 537)

complete graph   A complete graph is one that includes everything that is important about the graph (such as intercepts and other key points, asymptotes, or limitations on the domain or range), and that makes the rest of the graph predictable based on what is shown. For example, a complete graph of the equation $y = \frac{1}{3}(x-2)^2(x+3)$ is shown at right. (p. 9)

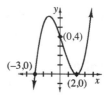

completing the square   A standard procedure for rewriting a quadratic equation from standard form to graphing (or vertex) form is called completing the square. Completing the square is also used to solve quadratic equations in one variable. For example, the expression $x^2 - 6x + 4$ starts with the first two terms of $(x-3)^2$. To "complete the square" we need to add 9 to $x^2 - 6x$. Since the original expression only adds 4, completing the square would increase the expression by 5, so $(x-3)^2 - 5$ is an equivalent form that is useful for solving or graphing. (p. 75)

complex conjugates   The complex number $a + bi$ has a complex conjugate $a - bi$. Similarly, the conjugate of $c - di$ is $c + di$. What is noteworthy about complex numbers conjugates is that both their product $(a+bi)(a-bi) = a^2 - b^2i^2 = a^2 + b^2$ and their sum $(a+bi) + (a-bi) = 2a$ are real numbers. If a complex number is a zero (or root) of a real polynomial function, then its complex conjugate is also a zero (or root). (p. 396)

complex numbers   Numbers written in the form $a + bi$ where a and b are real numbers, are called complex numbers. Each complex number has a real part, a, and an imaginary part, bi. Note that real numbers are also complex numbers with $b = 0$, and imaginary numbers are complex numbers where $a = 0$. (p. 392)

complex plane   A set of coordinate axes with all the real numbers on the horizontal axis (the real axis) and all the imaginary numbers on the vertical axis (the imaginary axis) defines the complex plane. Complex numbers are graphed in the complex plane using the same method we use to graph coordinate points. Thus, the complex number $1 + 3i$ is located at the point $(1, 3)$ in the complex plane. (p. 404)

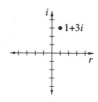

838

composite function A function that is created as the result of using the outputs of one function as the inputs of another can be seen as a composite function. For example the function $h(x) = |\log x|$ can be seen as the composite function $f(g(x))$ where $f(x) = |x|$ and $g(x) = \log x$. See *composition*. (p. 225)

composition When the output of one function is used as the input for a second function, a new function is created which is a composition of the two original functions. If the first function is $g(x)$ and the second is $f(x)$, the composition can be written as $f(g(x))$ or $f \circ g(x)$. Note that the order in which we perform the composition matters, and $g(f(x))$ will usually be a different function.

compound interest Interest that is paid on both the principal and the previously accrued interest. (p. 550)

compress A term used informally to describe the relationship of a graph to its parent graph when the graph increases or decreases more slowly than the parent. For example, the solid parabola shown at right is a compressed version of its parent, shown as a dashed curve. (p. 66)

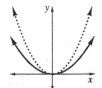

conjugate Every complex number $a + bi$ has a conjugate, $a - bi$, and both the sum and product of the conjugates are real. Similarly, an irrational number that can be written $a + \sqrt{b}$ where a and b are rational, has a conjugate, $a - \sqrt{b}$, and the product and sum of these conjugates are rational. (p. 396)

constant term A number that is not multiplied by a variable. In the expression $2x + 3(5 - 2x) + 8$, the number 8 is a constant term. The number 3 is not a constant term, because it is multiplied by a variable inside the parentheses. (p. 135)

constraint A limitation or restriction placed on a function or situation, either by the context of the situation or by the nature of the function.

continuous For this course, when the points on a graph are connected and it makes sense to connect them, we say the graph is continuous. Such a graph will have no holes or breaks in it. This term will be more completely defined in a later course. (p. 668)

continuously compounding interest For this course, continuously compounding interest can be thought of as interest that is computed and added to the balance of an account every instant.

control limit The upper and lower limits of a critical measurement that determines acceptable quality in a manufacturing process. See *statistical process control*. (p. 599)

convenience sampling A subgroup of the population for which it was easy to collect data. A convenience sample is not a random sample. (p. 456)

coordinate axes For two dimensions, two perpendicular number lines, the x- and y-axes, that intersect where both are zero and that provide the scale(s) for labeling each point in a plane with its horizontal and vertical distance and direction from the origin $(0, 0)$. In three dimensions, a third number line, the z-axis, is perpendicular to a plane and intersects it at origin $(0, 0, 0)$. The z-axis provides the scale for the height of a point above or below the plane. See *3-dimensional coordinate system*.

coordinates The numbers in an ordered pair (a, b) or triple (a, b, c) used to locate a point in the plane or in space in relation to a set of coordinate axes.

correlation coefficient, r A measure of how much or how little data is scattered around the least squares regression line. It is a measure of the strength of an association that has already been determined to be linear. The correlation coefficient takes on values between -1 and 1. The closer to 1 or -1 the correlation coefficient is, the less scattered the data is around the LSRL.

cosecant The cosecant is the reciprocal of the sine. (p. 651)

cosine In a right triangle (as shown at right) the ratio $\frac{\text{adjacent side}}{\text{hypotenuse}}$ is known as the cosine of the acute angle. At right, $\cos B = \frac{a}{c}$ since the side length a is adjacent to angle B. On a unit circle the cosine of an angle is the x-coordinate of the point the where the terminal ray of an angle in standard position intersects the unit circle. (p. 327)

cosine function The cosine of angle θ, denoted $\cos\theta$, is the x-coordinate of the point on the unit circle reached by a rotation angle of θ radians in standard position. The general equation for the cosine function is $y = a\cos b(x - h) + k$. This function has amplitude a, period $\frac{2\pi}{b}$, horizontal shift h, and vertical shift k. (p. 327)

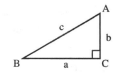

cosine inverse ($\cos^{-1} x$) Read as the inverse of cosine x, $\cos^{-1} x$ is the measure of the angle with cosine x. We can also write $y = \arccos x$. Note that the notation refers to the inverse of the cosine function, *not* $\frac{1}{\cos x}$. Because $y = \cos^{-1} x$ is equivalent to $x = \cos y$ and there are infinitely many angles y such that $\cos y = x$, the inverse *function* is restricted to select the *principal* value of y such that $0 \le y \le \pi$. The graph of the inverse cosine function is at right. (p. 636)

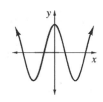

cotangent The cotangent is the reciprocal of the tangent. The graph of the cotangent function is at right. (p. 651)

counterexample An example showing that a statement has at least one exception; that is, a situation in which the statement is false. For example, the number 4 is a counterexample to the hypothesis that all even numbers are greater than 7. (p. 283)

cubic   A cubic polynomial is a polynomial of the form $y = ax^3 + bx^2 + cx + d$. "Cube" refers to the third (3) power.

cube root   In the equation $a = b^3$, the value b that is multiplied by itself three times to give the value a. For example, the cube root of 8 is 2 because $8 = 2 \cdot 2 \cdot 2 = 2^3$. This is written $\sqrt[3]{8} = 2$.

cycle   One cycle of a graph of a trigonometric function is the shortest piece that represents all possible outputs. The length of one cycle is the distance along the x-axis needed to generate all possible output values or the distance around the unit circle needed to generate all possible outcomes.

cyclic function   The term cyclic function is sometimes used to describe trigonometric functions, but it also includes any function that sequentially repeats its outputs at regular intervals. (p. 349)

data distribution   See *distribution*.

degree   One degree is an angle measure that is $\frac{1}{360}$ of a full circle or $\frac{\pi}{180}$ radians. (p. 333)

degree of a polynomial   The degree of a monomial is the sum of the exponents of its variables. For example, the degree of $3x^2 y^5 z$ is 8. For a polynomial the degree is the degree of the monomial term with the highest degree. Example: for the polynomial $2x^5 y^2 - 4x^4 z^6 + x^7 z$ the degree is 10. (p. 374)

degree of a polynomial in one variable   The highest power of the variable. The degree of a polynomial function also indicates the maximum number of factors of the polynomial and provides information for predicting the number of "turns" the graph can take. (p. 374)

dependent variable   When one quantity depends for its value on one or more others, it is called the dependent variable. For example, we might relate the speed of a car to the amount of force you apply to the gas pedal. Here, the speed of the car is the dependent variable; it depends on how hard you push the pedal. The dependent variable appears as the output value in an $x \rightarrow y$ table, and is usually placed relative to the vertical axis of a graph. We often use the letter y and the vertical y-axis for the dependent variable. When working with functions or relations, the dependent variable represents the output value. In Statistics, the dependent variable is often called the response variable. Also see *independent variable*. (p. 6)

depreciation   A decrease in value possibly because of normal wear and tear, age, decay, decrease in price. (p. 742)

description of a function   A complete description of a function includes: a description of the shape of the graph, where it increasing and/or decreases, all the intercepts, domain and range, description of special points, and description of lines of symmetry.

difference of squares A polynomial that can be factored as the product of the sum and difference of two terms. The general pattern is $x^2 - y^2 = (x+y)(x-y)$. For example, the difference of squares $4x^2 - 9$ can be factored as $(2x+3)(2x-3)$. (p. 128)

difference of cubes A polynomial of the form $x^3 \pm y^3$. It can be factored as follows: $x^3 \pm y^3 = (x \pm y)(x^2 \mp xy + y^2)$. For example, the difference of cubes $8x^3 - 27$ can be factored as $(2x-3)(4x^2+6x+9)$. (p. 427)

dilation A transformation which vertically compresses or stretches the graph of a function. For example, the graph of $g(x) = 2(x^2 + 3x - 5)$ is a dilation of the function $f(x) = x^2 + 3x - 5$ by a factor of 2.

dimensions The dimensions of a flat region or space tell how far it extends in each direction. For example, the dimensions of a rectangle might be 16 cm wide by 7 cm high.

direction (of an association) If one variable in a relationship increases as the other variable increases, the direction is said to be a positive association. If one variable decreases as the other variable increases, there is said to be a negative association. If there is no apparent pattern in the scatterplot, then the variables have no association. When describing a linear association, you can use the slope, and its numerical interpretation in context, to describe the direction of the association.

discrete graph A graph that consists entirely of separated points is called a discrete graph. For example, the graph shown at right is discrete. Also see *continuous*. (p. 668)

discriminant For quadratic equations in standard form $ax^2 + bx + c = 0$, the discriminant is $b^2 - 4ac$. If the discriminant is positive, the equation has two roots; if the discriminant is zero, the equation has one root; if the discriminant is negative, the equation has no real-number roots. For example, the discriminant

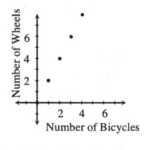

of the quadratic equation $2x^2 - 4x - 5$ is $(-4)^2 - 4(2)(-5) = 56$, which indicates that that equation has two roots (solutions). (p. 396)

distance formula An application of the Pythagorean Theorem to find the distance between two points in a plane. The <u>distance between any</u> two points (x_1, y_1) and (x_2, y_2) is $\sqrt{(x_2 - x_1)^2 + (y_2 - y_1)^2}$. In the example at right the distance is $\sqrt{4^2 + 5^2}$. (p. 76)

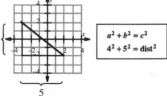

distribution The statistical distribution of a variable is a description (usually a list, table, or graph) of the number of times each possible outcome occurs. A distribution of data is often summarized using its center, shape, spread, and outliers, and can be displayed with a combination histogram and boxplot. (p. 765)

Distributive Property We use the Distributive Property to write a product of expressions as a sum of terms. The Distributive Property states that for any numbers or expressions a, b, and c, $a(b+c)=ab+ac$. For example, $2(x+4)=2\cdot x+2\cdot 4=2x+8$. We can demonstrate this with a generic rectangle.

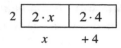

dividing line See *boundary line*.

dividing point See *boundary point*.

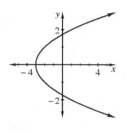

domain The set of all input values for a relation or function. For example, the domain of the function graphed at right is $x\geq-3$. For variables, the domain is the set of numbers the variable may represent. Also see *input*. (p. 6)

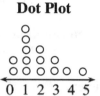

Dot Plot

dot plot A way of displaying one-variable data that has an order and can be placed on a number line. Dot plots are generally used when the data is discrete (separate and distinct) and numerous pieces of data are of equal value.

Double Angle Identities Trigonometric identities that involve doubling angle measures. They are: $\sin(2x)=2\sin(x)\cos(x)$ and $\cos(2x)=\cos^2(x)-\sin^2(x)$. (p. 651)

double-peaked See *shape (of a data display)*. (p. 765)

double root A root of a function that occurs exactly twice. If an expression of the form $(x-a)^2$ is a factor of a polynomial, then the polynomial has a double root at $x=a$. The graph of the polynomial does not pass through the x-axis at $x=a$ but is tangent to the axis at $x=a$. (p. 380)

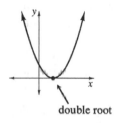

double root

e In mathematics, the base of a natural logarithm. $e\approx 2.71828...$ (p. 548)

Elimination Method A method for solving a system of equations. The key step in using the Elimination Method is to add or subtract both sides of two equations to eliminate one of the variables. For example, the two
$$5x+2y=10$$
$$2x-2y=4$$
equations in the system at right can be added together to get the simplified result $7x=14$. We can solve this equation to find x, then substitute the x-value back into either of the original equations to find the value of y.

Equal Values Method A method for solving a system of equations. To use the equal values method, take two expressions that are each equal to the same variable and set those expressions equal to each other. For
$$y=-2x+5$$
$$y=x-1$$
example, in the system of equations at right, $-2x+5$ and $x-1$ each equal y. So we write $-2x+5=x-1$, then solve that equation to find x. Once we have x, we substitute that value back into either of the original equations to find the value of y.

equation   A mathematical sentence in which two expressions appear on either side of an "equals" sign (=), stating that the two expressions are equivalent. For example, the equation $7x + 4.2 = -8$ states that the expression $7x + 4.2$ has the value -8. In this course, an equation is often used to represent a rule relating two quantities. For example, a rule for finding the area y of a tile pattern with figure number x might be written $y = 4x - 3$.

equivalent   Two expressions are equivalent if they have the same value. For example, $2 + 3$ is equivalent to $1 + 4$. Two equations are equivalent if they have all the same solutions. For example, $y = 3x$ is equivalent to $2y = 6x$. Equivalent equations have the same graph. (pp. 123, 133)

evaluate   To evaluate an expression, substitute the value(s) given for the variable(s) and perform the operations according to the order of operations. For example, evaluating $2x + y - 10$ when $x = 4$ and $y = 3$ gives the value 1.

even function   A function where $f(-x) = f(x)$ for all values of x defined for the function. The graph of the function will be symmetric about the y-axis. (p. 108)

event   One or more results of an experiment.

excluded value   A value that is undefined for a given function and therefore excluded from the domain of the function. (p. 152)

expected value   The expected value for an outcome is the product of the probability of the outcome and the value placed on that outcome. The expected value of an event is the sum of the expected values for its possible outcomes. For example, in a lottery where 7 numbers are drawn from 77 and you have to have chosen all seven to win, the probability that your ticket is the $1,000,000 winner is $\frac{1}{2404808340}$ and the expected value is $0.000416.

experiment   A process that applies a treatment (change) to a group of subjects to determine if there is a measureable difference from another group. If an experiment properly implements randomization, controls (balances) the effects of lurking variables between the groups, and is replicated with many subjects, cause and effect can often be determined. (p. 461)

explicit equation (for a sequence)   An equation for a term in a sequence that determines the value of any term $t(n)$ directly from n, without necessarily knowing any other terms in the sequence. Also see *recursive equation*. (p. 683)

exponent   In an expression of the form a^b, b is called the exponent. For example, in the expression 2^5, 5 is called the exponent. (2 is the base, and 32 is the value.) The exponent indicates how many times to use the base as a multiplier. For example, in 2^5, 2 is used 5 times: $2^5 = 2 \cdot 2 \cdot 2 \cdot 2 \cdot 2 = 32$. For exponents of zero, the rule is: for any number $x \neq 0$, $x^0 = 1$. For negative exponents, the rule is: for any number $x \neq 0$, $x^{-n} = \frac{1}{x^n}$, and $\frac{1}{x^{-n}} = x^n$. Also see *laws of exponents*. (pp. 724, 740)

exponential function   An exponential function in this course has an equation of the form $y = ab^x + c$, where a is the initial value, b is positive and is the multiplier, and $y = c$ is the equation of the horizontal asymptote. An example of an exponential function is graphed at right. (p. 57)

expression   An expression is a combination of individual terms separated by plus or minus signs. Numerical expressions combine numbers and operation symbols; algebraic (variable) expressions include variables. For example, $4 + (5 - 3)$ is a numerical expression. In an algebraic expression, if each of the following terms, $6xy^2$, 24, and $\frac{y-3}{4+x}$, are combined, the result may be $6xy^2 + 24 - \frac{y-3}{4+x}$. An expression does not have an "equals" sign. (p. 135)

extraneous solution   Sometimes in the process of solving equations, multiplying or squaring expressions involving a variable will lead to a numerical result that does not make the original equation true. This false result is called an extraneous solution. For example, in the process of solving the equation $\sqrt{x+3} = 9 - x$ both sides of the equation are squared to get $x + 3 = x^2 - 19x + 81$ which has solutions 6 and 13. 6 is a solution of the original equation, but 13 is extraneous, because $\sqrt{13+3} \neq 9 - 13$. (p. 173)

extrapolate   A prediction made outside the range of the observed data. Often extrapolations are not very reliable predictions.

$f^{-1}(x)$ Read this as "f inverse of x," the inverse function for $f(x)$. (p. 219)

factor   A factor is part of a product. A polynomial expression $p(x)$ is a factor of another polynomial expression $P(x)$ when there is a polynomial $q(x)$ such that $p(x)q(x) = P(x)$. In the equation $3x^2 - 9x + 6 = 3(x - 2)(x - 1)$, the expressions $(x - 2)$, $(x - 1)$, and 3 are factors.

Factor Theorem   States that if a is a root of a polynomial then $x - a$ is a factor, and if $x - a$ is a factor then a is a root. For example, the polynomial $x^2 - 5x - 6 = (x - 6)(x + 1)$ and the roots are 6 and –1. (p. 418)

factored completely   A polynomial is factored completely if none of the resulting factors can be factored further using integer coefficients. For example, $-2(x + 3)(x - 1)$ is the completely factored form of $-2x^2 - 4x + 6$. (p. 371)

factored form   A quadratic equation in the form $a(x + b)(x + c) = 0$, where a is nonzero, is said to be in factored form. For example, $-7(x + 2)(x - 1.5) = 0$ is a quadratic equation in factored form. (p. 371)

factorial   A shorthand notation for the product of a list of consecutive positive integers from the given number down to 1: $n! = n(n - 1)(n - 2)(n - 3) \cdot \ldots \cdot 3 \cdot 2 \cdot 1$. For example, $5! = 5 \cdot 4 \cdot 3 \cdot 2 \cdot 1 = 120$. (p. 648)

family of functions A group of functions that have at least one common characteristic, usually the shape and the form of the equation. For example the quadratic family of functions have graphs that are parabolas, and equations of the form $y = ax^2 + bx + c$. Examples of other families are linear functions, exponential functions, and absolute value functions. (p. 98)

Fibonacci Sequence The sequence of numbers $1, 1, 2, 3, 5, 8, 13, \ldots$. Each term of the Fibonacci sequence (after the first two terms) is the sum of the two preceding terms. (p. 684)

first quartile (Q1) The median of the lower half of a set of data which has been written in numerical order. (p. 757)

first term form (of a sequence) An equation of a sequence written in first term form uses the first term of the sequence and its common difference or ratio. The first term form of an arithmetic sequence is $a_n = a_1 + d(n-1)$, where a_1 is the first term and d is the common difference. The first term form of a geometric sequence is $a_n = a_1 r^{n-1}$, where a_1 is the first term and r is the common ratio. (p. 744)

five number summary A way of summarizing the center and spread of a one-variable distribution of data. The five number summary includes the minimum, first quartile, median, third quartile, and maximum of the set of data. Also see *boxplot*. (p. 757)

form (of an association) The form of an association can be linear of non-linear. The form can contain cluster of data. A residual plot can help determine if a particular form is appropriate for modeling the relationship.

fraction The quotient of two quantities in the form $\frac{a}{b}$ where b is not equal to 0. (p. 142)

fractional exponents Raising a number to a fractional exponent indicates a power as well as a root. $x^{a/b} = \sqrt[b]{x^a} = (\sqrt[b]{x})^a$. (p. 740)

function A relationship in which for each input value there is one and only one output value. For example, the relationship $f(x) = x + 4$ is a function; for each input value (x) there is exactly one output value. In terms of ordered pairs (x, y), no two ordered pairs of a function have the same first member (x). See also *description of a function* and *function notation*. (p. 6)

function notation When a rule expressing a function is written using function notation, the function is given a name, most commonly "*f*," "*g*," or "*h*." The notation $f(x)$ represents the output of a function, named f, when x is the input. It is pronounced "*f* of *x*." For example, $g(2)$, pronounced "*g* of 2", represents the output of the function g when $x = 2$. If $g(x) = x^2 + 3$, then $g(2) = 7$. (p. 6)

Fundamental Theorem of Algebra   The Fundamental Theorem of Algebra states that a polynomial of degree n with (real or) complex coefficients has exactly n roots, which may be real or complex. This also means that the polynomial has n linear factors since for every root a, $(x - a)$ is a linear factor.   (p. 418)

general equation   If $y = f(x)$ is a parent equation, then the general equation for that function is given by $y = af(x - h) + k$ where (h, k) is the point corresponding to $(0, 0)$ in the parent graph and, relative to the parent graph, the function has been: 1) vertically stretched if the absolute value of a is greater than 1; 2) vertically compressed if the absolute value of a is less than 1; and/or 3) reflected across the x-axis if a is less than 0.   (p. 98)

generator   The generator of a sequence tells what you do to each term to get the next term. Note that this is different from the function for the nth term of the sequence. The generator only tells you how to find the following term, when you already know one term. In an arithmetic sequence the generator is the common difference; in a geometric sequence it is the multiplier or common ratio.   (p. 692)

generic rectangle   A type of diagram used to visualize multiplying expressions without algebra tiles. Each expression to be multiplied forms a side length of the rectangle, and the product is the sum of the areas of the sections of the rectangle. For example, the generic rectangle at right can be used to multiply $(2x + 5)$ by $(x + 3)$.

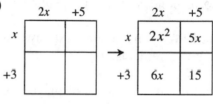

$$(2x + 5)(x + 3) = 2x^2 + 11x + 15$$

area as a product   area as a sum

geometric sequence   A geometric sequence is a sequence that is generated by a multiplier. This means that each term of a geometric sequence can be found by multiplying the previous term by a constant. For example: $5, 15, 45\ldots$ is the beginning of a geometric sequence with generator (common ratio) 3. In general a geometric sequence can be represented $a, ar, ar^2, \ldots + ar^{n-1}$.   (p. 537)

geometric series   The sum of a geometric sequence is a geometric series, for example: $5 + 15 + 45 + \ldots$ The sum of the first n terms of a geometric sequence, $a + ar + ar^2 + ar^3 + \ldots + ar^{n-1}$ is given by the formula at right.   (p. 510) $S = \dfrac{a(r^n - 1)}{r - 1}$

Giant One   A fraction that is equal to 1. Multiplying any fraction by a Giant One will create a new fraction equivalent to the original fraction.   (p. 152)

$$\frac{x+2}{x-3} \cdot \frac{x-2}{x-2} = \frac{(x+2)^2}{(x-3)(x-2)}$$

graph   The graph of an equation is the set of points representing the coordinates that make the equation true. The direction to "graph an equation" or "draw a graph" means use graph paper, scale your axes appropriately, label key points, and plot points accurately. This is different from *sketching* a graph. The equation $y = \frac{1}{3}(x - 2)^2(x + 3)$ is graphed at right.   (p. 9)

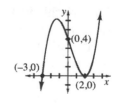

graphing form A form of the equation of a function or relation that clearly shows key information about the graph. For example, the graphing form for the general equation of a quadratic function (also called vertex form) is $y = a(x - h)^2 + k$. The vertex (h, k), orientation (whether a is positive or negative) and amount of stretch or compression based on $|a| > 1$ or $|a| < 1$ can be appear in the equation. (p. 68)

growth factor One way to analyze how the output value in a mathematical relation changes as the input value increases. Growth can be represented by constant addition, as the slope of a linear function or the constant difference in an arithmetic sequence, or by multiplication as the base of an exponential function or the multiplier in a geometric sequence. (p. 10)

(h, k) In this course h and k are used as parameters in general equations for families of functions $f(x) = af(x - h) + k$ and families of relations to represent the horizontal and vertical shifts of the parent graph. The point (h, k) represents location of a point that corresponds to $(0, 0)$ for parent graphs where $(0, 0)$ is on the graph.

half-life When material decays, the half-life is the time it takes until only half the material remains. (p. 723)

histogram A way of displaying one-variable data that is like a bar graph in that the height of the bars is proportional to the number of elements. However, a histogram is for numerical data. Each bin (bar) of a histogram represents the number of data elements in a range of values, such as the number of people who take from 15 minutes up to, but not including, 30 minutes to get to school. Each bin should the same width and the bins should touch each other. Also see *bar graph*. (p. 763)

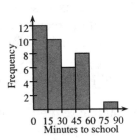

horizontal Parallel to the horizon. The x-axis of a coordinate graph is the horizontal axis.

horizontal lines Horizontal lines are "flat" and run left to right in the same direction as the x-axis. Horizontal lines have equations of the form $y = b$, where b can be any number. For example, the graph at right shows the horizontal line $y = 3$. The slope of any horizontal line is 0. The x-axis has the equation $y = 0$ because $y = 0$ everywhere on the x-axis.

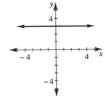

horizontal shift Used with parent graphs and general equations for functions and relations such as $y = a(x - h)^2 + k$. This type of transformation is a horizontal translation of a graph that moved left or right in relation to its parent graph. The horizontal shift will be h units to the right if h is positive, to the left if h is negative. (p. 66)

hypotenuse The longest side of a right triangle, the side opposite the right angle.

identity (trigonometric)   Equations that are true for all values for which the functions are defined. For example $\sin^2 x + \cos^2 x = 1$ which is true for all values of x, or $\cot x = \frac{1}{\tan x}$ which is true whenever the tangent and cotangent are defined.

imaginary numbers   The set of numbers that are solutions of equations of the form $x^2 = $ (a negative number) are called imaginary numbers. They are not positive, negative, or zero. The imaginary number i is a solution of the equation $x^2 = -1$, so $i^2 = -1$. In general, imaginary numbers follow the rules of real number arithmetic (e.g. $i + i = 2i$). Multiplying the imaginary number i by every possible real number yields all possible imaginary numbers. (p. 392)

independent variable   When one quantity changes in a way that does not depend on the value of another quantity, the value that changes independently is represented with the independent variable. For example, we might relate the speed of a car to the amount of force you apply to the gas pedal. Here, the amount of force applied may be whatever the driver chooses, so it represents the independent variable. The independent variable appears as the input value in an $x \rightarrow y$ table, and is usually placed relative to the horizontal axis of a graph. We often use the letter x and the horizontal x-axis for the independent variable. When working with functions or relations, the independent variable represents the input value. In Statistics, the independent variable is often called the explanatory variable. Also see *dependent variable*. (p. 6)

index (plural indices)   In summation notation, the indices are the numbers below and above the sigma that indicate which term to start with and which to end with. For a series they show the first and last replacement values for n. When the symbol above sigma is ∞ the series continues without ending. (p. 519)

Example: $\sum\limits_{n=1}^{8} 5n - 7 = -2 + 3 + 8 + ... + 33$.

inequality   An inequality consists of two expressions on either side of an inequality symbol. For example, the inequality $7x + 4.2 < -8$ states that the expression $7x + 4.2$ has a value less than 8. (p. 197)

inequality symbols   The symbol $\leq$ read from left to right means "less than or equal to." The symbol $\geq$ read from left to right means "greater than or equal to." The symbols $<$ and $>$ mean "less than" and "greater than," respectively. For example, "$7 < 13$" means that 7 is less than 13.

inequalities with absolute value   If k is any positive number, an inequality of the form: $|f(x)| > k$ is equivalent to the statement $f(x) > k$ or $f(x) < -k$; and $|f(x)| < k$ is equivalent to the statement $-k < f(x) < k$. For example, you can solve the inequality, $|5x - 6| > 4$ by solving the two inequalities $5x - 6 > 4$ or $5x - 6 < -4$. (p. 193)

inference   A statistical prediction.

infinite geometric series   An infinite geometric series is a geometric series which never ends. The sum of such a series with an initial value a and common ratio r, with $-1 < r < 1$, is given by the formula at right. (p. 537)

$$S = \frac{a}{1-r}$$

infinity   The concept that something is without limit or unending. The symbol for infinity is ∞. Note that infinity is an idea, not a number, even though it is often treated as such. (p. 18)

initial value   The initial value of a sequence is the first term of the sequence. (p. 57)

input   A replacement value for a variable in a function or relation. The first number in an ordered pair. The set of all possible input values is the domain of a function. (p. 26)

integer   Any whole number or the opposite of a whole number: $\ldots - 3, -2, -1, 0, 1, 2, 3, \ldots$

integral roots   Roots (or zeros) of functions that are integers. (p. 414)

Integral Zero Theorem   For any polynomial with integral coefficients, if an integer is a zero of the polynomial, it must be a factor of the constant term. (p. 418)

intercepts   Points where a graph crosses the axes. x-intercepts are points at which the graph crosses the x axis and y-intercepts are points at which the graph crosses the y axis. On the graph at right the x-intercept is $(3, 0)$ and the y-intercept is $(0, 6)$. (p. 10)

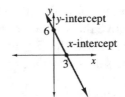

interest   An amount paid which is a percentage of the principal. For example, a savings account may offer 4% annual interest rate, which means they will pay $4.00 in interest for a principal of $100 kept in the account for one year. (p. 719)

interquartile range (IQR)   A way to measure the spread of data. It is calculated by subtracting the first quartile from the third quartile.

intersection   A point of intersection is a point that the graphs of two or more equations have in common. Graphs may intersect in one, two, several, many or no points. The set of coordinates of a point of intersection are a solution to the equation for each graph. (p. 21)

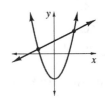

interval   A set of numbers between two given numbers.

inverse circular functions   See *inverse trigonometric functions*.

inverse function   A function that "undoes" what the original function does. It can also be seen as the x-y interchange of the function. The inverse of a function performs in reverse order the inverse operation for each operation of the function. The graph of an inverse function is a reflection of the original function across the line $y = x$. For example, $y = x^3 + 2$ is equivalent to $x = \sqrt[3]{y-2}$, its inverse function is written $y = \sqrt[3]{x-2}$. (p. 216)

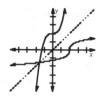

inverse operations   Subtraction is the inverse operation for addition and vice versa, division for multiplication, square root for squaring, and more generally taking the nth root for raising to the nth power.

inverse trigonometric functions   For each trigonometric function $\sin(x)$, $\cos(x)$, and $\tan(x)$, there is an inverse function written $\sin^{-1}(x)$, $\cos^{-1}(x)$, and $\tan^{-1}(x)$. Note: This symbol does not mean $\frac{1}{\sin(x)}$. It is a new function that "undoes" the original trig function, thus giving a specific angle measure when the input is $\sin x$, $\cos x$, or $\tan x$. For example: $\sin^{-1}(-\frac{1}{2}) = -\frac{\pi}{6}$. Note that the range of the inverse function is restricted to outputs for y such that $-\frac{\pi}{2} \le y \le \frac{\pi}{2}$ for $\sin x$, $-\frac{\pi}{2} < y < \frac{\pi}{2}$ for $\tan x$ and $0 \le y \le \pi$ for $\cos x$. Also see *cosine inverse, sine inverse,* and *tangent inverse.* (p. 629)

investigating a function   To investigate a function means to make a complete graph of the function and to write down everything you know about the function. Some things to consider are: domain, range, intercepts, asymptotes, inverse, and symmetry. (p. 33)

irrational numbers   The set of numbers that cannot be expressed in the form $\frac{a}{b}$, where a and b are integers and $b \neq 0$. For example, π and $\sqrt{2}$ are irrational numbers. (p. 389)

Law of Cosines   For any $\triangle ABC$, $a^2 = b^2 + c^2 - 2bc \cos A$. (p. 29)

Law of Large Numbers   A theorem stating that as the number of trials of a random process increases (for example, as the number of trials in a simulation increases), the results will approach the theoretical value closer. (p. 567)

Law of Sines   For any $\triangle ABC$, $\frac{\sin A}{a} = \frac{\sin B}{b} = \frac{\sin C}{c}$. (p. 29)

laws of exponents   The laws of exponents we study in this course are: (pp. 724, 740)

Law	Examples	
$x^m x^n = x^{m+n}$ for all x	$x^3 x^4 = x^{3+4} = x^7$	$2^5 \cdot 2^{-1} = 2^4$
$\frac{x^m}{x^n} = x^{m-n}$ for $x \neq 0$	$x^{10} \div x^4 = x^{10-4} = x^6$	$\frac{5^4}{5^7} = 5^{-3}$
$(x^m)^n = x^{mn}$ for all x	$(x^4)^3 = x^{4 \cdot 3} = x^{12}$	$(10^5)^6 = 10^{30}$
$x^0 = 1$ for $x \neq 0$	$\frac{y^2}{y^2} = y^0 = 1$	$9^0 = 1$
$x^{-1} = \frac{1}{x}$ for $x \neq 0$	$\frac{1}{x^2} = (\frac{1}{x})^2 = (x^{-1})^2 = x^{-2}$	$3^{-1} = \frac{1}{3}$
$x^{m/n} = \sqrt[n]{x^m}$ for $x \ge 0$	$\sqrt{k} = k^{1/2}$	$y^{2/3} = \sqrt[3]{y^2}$

least squares regression line (LSRL) A unique best-fit line that is found by making the squares of the residuals as small as possible.

line Graphed, a line is made up of an infinite number of points, is one-dimensional and extends without end in two directions. In two dimensions a line is the graph of an equation of the form $ax + by = c$.

line of best fit A line that represents, in general, data on a scatterplot. The line of best fit is a model of numerical two-variable data that helps describe the data. It is also used to make predictions for other data. Also see *least square regression line*. (p. 667)

line of symmetry A line that divides a figure into two congruent shapes which are reflections of each other across the line. (p. 217)

linear equation An equation with at least one variable of degree one and no variables of degree greater than one. The graph of a linear equation of two variables is a line in the plane. $ax + by = c$ is the standard form of a linear equation. (p. 10)

linear factor A factor of the form $(ax + b)$.

linear function A polynomial function of degree one or zero, with general equation $f(x) = a(x - h) + k$. The graph of a linear function is a line. (p. 41)

linear inequality An inequality with a boundary line represented by a linear equation. (p. 197)

linear programming A method for solving a problem with several conditions or constraints that can be represented as linear equations or inequalities. (p. 195)

linear regression A method for finding a best-fit line through a set of points on a scatterplot. Also see *regression* and *least squares regression line*.

locator point A locator point is a point which gives the position of a graph with respect to the axes. For a parabola, the vertex is a locator point. (p. 82)

Log base 10 $\log_{10} m = n$ if $10^n = m$. See *common logarithm*. (p. 282)

Log-Power Property See *Power Property of Logs*.

Log-Product Property See *Product Property of Logs*.

Log-Quotient Property See *Quotient Property of Logs*.

logarithm The logarithm of a given number, x, with respect to a base, b, is the exponent to which b must be raised to give x. For example, since we know that $32 = 2^5$, it follows that 5 is the logarithm, base 2, of 32, or $\log_2 32 = 5$. (p. 233)

logarithmic and exponential notation $m = \log_b(n)$ is the logarithmic form of the exponential equation $b^m = n$ ($b > 0$).

logarithmic functions Inverse exponential functions. The base of the logarithm is the same base as that of the exponential function. For instance $y = \log_2 x$ can be read as "y is the exponent needed for base 2 to get x," and is equivalent to $x = 2^y$. The short version is stated "log, base 2, of x," and written $\log_2 x$. (p. 240)

Looking Inside "Looking Inside" is a method of solving one-variable equations containing parentheses or an absolute value symbol. To use "looking inside," we first determine what the value of the entire expression inside the parentheses (or absolute value symbol) must be. We then use that fact to solve for the value of the variable. For example, to use "looking inside" to solve the equation $4(x + 2) = 36$, we first determine that $x + 2$ must equal 9. We then solve the equation $x + 2 = 9$ to find that $x = 7$. (p. 170)

lower control limit (LCL) See *control limit*. (p. 599)

lurking variable A hidden variable that was not part of the statistical study under investigation. Sometimes a lurking variable explains the true cause of an association between two other variables that are linked. (p. 461)

m When the equation of a line is expressed in $y = mx + b$ form, the parameter m gives the slope of the line. For example, the slope of the line $y = -\frac{1}{3}x + 7$ is $-\frac{1}{3}$.

margin of error Half of the spread between the upper and lower bounds of a statistical prediction. For example, if we predict weight is likely to be between an upper bound of 12 kg and lower bound of 18 kg, the margin of error is 3 kg, and we could write our prediction of the weight as 15 ± 3 kg. (p. 584)

maximize Make as large as possible. (p. 192)

maximum point The highest point on a graph. For example, the vertex of a downwardly oriented parabola.

maximum value The largest value in the range of a function. For example, the y-coordinate of the vertex of a downwardly oriented parabola. (p. 757)

mean The arithmetic mean, or average, of several numbers is one way of defining the "center" or "middle" or "typical value" of a set of numbers. The mean represents the center of a set of data well if the distribution of the data is symmetric and has no outliers. To find the mean of a numerical data set, add the values together then divide by the number of values in the set. For example, the mean of the numbers 1, 5, and 6 is $(1 + 5 + 6) \div 3 = 4$.

measure of central tendency   Mean and median are measures of central tendency, representing the "center" or "middle" or "typical value" of a set of data. See *center (of a data distribution)*.

mean absolute deviation   A way to measure the spread, or the amount of variability, in a set of data. The mean absolute deviation is the average of the distances to the mean, after the distances have been made positive with the absolute value. The standard deviation is a much more commonly used measure of spread than the mean absolute deviation. (p. 769)

median   The middle number of a set of data which has been written in numerical order. If there is no distinct middle, then the mean of the two middle numbers is the median. The median is generally more representative of the "middle" or of a "typical value" than the mean if there are outliers or if the distribution of the data in not symmetric. (p. 757)

midline   The horizontal axis of the graph of a trigonometric function. The midline is halfway between the maximum and minimum values of the function. (p. 360)

minimize   Make as small as possible.

minimum point   The lowest point on a graph. For example, the vertex of an upwardly oriented parabola.

minimum value   The smallest value in the range of a function. For example, the y-coordinate of the vertex of an upwardly oriented parabola. (p. 757)

model   A mathematical summary (often an equation) of a trend in data, after making assumptions and approximations to simplify a complicated situation. Models allow us to describe data to others, compare data more easily to other data, and allow us to make predictions. For example, mathematical models of weather patterns allow us to predict the weather. No model is perfect, but some models are better at describing trends than other models. Regressions are a type of model. Also see *regression*. (p. 113)

modified boxplot   See *boxplot*. (p. 765)

monomial   An expression with only one term. It can be a number, a variable, or the product of a number and one or more variables. For example, 7, $3x$, $-4ab$, and $3x^2y$ are each monomials.

multiple representations web   An organizational tool we use to keep track of connections between the four representations of relationships between quantities emphasized in this course. In this course, we emphasize four different ways of representing a numerical relationship: with a graph, table, situation (pattern), or rule (equation or inequality). (p. 9)

Core Connections Algebra 2

multiplicative identity   The number 1 is called the multiplicative identity because multiplying any number by 1 does not change the number. For example, $7(1) = 7$.

Multiplicative Identity Property   The Multiplicative Identity Property states that multiplying any expression by 1 leaves the expression unchanged. That is, $a(1) = a$. For example, $437x \cdot 1 = 437x$.

multiplier   In a geometric sequence the number multiplied times each term to get the next term is called the multiplier or the common ratio or generator. The multiplier is also the number you can multiply by in order to increase or decrease an amount by a given percentage in one step. For example, to increase a number by 4%, the multiplier is 1.04. We would multiply the number by 1.04. The multiplier for decreasing by 4% is 0.96. (p. 692)

natural logarithm   A logarithm base e. Abbreviated "ln". (p. 548)

negative exponent   Raising a number to a negative exponent is the same as taking the reciprocal of the number. $x^{-a} = \frac{1}{x^a}$ for $x \neq 0$. (p. 740)

non-function   A relation that has more than one output for one or more of its inputs.

normal distribution   A distribution of data that can be modeled with the normal probability density function. See *normal probability density function*. (p. 477)

normal probability density function   A very specific function that is used to model single-peaked, symmetric, bell-shaped data. (p. 485)

observational study   A study where data is collected by observing an existing situation without the researcher (or observer) imposing any type of change or treatment. (p. 461)

observed value   An actual measurement, as opposed to a prediction made from a model.

odd function   A function where $f(-x) = -f(x)$ for all values of x defined for the function. The graph of the function will be symmetric about the origin. (p. 108)

open question   A question that allows respondents to offer any answer they like. (p. 444)

one-dimensional   Not having any width or depth. Lines and curves are one-dimensional.

ordered pair   A pair of numbers written (x, y) used to represent the coordinates of a point in an xy-plane where x represents the horizontal distance from 0 and y is the vertical. The input and output values of a function or relation can be represented as ordered pairs were x is the input, and y is the output.

ordered triple   Three real numbers written in order (x, y, z) represent a point in space or replacement values for a situation involving three variables. See *3-dimensional coordinate system*. (p. 263)

orientation   Used informally in this course to describe some graphs. For example the direction a parabola opens might be referred to as its orientation. When describing the graph of a polynomial function, a positive orientation would mean the graph eventually continues upward as the value of x increases, as in the example above right. A negative orientation would mean it eventually heads downward as the value of x continues to increase, as in the example below right. (p. 358)

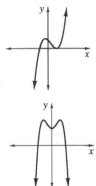

origin   The point on a coordinate plane where the x- and y-axes intersect is called the origin. This point has coordinates $(0, 0)$. The point assigned to zero on a number line is also called the origin. (p. 258)

outlier   A number in a set of data that is far away from the bulk of the data. (p. 765)

output   Used to describe the result of applying a function or relationship rule to an input value. For the function $f(x) = x^2 - 73$ when the input is 10, the output is 27. Function notation shows how the function operates on the input to produce the output: $f(10) = 10^2 - 73 = 27$. (p. 26)

parabola   The set of all points that are equidistant from a single point (the focus) and a line (the directrix). The general equation for a parabola that is a function (or a quadratic function) in graphing (or vertex) form, is $y = a(x - h)^2 + k$. The general equation of a quadratic function in standard form is $y = ax^2 + bx + c$. A general equation for parabolas that are not functions, "sleeping" parabolas, is $x - h = a(y - k)^2$. (p. 66)

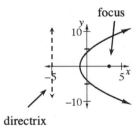

parallel   Two lines in a plane are parallel if they never intersect. Parallel lines have the same slope. Two line segments in a plane are parallel if the lines they lie on lines that never intersect. Two lines in space are parallel if they lie in the same plane and they do not intersect. There is a constant distance between parallel lines.

parameter   In a general equations where x and y represent the inputs and outputs of the function, variables such as a, b, c, m, h, and k are often referred to as parameters, and they are often replaced with specific values. For example, in the equation $y = a(x - h)^2 + k$ representing all parabolas that are functions, the $a, h,$ and k are (variable) parameters that give the shape and location, while x and y are the independent and dependent variables. (p. 41)

parent graph   The simplest version of a family of graphs. For instance, the graph of $y = x^2$, is considered the parent graph for parabolas that are functions. (p. 98)

Pascal's Triangle   The array of numbers at right. The triangular pattern continues downward. This array shows all the values of $_nC_r$ where n is the row number when the vertex is $_0C_0$. r is the number of places to the right in row n (when the counting begins with 0). For instance, $_5C_2$ is equal to 10. (p. 540)

```
        1
      1   1
    1   2   1
  1   3   3   1
 1  4   6   4  1
1  5  10  10  5  1
```

percent   A ratio that compares a number to 100. Percents are often written using the "%" symbol. For example, 0.75 is equal to $\frac{75}{100}$ or 75%.

percentile   A percentile ranking indicates the percentage of scores which are below the score in question. For example, if you scored at the 90th percentile on a test, your score was higher than the scores of 90% of the other test takers. (p. 482)

perfect square   Usually, a quadratic polynomial $ax^2 + bx + c$ that can be rewritten as the second power of a binomial, $(cx+d)^2$. For example, $x^2 - 6x + 9$ is a perfect square that can be rewritten as $(x-3)^2$. Also, any polynomial of even degree that can be rewritten as the square of one polynomial factor. For numbers, a whole number that can be written as the second power of another whole number. For example, $1, 4, 9, 16$, and 25 are perfect squares.

perfect square form   A quadratic equation in the form $a(x+b)^2 = c$, where a is nonzero, is said to be in perfect square form. For example, $3(x-12)^2 = 19$ is a quadratic equation in perfect square form. (p. 68)

perfect square trinomials   Trinomials of the form $a^2x^2 + 2abx + b^2$, where a and b are nonzero real numbers, are known as perfect square trinomials and factor as $(ax+b)^2$. For example, the perfect square trinomial $9x^2 - 24x + 16$ can be factored as $(3x-4)^2$.

perimeter   The distance around a figure on a flat surface.

Perimeter =
$5 + 8 + 4 + 6 = 23$ units

period   The length of one cycle of a graph, as shown by the dashed line in the graph at right. (p. 360)

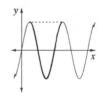

periodic function   A function which has a repetitive section or cycle such as the sine, cosine and tangent functions. In a periodic function, the cyclic pattern continues forever both to the left and to the right.

permutation   A permutation is an arrangement in which the order of selection matters. For example a batting line-up is a permutation because it is an ordered list of players. If each of five letters, A, B, C, D, E is printed on a card, the number of 3-letter sequences can you make by selecting three of the five cards is a permutation. Permutations can be represented with tree diagrams, decision charts, and their value calculated by using the formula for $_nP_r = \frac{n!}{(n-r)!}$. In the example given above, $_5P_3 = \frac{5!}{2!} = \frac{5\cdot4\cdot3\cdot2\cdot1}{2\cdot1} = 5\cdot4\cdot3 = 60$. (p. 503)

perpendicular   Two lines, rays, or line segments that intersect to form a right angle. A line and a plane can also be perpendicular if the line does not lie in the plane, but intersects it and forms a right angle with every line in the plane that passes through the point of intersection.

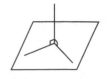

piecewise function   A function composed of parts of two or more functions. Each part is usually consists of a function with a restricted (limited) domain. (p. 105)

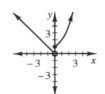

placebo   A treatment with no effect. A placebo is sometimes used in experiments involving people so that the psychological effects of participating in an experiment are the same in all the treatment groups. (p. 462)

plane   A plane is an undefined term in geometry. It is a two-dimensional flat surface that extends without end. It is made up of points and has no thickness. The part of a plane outlined by its xy-, xz- and yz-traces is often used to represent a plane on a 3-dimensional coordinate system. (p. 263)

point   An undefined term in geometry. A point has no dimensions but can be located by its coordinates on a number line, in a plane, or in space. (p. 263)

Point-Slope form $y - k = m(x - h)$ is called the point slope form of a linear equation or function because it shows the slope m and a point (h, k) that is on the graph of the line. For example, given a line that has slope $\frac{5}{3}$ and contains the point with coordinates $(3, -4)$ its equation can be written $y + 4 = \frac{5}{3}(x - 3)$. (p. 92)

polynomial   An algebraic expression that involves at most the operations of addition, subtraction, and multiplication. A polynomial in one variable is an expression that can be written as the sum of terms of the form: (any number) $\cdot$ $x^{(\text{whole number})}$. These polynomials are usually arranged with the powers of x in order, starting with the highest, left to right. The numbers that multiply the powers of x are called the coefficients of the polynomial. See *degree of a polynomial* for an example. (p. 135)

population   A collection of objects or group of people about whom information is gathered. (p. 445)

power   A number or variable raised to an exponent in the form x^n. See *exponent*.

power model or power curve   A best-fit curve of the form $y = ax^b$ that represents data on a scatterplot.

Power Property of Logs $\log_m(a^n) = n\log_m(a)$. For example, $\log_3 625 = 4\log_3 5$. (p. 289)

Core Connections Algebra 2

predicted value (of an association) The dependent (*y*-value) that is predicted for an independent (*x*-value) by the best-fit model for an association.

principal Initial investment or capital. An initial value.

probability The probability that an event *A*. with a finite number of equally likely outcomes, will occur is the number of outcomes for event *A* divided by the total number of equally likely outcomes. This can be written as $\frac{\text{number of outcomes for event A}}{\text{total number of possible outcomes}}$. A probability *p* is a ratio, $0 \le p \le 1$. (p. 567)

process control See *statistical process control*. (p. 598)

Product Property of Logs $\log_m(a \cdot b) = \log_m(a) + \log_m(b)$. For example, $\log_3 30 = \log_3 5 + \log_3 6$. (p. 289)

profit The amount of money after expenses have been accounted for.

proportion Equal ratios are described as a proportion. For example, the equation $\frac{x-8}{2x+1} = \frac{5}{6}$. (p. 472)

Pythagorean Identity For trigonometric functions, $\cos^2 x + \sin^2 x = 1$ for any value of *x*. (p. 343)

quadrants The coordinate plane is divided by its axes into four quadrants. The quadrants are numbered as shown in the first diagram at right. When graphing data that has no negative values, we sometimes use a graph showing only the first quadrant.

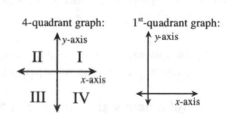

quadratic equation Any equation where at least one term has degree 2 and no term has degree higher than 2. The standard equation $Ax^2 + By^2 + Cxy + Dx + Ey + F = 0$ represents all quadratic relations in one or two variables. (p. 24)

quadratic expression An expression that can be written in the form $ax^2 + bx + c$, where *a*, *b*, and *c* are real numbers and *a* is nonzero. For example, $3x^2 - 4x + 7.5$ is a quadratic expression.

Quadratic Formula This formula gives you the solutions $x = \frac{-b \pm \sqrt{b^2 - 4ac}}{2a}$, for a quadratic equation in one variable that can be written in the standard form $ax^2 + bx + c = 0$. (p. 24)

quadratic function A quadratic equation that can be written $y = ax^2 + bx + c$ is also a quadratic function where *x* is the independent variable and *y* is the dependent variable. Its graph is a parabola with a vertical orientation. The graphing form of a quadratic function is $f(x) = a(x - h)^2 + k$.

quarterly Occurring four times a year. (p. 718)

quartile Along with the median, the quartiles divide a set of data into four groups of the same size. Also see *boxplot*. (p. 757)

quotient The result of a division problem is a quotient with a remainder (which could be 0). When a polynomial $p(x)$ is divided by a polynomial $d(x)$ the a polynomial $q(x)$ will be the quotient with a remainder $r(x)$. The product of $q(x)$ and $d(x)$ plus the remainder $r(x)$ will equal the original polynomial. $p(x) = d(x)q(x) + r(x)$.

Quotient Property of Logs $\log_m(\frac{a}{b}) = \log_m(a) - \log_m(b)$. For example, $\log_3 \frac{37}{5} = \log_3 37 - \log_3 5$. (p. 289)

R^2 See R-squared.

radian measure An arc of a unit circle equal to the length of the radius of the circle is one radian. The central angle for this arc has measure one radian. 1 radian $= \frac{180}{\pi}$ degrees. (p. 334)

radical An expression in the form $\sqrt{a}$, where $\sqrt{a}$ is the positive square root of a. For example, $\sqrt{49} = 7$. Also see *square root*. (p. 68)

radicand The expression under a radical sign. For example, in the expression $3 + 2\sqrt{x-7}$, the radicand is $x - 7$.

random sample A sample which was chosen as a result of a random process. A random sample can represent the whole population well.

range (of a data set) The range of a set of data is the difference between the highest and lowest values. (p. 771)

range (of a function) The range of a function is the set of possible outputs for a function. It consists of all the values of the dependent variable, that is every number that y can represent for the function $f(x) = y$. (p. 18)

ratio The comparison of two quantities or expressions by division.

rational equation An equation that includes at least one rational expression. For example, $5 - \frac{x+2}{x} = 7$. (p. 608)

rational expression An expression in the form of a fraction in which the numerator and denominator are polynomials. For example, $\frac{x-7}{x^2+8x-9}$ is a rational expression. (p. 135)

rational function A function that contains at least one rational expression. For example, $f(x) = \frac{5}{x-3}$. (p. 138)

rational number   A number that can be written as a fraction $\frac{a}{b}$ where a and b are integers and $b \neq 0$.

real numbers   The set of all rational numbers and irrational numbers is referred to as the set of real numbers. Any real number can be represented by a point on a number line. (p. 389)

rebound height   The height a ball reaches after a bounce.

rebound ratio   The ratio of the height a ball bounces after one bounce to the height from which it dropped. (p. 666)

reciprocal   The multiplicative inverse of a number or an expression.

reciprocal trigonometric functions   The functions $y = \frac{1}{\sin x} = \csc x$, $y = \frac{1}{\cos x} = \sec x$, and $y = \frac{1}{\tan x} = \cot x$. (p. 636)

rectangular numbers   The terms of the sequence $0, 2, 6, 12, 20, \ldots$. These numbers are called rectangular because they count the number of dots in rectangular arrays with the dimensions $n(n+1)$ where $n = 0, 1, 2, 3, 4, \ldots$

recursive equation (for a sequence)   An equation for a term in a sequence that requires knowing other terms in the sequence first. For example, the equation for the Fibonacci sequence is recursive because you need to know the previous two terms to find any other term. The equation for the Fibonacci sequence is $t(n) = t(n-2) + t(n-1)$, $t(1) = 1$, $t(2) = 1$. Also see *explicit equation*. (p. 692)

recursive sequence   A sequence which can be described by a recursive equation. See *recursive equation*. (p. 692)

reference angle   For every angle of rotation in standard position, the reference angle is the angle in the first quadrant $0 \leq \theta \leq \frac{\pi}{2}$ whose cosine and sine have the same absolute values as the cosine and sine of the original angle. (p. 338)

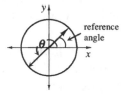

reflective symmetry   A type of symmetry where one half of the image is a reflection across a line of the other half of the image. You can fold the image on the line of symmetry and have both halves match exactly. Also see *line of symmetry*.

regression   A method for finding a best-fit line or curve through a set of points on a scatterplot. The most common type of regression is finding the least squares regression line. In this course we also do curved regressions: exponential regressions (fitting $y = a \cdot b^x$), quadratic regressions (fitting $y = ax^2 + bx + c$) and power regressions (fitting $y = ax^b$).

relation Functions are also relations, but relations are not necessarily functions. The equations for parabolas, ellipses, hyperbolas, and circles are all relations but only the equations that describe vertically oriented parabolas are functions.

relative frequency A ratio or percent. If 60 people are asked, and 15 people prefer "red," the relative frequency of people preferring red is $\frac{15}{60} = 25\%$. (p. 472)

relative maximum (minimum) A function that has a "peak" (or "valley") at a point P is said to have a relative maximum (minimum) at the point P. This is the point where the function changes direction.

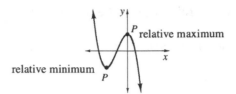

remainder When dividing polynomials in one variable, the remainder is what is left after the constant term of the quotient has been determined. The degree of the remainder must be less than the degree of the divisor. In the example below the remainder is $3x - 3$.
$(x^4 + 3x^3 - x^2 + x - 7) \div (x^2 + x + 1) = x^2 + 2x - 4 + \frac{3x-3}{x^2+x+1}$. Also see *quotient*. (p. 410)

Remainder Theorem For any number c, when a polynomial $p(x)$ is divided by $(x - c)$, the remainder is $p(c)$. For example, if the polynomial
$p(x) = x^4 - x^3 + 20x - 48$ is divided by $(x - 5)$, the remainder is
$p(5) = 552$. (p. 418)

repeated root A root of a polynomial that occurs more than once. The root r will occur as many times as $(x - r)$ is a factor of the polynomial. See *double root* and *triple root*. (p. 380)

residual The distance a prediction is from the actual observed measurement in an association. The residual is the y-value predicted by the best-fit model subtracted from the actual observed y-value. A residual can be graphed with a vertical segment that extends from the observed point to the line or curve made by the best-fit model. It has the same units as the y-axis.

residual plot A display of the residuals of an association. A residual plot is created in order to analyze the appropriateness of a best-fit model. If a model fits the data well, no apparent pattern will be made by the residuals—the residuals will be randomly scattered.

rewrite To rewrite an equation or expression is to write an equivalent equation or expression. Rewriting could involve using the Distributive Property, following the Order of Operations, using properties of 0 or 1, substitution, inverse operations, Properties of Logarithms, or use of trigonometric identities. We usually rewrite in order to change expressions or equations into more useful forms or sometimes, just simpler forms. (p. 170)

right angle An angle with measure 90°.

right triangle A triangle with a right angle.

roots of a function The number r is a root (or zero) of the function $f(x)$ if $f(r) = 0$. A root may be a real or a complex number. Real roots occur where the graph of the function $f(x)$ crosses the x-axis. Complex roots must be found algebraically. (p. 382)

_R_-squared The correlation coefficient squared, and usually expressed as a percent. R^2 is a measure of the strength of a linear relationship. Its interpretation is that R^2 % of the variability in the dependent variable can be explained by a linear relationship with the independent variable. The rest of the variability is explained by other variables not part of the study.

rule An algebraic representation or a written description of a mathematical relationship.

sample A subset (group) of a given population with the same characteristics as the whole population. (p. 445)

sample space With probability, all the possible outcomes.

scatter The variability in data. When the scatter of data forms a pattern, we can often describe and model the data. Random scatter has no discernable pattern. (Note that random scatter does not mean evenly scattered—randomly scattered data often forms clusters and gaps.) See *variability* and *spread*.

scatterplot A way of displaying two-variable numerical data where two measurements are taken for each subject (like height and forearm length, or surface area of cardboard and volume of cereal held in a cereal box). To create a scatterplot, the two values for each subject are written as coordinate pairs and graphed on a pair of coordinate axes (each axis representing a variable). Also see *association*.

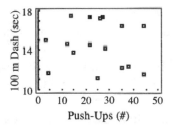

secant The reciprocal of the cosine. (p. 651)

sequence A function in which the independent variable is a positive integer (sometimes called the "term number"). The dependent variable is the term value. A sequence is usually written as a list of numbers. (p. 674)

series The sum of the terms of a sequence. (p. 500)

set A collection of data or items. (p. 139)

shape (of a data distribution) Statisticians use the following words to describe the overall shape of a data distribution: symmetric, skewed, single-peaked, double-peaked, and uniform. Examples are shown below. (p. 765)

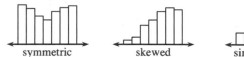 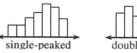

symmetric   skewed   single-peaked   double-peaked   uniform

sigma The Greek letter Σ which is used to mean sum. Using Σ provides a way to write a short, compact mathematical representation for a series. See *summation notation*. (p. 519)

simple interest Interest paid on the principal alone. (p. 719)

simplify To rewrite an expression or equation as an equivalent expression or equation in a form that is considered to be simpler or less cumbersome than the original.

simulation (probability) When conducting an experiment with an event that is unrealistic to perform, a simulation can be used. A simulation is a similar experiment that has the same probabilities as the original experiment. (p. 565)

sine In a right triangle (as shown at right) the ratio $\frac{\text{opposite side}}{\text{hypotenuse}}$ is known as the sine of the acute angle. At right, $\sin B = \frac{b}{c}$ since the side length b is opposite angle B. (p. 317)

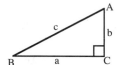

sine function For any real number θ, the sine of θ, denoted $\sin\theta$, is the y-coordinate of the point on the unit circle reached by a rotation angle of θ radians in standard position. The general equation for the sine function is $y = a\sin b(x-h) + k$. This function has amplitude a, period $\frac{2\pi}{b}$, horizontal shift h, and vertical shift k. (p. 360)

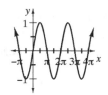

sine inverse ($\sin^{-1} x$) Read as the inverse of sine x, $\sin^{-1} x$ is the measure of the angle with sine x. We can also write $y = \arcsin x$. Note that the notation refers to the inverse of the sine function, *not* $\frac{1}{\sin x}$. Because $y = \sin^{-1} x$ is equivalent to $x = \sin y$ and there are infinitely many angles y such that $\sin y = x$, the inverse *function* is restricted to select the *principal* value of y such that $-\frac{\pi}{2} \le y \le \frac{\pi}{2}$. The graph of the inverse function, $y = \sin^{-1} x$ with $\frac{\pi}{2} \le y \le \frac{\pi}{2}$ is at right. (p. 636)

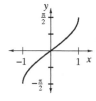

single-peaked See *shape (of a data display)*. (p. 765)

sketch a graph To sketch the graph of an equation means to show the approximate shape of the graph in the correct location with respect to the axes with key points clearly labeled. (p. 8)

skewed (data display) See *shape (of a data display)*. (p. 765)

"sleeping" parabola A "sleeping" parabola is a parabola which opens to the left or right, rather than upward or downward. These parabolas are not the graphs of functions. (p. 102)

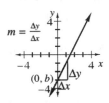

slope The ratio of the vertical change to the horizontal change between any two points on a line. For any two points (x_1, y_1) and (x_2, y_2) on a given line, the slope is $\frac{y_2 - y_1}{x_2 - x_1}$. For example, the slope of a line between points with coordinates $(3, -5)$ and $(-7, 2)$ is $\frac{2-(-5)}{-7-3} = -\frac{7}{10}$. (p. 10)

Slope-Intercept Form A linear equation written in the form $y = mx + b$ is written in slope-intercept form. In this form, m is the slope of the line and the point $(0, b)$ is the y-intercept. (p. 10)

solution Of an equation or inequality is a number or expression that makes the equation or inequality true when substituted for the variable. To find the numerical solution means to identify all the numbers that make a mathematical equation or inequality true. There may be any number of solutions for an equation or inequality, from 0 to infinitely many. Solutions to equations and inequalities in one variable are single numbers. For two variables they are ordered pairs, for three variables ordered triples. Equations with no solutions, such as $|x - 5| = -3$, are never true. Equations with one, several, or many solutions, such as $x(x + 3)(x - 7) = 0$ are sometimes true, and equations or identities such as $5(2x - 4) = 10x - 20$ are always true. (p. 200)

solve (1) To find all the solutions to an equation or an inequality (or a system of equations or inequalities). For example, solving the equation $x^2 = 9$ gives the solutions $x = 3$ and $x = -3$. (2) Solving an equation for a variable gives an equivalent equation that expresses that variable in terms of other variables and constants. For example, solving $2y - 8x = 16$ for y gives $y = 4x + 8$. The equation $y = 4x + 8$ has the same solutions as $2y - 8x = 16$, but $y = 4x + 8$ expresses y in terms of x and some constants. (p. 169)

special right triangles A right triangle with particular notable features that can be used to solve problems. Sometimes, these triangles can be recognized by the angles, such as the 45°-45°-90° triangle (also known as an "isosceles right triangle") and a 30°-60°-90° triangle. (p. 320)

spread (of a data distribution) A measure of the amount of variability, or how "spread out" a set of data is. Some ways to measure spread are the range, the mean absolute deviation, the standard deviation, and the interquartile range. For symmetric distributions with no outliers, the standard deviation or the interquartile range can represent the spread of the data well. However, in the presence of outliers or non-symmetrical data distributions, the interquartile range may be a better measure. Also see *variability*. (p. 757)

square root A number a is a square root of b if $a^2 = b$. For example, the number 9 has two square roots, 3 and –3. A negative number has no real square roots; a positive number has two; and zero has just one square root, namely, itself. Other roots, such as cube root, will be studied in other courses. Also see *radical*. (p. 83)

standard deviation   A way to measure the spread, or the amount of variability, in a set of data. The standard deviation is the square root of the average of the distances to the mean, after the distances have been made positive by squaring. The standard deviation represents the spread of a set of data well if the distribution of the data is symmetric and has no outliers. (p. 771)

Standard Form (linear function)   A linear equation written in the form $Ax + By = C$ is written in standard form. For linear functions, $B \neq 0$. (p. 10)

Standard Form (quadratic function)   The standard form for the equation of a quadratic function is $y = ax^2 + bx + c$ where $a \neq 0$. (p. 68)

Standard Form (quadratic relations in general)   The standard for parabolas, ellipses, and hyperbolas with axes parallel to the x- or y-axes is $Ax^2 + By^2 + Cx + Dy + E = 0$.

standard position   An angle is in standard position if its vertex is located at the origin and one ray is on the positive x-axis. (p. 343)

standard window   The graphing window on a calculator set to show the x- and y-axes for values $-10 \leq x \leq 10$ and $-10 \leq y \leq 10$.

statistic   A numerical fact or calculation that is formed from data. For example, a mean or a correlation coefficient is a statistic. With a capital "S," Statistics is the field of study which is concerned with summarizing data, and using probability to make predictions from data with natural variability. (p. 445)

statistical process control   The process of checking whether manufacturing quality remains stable over time. A process is "in control" if critical measurements of quality remain within the upper control limit and lower control limit as expected. (p. 598)

statistical test   A method of making decisions based on a statistical analysis of data. (p. 581)

step function   A special kind of piecewise function (a function composed of parts of two or more functions). A step function has a graph that is a series of line segments that often looks like a set of steps. (p. 728)

stoplight icon   The icon (shown at right) will appear periodically throughout the text. Problems that display this icon contain errors of some type.

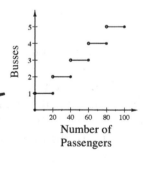

strength (of an association)   A description of how much scatter there is in the data away from the line or curve of best fit. If an association is linear, the correlation coefficient, r, or R-squared can be used to numerically describe and interpret the strength.

streak   Consecutive identical outcomes in a probabilistic situation. For example, if a baseball team wins four consecutive games, they have a winning streak of 4. (p. 572)

study   See *observational study*. (p. 461)

stretch factor   Used to describe the effect of a in the graphing form of a quadratic, cubic, absolute value, or exponential function. For $a > 1$ or $a < -1$ the outputs increase or decrease faster than the outputs for the parent functions, and the graphs are described as being stretched upwards or downwards in relation to the parent graph. (p. 66)

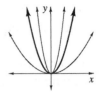

subjects   The people or items being measured in a statistical study.

substitution   Replacing a variable or expression with a number, another variable, or another expression. For example, when evaluating the function $f(x) = 5x - 1$, for $x = 3$, substitute 3 for x to get $f(3) = 5(3) - 1 = 14$.

Substitution Method   A method for solving a system of equations by replacing one variable with an expression involving the remaining variable(s). For example, in the system of equations at right the first

$$y = -3x + 5$$
$$2y + 10x = 18$$

equation tells you that y is equal to $-3x + 5$. We can substitute $-3x + 5$ in for y in the second equation to get $2(-3x + 5) + 10x = 18$, then solve this equation to find x. Once we have x, we substitute that value back into either of the original equations to find the value of y.

sum   The result of adding two or more numbers. For example, the sum of 4 and 5 is 9.

summation notation   A convenient way to represent a series is to use summation notation. The Greek letter sigma, Σ, indicates a sum.

For example, $\sum_{n=1}^{4} 3n = 3(1) + 3(2) + 3(3) + 3(4) = 30$. (p. 519)

The numbers below and above the sigma are called the indices. The index below, $n = 1$, tells us what value to start with for n. The top index tells us how high the value can go. In the example shown above, n starts at 1 and increases to 4.

symmetry   A figure that appears not to change when reflected across a line is said to have reflection symmetry. A figure that appears not to change when rotated through an angle of less than $360°$ is described as having rotation symmetry.

system of equations   A system of equations is a set of equations with more than one unknown or variable. The systems we solve most often in this course have two or three equations and two or three variables. Systems of equations are often solved using substitution or elimination to reduce the number of variables. A system of quadratic equations is shown at right. (p. 171)

$$y = x^2 + 8x - 4$$
$$y = 2x^2 + 5x - 8$$

system of inequalities A system of inequalities is a set of inequalities with the same variables. Solving a system of inequalities means finding one or more regions on the coordinate plane whose points represent solutions to each of the inequalities in the system. There may be zero, one, or several such regions for a system of inequalities. For example, the shaded region at right is a graph of the system of inequalities that appears below it. (p. 187)

$$y \le x^2 + x - 6$$
$$y > \tfrac{2}{3}x$$

tangent In a right triangle (at right) the ratio $\frac{\text{opposite side}}{\text{adjacent side}}$ is known as the tangent of an acute angle. At right, $\tan B = \frac{b}{a}$ since the side of length b is opposite angle B and the side length a is adjacent to (or next to) angle B. The function $f(\theta) = \tan(\theta) = \frac{y}{x}$ where (x, y) are the coordinates of the point on the unit circle where the radius makes an angle of θ with the positive horizontal axis.

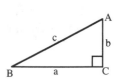

tangent function For any real number θ, the tangent of θ, denoted $\tan \theta$, is the slope of the line containing the ray which represents a rotation of θ radians in standard position. The general equation for the tangent function is $y = a\tan b(x - h) + k$. This function has period of $\frac{\pi}{b}$, vertical asymptotes at $\frac{\pi}{2b} + h \pm \frac{n\pi}{b}$ for $n = 1, 2, \ldots$, horizontal shift h, and vertical shift k. (p. 341)

tangent inverse ($\tan^{-1} x$) Read as the inverse of tangent x, $\tan^{-1} x$ is the measure of the angle that has tangent x. We can also write $y = \arctan x$. Note that the notation refers to the inverse of the tangent function, *not* $\frac{1}{\tan x}$. Because $y = \tan^{-1} x$ is equivalent to $x = \tan y$ and there are infinitely many angles y such that $\tan y = x$, the inverse *function* is restricted to select the *principal* value of y such that $\frac{\pi}{2} < x < \frac{\pi}{2}$. The graph of the inverse tangent function is at right. (p. 636)

term A single number, variable, or product of numbers and variables. A monomial is a term. Also a component of a sequence. (p. 135)

term number In a sequence, a number that gives the position of a term in the sequence. A replacement value for the independent variable in a function that determines the sequence. See *sequence*. (p. 676)

theoretical probability A probability calculation based on counting possible outcomes.

third quartile (Q3) The median of the upper half of a set of data which has been written in numerical order. (p. 757)

three-dimensional An object that has height, width, and depth. (p. 257)

transcendental number A number that is not the root of *any* polynomial equation with rational coefficients. Transcendental numbers are very common. The most prominent examples of transcendental numbers are π and e. (p. 548)

transformation (of a function) The conversion of a function to a corresponding function, often by a factor of constant k. Transformations often slide, reflect, stretch, and/or compress graphs of functions. For example, the transformation of $f(x) + k$ moves the graph of the function up or down by an amount k. The transformation $f(-x)$ reflects the graph of the function across the y-axis. (p. 83)

translation The result of moving a graph horizontally, vertically, or both but without changing its orientation.

treatment Some type of change imposed on one or more groups in an experiment so that a direct comparison can be made. (p. 461)

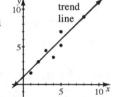

trend line Another name for a line of best fit. See *line of best fit*.

trigonometric identities The different trigonometric functions are related by many different equations, termed identities. A few examples of these identities are: $\cos(x) = \cos(-x)$ and $\sin(-x) = -\sin(x)$. (p. 651)

trigonometric ratios See *sine, cosine, tangent, secant, cosecant,* and *cotangent*. (p. 29)

trinomial A polynomial that is the sum or difference of exactly three terms, each of which is a monomial. For example, $x^2 + 6x + 9$ is a trinomial.

triple root A root of a function that occurs exactly three times. If an expression of the form $(x - a)^3$ is a factor of a polynomial, then the polynomial has a triple root at $x = a$. The graph of the polynomial has an inflection point at $x = a$. (p. 380)

two-dimensional An object having length and width. (p. 257)

Undoing Using inverse operations and reversing the order of operations to solve an equation in one variable or to "undo" a function rule in order to write its inverse. For example, in the equation $y = x^3 - 7$, add y and write the cube root. (p. 170)

uniform See *shape (of a data display)*. (p. 765)

unit circle A circle with a radius of one unit is called a unit circle. (p. 337)

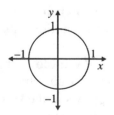

upper control limit (UCL) See *control limit*. (p. 599)

variable A symbol used to represent one or more numbers. In this course, letters of the English alphabet are used as variables. For example, in the expression $3x - (8.6xy + z)$, the variables are x, y, and z. (p. 41)

variability The inconsistency in measured data. Variability comes from two sources. Measurement error is the inconsistency in measurement of the same element repeated times and/or by different people. Element variability is the natural variation of the elements themselves. For example, even though in general people with larger shoe sizes are taller, not all people with the same shoe size have the same height. That is element variability. See *spread*. (p. 581)

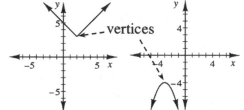

vertex (of a parabola) The vertex of a parabola is the highest or lowest point on the parabola (depending on the parabola's orientation). See *parabola*. (p. 60)

vertex form The vertex form for the equation of a quadratic function (also called graphing form) is written $y = a(x - h)^2 + k$. (p. 68)

vertical shift Used to describe the location of a graph in relation to its parent graph, the shift is the vertical distance (up or down) of each point on the graph from the corresponding point on the parent graph. This type of transformation is a vertical translation. For example, each point on the graph of $y = x^2 + 2$ is two units higher that its corresponding point on $y = x^2$. In a general equation such as $y = a(x - h)^2 + k$ the vertical shift is represented by k. (p. 66)

volume For a three-dimensional figure the number of non-overlapping cubic units that will fit inside.

x-bar process control chart A plot of the mean measurement of samples over time. x-bar process control charts are used to monitor whether a manufacturing process is proceeding within limits as expected. (p. 599)

x-intercept A point where a graph intersects the x-axis. In two dimensions, the coordinates of the x-intercept are $(x, 0)$. In three dimensions they are $(x, 0, 0)$. See *intercept*. (p. 10)

x-y interchange The result of exchanging the x and y variables and then solving for y. The resulting equation is the inverse of the original function.

$x \to y$ table A table that represents pairs of related values. The input value x appears in the first row or column, and the output value, y, appears in the second. The $x \to y$ table at right contains input and output pairs for the equation $y = x^2 - 3$.

x	y
-3	6
-2	1
-1	-2
0	-3
1	-2
2	1

Core Connections Algebra 2

_y_-intercept   A point where a graph intersects the _y_-axis. In two dimensions the coordinates of the _y_-intercept are $(0, y)$. In three dimensions, the coordinates are $(0, y, 0)$. See _intercept_. (p. 10)

_z_-score   A z-score indicates how many standard deviations a data value is from the mean. More formally, $z = \frac{\text{data value} - \text{mean}}{\text{standard deviation}}$.

zero factorial   Zero factorial is $1, 0! = 1$. (p. 648)

zero power   The result of raising any number (except zero) to the zero power is 1. $x^0 = 1$ for any number $x \neq 0$. (p. 740)

Zero Product Property   When the product of two or more factors is zero, at least one of the factors must equal zero. Used to solve equations in factored form. For example, given the equation $(x - 4)(x + 5) = 0$ you can see that 4 and −5 are solutions and that they are the only possible solutions because there are no other numbers that make either factor zero. (p. 24)

zeros of a function   The roots of a function or the values of _x_ for which the function value $y = 0$. The _x_-intercepts of the graph of a function in the real plane are zeros. These are also called the roots of the function. A function can have complex zeros. These complex zeros cause $y = 0$, but they are not _x_-intercepts since they do not exist in the real plane. See _roots of a function_. (p. 382)

Index
Student Version

Many of the pages referenced here contain a definition or an example of the topic listed, often within the body of a Math Notes box. Others contain problems that develop or demonstrate the topic. It may be necessary to read the text on several pages to fully understand the topic. Also, some problems listed here are good examples of the topic and may not offer any explanation. The page numbers below reflect the pages in the Student Version. References to Math Notes boxes are bolded.

Exponential
  application, 716
  decay, 670, 721
  equation, 714
    from a graph, 727, 731
    log form, 234
    solving, 282
      Checkpoint 9A, 460, 822
  function, **57**, 663, 716, 742
    from two points, 739
    inverse, 227, 228, 231, 232
    investigating, 707, 708, 709
    negative exponent, 724
    writing equation, 292
  graph
  from a situation, 731
  from an equation, 731
  growth, 661, 716
  writing a situation, 730
Expression, **135**
  equivalent, 123
  logarithmic
    Checkpoint 10, 552, 828
  rational, **135**, 142
    adding, 150
    Checkpoint 6A, 279, 807
    Checkpoint 6B, 300, 809
    dividing, 147
    multiplying, 147
    subtracting, 150
  rewriting, 736
  simplify
    Checkpoint 3A, 141, 790
    rational, **152**, **157**

F
Facilitator, 4
Factor Theorem, 418
Factored form
  polynomial equation, 371
Factoring, **24**
  difference of squares, 128, **427**
  of a polynomial, 414
  quadratics
    Checkpoint 5B, 242, 804
  stretch, 384, 386
  sum and difference of cubes, 416, **427**
  with substitution, 129
Factorial
  zero, 648

False positive, 606
Family of functions, 91, **98**
  log, 236
Fast Cars Lab, 742
Fibonacci numbers, 677
Fibonacci sequence, 684
First quartile, **757**
First term, 674, **744**
  form of an equation, **744**
Five number summary, **757**, 758
Formula, Quadratic, **24**
Fraction
  algebraic, 142
    operations with, **152**, **157**
Fractional exponents, 735, 736, **740**
Frequency, relative, 470, 472
Function, **6**
  amplitude, 358, **360**
  composite, 225, 243
  cyclic, 349
    period, 350, 353, 358
  decreasing, 707
  domain, **18**
  even, 97, 107, **108**
  exponential, **57**, 663
    writing equation, 292
  family, 33, 41, 91, **98**
  increasing, 707
  inverse, 212, 216
    Checkpoint 9B, 488, 825
    trigonometric, 629
  investigation, 33, 44
  machine, 5
  normal probability density, 477, **485**
  notation, **6**, 7
    Checkpoint 3B, 158, 792
  odd, 97, 107, **108**
  operations with, 138
  period, **360**
  polynomial, **374**
  piecewise-defined, 105
  range, **18**
  rational, 138
  reciprocal trigonometric, 634, **651**
  roots, **382**
  sequence, 695
  tangent, 341
  zeros, **382**
Fundamental Theorem of Algebra, **418**

Initial value, **57**, 680
Input, 26
Integral root, 414
Integral Zero Theorem, **418**
Intercept
  average of, 67, 69, **75**
  Checkpoint 7A, 331, 811
  x-intercept, **10**
  y-intercept, **10**
Interest, **719**
  compound, **550**, 716, **719**
    continuously, **550**
  simple, 716, **719**
Interquartile range, **757**, 770, **771**
Intersection, 21, 171, 172, 173
Inverse, 212, 216
  absolute value, 229
  cosine, 625, 630
    graph, **636**
  exponential function, 227, 228, 231, 232
  finding equation of, 222
    Checkpoint 9B, 488, 825
  function
    trigonometric, 629
  graph, 217, 224
  graphing, 216
  notation, **219**
  sine, 629
    graph, **636**
  tangent, 630
    graph, **636**
Investigating a Function, 33, 35
Irrational numbers, 389
Isometric dot paper, 258

J
Jackpot Fever, 509
Jumping Jackrabbits, 79

K
Keeping a Notebook, 7

L
Law of Cosines, **29**
Law of Sines, **29**
Law of Large Numbers, 567
Laws of exponents, **724**, **740**
Least common multiple, **157**

Line
  of best fit, 667
  of symmetry, 217
  trace, **271**
Linear equation, **10**
  point-slope form, 92
  writing
    Checkpoint 2A, 76, 783
Linear function, 41
Linear inequality
  two variables, 197
Linear programming, 195
Linear system of equations
  solving
    Checkpoint 2B, 104, 786
Locator point, 82, 98
Log function
  general equation, 240
  transformation, 239
Log Property Puzzles, 288
Logarithm, 232, **233**
  application, 296
  base, **233**
  base 10, 282, 239
  change of base, 592
  Checkpoint 10, 552, 828
  definition, **289**
  graphing, 232, 236, 237
  introduction, 228
  inverse relationship, **289**
  investigating properties, 286
  notation, **233**
  Power Property, 283, **289**
    proof, 289
  Product Property, 288, **289**
  Quotient Property, 288, **289**
  solving equations, 282
Logarithmic form, 234
Looking Inside, 170
Lower bound, 577, 582, **589**
Lower control limit, 599
Lurking variable, **461**

M
Making sense of problems, 113, 305, 556
Margin of error, 576, 577, **584**, **589**
  hypothesis test, **594**
Mathamericaland, 371, 385, 425
Mathematical practices, 113, 305, 556

Parent graph, 83, **98**
  cubic, 83
  exponential, 83
  hyperbola, 83
  parabola, 83, 91
Parent Graph Tool Kit, 91
Pascal's triangle, 540, 541
Patterns of Growth, 686
Pendulum, 313
Pendulum Experiment, 314
Penny Lab, 721
Percentile, 482
Perfect square
  form of a quadratic, **68**
Period, 350, 353, 358, **360**
Permutation, **503**, 540
  notation, **503**
Picking a Payout, 523, 525
Piecewise-defined function, 105
  step graph, **728**
Placebo, 462
Plane, **263**
  complex, 401, **404**
  graph, **271**
Point
  boundary, 186
  locating in space, **263**
  locator, 98
Point-slope form, 92
Polydoku, 407, 408, 409
Polynomial, **135**, 371, **374**, 375
  application, 425
  division, 407, **410**
  equation
    factored form, 371
    standard form, 371
  finding roots, 414
  function
    graph, 371, 379
  general equation, **387**
  minimum degree, 380
  multiplying
    Checkpoint 5A, 226, 801
  notation, **387**
  roots, **396**
  stretch factor, 384, 386
  theorems, **418**
  zeros, **396**
Polynomial Function Investigation, 372

Population, 441, **445**
  claim, **594**
  parameters, **474**
  standard deviation, 470, **474**
Power Property of Logarithms, 283, **289**
Precision, attend to, 114, 306, 557
Preface, 443
Probability
  conditional, **567**
  models, **567**
  simulation, 565, 571
Probability density function
  normal, 477, **485**
Process control, 598
  in control, 599
  nine points loss of control, 600
  out of control, 600
  x-bar chart, 599
Product as a sum, 127
Product Property of Logarithms, 288, **289**
Proportion, 472
Pythagorean Identity, 327, **343**, 641, **651**

Q
Quadratic
  equation, **24**
  factoring, **24**
    Checkpoint 5B, 242, 804
  from three points, 274
  graphing/vertex form, **68**, 71, **75**
  intercept
    Checkpoint 7A, 331, 811
  roots, **396**
  Shrinking Targets Lab, 55
  solution
    approximate decimal form, **68**
    exact form, **68**
  solving, **24**
  standard form, **68**
Quadratic Formula, **24**, **75**
Quality control, 593
Quantitative reasoning, 113, 305, 556
Quarterly interest, 718
Quartile, **757**
Question
  closed, 444
  open, 444
  order, 443
  two in one, 443
Quotient Property of Logarithms, 288, **289**

Core Connections Algebra 2

Trigonometric function
  sine, 317
  cosecant, 634
  cosine, 327
  cotangent, 635
  inverse, 629
  reciprocal, 634, **636**, **651**
  secant, 635
  tangent, 341
  transforming, 345
Trigonometric identitiy, 640
  Angle Difference Identity, 649, 650, **651**
  Angle Sum Identity, 649, 650, **651**
  Cofunction Identities, **651**
  Double Angle Identities, 640, **651**
  graphically, 641
  proving, 645
  Pythagorean Identity, 641, **651**
Trigonometric ratios, **29**
Triple root, 380
Two-dimensional, 257
Two questions in one, 443

U
Undoing, 170, 211
Uniform, **765**
Unit circle, 337
  graph, 324, 328
  Pythagorean Theorem, 327
Upper bound, 577, 582, **589**
Upper control limit, 599

V
Value, excluded, 142
Variability, 581, **757**
  experimental results, 587
  sample-to-sample, **584**, 587
  sampling, 576
Variable, 41
  dependent, **6**, 667
  independent, **6**, 667
  lurking, **461**

Vertex, 60
  form of a quadratic, **68**, 71, **75**
  parabola, 60
    Checkpoint 7B, 352, 813
Vertical
  asymptote, **37**
  compression, 66
  shift, 66
  stretch, 66
Visors for Runners, 471, 479

W
Wait time, 573
Word problem
  solving with systems of equations, 182
Wording, biased, 443

X
x-bar process control chart, 599
x-intercept, **10**, **382**
    Checkpoint 7A, 331, 811

Y
y = form, 673
y = *x*, 217
y-intercept, **10**
    Checkpoint 7A, 331, 811

Z
Zero
  exponent, **740**
  factorial, 648
  of a function, **382**
  of a polynomial, **396**
Zero Product Property, **24**
Zeroth term, **744**